Comparative anatomy
of the vertebrates

Comparative anatomy of the
Vertebrates

George C. Kent

Alumni Professor Emeritus, Department of Zoology,
Louisiana State University, Baton Rouge,
Louisiana

FIFTH EDITION

with **890** illustrations including **253** in color

The C. V. Mosby Company

ST. LOUIS · TORONTO · LONDON   1983

MOSBY

A TRADITION OF PUBLISHING EXCELLENCE

Editor: Diane L. Bowen
Assistant editor: Tim Arnold
Manuscript editor: Mary C. Wright
Book design: Nancy Steinmeyer
Cover design: Diane Beasley
Production: Linda R. Stalnaker, Susan Trail

FIFTH EDITION

The C.V. Mosby Company
11830 Westline Industrial Drive, St. Louis, Missouri 63141

Library of Congress Cataloging in Publication Data

Kent, George Cantine, 1914-
    Comparative anatomy of the vertebrates.

    Bibliography: p.
    Includes index.
    1. Vertebrates—Anatomy.   2.   Anatomy, Comparative.
I. Title.
QL805.K43   1983   596'.04   82-2078
ISBN 0-8016-2651-X   AACR2

C/VH/VH   9   8   7   6   5   4   3   2   1   02/B/244

Preface

This is a textbook of descriptive and functional morphology with an evolutionary perspective. It examines the architecture of vertebrate systems, speculates on survival values of successive modifications of earlier structural patterns, and points out how functional combinations of modern characters contribute to survival in the contemporary environment. It is repeatedly expressed or implied that existing structural patterns are modifications of earlier ones, that the adult is a modification of the embryo, that individual differences exist, and that structure is broadly determined by heredity and adaptively modified through natural selection. Inevitably, the approach evokes a critical examination of the concept of organic evolution. A statement of what organic evolution implies and, equally important, what it does not imply is found in Chapter 18, which should be read early in the course.

This edition features expanded coverage of birds, increased emphasis on evolutionary trends, and new or expanded discussions of mechanisms of locomotion, feeding and mastication, respiration in fishes, thermoregulation in ectothermic amniotes, and visual accommodation, among other functional topics. There are more than 50 new illustrations, and additional ones have been redrawn or had color added.

As in earlier editions there is an abridged classification of vertebrates, a list of nearly 800 prefixes, suffixes, and stem words used in anatomy in a format designed to encourage maximum use, and a short list of comprehensive references that supplements the selected readings at the end of each chapter.

To all who offered criticism in the past or suggestions for future editions, I extend my sincere thanks. You have contributed immeasurably to this work. In addition to acknowledgments in earlier editions I extend special thanks to the curatorial staff of the Museum of Zoology of Louisiana State University, Professor Stanley Rhodes of Bloomsburg State College, and Karen Westphal, who executed most of the new drawings. The frontispiece is courtesy of the Macmillan Company, Ltd., from *A History of Comparative Anatomy* by F.J. Cole. In conclusion, I gratefully acknowledge the continuing aid and encouragement of my wife, Lila, to whom the original edition of this work was affectionately dedicated.

George C. Kent

Contents

Prologue

Cavemen had some knowledge of the internal organs of mammals, as did the Babylonians and ancient Egyptians, who practiced surgery and embalming. Embalming, which involved removal of most of the internal organs, was an advanced art. Aside from a small number of Egyptian medical papyri dating to about 3000 BC, the oldest anatomical works were written during the last 400 years BC by Greek philosophers and physicians. These works were incomplete, mostly superficial, and often imaginative. Anatomy of the classical era culminated in the works of Galen, a Greek philosopher-physician who practiced in Rome between AD 165 and 200. He assembled all available Greek anatomical writings, supplemented them with his own dissections of apes from the Barbary Coast (human dissection was at that time prevented by public opinion and superstition), and, in addition, wrote more than 100 treatises on medicine and human anatomy. Shortly thereafter, scholasticism took over, and during the next 1300 years Galen's descriptions were considered infallible and dissent was punishable. Subservience to authority became so accepted that (as has been said, probably partly in jest) if a scholar wanted to know how many teeth horses have, he saddled up and rode 100 miles, if necessary, to the nearest library to see what Galen said. (No doubt the peasants looked into the horse's mouth—an application of the experimental method.)

It was not until the fifteenth century that Leonardo da Vinci (1452-1519) and other Italian artists began to make anatomical observations of their own (at the peril of excommunication from the church), and a renaissance in anatomy began. In 1533 a young Flemish medical student named Vesalius at the University of Paris attended classes where Galen's works were read (by a "reader") while the professor tried, often with embarrassing lack of success, to harmonize Galen's descriptions with the dissection. (Recall that many of Galen's descriptions of man were written from dissections of apes.) After 3 years Vesalius quit Paris, earned a degree at Padua, stayed on to teach, and recorded his own anatomical observations. In 1543 he published *De humani corporis fabrica (On the Structure of the Human Body)*, and anatomy entered the modern investigative period.

Twelve years after publication of Vesalius's anatomy, Pierre Belon (1555) published what has become a classical illustration of a human and bird skeleton side by side, showing that the parts correspond, almost bone for bone (frontispiece). The bird was drawn in an upright position facing the viewer, with wings hanging like arms. The bones of the bird and of man were similarly labled. Belon, a botanist and a physician, was therefore also a pioneer in comparative anatomy.

It was another century, however, before anatomists became interested in cataloging other examples of what we today call "homologous structures"—structures in two different species that develop in the same way from the same embryonic precursor and are really the same structure even though they may not look alike or even perform the same function. Each newly discovered instance of homologous structure in two species was dutifully explained as being a manifestation of a basic architectural plan or archetype in the Creator's mind. The idea that these similarities might be the result of inheritance of a similar genetic code from a common ancestor, with modifications, had not yet been openly expressed. When it finally was, the idea met with the same almost universal condemnation in the Western world that Copernicus (1473-1543) encountered earlier when he announced that the earth revolved around the sun. Both theories were considered atheistic, which they are not, since neither concept in any way denies (or confirms) the validity of the concept of a Creator.

Comparative anatomy today is the study of structure, of the functional significance of structure, and of the range of variation in structure and function in different species. Its methods are descriptive and experimental. The data are employed partly to attempt to deduce the history of the different species on our planet and the environmental conditions under which they rose, flourished, and became extinct. The data also help to satisfy the curiosity of the human mind. Like other scientific disciplines, comparative anatomy has its roots in philosophy, and its aim is enlightenment.

CHAPTER 1

The vertebrate body

A study of comparative vertebrate anatomy is, in a sense, a study of history. It is the history of the struggle of vertebrate animals for compatibility with an ever-changing environment. It is the history of the extermination of the unfit and the invasion of a new territory by those best equipped for survival. It is a study of history, just as is the study of man's conquests, political fortunes, and social evolution.

The study of vertebrates is, by definition, a study of man, although not of man alone. It leads to a better understanding of man's past and to an assay of his present state. As for predicting the future, a most important, although often neglected, objective of history, the biologist can predict that neither the earth nor that which grows on the earth will remain unchanged. The prediction is based in part on the fact that there has been a succession of animals and plants on the earth and that the species of today are not the same species that would have been seen 300 million years ago. On the basis of probability, it can be predicted that they will be still more different tomorrow. Since there has been a succession of species, and since all life seems to come from preexisting life, logic tells us that the species have been changing. This is the premise of the discipline of comparative anatomy.

The discipline has an important function. It is not that of promoting the premise. It is, instead, one of continually seeking new insights, of finding additional interrelationships, of periodically reevaluating our tentative conclusions, and of drawing new ones. When comparative anatomy ceases to be a search for the truth, it will have surrendered its status as a science and will have become a body of meaningless facts. The facts are important, but their meaning, devoid of speculation, is immeasurably more so. To the study of no discipline is the dictum of *Proverbs* more applicable, ". . . in all thy getting, get understanding."

Vertebrates, past and present, are constituted in accordance with a basic architectural pattern. This phrase has two implications. The

In this chapter we will preview the basic architectural features of vertebrate animals. We will learn what happens to their embryonic notochords, examine the embryonic pharynx, and find out why brains and spinal cords are hollow from fish to man. Finally, we will note some additional features that, although not unique, are found in animals with backbones.

General body plan
Vertebrate characteristics: the big four
   Notochord and vertebral column
   Pharynx
   Dorsal, hollow central nervous
     system
Satellite characteristics
   Skin
   Respiratory mechanisms
   Coelom
   Digestive organs
   Urinogenital organs
   Circulatory system
   Sense organs

1

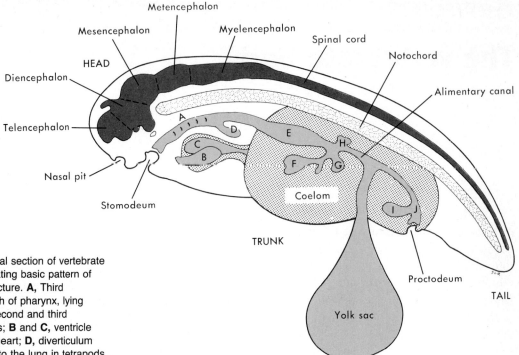

Fig. 1-1. Sagittal section of vertebrate embryo, illustrating basic pattern of vertebrate structure. **A,** Third pharyngeal arch of pharynx, lying between the second and third pharyngeal slits; **B** and **C,** ventricle and atrium of heart; **D,** diverticulum that gives rise to the lung in tetrapods and swim bladder in fishes; **E,** stomach; **F,** liver bud and associated gallbladder; **G,** ventral pancreatic bud; **H,** dorsal pancreatic bud; **I,** urinary bladder of tetrapods; **J,** cloaca. The stomodeum is separated from the pharynx by a thin oral plate. The proctodeum is separated from the cloaca, **J,** by a cloacal membrane. The brain has five major subdivisions: telencephalon and diencephalon (forebrain), mesencephalon (midbrain), and metencephalon and myelencephalon (hindbrain).

first is that vertebrates conform quite closely to a **generalized pattern of anatomical structure.** This is revealed by dissection and study of adult vertebrates. The second implication is that there is a **uniformity of developmental processes,** which is revealed by studies of embryos. In this book we will examine this generalized pattern and learn in what directions the pattern has been modified in later populations. It would be useful, also, to be able to describe the historical selective forces in the external environment that resulted in the modifications, and this will be attempted on occasion, but with reservations, since most of what has been written on that topic is highly speculative. We will, however, look at functional morphology, that is, the manner in which established anatomical features serve the animal today.

GENERAL BODY PLAN

The vertebrate body is divided into head, trunk, tail, and appendages. Concentrated on or in the head of vertebrates are special sense organs for monitoring the external environment, jaws for capturing or processing food, and, in fishes, gills for respiration. These structures necessitate a brain large enough to receive and process incoming information and to provide stimuli to the muscles that operate the or-

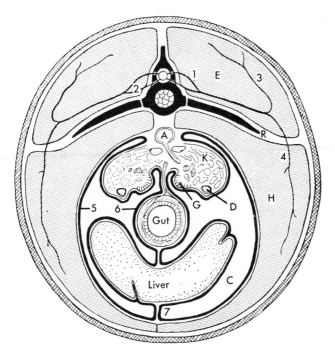

Fig. 1-2. Typical vertebrate body in cross section. **A,** Dorsal aorta, giving off renal artery to kidney; **C,** coelom; **D,** kidney duct; **E,** epaxial muscle; **G,** future gonad (gonadal ridge); **H,** hypaxial muscle in body wall; **K,** kidney; **R,** rib projecting into a horizontal septum from the transverse process of a vertebra. **1,** Dorsal root of spinal nerve; **2,** ventral root; **3,** dorsal ramus of spinal nerve; **4,** ventral ramus; **5,** parietal peritoneum; 6, visceral peritoneum; 7, ventral mesentery. A remnant of the notochord lies within the centrum of a vertebra (immediately dorsal to **A**). The spinal cord lies above the centrum surrounded by a neural arch.

gans. Increasing brain size over hundreds of millions of years has resulted in larger braincases that are increasingly movable independently of the trunk and, ultimately, separated from it by a neck. Cephalization has therefore developed to a greater degree in vertebrates than in any other group of animals.

The trunk contains the body cavity, or **coelom** (Fig. 1-1). Surrounding the coelom is the **body wall,** covered by skin, lined by **parietal peritoneum,** and consisting chiefly of muscle, vertebral column, and ribs (Fig. 1-2). The body wall must be cut open to expose the viscera. The latter are covered by **visceral peritoneum,** which is continuous with the parietal peritoneum via dorsal and ventral mesenteries. The few visceral organs that do not develop dorsal mesenteries lie against the dorsal body wall just external to the parietal peritoneum, in which position they are said to be retroperitoneal.

The neck is a narrow extension of the trunk that lacks a coelom. It consists primarily of vertebrae, muscles, spinal cord, nerves, and elongated tubes—esophagus, blood vessels, lymphatics, trachea—that connect the head and trunk.

The tail begins at the anus or vent. It consists almost exclusively of a caudal continuation of body wall muscles, axial skeleton, nerves,

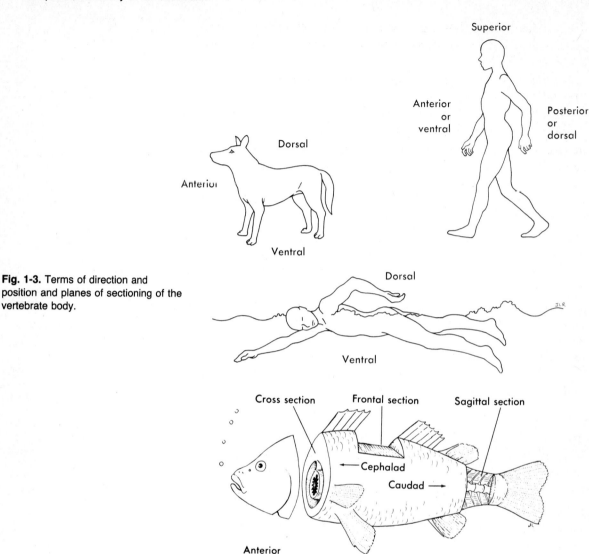

Fig. 1-3. Terms of direction and position and planes of sectioning of the vertebrate body.

and blood vessels. Frogs and toads have a tail as swimming larvae, but it is resorbed at metamorphosis. Modern birds have reduced the tail to a nubbin, but the first birds had long tails (Fig. 3-20); and human beings have a tail early in embryonic life (Fig. 1-10).

Vertebrates have three principal **body axes:** an anteroposterior (longitudinal) axis, a dorsoventral axis, and a left-right axis. With reference to the first two, structures at one end of each axis are different from those at the other end. The left-right axis terminates in identical structures on each side. Thus the head differs from the tail and the dorsum differs from the venter, but right and left sides are mirror images of each other. An animal with this arrangement of body parts exhibits **bilateral symmetry.**

It is sometimes convenient to discuss parts of the vertebrate body with reference to three **principal anatomical planes.** Two axes define a plane. The transverse plane is established by the left-right and the dorsoventral axes. A cut in this plane is a cross section (Fig. 1-3). The frontal plane is established by the left-right and longitudinal axes. A cut in this plane is a frontal section. The sagittal plane is established by the longitudinal and dorsoventral axes. A cut in this plane is a sagittal section. Sections parallel to the sagittal plane are parasagittal. Acquainting oneself with these concepts is a simple exercise in anatomy and logic.

Vertebrates exhibit a basic **metamerism,** the serial repetition of body structures in the longitudinal axis. It is clearly expressed in embryos (Fig. 15-6) and is retained in many adult systems. No external evidence is seen because the skin is not metameric. If, however, the integument is stripped from the body of fishes, amphibians other than anurans, and some reptiles, one sees a series of muscle segments used chiefly for locomotion (Fig. 10-4). In addition, the serial arrangement of vertebrae, ribs, spinal nerves, embryonic kidney tubules, and segmental arteries and veins is a further expression of the metamerism of vertebrates.

VERTEBRATE CHARACTERISTICS: THE BIG FOUR

Vertebrates constitute the subphylum **Vertebrata (Craniata)** in the phylum **Chordata.** They exhibit four definitive structural characteristics: (1) a notochord, at least in the embryo; (2) a pharynx with pouches or slits in its wall, at least in the embryo; (3) a dorsal, hollow nervous system; and (4) a vertebral column. These are the "big four" vertebrate characteristics. The first three are chordate characteristics and are found also in protochordates. Other features associated with vertebrates but not necessarily unique among them will be mentioned later as satellite characteristics.

Notochord and vertebral column

The notochord is the first skeletal structure to appear in vertebrate embryos. At its peak of embryonic development it is a rod of living cells located immediately ventral to the central nervous system and dorsal to the alimentary canal extending from the midbrain to the tip of the tail (Fig. 1-1). The part of the notochord in the head becomes incorporated in the floor of the skull, and, except in agnathans, the part in the trunk and tail becomes surrounded by cartilaginous or bony rings called **vertebrae.** These provide more rigid support for

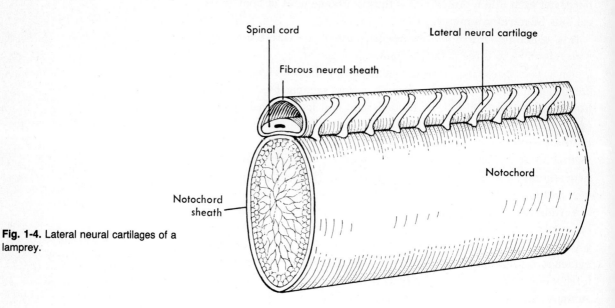

Fig. 1-4. Lateral neural cartilages of a lamprey.

the body than does a notochord alone. A typical vertebra consists of a centrum that is deposited around and within the notochord, a neural arch that forms over the spinal cord, and various processes. In the tail a hemal arch may surround the caudal artery and vein (Figs. 7-1, *C* and *D*, and 7-2).

The fate of the notochord in adult vertebrates is variable. In almost all fishes it persists the length of the trunk and tail, although usually constricted within each centrum (Fig. 7-6). The same is true in many urodeles and some primitive lizards. However, in modern reptiles, birds, and mammals the notochord is almost obliterated during development. A vestige remains in mammals within the intervertebral discs that separate successive centra (Fig. 7-7, *D*). The vestige consists of a soft spherical mass of connective tissue called the **pulpy nucleus.** Modern reptiles and birds lack even this vestige.

In agnathans the notochord grows along with the animal and paired **lateral neural cartilages** become perched on the notorchord lateral to the spinal cord (Fig. 1-4). These cartilages are reminiscent of neural arches, but whether they are primitive vertebrae, vestigial vertebrae from an ancestor that had a typical vertebral column, or entirely different structures is not known. When a notochord persists as an important part of the adult axial skeleton, it develops a strong outer elastic and inner fibrous sheath (Fig. 1-4).

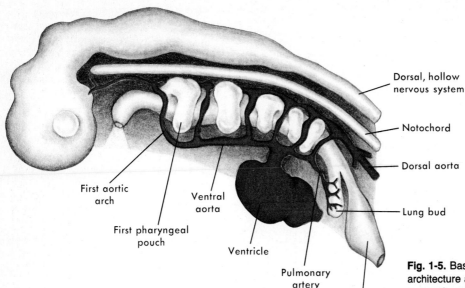

First aortic
arch

First pharyngeal
pouch

Ventral
aorta

Ventricle

Pulmonary
artery

Digestive
tract

Dorsal, hollow
nervous system

Notochord

Dorsal aorta

Lung bud

Fig. 1-5. Basic pattern of pharyngeal architecture as exemplified by a composite vertebrate embryo. The notochord lies ventral to the nervous system and extends from the midbrain caudad. A series of pharyngeal pouches has evaginated from the lateral walls of the digestive tract. Six aortic arches (red) connect the heart and ventral aorta with the dorsal aorta. (Typically, the first aortic arch disappears before the sixth one has formed.) The anterior end of the dorsal, hollow nervous system is enlarging to form the brain. Although a lung does not form in all vertebrates, it is an ancient structure and is represented by a swim bladder in most fishes.

It is apparent that the notochord has been disappearing as an adult structure. But the development of a notochord in every vertebrate embryo—even the human embryo—is a reminder that all vertebrates are built in accordance with a basic architectural pattern.

Pharynx

The pharynx is the region of the alimentary canal exhibiting pharyngeal pouches in the embryo (Fig. 1-5). The pouches may rupture to the exterior to form pharyngeal slits. These slits may remain throughout life, or they may be temporary. If they remain throughout life, the adult pharynx is the part of the alimentary canal having slits. If the slits are temporary, the adult pharynx is the part of the alimentary canal connecting the oral cavity and esophagus.

PHARYNGEAL POUCHES AND SLITS

The basic pattern of the vertebrate pharynx is expressed in all vertebrate embryos. A series of paired **pharyngeal pouches** arises as diverticula of the pharyngeal endoderm (Figs. 1-5 to 1-7). The pouches invade the pharyngeal wall and grow toward the surface of the animal. Simultaneously, an **ectodermal groove** grows toward each pharyngeal pouch (Figs. 1-6 and 1-7). Soon only a thin **branchial plate** separates the groove from the pouch. When the branchial plate rup-

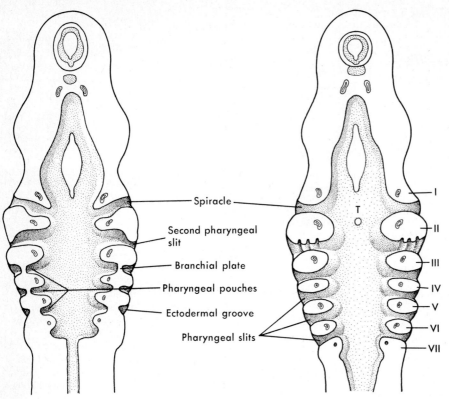

Spiracle

Second pharyngeal slit

Branchial plate

Pharyngeal pouches

Ectodermal groove

Pharyngeal slits

I
II
III
IV
V
VI
VII

Fig. 1-6. Pharyngeal arches (**I** to **VII**) and slits in embryonic shark, frontal section, looking down onto floor of pharynx. Early stage, *left;* later stage, *right.* **T,** Thyroid evagination.

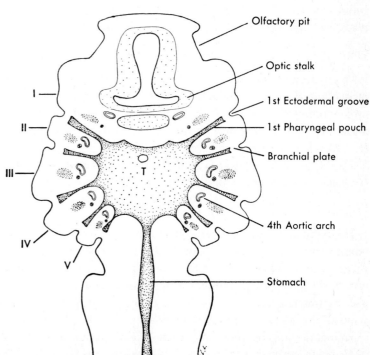

Olfactory pit

Optic stalk

1st Ectodermal groove

1st Pharyngeal pouch

Branchial plate

4th Aortic arch

Stomach

I
II
III
IV
V

Fig. 1-7. Frontal section of embryonic frog pharynx. **I** to **V,** First five pharyngeal arches; **T,** thyroid evagination.

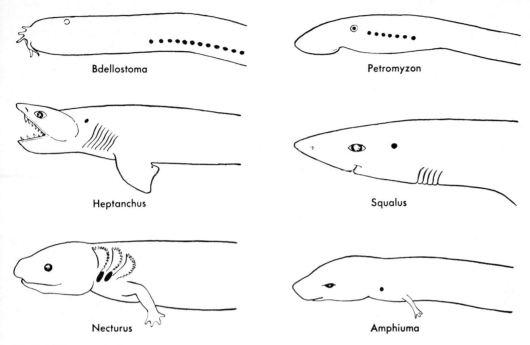

Fig. 1-8. Pharyngeal slits in selected agnathans (top), sharks (center), and tailed amphibians (bottom).

tures, as it usually does, a passageway is formed between the pharyngeal lumen and the exterior. This embryonic passageway is a **pharyngeal slit.** The slits may be permanent or temporary.

Pharyngeal slits are permanent in adults that live in water and breathe by gills (Fig. 1-8). Eight is the largest number of pouches and slits that forms in any jawed vertebrate, and that many are found only in primitive sharks. Agnathans have as many as 15 pouches and slits. Some urodeles retain one to three slits throughout life (Fig. 1-8, *Necturus* and *Amphiuma*, and Table 3-1).

Pharyngeal slits are temporary if the animal is going to live on land. Of the six pharyngeal pouches that form in frog embryos, four give rise to gill slits in tadpoles. These slits close when the tadpole metamorphoses into a frog. In reptiles, birds, and mammals no gills develop in the pouches, and the slits are transitory. Of the five pouches that develop in chicks, the first three rupture to the exterior and close again. Only one or two of the more anterior pouches of mammals may rupture. Cervical fistulas occasionally seen in human beings are usually the result of the failure of the cervical sinus (third and fourth slits) to close (Figs. 1-9 and 17-16).

Although the pharyngeal pouches of embryonic tetrapods rarely give rise to permanent slits, the first one becomes the auditory tube

Fig. 1-9. Cervical fistula resulting from persistent pharyngeal slit.

and middle ear cavity of tetrapods, and the second persists as the pouch of the palatine tonsil of mammals. The walls of several pouches give rise to endocrine tissue in all vertebrates.

PHARYNGEAL ARCHES

Each pharyngeal pouch or slit is separated from the next by a column of tissue called a pharyngeal arch (Figs. 1-6, 1-7, and 1-10). Each pharyngeal arch, whether in an adult fish or an embryonic human being, typically contains four basic structures, or the blastemas from which these structures develop. They are (1) a pharyngeal skeletal element (illustrated in an adult shark in Fig. 8-1), (2) branchiomeric muscles (Fig. 10-16, A), (3) branches of certain cranial nerves, and (4) an aortic arch (Fig. 1-5), which, at least in embryos, directly connects the ventral and dorsal aortas. These basic components are also found in front of the first pouch and, with perhaps some omissions, directly behind the last. Therefore a pharyngeal arch is a column of tissue located between two successive pharyngeal pouches or slits, and in front of the first pouch or slit and immediately behind the last. It is covered externally by ectoderm and internally by endoderm.

The upper and lower jaws and associated muscles, nerves, and vessels constitute the first, or **mandibular, arch.** The second, or **hyoid, arch** is behind the first pouch or slit. The remaining pharyngeal arches are referred to by number. Arches supporting a gill are often called **branchial arches.**

The boundaries of a pharyngeal arch can be determined from the exterior when there are ectodermal grooves or pharyngeal slits to serve as landmarks, and only then. If the grooves disappear or the slits close, the boundaries of the arches are lost and the components become reoriented. In most tetrapods, therefore, pharyngeal arches are anatomical entities in embryos only.

The primitive vertebrate pharynx was evidently a device for filtering food out of a respiratory water stream as does the pharynx of an amphioxus. The modifications that occurred in the pharynx of vertebrates that shifted from branchial to pulmonary respiration constitute one of the fascinating chapters of vertebrate history.

Dorsal, hollow central nervous system

The central nervous system consists of a brain and spinal cord and contains a central cavity, or **neurocoel.** Dorsal, hollow central nervous systems are found only in chordate animals. Their dorsal location and the cavity result from the fact that the central nervous system typically arises as a longitudinal **neural groove** in the dorsal ectoderm (Fig. 1-11). The groove subsequently sinks into the dorsal body wall

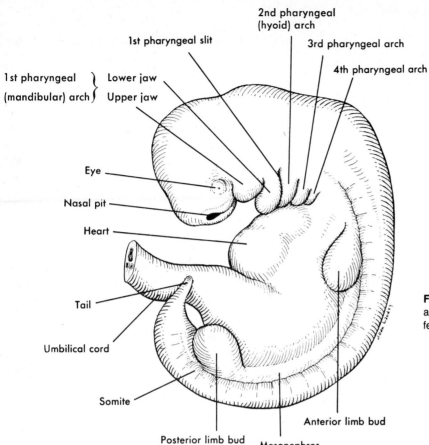

2nd pharyngeal
(hyoid) arch

3rd pharyngeal arch

4th pharyngeal arch

1st pharyngeal slit

1st pharyngeal
(mandibular) arch

Lower jaw

Upper jaw

Eye

Nasal pit

Heart

Tail

Umbilical cord

Somite

Posterior limb bud

Mesonephros

Anterior limb bud

Fig. 1-10. Human embryo approximately 4½ weeks after fertilization (5-mm stage).

Actual crown-rump length

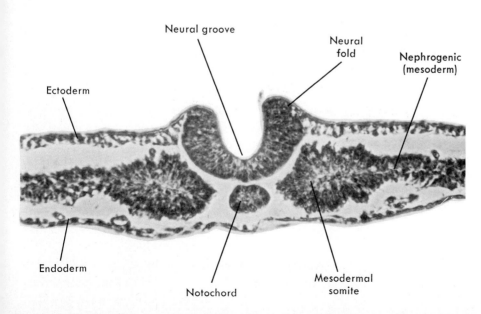

Neural groove

Neural
fold

Nephrogenic
(mesoderm)

Ectoderm

Endoderm

Notochord

Mesodermal
somite

Fig. 1-11. Cross section of 24-hour chick embryo showing neural groove, notochord, and mesodermal somites.

to form a hollow **neural tube.** The tube is wider anteriorly, and this part becomes the brain with its ventricles (Figs. 1-5 and 15-6).

Cyclostomes, teleosts, and ganoid fishes modify the basic pattern of neurocoel formation. Instead of forming a groove, the surface neural ectoderm forms a wedge-shaped **neural keel** that sinks into the tissue above the notochord. Eventually the keel separates from the surface and a·cavity forms within it by rearrangement of the cells in the center. The result is a typical dorsal, hollow nervous system.

Cranial and spinal nerves connect the central nervous system with the various organs of the body. The nerves, along with associated ganglia and plexuses, constitute the peripheral nervous system. The spinal nerves of most vertebrates are metameric (Fig. 15-8), arising at the level of each body segment and passing to the skin and muscles of that segment and to the viscera. Ten cranial nerves arise from the brain in fishes and amphibians and twelve in amniotes. The extra two nerves in higher vertebrates are spinal nerves that have become "trapped" within the skull.

SATELLITE CHARACTERISTICS
Skin

The skin of vertebrates is unique in that it consists of two layers, an epidermis of ectodermal origin and an underlying dermis of mesodermal origin (Fig. 5-10). Many types of defensive, lubricatory, nutritive, pheromonal, and homeostasis-maintaining glands develop from the skin, and the skin is modified locally to form membranes such as the transparent conjunctiva of the eye and the mucous membranes of the lips. It also forms a variety of appendages, such as cornified scales, nails, feathers, and hair. Also, the epidermis of vertebrates that live in water is different from that of vertebrates exposed to air.

Respiratory mechanisms

Most vertebrates carry on external respiration (exchange of respiratory gases between the animal and environment) by means of highly vascularized membranes located on the pharyngeal arches in the case of gills, and derived from the pharyngeal floor in the case of lungs (Fig. 1-5). In some species respiration takes place through the skin, the buccopharyngeal lining, and, in embryos, through special extraembryonic membranes that usually lie just inside the eggshell or in contact with the lining of the mother's uterus.

Coelom

Like many invertebrates, vertebrates are built like a "tube within a tube," having in the trunk a body cavity, or coelom, between the

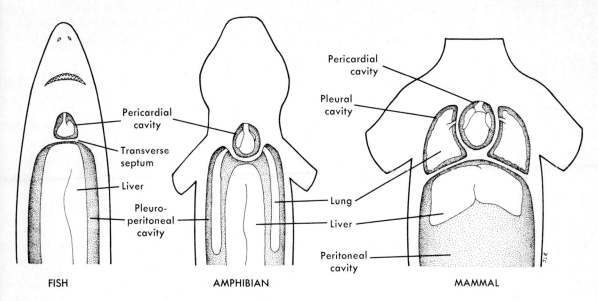

Fig. 1-12. Chief subdivisions of the coelom of vertebrates.

body wall and digestive tube. The coelom is subdivided in fishes, amphibians, and many reptiles into a **pericardial cavity** housing the heart and a **pleuroperitoneal cavity** housing most of the other viscera, including the lungs (Fig. 1-12). The pericardial and pleuroperitoneal cavities in these vertebrates are separated by a fibrous **transverse septum.** In some reptiles and in birds and mammals the lungs occupy separate **pleural cavities.** The transverse septum is then supplemented by other septa including, sometimes, muscular diaphragms. In many male mammals caudal outpocketings of the coelom house the testes, and these **scrotal cavities** are a fourth subdivision of the coelom.

Digestive organs

The digestive tract has specialized regions for the acquisition, processing, temporary storage, digestion, and absorption of food and for the elimination of the unabsorbed residue. Typical are the oral cavity, pharynx, esophagus (which is as long as the neck), stomach, and intestine. The last is often coiled, which increases the absorptive area without increasing the body length. The tract usually has a number of ceca, or diverticula, including a liver and pancreas.

The terminal segment of the digestive tract in all but a few vertebrates is the **cloaca,** which opens to the exterior via the **vent.** All vertebrate embryos develop a cloaca, but in modern fishes it becomes so shallow as to be nonexistent, and in mammals other than monotremes it becomes subdivided into two or three passageways, each with its own exit to the outside. The opening of the intestine is then the **anus**.

Urinogenital organs

Kidneys and gonads arise close together in the roof of the coelom (Fig. 1-2, *G* and *K*), and the two systems share certain passageways. Kidneys (nephroi) are the chief organs for elimination of water in those species in which this is necessary. (It is not necessary in marine or desert animals.) They also assist in maintaining an appropriate electrolyte balance. In the most primitive vertebrates, fluid and certain wastes were removed from the coelom by microscopic kidney tubules resembling somewhat the nephridia of earthworms. In most vertebrates, however, the substances to be excreted are collected by the tubules directly from the blood. The tubules transmit the substances to a pair of longitudinal ducts that empty into the cloaca or urinary bladder or to the exterior.

Reproductive organs include gonads, ducts, accessory glands, storage chambers, and copulatory mechanisms. Early in development all vertebrate embryos are bisexual, having gonadal and duct primordia for both sexes. If the animal is genetically constituted to become a female, the gonad primordia develop into ovaries, and only the female ducts differentiate. If the animal is to become a male, the gonad primordia become testes, and the male ducts differentiate. The duct system associated with the opposite sex largely disappears. Cyclostomes lack reproductive ducts. Their sperm and eggs are shed into the coelom and exit via a urinogenital papilla behind the anus.

Circulatory system

Whole blood is confined to arteries, veins, capillaries, and sinusoids. The heart, located ventral or caudal to the pharynx, pumps blood into a ventral aorta and then through aortic arches to the dorsal aorta. The latter conducts the blood caudad (Fig. 1-5). Vertebrates also have a lymphatic vascular system.

Sense organs

Vertebrates have a wide variety of general and special sense organs (**receptors**) that monitor the constantly changing external and internal environments. Receptors will be discussed in Chapter 16.

CHAPTER SUMMARY

1. The vertebrate body consists of head, trunk containing a coelom, tail beginning at the vent or anus, paired fins or limbs, and median fins in fishes.

2. Vertebrates have a dorsal, hollow nervous system, a notochord and pharyngeal pouches in the embryo at least, and a vertebral column except in agnathans.

3. The notochord is the first axial skeletal structure to appear in embryos. In agnathans it is surmounted by lateral neural cartilages. In jawed vertebrates it is typically surrounded by cartilaginous or bony vertebrae, and it either is constricted within vertebrae or disappears except for intervertebral vestiges such as the pulpy nucleus of mammals.

4. Pharyngeal pouches tend to rupture to the exterior to form temporary or permanent pharyngeal slits. They become gill slits in fishes and larval amphibians, and they close again in lung-breathing tetrapods. Separating each pharyngeal pouch, and in front of the first and behind the last, is a pharyngeal arch.

5. Pharyngeal arches contain a skeleton, branchiomeric muscles, a branch of a cranial nerve, and an aortic arch. They are not readily distinguishable after the pharyngeal slits close. They support gills in gill-breathing species. The first two constitute the mandibular and hyoid arches.

6. The nervous system consists of central and peripheral systems. The central nervous system typically arises as a dorsal ectodermal groove that sinks into the body to form a tube above the notochord. In some fishes it arises as a neural keel. The peripheral nervous system consists of nerves and associated ganglia and plexuses. There is a wide variety of general and special receptors.

7. Vertebrates have bilateral symmetry and are metameric in numerous systems. They have a two-layered skin, and they respire chiefly via gills, lungs, skin, or buccopharyngeal lining and via extraembryonic membranes in embryos.

8. There are at least two coelomic chambers (pericardial and pleuroperitoneal) and sometimes four (pleural, pericardial, peritoneal, scrotal).

9. A typical digestive tract consists of oral cavity, pharynx, esophagus, stomach, intestine, cloaca or its derivative, and numerous glandular or nonglandular diverticula.

10. The urinogenital system includes kidneys, gonads, ducts, storage chambers, accessory glands, and copulatory organs.

11. The circulatory system includes circulating cells, heart, arteries, veins, capillaries, sinusoids, and lymphatics.

SELECTED READING

Wessells, N.K.: An essay on vertebrates. In Vertebrate structures and functions, San Francisco, 1974, W.H. Freeman and Co., Publishers.

CHAPTER 2

Vertebrate beginnings and some simple chordates

OSTRACODERMS AND THE ORIGIN OF CHORDATES

The oldest vertebrates that we have knowledge of are the ostracoderms (Fig. 2-1). These fishes lived chiefly in fresh water from the early Ordovician to the late Devonian periods. They had no jaws and no paired fins and are thought to have been mostly filter feeders. This means that they filtered food particles out of the stream of respiratory water that was continually flowing into their pharynx and over their gills. Broad plates of bone were embedded in the dermis of their head and anterior trunk, and the more caudal parts of the body had smaller bony scales. These bony plates and scales provided a protective armor that inspired their nickname, "armored fishes." The oldest ostracoderms belong to the order Heterostraci, class Agnatha. We know about these fishes because their bony skin made it possible for them to become fossilized and for humans to examine them nearly 500 million years later.

The broad outlines of vertebrate history after the ostracoderms have been remarkably well determined. The jawless ostracoderms were followed by placoderms—jawed fishes (Fig. 3-4)—which were followed by the rest of the known jawed fishes and, eventually, by tetrapods (Fig. 3-10). The perplexing problem is, "Who preceded the ostracoderms?"

In this chapter we will meet the oldest known vertebrates. We will speculate concerning their invertebrate predecessors and possible kinship with protochordates. Then the best-known protochordates—sea squirts and the amphioxus—will be described. Finally, we will examine the structure of the ammocoete, a vertebrate larva that bears a remarkable resemblance to protochordates.

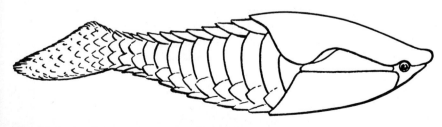

Fig. 2-1. Ostracoderm, a very ancient armored, jawless fish.

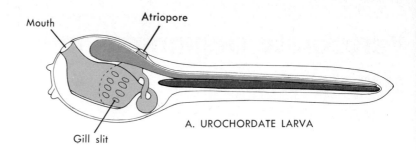

A. UROCHORDATE LARVA

Fig. 2-2. Chordate larvae showing basic architectural pattern. *Dark red,* notochord; *medium red,* dorsal nervous system; *light red,* alimentary canal. In **A,** a larval sea squirt, the left wall of the pharynx has been removed to show the gill slits in the right wall leading to the atrium.

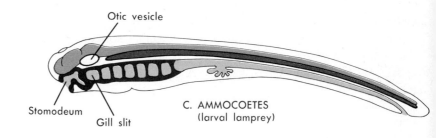

B. AMPHIOXUS LARVA

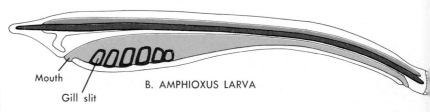

C. AMMOCOETES
(larval lamprey)

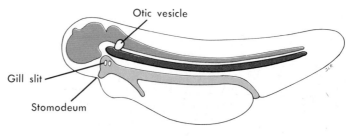

D. LARVAL AMPHIBIAN

Although we can follow vertebrate history forward from ostracoderms with reasonable confidence, we can do little but speculate as to the most probable invertebrate ancestors of ostracoderms. This is because there are no fossil links in pre-Ordovician rocks that might suggest the nature of transitional forms. The absence of fossilization suggests a paucity of mineralized tissues in the ancestors of ostracoderms. Therefore dermal bone may have appeared with comparative suddenness in soft-bodied invertebrates that already possessed a notochord, dorsal nervous system, and pharyngeal slits. It is not necessary to design such a soft-bodied animal out of pure imagination; similar animals already exist. We call them protochordates, and they include urochordates and the amphioxus (Fig. 2-2, *A* and *B*). Perhaps they provide some clue, however meager, to the ancestors of ostracoderms. It may be that some protochordate-like organism gave rise to the known protochordates and to a divergent line that led to ostracoderms.

We are not at a dead end in our thinking when we derive protochordates and vertebrates from a common ancestor. We find genetic codes very similar to those of larval chordates in acorn tongue worms and larval echinoderms. Acorn tongue worms (Fig. 2-15) have pharyngeal slits and a dorsal nerve cord, like chordates, and a ventral nerve cord, like invertebrates. However, they have no recognizable notochord. Some acorn tongue worms have ciliated larvae, and all are filter feeders. These hemichordates evidently have genetic affinities with chordates. They also have affinities with echinoderms. Larval echinoderms are so similar to larval acorn tongue worms that the latter were at one time mistaken for starfish larvae. Echinoderms, like ostracoderms, have mineralized tissue in their mesoderm (not in their ectoderm, as in molluscs, for instance), and, like amphioxus, they form their mesoderm and coelom as outpocketings of their archenteron (Fig. 4-5). Finally, echinoderms, acorn tongue worms, amphioxuses, urochordates, and vertebrates are all deuterostomes, meaning that they convert their blastopore, the original opening into their archenteron, into an anus and develop a new mouth. This trait, shared with only one other invertebrate group (Chaetognatha), is further evidence of a genetic affinity among these organisms.

Perhaps the most convincing evidence for genetic ties between vertebrates on the one hand and protochordates, hemichordates, and echinoderms on the other hand is the ammocoete, a free-swimming, filter-feeding larval stage of lampreys. The ammocoete larva resembles protochordate larvae very closely (Fig. 2-2).

A chart summarizing possible phylogenetic relationships among echinoderms, hemichordates, protochordates, and vertebrates is

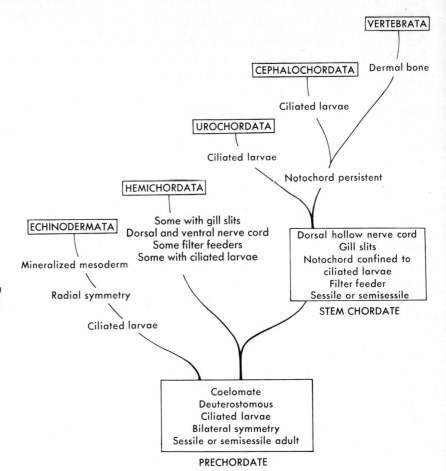

Fig. 2-3. One of several possible hypothetical relationships between echinoderms, protochordates, and vertebrates.

given in Fig. 2-3. It derives vertebrates from a hypothetical sessile or semisessile, bilaterally symmetrical, filter-feeding, deuterostomous stem chordate having a dorsal, hollow nerve cord, pharyngeal gill slits, and a notochord confined to the larva, where it stiffened the muscular tail for locomotion. The presence of a notochord throughout life in any chordate would then be an instance of **neoteny.** (Neoteny is the prolonged retention of a larval character.)

One of the unsettled problems about the origin of vertebrates is whether they originated in fresh or salt water. Paleontologists who think that they originated in fresh water point to the absence of vertebrate fossils in *marine* Ordovician rocks. This is a formidable argument. Others believe that such fossils may well exist but have not yet been found because at that time vertebrates were few in number and therefore fossils would be rare. They point out that negative evidence cannot be conclusive. Arguments supporting both sides have been reviewed by Stahl.[9]

PROTOCHORDATES

In 1874 Ernst Haeckel established the phylum Chordata, incorporating the subphyla Urochordata, Cephalochordata, and Vertebrata. The phylum was erected to accommodate all organisms having a notochord, pharyngeal slits, and a dorsal, hollow nervous system. Members of the two lower subphyla have come to be known as protochordates. They are all marine organisms. Our interest in them stems from the hypothesis that they share a common ancestor with animals with backbones.

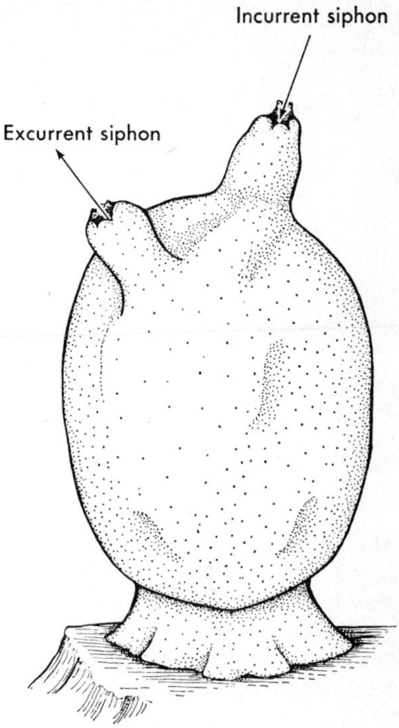

Urochordates (Tunicata)

The notochord in urochordates is confined to the tail of larvae. Urochordates that metamorphose, that is, the **sea squirts** (Figs. 2-4 and 2-5), lose the notochord during metamorphosis and usually become sessile adults. A second group of urochordates, the tiny **larvaceans** (Fig. 2-6), remain free-swimming larvae throughout life.* The notochord strengthens the tail for locomotion. The third group of urochordates, **thaliaceans** (Fig. 2-7), have no tail at all and, therefore, no notochord. They are propelled forward by a stream of water that is forcefully expelled from their excurrent siphon. All urochordates are surrounded by a tough cellulose-like tunic that is often beautifully colored and usually transparent. This tunic earned them their alternate name, tunicates.

Larval sea squirts are free-swimming organisms about 6 mm long. They have no separate head, so the nerve cord commences in the trunk in a brainlike swelling containing a ventricle. Respiratory water enters the pharynx and passes through pharyngeal gill slits into the atrium, a chamber surrounding the pharynx that also receives the end of the digestive tract and genital ducts. From the atrium, water, digestive tract residues, and reproductive cells are flushed to the exterior via an atriopore.

At metamorphosis the larva attaches to a substrate via its three adhesive papillae, the tail is resorbed, the notochord disappears, and a rearrangement of internal organs takes place. The larval mouth becomes an incurrent siphon, and the atriopore becomes an excurrent siphon. A water stream laden with food particles and oxygen passes via the incurrent siphon into the pharynx (now the largest organ in the body). Here, food is filtered out of the water stream and ensnared in mucus secreted by the endostyle, a glandular groove in the pharyngeal floor. The particles are then moved by papillae and ciliary action into the stomach while water passes over the gills and into the

MOLGULA

Fig. 2-4. Adult sea squirt.

---

*This is an instance of paedogenesis, the attainment of sexual maturity while in the larval state.

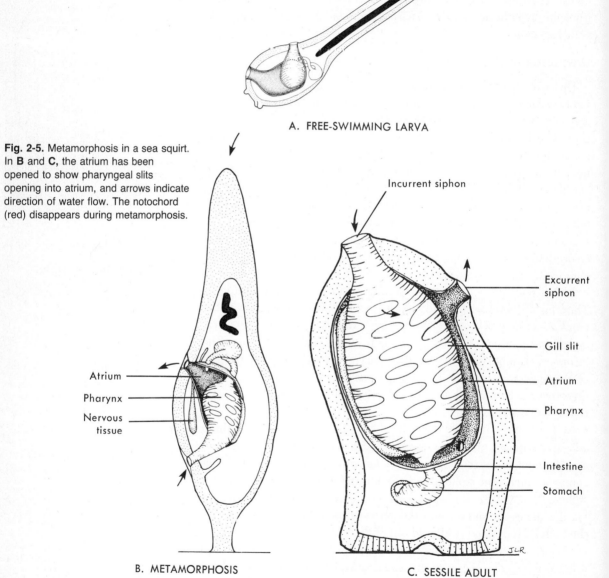

A. FREE-SWIMMING LARVA

Fig. 2-5. Metamorphosis in a sea squirt. In **B** and **C,** the atrium has been opened to show pharyngeal slits opening into atrium, and arrows indicate direction of water flow. The notochord (red) disappears during metamorphosis.

Incurrent siphon

Excurrent siphon

Gill slit

Atrium

Pharynx

Intestine

Stomach

Atrium

Pharynx

Nervous tissue

B. METAMORPHOSIS

C. SESSILE ADULT

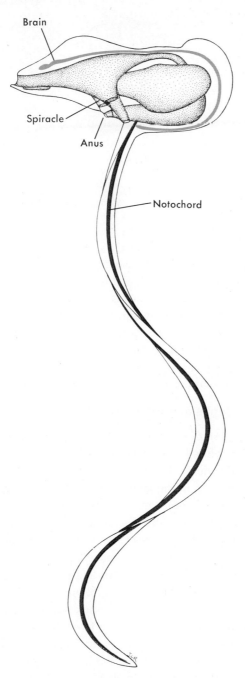

Brain

Spiracle

Anus

Notochord

Fig. 2-6. A larvacean. The neural tube continues into the tail along with the notochord.

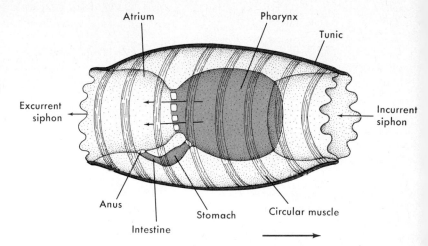

Fig. 2-7. Thaliacean showing direction of respiratory current through gill slits (small arrows) and direction of locomotion (large arrow). Digestive tract (red) is seen through semitransparent tunic and body wall.

atrium. The animal is, therefore, a filter feeder. The forceful discharge of water from the atrium via the excurrent siphon whenever the animal is irritated inspired the descriptive name, sea squirt.

In adult sea squirts the nervous system is reduced to a solid elongated neural ganglion, a remnant of the "brain" of the larva, with nerve strands radiating to all parts of the body. There are no known special sense organs. Arising from each end of the heart, located near the pharynx, is a vessel. Blood is propelled first into one vessel for several pulsations and then into the other.

Cephalochordates: amphioxus

Amphioxus means "sharp at both ends." Any member of the subphylum Cephalochordata may be called an amphioxus, or lancelet (little spear), but the correct generic name for the lancelet commonly studied in the laboratory is *Branchiostoma* (Fig. 2-8). *Asymmetron* is the only other genus in the subphylum.

Lancelets are found a short distance out from sandy beaches throughout most of the globe. They quickly burrow into sand with eel-like movements, make a U turn, and then emerge until only the oral hood area is protruding for filter feeding. Adults vary from less than 2 cm to more than 8 cm in length, the largest being *Branchiostoma californiense*. Off the coast of China, amphioxuses are collected in quantity and sold as a table delicacy.

An amphioxus is semitransparent but becomes opaque when immersed in preserving fluids. The body is practically all trunk and tail. A pair of longitudinal ridges of unknown function, the **metapleural folds,** hang along each side of the midventral line beneath the pharynx (Fig. 2-10, *C*).

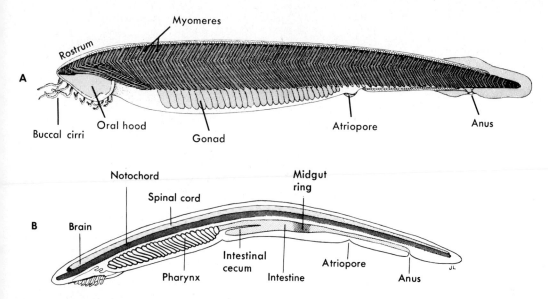

Fig. 2-8. *Branchiostoma.* **A,** Mature adult. **B,** Internal structure of young specimen.

Notochord. The notochord extends from the tip of the rostrum to the tip of the tail (Fig. 2-8, *B*). It consists of muscular discs arranged like a long column of coins separated by fluid-filled spaces. The muscle fibers in each disc run transversely and have dorsal extensions that end near nerve terminals from which they evidently receive their motor innervation.[7] The muscle resembles that of invertebrates in that the protein is paramyosin. Contraction of the muscles increases the stiffness of the notochord, which may aid in swimming. Its continuation to the very tip of the rostrum—unlike in any other chordate—may be an adaptation for burrowing in sand (Fig. 2-9). Surrounding the notochord is a thick collagenous connective tissue sheath. The only other skeleton is fibrous rods that support the gill bars, buccal cirri, and fins.

Skin (Fig. 5-1). The skin consists of a single layer of epidermal cells and a thin dermis. Interspersed among the epidermal cells are unicellular glands. Larval skin is ciliated but the cilia later disappear, and the epidermis secretes a cuticle resembling that of annelids. Immediately internal to the dermis is the body wall muscle.

Body wall musculature. The body wall muscle is used for locomotion. It consists of an uninterrupted series of <-shaped muscle segments called **myomeres,** extending from the anterior tip of the body to the tip of the tail. Each myomere is separated from the next by a connective tissue partition, the **myoseptum,** to which the anteroposteriorly directed muscle bundles attach. Since the myomeres are

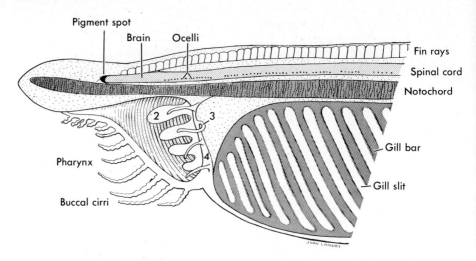

Fig. 2-9. Cephalic end of an amphioxus shown in sagittal section. **1,** Vestibule bounded by oral hood; **2,** part of the wheel organ projecting into vestibule; **3,** velar tentacle; **4,** velum.

<-shaped, cross sections of the body wall include several successive myomeres (Fig. 2-10).

Nervous system. The amphioxus exhibits a hollow central nervous system resembling that of vertebrates in basic structure. However, only two brain subdivisions can be detected: an anterior **prosencephalon,** containing a single ventricle, and a more posterior **deuteroencephalon.** The prosencephalon is lined with cilia and long filamentous projections of the ependymal cells, demonstrable only with electron microscopy.

Attempts to homologize the parts of the brain of the amphioxus with those of a vertebrate have not been entirely successful. In an amphioxus the notochord extends anterior to the brain. Does this indicate the absence of a forebrain? The answer must await further research. Whether or not the nerves that supply the gills should be considered cranial nerves complicates the problem. If the branchial nerves are omitted, there are seven cranial nerves (including the apical, or terminal, nerve). If the branchial and oral nerves are included, there are 39. The absence of semicircular canals, eyes, lateral-line system, and foramen magnum deprives us of landmarks that would be helpful. Because of these difficulties, it is not possible to decide just where the brain ends and the spinal cord begins.

The canal within the spinal cord is lined by nonnervous supporting elements called **ependymal cells.** Near the caudal end of the cord the nervous elements disappear, and the cord is composed of ependymal

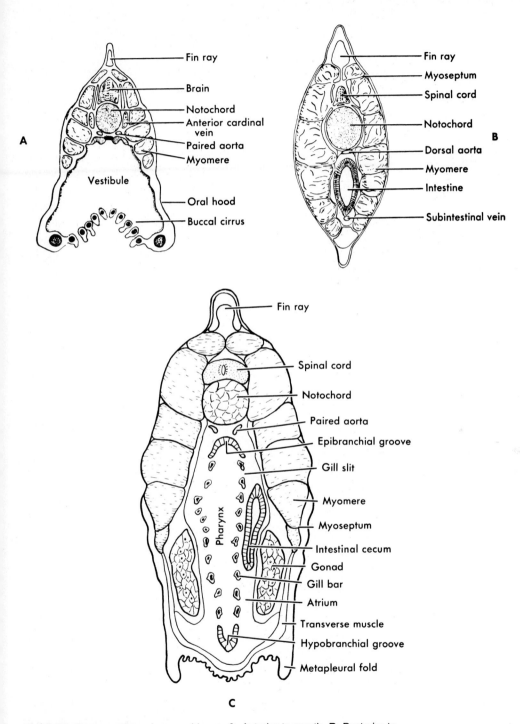

Fig. 2-10. Cross sections of an amphioxus. **A,** Anterior to mouth. **B,** Posterior to atriopore. **C,** Level of pharynx.

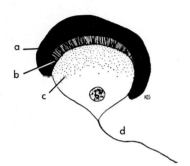

Fig. 2-11. Ocellus (light receptor) from spinal cord of an amphioxus. **a,** Melanocyte; **b,** apical border of receptor cell; **c,** receptor cell; **d,** process for conduction of impulse.

cells alone. A similar situation occurs in vertebrates. A single membrane (**meninx**) surrounds the brain and cord.

Spinal nerves emerge from the cord metamerically. They consist of dorsal roots that contain sensory and motor fibers, the latter supplying only visceral organs. The "ventral roots" are not nerve roots at all but tubes that conduct extensions of the body wall muscle cells into the spinal cord where they receive their innervation.[6] Since the somites of the two sides are not exactly opposite one another, the roots of the left and right sides do not arise directly opposite one another.

Special sense organs. The relatively small size of the brain is correlated with the paucity of organs of special sense. There are no retinas, semicircular canals, or lateral-line organs. It is doubtful whether an olfactory epithelium is present. Chemoreceptors are particularly abundant on the buccal cirri and velar tentacles, where they monitor the incurrent water stream. They are also scattered on other surfaces of the body, the tail being more sensitive than the trunk. Touch receptors, which elicit withdrawal, are present over the entire body surface.

The most characteristic sense organs are the light-sensitive, pigmented **ocelli** embedded within the ventrolateral walls of the spinal cord (Fig. 2-11). Each ocellus consists of a receptor cell and a caplike melanocyte. The melanocyte lies between the receptor cell and the incoming light rays and is a cell packed with large melanin pigment granules. A conducting process extends from the base of the receptor cell. Ocelli probably assist in orienting the animal as it burrows in the sand.

Filter feeding and respiration. The vestibule (Fig. 2-9) is broadly open to the sea ventrally. The mouth is an opening in the velum and leads to the pharynx. Cilia on the pharyngeal surface of the gill bars create a steady flow of water through the mouth and into the pharynx. A set of stubby projections in the vestibule, the wheel organ, is covered with sticky mucus that retrieves some of the heavier food particles that miss the mouth, and it directs these through the mouth along with the water stream. Buccal cirri partially strain the water as it enters the vestibule and monitor it chemically.

Food is processed as follows: In the pharyngeal floor there is a **hypobranchial groove,** or endostyle (Fig. 2-10, *C*). In the roof is an **epibranchial groove.** On the gill bars, ciliated peripharyngeal bands connect the two grooves. The cells of these bands and grooves secrete mucus. Food particles trapped in the mucus are incorporated into a stringy food cord that is propelled by cilia dorsally into the epibranchial groove and then caudad into the midgut behind the pharynx. Here it is temporarily arrested by the **midgut ring** (Fig. 2-8, *B*) and mixed with digestive juices. Some of the digesting foodstuffs then

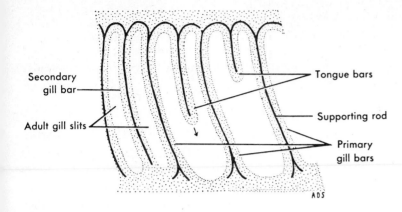

Secondary gill bar

Adult gill slits

Tongue bars

Supporting rod

Primary gill bars

A D S

Fig. 2-12. Tongue bars in the pharyngeal wall of an amphioxus growing ventrad (arrow), subdividing the larval slits in two.

pass beyond the ring into the hindgut, and some are driven forward by cilia into the **intestinal cecum.** This is an evagination of the midgut that arises in the same way as the liver of vertebrates, although the two do not function alike. The cecum secretes enzymes, and its lining cells phagocytose the smallest food particles and digest them by intracellular digestion. Extracellular digestion takes place in other parts of the digestive tract. The intestine opens to the exterior via an anus.

Relieved of food particles, water passes between the gill bars into the atrium and then to the outside via an atriopore. The number of gill slits varies, but it exceeds 60 in adults. During metamorphosis each larval slit is divided into two by the down growth of a tongue bar (Fig. 2-12). Much respiration takes place through the skin.

Circulatory system. The heart consists only of a fibrous venous sinus (sinus venosus), and the colorless blood is pumped by two muscular pulsating vessels. These are the cecal vein leading to the sinus venosus and the ventral aorta emerging from it (Fig. 2-13). The remaining blood vessels have thin walls, and histologically the arteries, veins, and capillaries are alike. Arteries are vessels that carry blood from the sinus venosus to the gills and then to the body wall and viscera. Veins collect blood from these locations and return it to the sinus venosus.

Arterial blood courses forward beneath the pharynx in the muscular, contractile ventral aorta that commences in the sinus venosus. From the ventral aorta, afferent branchial arteries pass up the gill bars. Before joining the dorsal aorta, these arteries contribute to vascular channels supplying protonephridia (excretory organs). The blood then enters the paired dorsal aortas. These pass caudad above the pharynx and unite just behind it to form an unpaired aorta. This distributes blood by paired vessels to the body wall and by median vessels to the visceral organs. The dorsal aorta continues into the tail as the caudal artery.

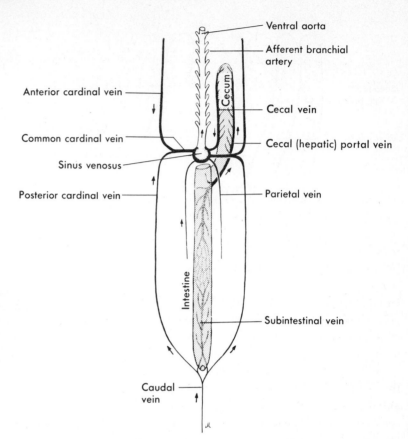

Fig. 2-13. Basic venous channels and ventral aorta of an amphioxus, dorsal view. The cecum has been rotated 90 degrees around the long axis. The cecal portal vein in life is ventral to the cecum, and the cecal vein is dorsal. The conventional term "hepatic portal" for the cecal portal vein is not appropriate.

The venous channels (Fig. 2-13) are similar to the embryonic venous channels of vertebrates. From the capillaries of the tail a single caudal vein courses forward and divides into right and left posterior cardinal veins. These pass forward in the lateral body wall to a point just behind the pharynx. Here the posterior cardinal veins meet the anterior cardinal veins from the rostrum and pharyngeal wall. The blood then enters a common cardinal vein leading to the sinus venosus. Two parietal veins drain the dorsolateral body wall of the trunk. These also terminate in the sinus venosus.

Drainage from the visceral organs is via a median subintestinal vein arising from the caudal vein. The subintestinal vein passes cephalad along the ventral surface of the intestine. There it breaks up into smaller channels, receives tributaries, and reconvenes to continue forward as a portal vein ending in the capillaries of the cecum. From the cecum the contractile cecal vein pumps blood to the sinus venosus.

Urinogenital system. The amphioxus is **dioecious;** that is, ovaries and testes are not in the same individual. Mature gonads are visible

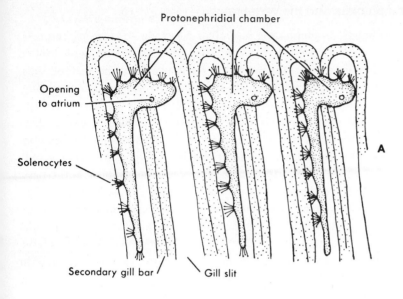

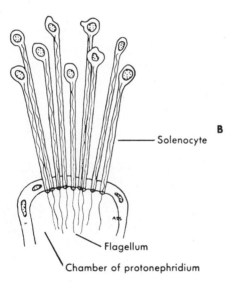

Fig. 2-14. Excretory organs of an amphioxus. **A,** Three protonephridia. **B,** A cluster of solenocytes. They project into the coelom at their free end and empty into the protonephridial chamber at their base.

through the muscle and skin of the trunk. Sperm or eggs are shed directly into the water within the atrium.

Removal of coelomic wastes is accomplished by protonephridia lying beside the secondary gill bars. Each protonephridium consists of clusters of solenocytes that project into the coelom and a chamber that opens into the atrium via a small pore (Fig. 2-14). The flagellum causes a current of coelomic fluid to enter a solenocyte and pass down the stalk. The excretory mechanism resembles the nephridia of marine annelids and the flame cells of some other invertebrates.

Amphioxus and the vertebrates

Although an amphioxus resembles a vertebrate in many respects, differences are evident. An amphioxus has almost no cephalization and no paired sense organs; it has a notochord but no vertebral column; it has gill slits but in large numbers, emptying into an atrium; it has a dorsal, hollow nervous system, but the brain lacks the major vertebrate subdivisions; it has a segmented musculature, but the segments extend to the anterior tip of the head; it has median fins but no paired ones; it has a two-layered skin, but the outer layer is only one cell thick; it has arterial and venous channels similar to the basic channels of vertebrates but no muscular heart; it is coelomate, but the coelom is greatly restricted; liquid wastes are removed from coelomic fluid as in lower vertebrates, but the excretory protonephridia resemble those of nonchordates. A hypothetical relationship of the amphioxus to other protochordates and to vertebrates is diagramed in Fig. 2-3.

HEMICHORDATES

Ten years after the phylum Chordata was established William Bateson added acorn tongue worms as a subphylum, Hemichordata (Fig. 2-15). He did this because acorn tongue worms exhibit certain fea-

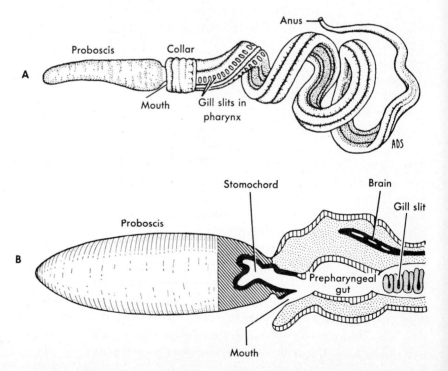

Fig. 2-15. An acorn tongue worm, *Saccoglossus.* **A,** Entire worm. **B,** Head, sagittal section (except proboscis).

tures characteristic of lower chordates. First, they have a dorsal nerve cord that arises as a groove of ectodermal cells, which, in the collar region only, sinks under the skin to establish a dorsal, hollow brain-like vesicle (Fig. 2-15, *B*). Second, they have gill slits in the pharyngeal walls. Third, they have a short diverticulum of the foregut extending forward into the proboscis and called a **stomochord.** Bateson was convinced that the stomochord was either a primitive or an aberrant notochord. Therefore he felt justified in enlarging the phylum Chordata.

Hemichordates are not widely accepted as protochordates, chiefly because there is little evidence for homologizing the stomochord with a notochord. Instead, hemichordates are most often classified as a phylum close to echinoderms, with which they have marked affinities expressed especially in their free-swimming larvae. The phylum Hemichordata usually includes, in addition to acorn tongue worms (class Enteropneusta), two other classes (Pterobranchia and Planctosphaeroidea) that have little resemblance to one another or to enteropneusts.

THE AMMOCOETE LARVA

Ammocoete is the name given to the larval lamprey (Fig. 2-2, *C*). *Ammocoetes* was a genus at one time when these larvae were erroneously believed to be adult protochordates. The ammocoete, which lives from 2 to 6 years as a burrowing freshwater larva, is a filter feeder with all the basic and satellite features of a vertebrate except a vertebral column. The existence of such a larva in the lowest vertebrates strengthens the hypothesis that vertebrates share a common ancestry with protochordates.

The dorsal, hollow nervous system consists of a brain with the three vertebrate subdivisions—forebrain, midbrain, hindbrain—and spinal cord. The notochord underlies the hindbrain and extends almost to the tip of the tail. The pharynx has seven pairs of gill pouches opening directly to the outside via gill slits. A complicated subpharyngeal gland (endostyle) lies ventral to the pharynx and opens into it by a short duct (Fig. 17-12). The gland secretes mucus that entraps food particles entering the pharynx with the respiratory water stream. The *adult lamprey* is not a filter feeder, and much of the gland degenerates when the larva metamorphoses. The cells that remain organize thyroid follicles like those of higher vertebrates.

The lateral body wall is chiefly muscle arranged as myomeres that provide locomotion (Fig. 2-16). The epidermis contains many unicellular mucous glands, but, unlike that of the amphioxus, it is stratified (Fig. 5-4). The dermis is thin and fibrous.

Special sense organs are more numerous than in the amphioxus.

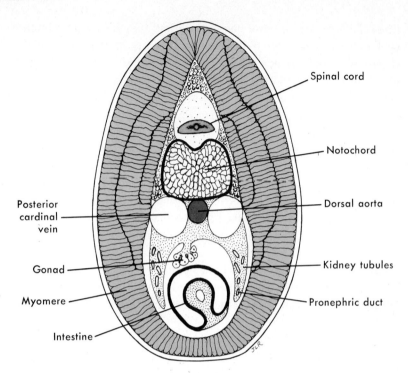

Spinal cord

Notochord

Dorsal aorta

Posterior cardinal vein

Kidney tubules

Gonad

Pronephric duct

Myomere

Intestine

Fig. 2-16. Relatively old ammocoete in cross section just behind liver. Several myomeres are cut in a single section because they curve caudad in passing inward from the skin.

From a median naris on the dorsum of the head a nasal canal slants downward and backward to open into a median olfactory sac, the receptor for smell. The sac lies just anterior to the brain, to which it is connected by a pair of olfactory nerves.

Two middorsal eyes are located just under the skin of the head, attached to the roof of the forebrain by stalks containing nerve fibers. These are the pineal and parapineal organs (Fig. 16-15, *A*). Each consists of a simple lens and receptor cells. Paired lateral eyes are deep under the skin and functionless.

An otic vesicle is located at the cephalic end of the hindbrain above the first gill chamber on each side (Fig. 2-2, *C*). The vesicles arise as fluid-filled invaginations of the ectoderm and develop into inner ears. Other fluid-filled receptors, the neuromast organs (Fig. 16-1), lie in the skin of the head and open onto the surface via pores. Their functions are discussed in Chapter 16.

The digestive tract is simple and straight from mouth to anus. The most cephalic part of the early larval tract is the stomodeum (Fig. 2-2, *C*), an invagination of the embryonic ectoderm that grew inward until it met and opened into the embryonic pharynx. In older larvae the stomodeum becomes a buccal funnel leading via a mouth into a buccal cavity at the end of which is a velum. Beyond the velum is the pharynx. Water is drawn into the mouth and pharynx by a pumping action of the pharyngeal muscles. The velum, consisting of two muscular flaps anchored to the wall of the buccal cavity, acts as a valve preventing the water from returning to the mouth when water pressure is high in the pharynx. Thus water is forced to exit by way of the gill slits. The food is chiefly diatoms that are ensnared in mucus from the subpharyngeal gland and propelled slowly toward the intestine, where digestion takes place. A short distance beyond the pharynx is a liver diverticulum and embedded in it is a gallbladder that disappears at metamorphosis when the nature of the food changes from diatoms to tissue fluids from the fish on which the adult lamprey is parasitic. There is no stomach. By relaxing the velum and closing the gill slits, which are also valved, the ammocoete can force debris out of its pharynx by way of the mouth in a kind of coughing action.

The circulatory system is typically vertebrate. The heart lies in a pericardial cavity just behind the pharynx. It has a sinus venosus, atrium, and ventricle. The pericardial cavity is broadly open to the main coelom, although it becomes a separate cavity in adults. Blood is pumped forward by the ventricle into the ventral aorta, which is unpaired near the heart but paired farther cephalad. From the ventral aorta, blood passes via afferent branchial arteries to the capillaries of the gills. Oxygenated blood then passes via efferent branchial arteries into the dorsal aorta, which courses caudad.

Venous blood returns from the head via a pair of anterior cardinal veins and from the trunk and tail by two posterior cardinal veins (Fig. 2-16). Anterior and posterior cardinals flow into a common cardinal vein that empties into the sinus venosus. Blood returns from the intestine via a ventral intestinal vein that ends in the capillaries of the liver. The ventral intestinal vein and its tributaries therefore constitute a hepatic portal system. From the liver, blood proceeds forward in a hepatic vein to the sinus venosus, atrium, and ventricle.

Because the ammocoete lives in fresh water it is faced with the constant necessity of eliminating excess water. This is accomplished by a pair of kidneys located anteriorly in the coelom (Fig. 2-16). The kidney of an early larva consists of three to six tubules with funnel-like nephrostomes that collect coelomic fluid secreted by vascular tufts called glomeruli (Fig. 14-2, *A*). Some of the constituents of the fluid are reabsorbed by the lining of the tubules. What remains is urine, and this passes into paired longitudinal ducts (Fig. 2-16, pronephric duct) that empty to the exterior via a median papilla just behind the anus. Between the kidneys is a rudimentary gonad that is paired in early larvae but unpaired in older ones.

CHAPTER SUMMARY

1. Ostracoderms are the oldest known vertebrates. Fossils are found chiefly in freshwater rocks of the Ordovician, Silurian, and Devonian periods. Whether they arose in fresh or salt water is not settled. Their dermis contained large bony plates and smaller bony scales. They had no jaws, generally lacked paired appendages, and were filter feeders. They have been placed in the class Agnatha.

2. Vertebrates may share ancestors with the echinoderms, hemichordates, urochordates, and cephalochordates. The common precursor may have been a filter-feeding, bilaterally symmetrical invertebrate with ciliated larvae and sessile or semisessile adults.

3. Protochordates have a notochord, gill slits, a dorsal, hollow nervous system, but no vertebral column. There are two groups, urochordates (tunicates) and cephalochordates.

4. Urochordates include sea squirts, permanently larval larvaceans, and tailless, notochordless thaliaceans. They have a tunic and a notochord confined to the larval tail.

5. Cephalochordates are represented by the amphioxus. The notochord is retained throughout life.

6. Hemichordates are of uncertain taxonomic status. They have a stomochord and are usually excluded from the phylum Chordata.

7. The ammocoete is the free-swimming, filter-feeding larva of lampreys. It provides evidence for genetic ties between protochordates and vertebrates.

LITERATURE CITED AND SELECTED READINGS

1. Barrington, E.J.W.: The biology of Hemichordata and Protochordata, San Francisco, 1965, W.H. Freeman and Co. Publishers.
2. Barrington, E.J.W., and Jefferies, R.P.S., editors: Protochordates. Symposium of the Zoological Society of London, no. 36, New York, 1975, Academic Press, Inc.
3. Berrill, N.J.: The tunicata, London, 1950, The Ray Society.
4. Berrill, N.J.: The origin of vertebrates, London, 1955, Oxford University Press.
5. Conklin, E.G.: The embryology of amphioxus, Journal of Morphology **54:**69, 1932.
6. Flood, P.R.: A peculiar mode of muscular innervation in amphioxus: light and electron microscopic studies of the so-called ventral roots, Journal of Comparative Neurology **126:**181, 1966.
7. Flood, P.R.: The connection between spinal cord and notochord in amphioxus *(Branchiostoma lanceolatum)*, Zeitschrift für Zellforschung und mikroskopische Anatomie **103:**115, 1970.
8. Grassé, P.-P., editor: Traité de zoologie, vol. 11. Echinodermes, stomochordes, procordes, Paris, 1948, Masson & Cie Editeurs.
9. Stahl, B.J.: Vertebrate history: problems in evolution, New York, 1974, McGraw-Hill Book Co.

CHAPTER 3

Parade of the vertebrates in time and taxa

In this chapter we will look at the major groups of vertebrates, meet representatives of each group, learn something about the natural history of a few, and note some opinions about who came from whom. At the end we will be reminded of the enormous potential for variation among individuals, which is a prerequisite for speciation.

There are probably 40,000 different known species of animals exhibiting vertebral columns. Fortunately for Noah one half of these are fishes. However, many amphibians and some reptiles and mammals share with fishes the freshwater ponds or streams as their permanent abode, and a much smaller number share the seas. Amphibians that can tolerate salt water are rare and do not live in the sea. A few snakes, iguanid lizards that live on marine algae, turtles, and crocodiles are predominantly or permanently marine. Among mammals, whales, porpoises, sea cows, and most dolphins are marine. Although birds are not permanent residents of water, many are entirely dependent on marine organisms for food. All the foregoing animals other than fishes, however, are evidently descendants of terrestrial ancestors and have returned to the water.

The purpose of this chapter is to present to the reader vertebrates that are referred to in other chapters, and to introduce their probable ancestors and nearest living relatives. The printed program for this parade is the abridged classification of vertebrates at the end of the book.

VERTEBRATE TAXA

Natural classification is a device for lumping into groups (taxa) animals that are genetically similar. The chief vertebrate taxa are classes, subclasses, superorders, orders, suborders, families, genera, and species. Fig. 3-1 lists the classes that are generally recognized, although Agnatha and Acanthodii are not always given class status.

Agnathans lack jaws and hence are **agnathostomes;** all other vertebrates are **gnathostomes.** Commencing with amphibians, vertebrates typically have four legs (sometimes modified as wings or paddles);

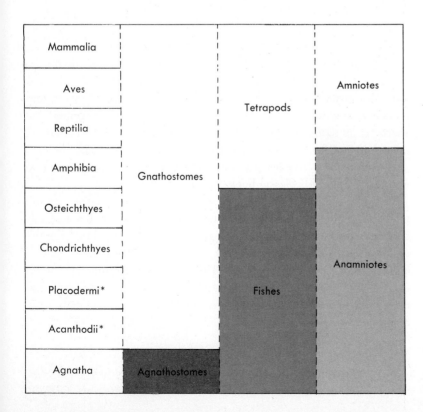

Fig. 3-1. Major categories of vertebrates. Classes are listed in the first column. Asterisks indicate extinct groups.

	Spiny dogfish	**Spotted necturus**	**Domestic cat**
Class	Chondrichthyes	Amphibia	Mammalia
Subclass	Elasmobranchii	Lissamphibia	Eutheria
Superorder			Ferae
Order	Selachii	Caudata	Carnivora
Suborder	Squaloidea		Fissipedia
Family		Proteidae	Felidae
Genus and species	*Squalus acanthias*	*Necturus maculosus*	*Felis cattus*

hence they are **tetrapods.** Commencing with reptiles, vertebrates exhibit a special membrane that surrounds the developing embryo. This membrane is the **amnion,** and animals that possess it are said to be **amniotes.** Fishes and amphibians do not exhibit this membrane and are **anamniotes.**

Since the time of Carl von Linné (Latin, Linnaeus), a Swedish naturalist, taxonomic nomenclature has been latinized by agreement among zoologists of the world. This enables zoologists of all languages to understand one another without translation when the name of any animal is mentioned. For instance, not every zoologist knows what "un chat," "die Katze," or "el gato" is. All these words refer to the common domestic cat, but *Felis cattus* is the taxonomic name for this species. The generic name *Felis* separates certain cats—mountain lion, European wildcat, domestic cat, and others—from lions, tigers, leopards, and so forth, which have been placed in the genus *Panthera*. *Felis cattus* separates domestic cats from mountain lions (*F. concolor*) and from European wildcats (*F. sylvestrus*). The binomial designation for a species was introduced by Linnaeus in the tenth edition (1758) of his classic book *Systema Naturae*.

In the box above is one classification for the spiny dogfish, spotted necturus, and domestic cat. Many taxonomic names, when translated, characterize the taxon, making it easier to remember. Thus Chondrichthyes means "cartilaginous fishes," Carnivora means "flesh eaters," and *maculosus* means "spotted." The anatomical terminology at the end of the book contains the stems from which many taxonomic names have been derived. Others can be found in an unabridged dictionary.

AGNATHA: THE FIRST VERTEBRATES

The class Agnatha includes two groups of jawless fishes—the ancient, bony **ostracoderms** and the boneless **cyclostomes.** Ostraco-

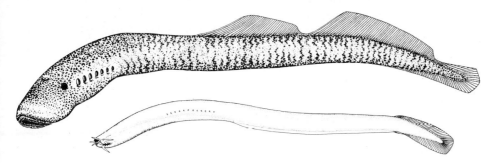

Fig. 3-2. Lamprey *Petromyzon* above; hagfish *Bdellostoma* below.

Fig. 3-3. Fossil lamprey *Mayomyzon* from the Carboniferous period.
(From Bardack and Zangerl.[4])

derms (Fig. 2-1) are the oldest known vertebrates. A bony armor was present in the skin of the entire body, and, in addition, their head contained a deeper skeleton of bone and considerable cartilage. Some were 2-3 cm long, and others attained a length of up to 30 cm. Ostracoderms are found in four extinct orders ranging from the Cambrian to the Devonian periods.

Living cyclostomes include lampreys and hagfishes (Fig. 3-2). They became separated from the mainstream of vertebrate evolution some 400 or more million years ago, and, while displaying what are evidently primitive traits (no jaws, median nostril and olfactory sac, no paired fins, a pineal eye, only two semicircular ducts, large gill pouches with small round external openings), they lost all capacity to form bone in the skin or elsewhere and became eel-like. Lampreys developed a buccal funnel with a rasping tongue, and many became parasitic. Little is known of the axial skeleton of the trunk and tail of ostracoderms, but living cyclostomes retain a prominent notochord throughout life and have no recognizable vertebral column (Fig. 1-4). Although cyclostomes are the lowest living vertebrates taxonomically, it must not be assumed that, because of this, all systems are primitive. Many features are highly specialized.* Cyclostomes are sometimes placed in two orders, Petromyzontiformes (lampreys) and Myxiniformes (hagfishes), and sometimes in one (Cyclostomata). Lampreys have existed and remained unchanged for a long time. A fossil lamprey from the Carboniferous period is seen in Fig. 3-3.

Lampreys

The ammocoete larvae of lampreys have been described in Chapter 2. Many larval traits are retained by adults. A large buccal funnel lined with horny denticles helps keep the parasitic adult lamprey attached to the host while a tonguelike rod covered with horny teeth rasps the flesh of the victim. A single nostril is located dorsally on the head, and a nasohypophyseal canal leads from the nostril to the olfactory sac and then terminates blindly in a nasohypophyseal sac (Fig. 12-5). Seven pairs of gill pouches open separately via gill slits that conduct water in and out of the pouches, thus freeing the buccal funnel for feeding on the host.

Petromyzon marinus marinus is a species of **anadromous** lampreys. That is, members live in the sea but migrate upstream to lay their eggs. In 20 to 21 days the small, nonparasitic larvae emerge. After several years upstream they metamorphose into immature adults and migrate to the sea. There they attain sexual maturity and become physiologically adapted for the journey back to the spawning place.

---

*A discussion of *primitive, specialized,* and related terms is found in Chapter 18.

Petromyzon marinus dorsatus is a land-locked population inhabiting the freshwater Great Lakes between Canada and the United States. They, too, enter rivers to spawn. Most *Lampetra* are freshwater lampreys that do not migrate. They spawn on reaching sexual maturity and promptly die without even eating!

Hagfishes

Hagfishes are nonparasitic, slimy marine cyclostomes with a shallow buccal funnel lacking denticles. They feed on live and dead fish and a variety of small invertebrates. A fringe of stubby, fingerlike papillae surrounds the buccal funnel, and a single nostril is located just above the funnel. A canal leads from the nostril to the olfactory sac and then on to the pharyngeal cavity, carrying respiratory water (Fig 12-4). The eyes are vestigial.

Myxine glutinosa, the Atlantic hagfish, has six pairs of gill pouches (occasionally five or seven) that open into a common efferent duct (Fig. 12-4). *Bdellostoma stouti*, common off the coast of California, has 10 to 15 pairs of gill pouches opening directly to the exterior. Hagfishes are not anadromous, and the larvae stay within the egg membranes until metamorphosis. This may be an adaptation to the saltwater environment in which the eggs are laid.

ACANTHODIANS AND PLACODERMS: EARLY JAWED FISHES

Acanthodians date back to the Silurian period and may be the oldest jawed fishes (Fig. 9-13). Like ostracoderms, their head and body were protected by a dermal armor of bony plates and scales. Most of them were only a few inches in length. Although called "spiny sharks," they were not sharks. Their skeleton consisted of bone as well as cartilage, and they had a large operculum. Their paired fins, supplemented by as many as five accessory pairs, were supported by hollow spines. At one time acanthodians were classified with placoderms. Currently, they are assigned either class status, or they are assigned subclass status in the class Osteichthyes.

Placoderms were armored fishes that appeared a little later than acanthodians. They were abundant in the fresh waters of the Devonian while ostracoderms were disappearing. They had paired fins and were swift predators. The best-known placoderms are the arthrodires (Fig. 3-4, *Coccosteus*). A heavy bony dermal shield covered the head and gill region and another covered much of the trunk, the two shields meeting in a movable joint. The remainder of the body was naked in late species. Antiarchs (Fig. 3-4, *Bothriolepis*) were small placoderms with atypical pectoral fins, dorsal eyes, and a flattened ventral surface that suggests they were bottom feeders.

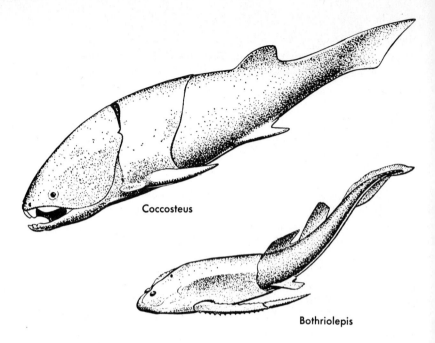

Fig. 3-4. Two Devonian placoderms, each about one-third natural size. *Coccosteus* is an arthrodire; *Bothriolepis* is an antiarch. (From Colbert.[11])

Acanthodians and placoderms are the oldest known jawed fishes, but data are lacking—perhaps never to be uncovered—that would enable us to sort out the phylogenetic relationships between them and later cartilaginous and bony fishes. We simply cannot say who came from whom during those early periods of the Paleozoic.

CHONDRICHTHYES: CARTILAGINOUS FISHES

Chondrichthyes (Fig. 3-5) have no bone other than that in their scales and teeth. Their ancestors had a bony skeleton, and the absence of bone is a specialization. The pelvic fins of males are modified as claspers for transfer of sperm to the female. They have placoid scales made of dentin and enamel.

Chondrichthyes are numerous at present but were far more so in ancient times. This is confirmed by the large number of fossil species known, some of which are identified only by a horny spine, by otoliths (calcareous concretions in the inner ear), or by their teeth. Let it not be assumed, however, that fragments alone remain of these ancient hordes. Many remarkably preserved cartilaginous fishes with intact viscera and muscle fibers have been uncovered within comparatively recent years, and it is likely that further discoveries will be forthcoming. Some of the ancient forms were heavily armored, as may be expected, and placoid scales are remnants of that armor. The most common cartilaginous fishes are elasmobranches.

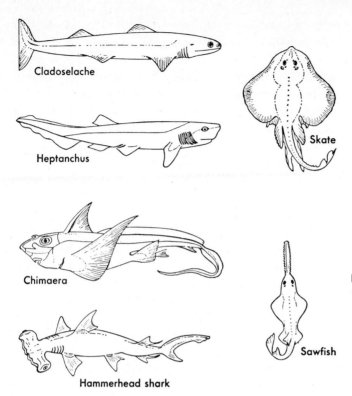

Fig. 3-5. Group of Chondrichthyes. *Cladoselache* is primitive and extinct.

Elasmobranchs

Elasmobranchs can be divided into **Cladoselachii** and **Pleuracanthodii** (Paleozoic sharks), **Squaliformes** (later extinct and living sharks), and **Rajiformes** (skates, rays, sawfishes). The first pharyngeal slit is small, contains only a miniature gill-like surface (**pseudobranch**), and is called a **spiracle.** The gill slits are "naked," that is, visible on the side of the pharynx rather than covered by an operculum. Except in primitive forms such as *Cladoselache* (Fig. 3-5), the mouth is on the ventral surface rather than terminal.

Sharks are of interest to students of vertebrate anatomy because of their generalized structure. If one were to seek a living blueprint of the vertebrate body—an architectural pattern that, by modifications here and deletions there, would serve for all vertebrates—the shark would be one. The anatomy of the eye is in basic respects the anatomy of the human eyeball. The distribution of the nerves to the jaws, to the olfactory epithelium, to the inner ear, and to the musculature is essentially the arrangement found in other vertebrates. The arrangement of the visceral skeleton, aortic arches, chief venous channels, and urinogenital system of sharks is, in essential features, comparable with that in the embryos of higher vertebrates. Thus knowledge of the anatomy of the shark constitutes a point of departure for the study of higher vertebrates. Often studied is the spiny dogfish of the Atlantic, *Squalus acanthias*, named for the prominent spine associated with each dorsal fin. *Squalus suckleyi* is the Pacific spiny dogfish. *Mustelus* is the "smooth dogfish" in the sense that it lacks dorsal spines. These species have a spiracle and five gill slits. Hexanchid sharks have six gill slits, and heptanchild sharks have seven. This seems to be a primitive number for sharks, was the number in *Cladoselache*, and is the largest number in any jawed fish.

Rays, skates, and **sawfish** are elasmobranch fishes whose bodies are more or less flattened. If one could grasp the lateral body wall of a dogfish just above the gill slits and stretch the body wall laterad to form a "wing" without interfering with the location or shape of the coelomic cavity, this would produce the body form of a ray or skate. The mouth and gill slits are ventral (Fig. 12-20, *A*), but the spiracle is dorsal. Movement is accomplished by undulation of the winglike lateral body wall. The ventral location of the mouth and dorsal location of the spiracle are adaptations for bottom feeding. They scoop up food with their ventral mouth and sometimes stir up mud and sand while doing so. The spiracle, which is the chief incurrent route for respiratory water, is removed from this debris.

The tail in sting rays has become an organ of defense and offense. In some rays it becomes an electric organ capable of delivering a high-voltage electric discharge. The giant ray of tropical waters weighs nearly half a ton and has a pectoral finspread of more than 20 feet! Sawfish (Fig. 3-5) do not become as flattened as rays and skates, but the gill slits are ventrally located.

Holocephalans

Holocephalans are the chimaeras (Fig. 3-5), an atypical group of Chondrichthyes that lacks scales on most of the body. The gill slits are covered by a fleshy operculum, and the spiracle is closed. The upper jaw, unlike in elasmobranchs, is solidly fused with the cartilaginous braincase. Instead of teeth there are hard, flat, bony plates on the jaws.

OSTEICHTHYES: BONY FISHES

Osteichthyes can be traced to the early Devonian. They have a skeleton composed partly or chiefly of bone, the gill slits are covered by a bony operculum that grows from the second visceral arch, and the skin has scales with more or less bone. Most bony fishes also have a gas-filled swim bladder. The cloaca in all but lungfishes is so shallow that it is practically nonexistent, and there are no more than five gill apertures. Osteichthyes are either ray finned or lobe finned.

Ray-finned fishes

Ray-finned fishes (**Actinopterygii**) are bony fishes in which slender fin rays are essentially the sole support for the fins and internal nares are lacking. There are three groups, chondrosteans, holosteans, and teleosts. Chondrosteans and holosteans are called **ganoid fishes** because, when they were dominant, they were covered with bony plates or scales on the surface of which was a shiny enamel-like substance called ganoin. Ganoid fishes are represented today by only a handful of survivors, modern teleosts having taken their place in the Cretaceous.

Chondrosteans. Chondrosteans (sometimes called paleoniscoids) are represented today by only the sturgeons, two genera of spoonbills, or paddlefishes, and two freshwater African genera, *Polypterus* and *Calamoichthys* (Fig. 3-6). The African genera, like ancient ganoids, have a well-ossified skeleton and the most ancient variety of ganoid scales. They have lungs and gulp air for breathing, as did many ancient fishes; and they have a fleshy lobe at the base of the pectoral fins. However, within the lobe are typical fin rays rather than the bony skeleton characteristic of lobe fins. Sturgeons and spoonbills are quite different from the African genera. They have an endoskeleton primarily of cartilage—a modification of a more ancient bony condition—and ganoid scales have been replaced over most of

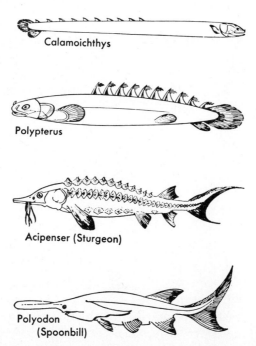

Calamoichthys

Polypterus

Acipenser (Sturgeon)

Polyodon
(Spoonbill)

Fig. 3-6. Group of chondrosteans.

the body by more modern ones. They are sometimes placed in a separate superorder.

Holosteans. Only two genera of holosteans have survived, *Lepisoteus* (or *Lepidosteus*), the various garfishes, and *Amia*, the sole surviving species of which is *Amia calva*, the bowfin (Fig. 3-7). Both are freshwater fishes. Gars are completely covered with ganoid scales that are somewhat modified from the older paleoniscoid scales seen in the African species (compare paleoniscoid and lepidosteoid ganoid scales, Fig. 5-30, and see Fig. 5-31, A). Bowfins are more modern in ap-

Fig. 3-7. The sole living holosteans.

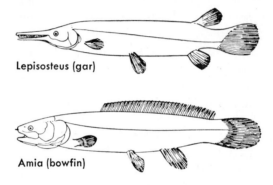

Lepisosteus (gar)

Amia (bowfin)

Fig. 3-8. Group of teleosts.

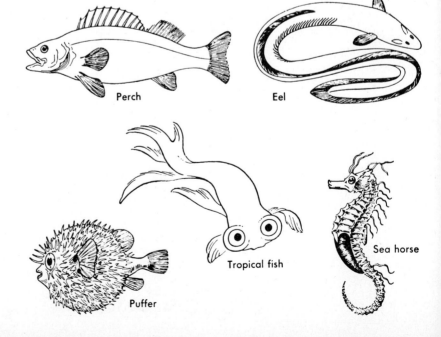

Perch

Eel

Tropical fish

Sea horse

Puffer

pearance. The ganoid scales are broad plates limited to the head (Fig. 8-7), and the surface ganoin has been lost. The rest of the body is covered with modern fish scales.

Teleosts. Unless interested in ichthyology, one may gain little notion of the enormous variety of modern teleosts, who represent 95% of all living fishes (Fig. 3-8). There are long, slim teleosts without paired appendages; short, fat ones with sails; transparent ones; fishes that stand on their tails; fishes with both eyes on the same side of the head; fishes that carry lanterns, that climb trees, that carry their eggs in their mouth, that appear to be smoking pipes, that possess periscopical eyes; and hundreds of other bizarre genera. They inhabit the abyssal depths far out from the continental shelf, they cavort in modest brooks, and some make nightly sorties onto land. They run the gamut of colors, although a relatively small number of pigments assisted by myriads of light-dispersing crystals are responsible for all hues.

The skeleton of teleosts is well ossified, but their overlapping cycloid and ctenoid scales are flexible because they have only a thin layer of bone. The pelvic fins are often far forward, and there is no spiracle. These are only a few of the many characteristics of teleosts. With the exception of the fishes already discussed and the lobe fins, any fish caught on a hook or seen in an aquarium or in the marketplace is a teleost.

Lobe-finned fishes (Fig. 3-9)

Lobe-finned fishes (**Sarcopterygii**) have a fleshy lobe at the base of their paired fins. The lobe contains part of the fin skeleton. They also have internal nares that open into the oral cavity. There are two groups, crossopterygians and dipnoans. These were differentiated by the start of the Devonian.

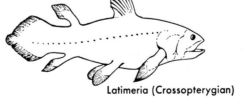

Latimeria (Crossopterygian)

Fig. 3-9. Lobe-finned fishes.

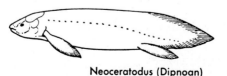

Neoceratodus (Dipnoan)

Crossopterygians. With the exception of *Latimeria*, crossopterygians are all yesterday's animals, having been the most common bony fishes of the Devonian. They are of special interest because of their resemblance to early amphibians. The skeletal elements within the fin lobe corresponded closely to the proximal skeletal elements of early tetrapod limbs (Fig. 9-40). The skull was similar to that of the earliest amphibians (Fig. 8-9). They had swim bladders that some may have used as lungs; and most of them had internal nares, although these were probably not used for breathing. Because of these and other traits, crossopterygians (probably the freshwater rhipidistians) are thought to have been the stem from which amphibians evolved.

Dipnoans. There are three living genera of lungfishes. These are *Protopterus* from Africa, *Neoceratodus* from Australia, and *Lepidosi-*

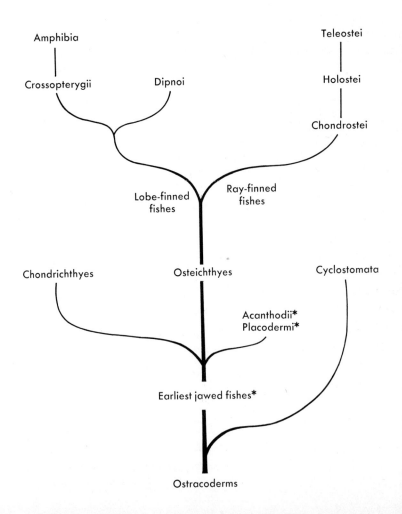

Fig. 3-10. Theoretical phylogenetic lines leading to the major groups of fishes and to amphibians. The distribution of fishes in geological time is given in Fig. 3-33. The phylogenetic relationship of asterisked groups to each other is not known.

ren from Brazil. *Protopterus* and *Lepidosiren* have inefficient gills and suffocate if held under water, but *Neoceratodus* relies on gills for oxygen except when the oxygen content of the water is low. During the wet season these animals enjoy life in their freshwater habitats; but when the sun dries the streams, the African and Brazilian species dig deep burrows in the moist, muddy banks and spend the dry, hot season in a state of lowered metabolism (aestivation). This minimizes water loss and reduces the need for nutrients and oxygen.

Lungfishes and amphibians are derived from ancient crossopterygians and have undergone a number of similar mutations. In both, the swim bladder became supplied by a branch from the sixth aortic arch instead of from the dorsal aorta as in their crossopterygian ancestors, the atrium of the heart became partially divided into two chambers, both usually have a larval stage with external gills, both have internal nares, and in both the swim bladders or lungs have ducts leading to the pharynx. The approximate phylogenetic lines leading to the major groups of fishes and to amphibians are given in Fig. 3-10.

AMPHIBIANS: THE LOWEST TETRAPODS
Who they are and where they came from

The oldest known amphibians are the swamp-dwelling **labyrinthodonts,** so named because the dentin of their teeth was so infolded as to resemble a labyrinth when seen in cross section (Fig. 3-11). They were discovered in rocks from the end of the Devonian or the beginning of the Carboniferous period in Greenland. Although they resembled later tailed amphibians, they had many fishlike features not found in today's amphibians. Among these were minute bony scales in the skin (today found only in burrowing amphibians) and a tail containing fin rays. Their skulls were so similar to certain crossopterygian skulls that the two are easily confused (Fig. 8-9). Grooves in the bones just under the skin of the head show that labyrinthodonts had a sensory canal sytem of neuromast organs that monitor an aquatic environment. Today's aquatic amphibians still have this system, but terrestrial species lose it at metamorphosis. Labyrinthodonts were as small as today's newts and as large as crocodiles. Most authorities consider them to be the ancestors of modern amphibians and of the first reptiles.

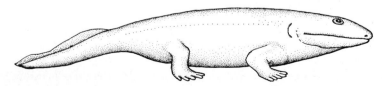

Fig. 3-11. A labyrinthodont, *Ichthyostega,* from the Devonian period.

A second major group of Paleozoic amphibians are the **lepospondyls.** Attempts to trace their ancestry have not been successful because of lack of fossil evidence. There are authorities who, although in the minority, think that lepospondyls arose from some crossopterygian completely independently of labyrinthodonts or even from an ancient dipnoan and that they gave rise to urodeles, whereas labyrinthodonts gave rise to anurans, apodans, and cotylosaurs. This viewpoint is based on interpretation of anatomical evidence alone and is known as the diphyletic theory of the origin of tetrapods. The monophyletic theory is that all tetrapods are derived from a common crossopterygian ancestor, probably a rhipidistian, and that lepospondyls are side branches from this common stem. Arguments for and against these viewpoints have been summarized by Stahl.[31]

The remaining amphibians are in the subclass **Lissamphibia,** which incorporates **Proanura,** the Triassic precursors of modern frogs and toads, and three extant orders, **Anura** (frogs and toads), **Urodela** (or Caudata, modern tailed amphibians), and **Apoda** (or Gymnophiona, wormlike burrowing caecilians). Since they lack the necessary egg membranes that would protect developing eggs in air, terrestrial amphibians, with exceptions to be noted shortly, must return to water to lay their fishlike eggs. There is usually an aquatic larval stage with external gills and neuromast organs. At metamorphosis the gills are usually lost, even in aquatic species, although the latter usually retain neuromast organs.

Amphibians are the lowest vertebrates to exhibit a middle ear cavity with an ear ossicle (columella) for transmitting airborne sound waves. The middle ear complex is a contribution from the branchial apparatus of crossopterygian forebears. The skin has lost all traces of ancestral bony scales except in apodans, and the surface layer tends to develop a stratum corneum of keratinized (cornified) cells that help prevent desiccation in air. The limbs exhibit the usual tetrapod skeleton but have little ability to support the body on land. The pelvic girdle has become modified to brace the hind limbs against the vertebral column by articulating with a single trunk vertebra, called sacral. The first vertebra (now called cervical) has been modified to articulate against the two occipital condyles of the amphibian skull, which enables amphibians to move their heads up and down as in saying "yes." (Shaking their head "no" is anatomically impossible.) The skull exhibits many uniquely amphibian traits. These and other amphibian features are discussed in later chapters.

Caudata (Urodela)

Tailed amphibians resemble, in body form, the ancient amphibians from which they are descended. Some retain external gills throughout life, even though lungs develop, and these are neotenic.* Plethodontidae lose their gills but do not develop lungs. The eight urodele families of the world are listed in Table 3-1, and representative genera are discussed below and illustrated in Fig. 3-12.

Necturus, the mud puppy, is the only genus of Proteidae in the United States and Canada, where there are six species and subspecies. Its European counterpart is *Proteus*, a blind cave dweller. As a 2-cm larva, *Necturus* has tiny imperfect tetrapod appendages, the belly is distended by the presence of yolk, and the tail is keeled and has dorsal and ventral fins. There are three pairs of external gills and

---

*Neoteny is the prolonged retention of larval or juvenile characters. When the larval trait retained is external gills, the animal may be said to be "perennibranchiate."

Table 3-1. Distribution of gills, pharyngeal slits, and lungs among adult urodeles

| Family | Representative genera | Number of pairs | | Lungs |
		Gills	Slits	
Proteidae	*Necturus*	3	2	Yes
Amphiumidae	*Amphiuma*	0*	1	Yes
Hynobiidae	*Hynobius*	0*	0	Occasionally
Cryptobranchidae	*Cryptobranchus*	0*	1	Yes
Salamandridae	*Notophthalmus*	0*	0	Yes
Ambystomatidae	*Ambystoma*	0*	0	Yes
Plethodontidae	*Plethodon*	0*	0	No
Sirenidae	*Siren*	3	3 to 1	Yes

*Some species or individuals are perennibranchiate.

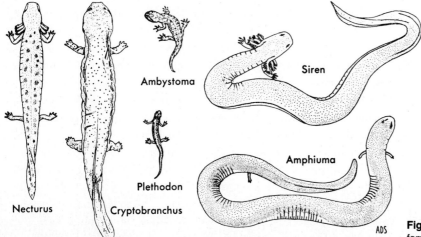

Necturus   Cryptobranchus   Plethodon   Ambystoma   Siren   Amphiuma

ADS

Fig. 3-12. Representatives of six families of urodeles.

three pairs of gill slits. As the larva grows, toes become more pronounced, the skin darkens, and the yolk is used up. At about 5 years of age *Necturus* attains 20 cm in length and is sexually mature. Lungs have developed, but they are hydrostatic organs; the external gills and two pairs of slits remain. The tail is still finlike. Thus *Necturus* is neotenous, but unlike neotenous populations of *Ambystoma* and *Siren*, *Necturus* cannot be induced to discard its gills by administration of thyroxin. One or more enzymes necessary for thyroid hormone to bring about metamorphosis are either lacking or are blocked by other metabolic substances.

Amphiuma (family Amphiumidae) is a large, aquatic, North American, eel-like urodele that attains a length of 1 m. One pair of slits remains in adults (Fig. 1-8). The appendages are very small and entirely inadequate for bearing weight. There are two species, *Amphiuma pholeter* and *A. means*. *A. pholeter* has one digit, *A. means means* has two, and *A. means tridactylum* has three.

Hynobius and *Ranodon* are genera in the family Hynobiidae, which are Asiatic land salamanders. The family has primitive caudate characteristics.

Cryptobranchus is a genus in the family Cryptobranchidae of Asia and North America. It looks ferocious because of its broad, flattened head, its compressed tail with a thin, deep dorsal keel, the longitudinal wrinkles on its chin, and the wrinkled, fleshy fold along the trunk on each side. *Cryptobranchus* attains a length of 70 cm. One gill slit usually remains on each side, sometimes concealed beneath folds of skin.

Salamandra and *Notophthalmus* are Salamandridae (Eurasian and American aquatic and terrestrial salamanders). *Notophthalmus viridescens* typically exhibits three phases of postembryonic life (Fig. 3-13). The larva lives in water. After several months gills and slits are lost, four legs appear, and the animal, now an **eft,** emerges from the water to commence a term of residence on land, often ascending to 4,000-foot altitudes. The skin develops a thick stratum corneum that blocks the sensory canals and skin glands. The body gradually assumes a bright orange-red color, and a series of black-bordered red spots develops along the dorsolateral aspect. The land phase lasts 1 to 3 years, depending on the locality. It ends as the eft approaches sexual maturity under the stimulus of gonadotropic hormones. As the time for mating draws near, the efts commence mass migrations down the hills, through the lowlands and meadows, toward the freshwater ponds. The migration is a manifestation of the water drive brought about by the pituitary hormone prolactin. The thick stratum corneum is shed, exposing the mucous glands and sensory canals. The skin

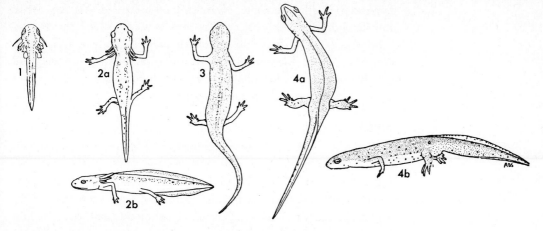

Fig. 3-13. Life history of the salamander *Notophthalmus*. **1,** Newly hatched larva (7 mm); **2a,** fully formed larva (30 mm); **2b,** fully formed larva, lateral view; **3,** red eft (70 mm); **4a,** male newt (95 mm); **4b,** male newt, lateral view.

loses its brilliant color, and by the time the animals enter the ponds, many have assumed the adult coloration, olive green on the back and light yellow ventrally. The tail changes from round to laterally compressed and again develops dorsal and ventral fins. The animal is now a sexually mature water-phase individual known as a **newt.** In some localities the larvae remain in the water and retain vestigial gills throughout life. *Salamandra atra* is viviparous.

Ambystoma belongs to a family (Ambystomatidae) of terrestrial North American urodeles. In certain localities they retain external gills and remain aquatic throughout life. However, these reluctant individuals can be caused to discard their gills by being provided with thyroid hormone or iodine. Perhaps the most widely known species is the neotenic *Ambystoma mexicanum,* commonly known as the Mexican axolotl.* Even among neotenic populations some individuals metamorphose spontaneously.

Plethodon belongs to the American and European family of terrestrial and aquatic urodeles, Plethodontidae. At metamorphosis most of them lose their gills but none develop lungs. They breathe via their skin. Plethodons live at considerable distances from bodies of water and, except for some tropical forms, lay their eggs in moist places such as the undersides of logs or in damp caves. The larvae hatch with legs already formed and may never enter water. In such in-

---

*Xolotl was an Aztec god of twins and monsters.

stances larval gills are of no advantage and are discarded a few days after hatching.

Siren and *Pseudobranchus* are two genera in the American family Sirenidae, which lives in muck or swamplands. They are perennibranchiates that lack hind limbs. *Siren* usually has three gill slits, but not all of these may be open. *Pseudobranchus* retains one gill slit.

Anura

Frogs and toads are tailless amphibians in which several caudal vertebrae are fused into one elongated urostyle (Fig. 7-10). The adult anuran breathes by lungs and skin and lives on land or in fresh water. A few anurans, such as *Rana cancrivora,* the crab-eating frog of the marshes of Thailand, and *Bufo viridis,* can tolerate salt water by hormonally maintaining a higher than usual level of salt in their tissues.

A few anurans do not live near water and do not deposit their eggs in water. But what would happen if larvae with external gills, no legs, and fishlike bodies for swimming were to hatch from their jelly envelopes only to find they were not in water? The species would almost surely perish. But such species, robber frogs, for example, survive because of an adaptive mutation. The larval stage occurs within the jelly envelopes, and miniature adults emerge to assume life on land. (Remarkable as this seems, reptiles and birds regularly do essentially this!) Some 30 species of tree frogs do not lay their eggs in water either. Instead, they carry developing eggs in a brood pouch under the skin of the back. Later, fully metamorphosed young frogs escape through a small posteriorly directed opening in the skin. A similar condition is found in the Surinam frog, *Pipa pipa.* The East African toad *Nectophrynoides vivipara* is viviparous. As many as 100 young develop in the female reproductive tract and are born alive.

The earliest fossil frog, or prefrog, is *Triadobatrachus (Protobatrachus),* a proanuran. It had a skull quite similar to today's frogs and toads, and the body was shortened as a result of reduction in the number of trunk vertebrae, approaching the condition in modern anurans. It had a tail with separate caudal vertebrae, the ribs were longer than in modern anurans and were not fused with the vertebrae as they are today, the tibia and fibula of the leg were not fused as they are today, and the abdomen was covered with bony scales. Their precise ancestry is unknown. Schmalhausen[28] cites evidence that anurans may have originated in the mountains, their small ancestors having retreated upstream in the face of threats from lowland enemies, and that they returned to the lowlands only after extinction of the large reptiles. He points out that the more primitive living anurans—*Ascaphus,* for example—live in the mountains today.

Fig. 3-14. An apodan. The annular structure is a specialization that evidently aids in burrowing.

Apoda

Apodans (Fig. 3-14), or caecilians, are circumtropical limbless amphibians, which, except for a few aquatic species, live in burrows on land. Their eyes are small and sometimes buried beneath the bones of the skull. They have minute scales in their skin, vestiges of the dermal scales of ancestral amphibians. Some are a half meter long and have as many as 250 vertebrae. They have a very short tail with the result that the vent is almost at the end of the body. Burrowing species lay large yolky eggs, and the larval stage is passed in the egg envelopes. Several aquatic genera are vivparous. Only one fossil apodan has been found.

REPTILES: THE LOWEST AMNIOTES

From the ancient labyrinthodonts there arose, if we read correctly Nature's handwriting in the earth, a group of tetrapods destined to be named, 300 million years later, the **cotylosaurs** (Fig. 3-15, *A*). These, or a tetrapod very much like them, were the first, or stem, reptiles. The earliest cotylosaurs had made few advances over the labyrinthodonts, but from the cotylosaurs developed a distinguished and hoary group of descendants, the members of the class Reptilia.

The cotylosaurs have vanished. Gone with them are their descendants the dinosaurs, the flying reptiles (pterosaurs), and the aquatic,

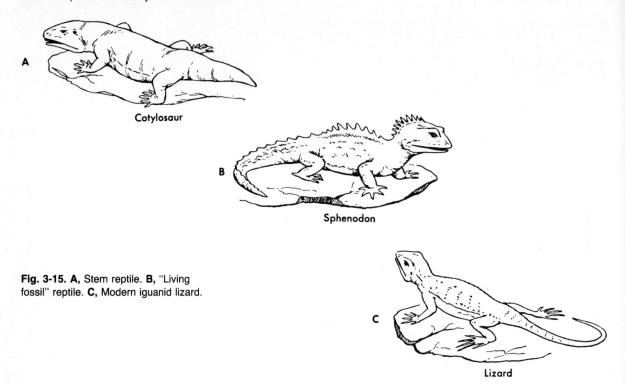

Fig. 3-15. A, Stem reptile. **B,** "Living fossil" reptile. **C,** Modern iguanid lizard.

viviparous ichthyosaurs that had paddles for limbs. Vanished are hundreds upon hundreds of the mighty or weak, great or small, fast or lumbering reptiles, which one by one bowed out of the vertebrate parade while mammals were first raising their voices in the forests and at the edges of the bogs. Remaining with us are a few successful cotylosaur descendants: the turtles, an ancient group that thus far has doggedly persevered in the struggle for existence; *Sphenodon,* a "living fossil" lizard; modern lizards, more recent additions to reptilian society; snakes, which are lizards deprived of their appendages through some fortuitous circumstance; and crocodilians. These few survivors mirror the effect of mutations and the ravages of a changing environment on cotylosaurs and descendants. Birds and mammals represent still other mutations of reptilian chromosomes, but they have become so different as to no longer be classified with reptiles.

Reptiles made significant advances over amphibians and fishes in the acquisition of three extraembryonic membranes (**amnion, chorion, allantois**), which emancipated them and their descendants (birds and mammals) from the necessity of laying eggs in water. The amnion (Fig. 4-9) is a membranous sac filled with watery, salty amniotic fluid. The embryo develops in this fluid just as the embryos of

Fig. 3-16. *Anolis* in process of hatching. (Courtesy Carolina Biological Supply Co., Burlington, N.C.)

fishes and amphibians develop in the pond or sea. The fluid is secreted by the cells of the amnion. To state the situation fancifully, instead of the mother going to the water to deposit her eggs, the developing embryo has its own private pond. Thus reptiles became the first amniotes. The chorion and allantois usually constitute a vascular chorioallantoic membrane that lies against the porous eggshell (another reptilian innovation), taking the place of larval gills for respiration. In viviparous reptiles and in mammals it performs the same function, absorbing oxygen from the uterine environment.

Because of these three extraembryonic membranes, oviparous reptiles found themselves able, and indeed forced, to lay their eggs on land. Their young hatch fully formed (Fig. 3-16), skipping the larval stage, ready to seek food on land. Not only were reptiles liberated from returning to water to lay their eggs, but aquatic, oviparous reptiles must go onto the land to do so, since porous eggs would become water logged in an aqueous environment.

Reptiles have a thicker stratum corneum than amphibians, and the epidermis becomes especially scaly. These cornified epidermal scales are relatively impervious to water, which results in water conservation, an advantage to animals living in air and often remote from water. The digits are supplied with claws; a new kidney, the metanephros, has come into existence; the ventricle of the heart is partially or completely divided into right and left chambers; there is a single occipital condyle, and the pelvic girdle articulates with two sacral vertebrae instead of one as in amphibians, thereby providing stouter bracing of the hind limbs against the vertebral column.

All living reptiles, like their piscine and labyrinthodont ancestors, are **ectotherms.** That is, they cannot produce sufficient heat through metabolism to maintain a body temperature that is more or less constant and above that of the external environment. Consequently, many are semitropical or tropical, and those that are not exhibit various behavior patterns, structural adaptations, and radiation-monitoring devices that enable them to thermoregulate.

These then are reptiles: scaly, clawed, mostly terrestrial tetrapods lacking feathers and hair, which (except for a few viviparous forms) lay large, yolk-laden, shell-covered (**cleidoic**) eggs on land, the embryos of which are surrounded by an amnion, and the young of which are hatched fully formed. The temporal region of the skull (Fig. 8-15) is accorded special consideration in dividing the reptiles into groups (Chapter 8). We will look briefly at a few representatives of the five subclasses.

Anapsida

The subclass Anapsida includes cotylosaurs and turtles. The name "anapsid" refers to the absence of the bony temporal arch found in all other reptiles and their avian and mammalian descendants. The arch is absent because there are no temporal fossae (Chapter 8).

Turtles (**order Testudinata**) are ancient reptiles that probably have remained relatively unchanged for 175 million years. They are identified by their shell of bony dermal plates, to which the ribs and trunk vertebrae are solidly fused. A loss of most trunk muscles occurred, but this was not detrimental, since the rigid shell rendered them useless anyway. Turtles, like birds, have also lost their teeth.

Lepidosauria

There are two orders of living lepidosaurians, **Rhynchocephalia,** with only one survivor, *Sphenodon;* and **Squamata,** the scaly (squamate) reptiles, which include lizards, amphisbaenians, and snakes. The scales, unlike those of fishes, are epidermal (Fig. 5-14).

Sphenodon (Fig. 3-15, *B*) is a primitive, generalized lizardlike reptile that at one time inhabited New Zealand but is now confined to the islands of Tasmania and New Guinea, all of which were once connected. It is destined to become extinct. *Sphenodon* reaches a length of 0.75 m (2$\frac{1}{2}$ feet).

Lizards (**suborder Lacertilia**) are the most versatile of reptiles. Because of well-differentiated appendicular muscles and a suitably structured skeleton some lizards run with agility on their hind limbs alone; some are amazing broad jumpers; some, such as the nocturnal arboreal geckos, have a suction disc on their toes that adheres to a smooth surface when the animal is climbing; some, such as skinks, burrow in sandy soil; and some, such as *Draco*, the flying dragon, glide through the air on rib-supported extensions of the lateral body wall. A few lizards are limbless, some are blind, and some have transparent eyelids (**spectacles**). The scales may assume grotesque shapes, and the eardrum lies in a shallow depression or at the end of an outer ear canal (Fig. 16-10). (The latter is also true of other reptiles except snakes.) The paired eyes have a third eyelid (nictitating membrane), and the teeth are usually in sockets. Lizards in the iguanid family are more generalized. They are from 10 to 210 cm long, the teeth are not socketed, and the tongue is not retractable. *Iguana* is herbivorous, partly arboreal, and frequents the vicinity of water. The largest lizard alive is the carnivorous Komodo dragon of Indonesia. It reaches 2.75 m in length and 115 kg in weight. The horned toad of the North American desert, *Phrynosoma*, is a lizard.

Amphisbaenians (**suborder Amphisbaenia**) are small- to medium-sized (30 to 70 cm), wormlike, burrowing, mostly limbless lizards. They live underground, and their bodies are cylindrical and annulated like those of the burrowing apodans. Covering the eardrum and cornea is typical skin, so these organs are not apparent. There are about 120 species of amphisbaenians.

Snakes (**suborder Serpentes**) have evolved from lizards. Lacking limbs, snakes have achieved other modes of locomotion using body wall muscles, including a unique group that connects the ribs with scutes. Despite the absence of limbs, snakes inhabit fields, mountains, deserts, trees, ponds, rivers, and the sea. A number of marine snakes are viviparous, which eliminates the need to go to land to lay their eggs.

Archosauria

Archosaurs (Fig. 3-17) were the dominant land vertebrates during the Mesozoic, the Age of Reptiles. The subclass includes **Thecodontia**, the earliest archosaurs, named for their teeth, which were in sockets; **Pterosauria**, flying reptiles; **Saurischia**, dinosaurs with a reptilian pelvis; **Ornithischia**, dinosaurs with a birdlike pelvis; and **Crocodilia**, the sole survivors of the horde of Mesozoic reptiles.

Crocodilians include crocodiles, alligators, caimans, and gavials (one species). These are amphibious reptiles with bony plates under leathery scaly skin on the back or belly (Fig. 5-35). They have an

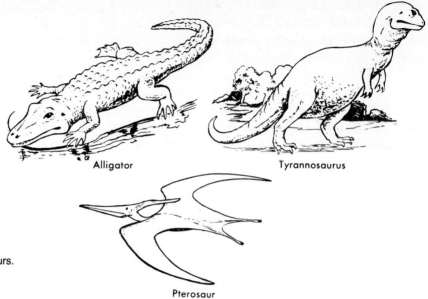

Fig. 3-17. Representative archosaurs.

Fig. 3-18. Therapsid reptile about the size of a large dog. (From Colbert.[11])

exceptionally long secondary palate that separates the nasal passage-way from the oral cavity all the way to the pharynx. Their heart has a completely divided ventricle, and there are abdominal ribs. Croco-diles are common in the subtropical and tropical water of Asia, Africa, the Americas, and Australia. Alligators live in the warm southern re-gions of North America *(Alligator mississippiensis)* and China *(A. si-nensis)*. Crocodiles may be distinguished from alligators by the shape of the snout, which is more slender and triangular in croco-diles, and broad and rounded in alligators; and by the fact that the enlarged fourth tooth of the lower jaw in crocodiles fits into a lateral notch on the upper jaw and can be seen in living crocodiles when the mouth is closed, whereas in alligators this tooth fits into a pit that is sufficiently deep and medial to the upper tooth line that it is hidden when the mouth is shut. Caimans and alligators look very much alike and belong to the same family (Alligatoridae). Caimans live in South America, and gavials live in northern India. The snout of gavials is long and very slender because the left and right halves of the mandible are united medially by a symphysis that extends all the way to the fifteenth tooth.

Pterosaurs were flying reptiles. Their bones were pneumatic, as in modern birds, but their wings were more like those of bats, since the wing membrane, or patagium, was supported by an elongated finger—the fourth, in pterosaurs. They had a long neck and a long or short tail. Well-preserved fossils of one species, *Sordus pilosus*, show that they were insulated with a dense growth of what appears to have been either hair (why not?) or hairlike feathers and that they may have been endothermic.* The largest known pterosaur had a wingspread of about 10 m (35 feet).

Dinosaurs came in all sizes and many shapes, and the massive ones such as *Tyrannosaurus* (Fig. 3-17) were not at all characteristic of the group. Many saurischians were swift, bipedal hunters. Ornithischians were herbivores with no front teeth, although some had horny platypus-like beaks. Bakker[3] has summarized recent arguments that dinosaurs were endothermic and that birds inherited endothermy from some small bipedal dinosaur.

Euryapsida

Euryapsida is a varied group that includes extinct large marine reptiles, the best known of which are the **plesiosaurs** and **ichthyosaurs.** They had an elongated snout armed with sharp teeth used for spearing fish, and their limbs were modified flippers. Plesiosaurs were up to 12 m long and had short tails. Some had a tiny head (small brain) and a very long neck that may have held the head above the sea while foraging for fish. Ichthyosaurs were smaller (up to 3 m or more) and fishlike in outward appearance with no visible neck (Fig. 9-25).

Synapsida

Synapsids diverged early from other reptilian lines and are the reptiles from which mammals emerged. Like mammals, they had a single lateral temporal vacuity (Fig. 8-15, *B*). Early synapsids (pelycosaurs) had a parietal foramen, indicating the presence of a functional third eye. Later synapsids in the mammalian line (therapsids, Fig. 3-18) had two occipital condyles, like mammals, and a secondary palate and

---

*Endothermy is the ability to produce internal heat sufficient to maintain a relatively stable temperature over a long period of time despite cyclic environmental temperature fluctuations. A less precise term is "warm blooded."

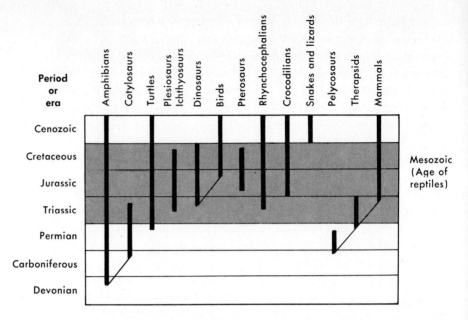

Fig. 3-19. Range of selected reptiles through time. Connecting lines indicate probable origins of cotylosaurs, birds, and mammals.

dentition consisting of incisors, canines, and grinding molars. The dentary was the largest bone in the lower jaw, presaging the condition in mammals (Fig. 8-16). Like other reptiles, synapsids had only one bone in the middle ear and a tiny braincase. Nothing is known of the skin. The distribution of selected reptiles in geological time is shown in Fig. 3-19.

BIRDS: FEATHERED VERTEBRATES

Birds are endothermic vertebrates with feathers. They are descendants of some archosaurian reptile, probably a small bipedal dinosaur, and are known first from the Upper Jurassic, which makes them over 200 million years old. Dinosaurs, because of the structure of their pelvis, could stand and run on their hind limbs, which freed the forelimbs for other functions including, ultimately, flight. (This probably happened also in the evolution of pterosaurs from archosaurian stock.) Bipedal dinosaurs needed the long muscular tail to complete a tripod with the hind limbs for balance. Birds have a restructured trunk that provides a new center of gravity and made it possible for birds to lose the tail, although it was still present when the earliest birds were flying. Birds have retained reptilian claws, epidermal scales on legs and feet, a single occipital condyle, and a diapsid skull.

Feathers are exquisitely structured keratinized appendages of the epidermis that have replaced reptilian scales on all surfaces except the beak, legs, and feet. Feathers make bird flight possible. Whereas pterosaurs and bats have a wing membrane stretched between the forelimbs and trunk, or even the tail, that serves as an airfoil, feathers attached to the bones of the forearm and hand are the only airfoil birds have. Feathers also insulate against seasonal heat and high-altitude cold. (When birds produce excessive heat during flight, it is eliminated in expired air.) Feather pigments facilitate recognition by other members of the species and often provide protective coloration. Seasonal pigmentation is the result of molting; it signals the sex and reproductive state of the individual.

In addition to feathers and wings birds have other features that are adaptations for flight. Body weight has been reduced in several ways. Long bones have become slender, and most bones, including vertebrae, have lost the central marrow, which leaves cavities that contain air-filled extensions of air sacs from the lungs. The skull has been lightened by a thinning of the compact layers of the membrane bones, but it remains durable because sutures have been eliminated and the spongy bone that remains is architecturally strong. All teeth have been lost, having been replaced functionally by a lighter-weight horny beak that is used also in many species for getting food into the mouth. The bones of the wrist, palm, and digits have been reduced in number and size (Fig. 9-23); consequently the volume of muscle within the forelimb has been greatly reduced. The urinary bladder has been lost, and the large intestine has been shortened.

Modifications of the skeleton include a large keel, or **carina,** on the sternum for attachment of the massive flight muscles. It is absent in most birds that do not fly. The entire skeleton of the trunk except the ribs has become a rigid unit by ankylosis of trunk vertebrae and their fusion with the pelvic girdle to form a **synsacrum** (Fig. 7-17). The ankle is rigid, and the angle of approach of the femur to the ornithischian-type girdle has been altered. Uncinate processes of ribs strengthen the thoracic wall and provide additional surfaces for attachment of some of the flight muscles of the scapula (Fig. 7-21).

Many soft parts have been modified. The esophagus often has a crop for storage of seeds and grain, and the stomach has become a grinding gizzard like that of crocodilians, which are close relatives. The size and shape of the eyes have been modified, which result in increased acuity of vision from high in the air, and the orbits have become correspondingly enlarged. The cerebral hemispheres have a thick new stratum of nerve cells, the hyperstriatum (Fig. 15-21), which is responsible for stereotyped avian behavior patterns such as

Fig. 3-20. Fossil *Archaeopteryx* embedded in limestone. Wings and their skeleton are near bottom of photograph, the long feathered tail is at top. (Photograph courtesy The Museum für Naturkunde an der Humboldt-Universität, Berlin.)

nest building. The cerebellum is enlarged as a consequence of increased neural input from wing and hind limb muscles. The modified lungs and air sacs are discussed in Chapter 12.

Archaeornithes: the earliest birds

The oldest known birds are in the genus *Archaeopteryx*. Two fossils about the size of a crow were found during the nineteenth century in Late Jurassic limestone in Bavaria, West Germany. The first specimen was complete except for a few cervical vertebrae, the right foot, and lower jaw. The second specimen, illustrated in Fig. 3-20, was even more complete; and three additional specimens, not exactly alike, have been recovered elsewhere. Archaeopterygians had a long reptilian tail, thecodont teeth on both jaws, and feathers on the wings

A

B

Fig. 3-21. A, *Archaeopteryx,* the earliest known bird of the Jurassic period. **B,** A carinate bird (pigeon) for comparison. How many skeletal changes can you find? (From Colbert.[11])

and tail that were no different from today's. The skull was more reptilian than avian, the nostrils were far forward, there was no beak, and the braincase had not expanded to accommodate an enlarged brain. The cervical vertebrae were not saddle shaped at the ends as in today's birds, trunk vertebrae were not rigidly fused, and the synsacrum was not well developed. The sternum was small, indicating weak flight muscles. These birds may have soared more than they flew. Fig. 3-21 contrasts some of the more obvious features of the skeleton with that of a pigeon. *Archaeopteryx* has been placed in the **subclass Archaeornithes.** All other birds are currently in the **subclass Neornithes.**

Neornithes

The subclass Neornithes includes all extinct and living birds other than *Archaeopteryx*. It is separated into two groups, **Odontognathae** (birds with teeth) and **Neognathae** (toothless birds). The only odontognath known for sure is *Hesperornis* (Fig. 3-22) from marine deposits in Kansas. The wings were vestigial, so it did not fly; but it swam and dove for fish, catching and holding them with sharp, conical teeth.

Most neornithes fly, but some, the **ratites,** cannot. They have small incompetent wings, but they have powerful leg muscles that enable them to run well. It is likely that their ancestors could fly. Many are known only as fossils, and the survivors are in danger of extinction by humans. Ostriches, emus, cassowaries, rheas, kiwis, and penguins are the living ratites. The extinct moas were nearly 4 m (13 feet) tall and laid eggs more than 30 cm (1 foot) in diameter.

Fig. 3-22. *Hesperornis,* a flightless toothed bird from the Cretaceous seas of Kansas in the United States. Reconstructed.

Neornithes that fly are **carinates;** that is, they have a large carina. Penguins have a large carina but they cannot fly, partly because their forelimbs are powerful flippers that make them good swimmers but prevent them from flying. The largest living carinate is the Andean condor, with a wingspread of about 3 m (10 feet) and weighing about 15 kg (35 pounds). But the Giant Teratorn *(Teratornis)*, which lived in Argentina 5 million years ago and is thought to have been a flier, had a wingspread of 7.5 m (25 feet), weighed 360 kg (160 pounds), and measured 3.5 m (11 feet) from beak to tip of tail. It was not as large as some pterosaurs, however.

Many carinates are annual migrants, passing part of a year in one geographical region and the remainder elsewhere, sometimes migrating great distances. The Arctic tern spends several months above the Arctic Circle and the remaining months in the Antarctic, traveling 22,000 miles round trip each year! During migration, birds move in mass flights, often at night and at an elevation of approximately 2,000 feet. Those destined for the same geographical location may pass over approximately the same routes (flyways) year after year. A great flyway is located directly over the Gulf of Mexico between the Yucatan peninsula and the Gulf Coast of the United States. Other flyways are located overland between Central American and the United States and from the West Indies via the Florida peninsula. Migration is associated in part with mating and is triggered by a specific hormonal balance. How birds navigate has long challenged ornithologists. The sun, stars, barometric pressure, polarized light, and low-frequency sound all seem to provide input during flight at one time or another.

There are fewer species of birds today than at the start of the Cenozoic. Climate changes resulting from glaciation of the northern hemispheres probably accounted for much of the loss, but increasing populations of mammals that competed with birds for food, especially insectivorous and carnivorous birds, may have played a role. The spread of human civilization has been the most recent threat to many avian species.

MAMMALS: VERTEBRATES WITH HAIR

Mammals succeeded therapsid reptiles at the end of the Triassic. They are vertebrates with hair and, except monotremes, with mammary glands and nipples. Further distinguishing modern mammals from other vertebrates are the single dentary bone on each side of the lower jaw articulating with the squamosal bone; three bones in the middle ear cavity; a muscular diaphragm separating thoracic and abdominal cavities; sweat glands (in most mammals); absence of an adult cloaca in all but the lowest order; heterodont dentition (except in toothed whales); two sets of teeth (milk teeth and a permanent set);

biconcave, enucleate red blood cells that are circular (except in camels and llamas); loss of the right fourth aortic arch; a pinna, or sound-collecting lobe, accessory to the outer ear; a more specialized larynx; and extensive development of the cerebral cortex.

Because of the many variations in limb structure, mammals have been able to achieve a greater diversity of habitats than any other vertebrates except perhaps reptiles during their days of dominance. They burrow in the ground, hop, lumber, or gambol over the plains, scramble over mountain crags, swing through trees, propel themselves through the air in true flight, and inhabit the oceans, each lifestyle made possible by modifications of body structure.

Mammals can be divided into three groups. **Prototherians** are reptilelike mammals that lay eggs and have a cloaca throughout life. There is only one order, **Monotremata.** The single cloacal opening, or vent, inspired their name. **Metatherians** are viviparous mammals that use the embryonic yolk sac as a placenta. There is a single order, **Marsupialia.** The remaining mammals are **Eutheria,** which use the chorioallantoic membrane or an extension of it as a placenta. Unless prototherians emerged independently from reptilian ancestors, they diverged very early from other mammals.

Monotremata

The platypus, or duckbill (Fig. 3-23), and two genera of spiny ant-eaters, or echidnas, all from Australia or nearby Tasmania and New Guinea, are the sole surviving monotremes. Like reptiles, they lay heavily yolked eggs and have a cloaca. Like reptiles, too, they have a ventral mesentery extending the length of the abdominal cavity, the testes are within the abdomen, the outer ear has no pinna, and the brain lacks the great transverse fiber tract, corpus callosum, that connects the two cerebral hemispheres in other mammals. The malleus and incus are larger than in other mammals, resembling the articular and quadrate bones of therapsids. They have no nipples, but a milky fluid exudes from modified sweat glands onto tufts of hairs in shallow

Fig. 3-23. The platypus *(Ornithorhynchus),* a monotreme.

pits on the abdomen, from which it is licked up by the young. Monotremes are endothermic, but their body temperature is less stable than that of higher mammals, fluctuating as much as 13° C.

Duckbills live in pairs in burrows at the edges of streams. They have webbed feet that enable them to walk on muddy river bottoms, and a soft, rubbery, sensitive, beaklike muzzle with which they detect freshwater invertebrates, especially molluscus, in the mud and dredge them. The food is then stored in a cheek pouch until it is crushed later with horny teeth that replace a prenatal set of regular ones. During breeding seasons the female moves out of the burrow and constructs a new one just above the water line, where she lays one to three eggs in a nest she has constructed. The eggs are nearly round, about 2 cm in diameter, and covered with a pliable white shell. She incubates the eggs for about 2 weeks, after which they hatch.

Echidnas are terrestrial and have a long sticky tongue that is used to gather insects. Except on the abdomen they are armed with sharp quills interspersed among coarse hairs, and they roll into a ball for protection. A single egg, about 4 mm in diameter, is incubated in a temporary pouch that develops as a thin flap of abdominal skin in females. The milk-secreting glands are on the abdominal wall in the pouch, and the young hatch and are carried in the pouch for several weeks until they can seek food.

Marsupialia

Marsupials (Fig. 3-24) are primitive mammals in which the fetal yolk sac (in contact with the chorion) serves as a placenta. The young are born in almost a larval state and are transported, incubated, and nursed after birth in a maternal abdominal pouch (**marsupium**) of muscle and skin until they are old enough to become independent. The walls of the pouch are supported by two slender marsupial (epipubic) bones that project forward from the pelvic girdle. In several South American genera the pouch is incomplete or absent. Newborn young make their way to the pouch by squirming and wriggling and by using the claws on their forelimbs, which are considerably larger than the hind limbs at birth. The lips are sealed at the angles of the mouth, which therefore consists of only a small circular opening. Once the young has taken a nipple into its mouth the tip of the nipple swells and the young cannot easily drop off.

All native Australian mammals except bats are marsupials or monotremes. Among Australian marsupials are kangaroos, the Tasmanian wolf, bandicoot rabbit, wallaby, wombat, Australian anteater, and phalangers. Australian marsupials resemble many eutherian mammals such as wolves, foxes, bears, rabbits, mice, and cats in surprising

A

Tasmanian wolf

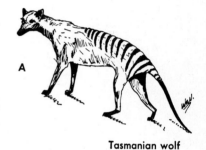

B

Wallaby

Opossum

C

Fig. 3-24. A and **B,** Marsupials from Australia. **C,** One of the few American marsupials.

details. Some phalangers resemble flying squirrels, and there are marsupial moles. Opossums are one of the few surviving marsupials in the Americas.

Why should there be no native mammal higher than a marsupial in Australia? It is now accepted that continental drift separated Australia from Gondwanaland (South America, Africa, Australia, Antarctica), and it is theorized that eutherian mammals had not yet reached Australia when the isolation of that continent occurred. As a result, only marsupials and monotremes would be found in Australia.

Insectivora

Insectivores (Fig. 3-25) are generalized mammals closely related to the primitive stock from which higher mammals arose. Although at one time abundant, they are represented today chiefly by small, retiring, often subterranean survivors: moles, shrews, shrewlike animals, tenrecs, spiny hedgehogs, and "flying" lemurs that do not fly, but glide, and are not lemurs. Insectivores subsist primarily on a diet of insects, worms, molluscs, and other small invertebrates.

Among primitive characteristics are a flat-footed (plantigrade) gait; five toes; smooth cerebral hemispheres; small, sharp pointed teeth with incisors, canines, and premolars poorly differentiated (Fig. 11-14, shrew); a large allantois and large yolk sac in the embryo; and sometimes a shallow cloaca. The testes are retained in the abdominal cavity in some genera (a primitive trait), and they never descend fully into scrotal sacs in any.

Moles have short, stout anterior limbs, with forefeet that are broad and more than twice as large as the hind feet, an adaptation for digging (Fig. 3-25). The neck is short, and the shoulder muscles are so powerful that head and trunk seem to merge. Their tiny eyes are practically useless, but an acute sense of smell locates distant food, and the sensitive tip of the elongated snout tells them when they have encountered it.

Shrews superficially resemble mice. They are shy, busy little fighters with a keen sense of hearing. They have an elongated, bewiskered, sensitive snout, and their incisor teeth are long and curved. The pigmy shrew, weighing about 3 g, is the smallest mammal on earth.

The tree shrew (Fig. 3-26) is classified by some authorities in the order Insectivora, by others as the most primitive primate. It has traits that bridge the gap between the two orders.

Chiroptera

Bats are the only known vertebrates in addition to pterosaurs and birds that have achieved true flight. This is possible because of the

Fig. 3-25. The mole, an insectivore.

Fig. 3-26. Tree shrew. (Courtesy Delta Regional Primate Research Center, Covington, La.)

well-developed wing (patagium) extending between the neck, limbs, and tail and incorporating four greatly elongated, clawless fingers. The thumbs project from the anterior margins of the wings and bear claws, which aid in locomotion when not in flight. The five digits of the hind limbs all bear claws, which are used for hanging upside down, wings folded, from rafters or ledges in caves. Nipples, usually two, are limited to the thoracic body wall. The pectoral muscles are strong, and the sternum is keeled, although not as much as in birds. All bones are slender, and those of the hand are greatly elongated (Fig. 9-24). Bats have large pinnas (external earlobes), and the face and head glands are unusually numerous and enlarged. They constitute a large order and probably arose from an insectivore ancestor.

Bats are insectivorous, frugivorous (fruiteaters), or sanguinivorous (subsisting on the blood of other mammals). Vampire bats have received attention because of sanguinivorous habits. Incisor teeth occur on the upper jaw only, and there is just one pair. They are razor sharp and point toward one another so they slit the skin of prey. As blood oozes from the wound, the bat licks it up without awakening the sleeping victim, which is often a domestic animal. Associated with the vampire habit of taking only fluid nourishment is the very small lumen of the esophagus, through which no solid food could possibly pass.

Vampire bats and Lamarckism. The adaptations of the teeth and the esophagus of vampire bats and the fluid diet inspire the speculative question of whether a small esophageal luman forced bats to adopt a fluid diet of blood (the only available fluid containing all the nourishment needed by a mammal) or whether the fluid diet during many generations was in any way a *cause* of the decrease in the size of the esophageal lumen. If the former is the case, it is fortunate that vampire bats hit on blood as a source of nourishment; otherwise, they could not have survived the change. If, as thought by Lamarck, the change in the esophageal lumen resulted from disuse of this part for solid foods, modern genetics has thus far been unable to fathom the mechanism whereby the change in any generation became hereditary. The possibility also exists that sanguinivorous bats were already sanguinivorous before chance mutations altered the esophagus. If so, decrease in size of the esophageal lumen would have had no deleterious effect on these bats.*

Convergent evolution.* The evolution of pterosaurs, birds, and bats, all of which develop a wing for aerial locomotion, is an illustration of convergent evolution. The term is applied when two species occupying the same kind of environment, concurrently or separated

---

*Lamarckism and the Theory of Organic Evolution are discussed in Chapter 18.

by millions of years, develop a similar adaptation even though the two species do not have a common ancestor that could have contributed similar genetic information to both. The concept implies that unrelated species may, through adaptive mutations, approach each other with respect to some trait. Another instance of convergence is development in whales and ichthyosaurs of flippers that superficially resemble fins.

Primates

Primates (prī-mā´-tēz) are primarily arboreal mammals that arose as an offshoot of Cretaceous insectivore stock. One of many classification schemes divides them into four suborders, **Lemuroidea,** lemurs and lorises; **Tarsioidea,** tarsiers and their relatives; **Platyrrhini,** South American monkeys and small squirrel-like marmosets; and **Catarrhini,** Old World monkeys, apes, and man. Platyrrhines and catarrhines are often referred to as anthropoids.

Among primate specializations is the grasping hand so built that the thumb can be made to touch the ends of the other four fingers of the same hand. The big toe is also opposable in most primates. At least some of the digits are provided with nails instead of claws. Often there is a prehensile tail, which supplements the hands for grasping during arboreal locomotion. The cerebral hemispheres of the brain are larger than those of any other mammal. The snout has been shortened, with the result that both eyes can look forward. There is frequently only one pair of nipples, and these are on the thorax. Among primitive features are a flat-footed gait, five digits, a large clavicle, a central wrist carpal in many primates, and generalized dentition.

Lemuroids. Lemurs, the largest of which is the size of a domestic cat, receive their ghostly name from the habit of swinging silently through the trees while most higher primates are asleep. The long axis of the head is in line with the long axis of the body, as in most other mammals. The long tail is not prehensile. The second finger and toe have a claw instead of a nail. The uterus is duplex. The placenta is nondeciduate; that is, the fetal part of the placenta does not become rooted into the uterine lining of the mother, and so there is no trauma of the uterus at birth. These are primitive traits.

Lorises include the nocturnal pottos and bush babies. They inhabit Africa, India, and the East Indies.

Tarsioids. Tarsiers (Fig. 3-27) resemble higher primates more than lemurs do. Their eyes are close together and directed forward so there is an overlap in the left and right fields of vision; the head is more nearly balanced at right angles to the vertebral column; all five fingers have nails and so do all toes except the second and third; and the placenta is deciduate.

Fig. 3-27. *Tarsius,* a prosimian.

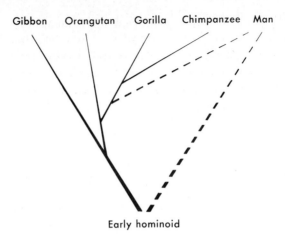

Fig. 3-28. Theoretical relationships of hominoids. Broken lines indicate alternative current hypotheses.

Platyrrhines and catarrhines. Platyrrhines and catarrhines are differentiated on the basis of the direction in which the nostrils open. The nostrils of platyrrhines (South American monkeys and marmosets) are separated by a broad internarial septum and open to the side. Those of catarrhines (Old World monkeys, apes, humans) lie close together and open downward as in humans. In both, the head is at a right angle to the long axis of the vertebral column, the eyes are directed forward and are close together, the cerebral hemispheres are maximally developed, there are 32 teeth in the permanent set, the placenta is deciduate, and only one offspring is usually born at a time. Platyrrhines include *Cebus* (the capuchin), *Ateles* (spider monkey), and *Alouatta* (howler monkey). Howlers are named for the loud screeching cries made with the enlarged hyoid bone and larynx (Fig. 12-11). Catarrhines are in two groups, **cercopithecoids** and **hominoids.** Among the former are baboons, mandrills, and the macaque, or rhesus, monkey from which the symbol "Rh" designating blood groups was derived. The best-known hominoids are listed in Fig. 3-28. "Man" probably diverged very early from other hominoids.

Since the discovery in 1856 of Neanderthal man, who lived in Europe 100,000 years ago, fossil parts of prehistoric man have been found in considerable numbers. The latest fossils indicate that man lived in Africa 4 million years ago. With each discovery the problem arises whether to include the new member in existing species, or to erect new species, or even genera. For example, Neanderthal man is sometimes classified as a subspecies of modern man *(Homo sapiens neanderthalensis)* and sometimes placed in a separate species *(Homo neanderthalensis)*. The rules for classifying other vertebrates are applied to the taxonomy of man. The oldest known manlike (hominid) remains are presently assigned to the genus *Australopithecus*. These hominids walked upright and were about 5 feet tall; males were considerably larger than females. They had a humanlike body but the facial contours of an ape, and they had an ape-sized brain. They used simple bone tools. *Homo erectus* is a more recent hominid. He fashioned tools and used fire. Modern man, *Homo sapiens sapiens*, who added atomic and nuclear energy to his array of tools, occupied Europe with Neanderthal man and replaced him either by competition or absorption.

In the emergence of man from an earlier anthropoid many changes occurred. An **S**-shaped curve in the vertebral column permitted an erect posture; the facial angle became less acute (Fig. 3-29); the teeth, especially the canines, became smaller; the frontal lobes of the cerebral hemispheres enlarged, resulting in an enlarged braincase and a more prominent forehead; the eyebrow ridges became reduced; the nose became more prominent; the tail became confined to embryonic stages; the arms became shorter; a metatarsal arch developed in the otherwise flat feet; the big toe moved in line with the other toes and ceased to be opposable; articulate speech appeared; and many other changes occurred.

It is to the massive development of the frontal lobes of the cerebral hemispheres, to the opposable thumb, and to articulate speech that man owes his present dominance in the animal kingdom. With his fingers he can construct instruments of offense and defense and machines to lighten his burden, and with them he can scrawl symbols that convey experiences and techniques to the corners of the earth and to generations unborn. With his voice he can communicate with contemporary fellow creatures and exchange ideas with delicate shades of meaning. With his brain he can associate sensory stimuli that are currently received with those recalled from earlier experiences, and after meditation elect a mode of action that he calls "intelligent." With his brain, too, he can enjoy the esthetic beauty of the imponderable universe, search for ultimate truth, and dream of Utopia, which, but for his residual animal nature, might be his heritage.

Carnivora

Carnivores are a large and diverse group of flesh eaters that includes aquatic and terrestrial species. They have powerful jaws and, except in water forms, elongated, sharp canine teeth capable of spearing and tearing flesh (Fig. 11-15, *B*). The cerebral cortex is convoluted, and the animals are capable of considerable learning.

Terrestrial carnivores include "cats" of many kinds (domestic cats, panthers, lynx, etc.), dogs and related forms, bears and pandas, hyenas, and numerous species important economically for their furs,

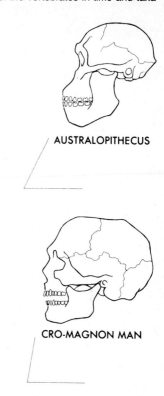

AUSTRALOPITHECUS

CRO-MAGNON MAN

Fig. 3-29. Facial angles of two hominids. The angles are shown beneath the skulls.

Fig. 3-30. Aquatic carnivores (sea lions). (Courtesy The American Museum of Natural History, New York.)

such as racoons, mink, otters, skunks, and badgers. Terrestrial carnivores typically have five toes with sharp, sometimes retractable, claws.

Aquatic carnivores are sometimes placed in a separate order, **Pinnipedia,** which includes sea lions (Fig. 3-30), seals, and walruses. They have many adaptations for life in the water. They have webbed, paddlelike, and often nailless limbs that are more or less included within the body wall. In "wriggling" seals the hind limbs are permanently bound to the tail, and movements on land consist of pulling themselves awkwardly along or flopping about. Despite their aquatic adaptations the young are born on land (in rookeries) and cannot even swim.

Cetacea

Whales, dolphins, and porpoises are moderately large or massive aquatic mammals, sometimes attaining 30 m (100 feet) in length and 150,000 kg (200,000 pounds) in weight. This is 22 million times the weight of the smallest shrew. The tail has a horizontal terminal fin (fluke) filled with fibrous tissue, which provides forward thrust by its up-and-down motion. A dorsal fin, similarly constructed, is sometimes present and serves as a rudder and stabilizer. The forelimbs are paddlelike and serve chiefly as balancers. Although the fingers are not separated from the paddle, finger bones are present (Fig. 9-27). Hind limbs and girdle are mere vestiges embedded in the trunk wall or are missing entirely.

A few hairs, which can be easily counted, usually occur on the muzzle; otherwise, the skin is smooth and naked. The frontal and nasal bones are shortened so that the nostrils are far back on the skull and frequently united to form a single large "blowhole." The diaphragm is unusually muscular, and the water spout (composed of vapor from the expired air) may last from 3 to 5 minutes. Most cetaceans have teeth, but whalebone whales (right whales, rorquals, Pacific gray whales, pigmy right whales) have frayed horny sheets of whalebone (baleen) hanging from the roof of the mouth (Fig. 5-27). These immense carnivores strain several tons of small fish, shellfish, and other invertebrates out of the sea each day. A heavy layer of fat, called blubber, under the skin conserves body heat while the animal swims in the cold depths of the ocean. Because of their great bulk, they dare not approach too close to shore lest they become marooned and die, crushed by tons of their own flesh.

Cetaceans are the only completely adapted seagoing mammals. All other aquatic mammals must return to land to breed. Baby whales are born in the sea and when feeding, hang onto one of the two inguinal teats of the mother as she swims about. Whales have lost their olfactory nerves,* and the nostrils have valves that close during diving.

Edentata

Edentates are chiefly South American mammals that have diverged from insectivores. They include tree sloths, South American anteaters, and armored edentates, best known of which is the armadillo. Several giant armored fossil edentates are known. All teeth are absent in South American anteaters (hence the name "edentate"), but many other species have cheek teeth that lack enamel. Histological evidence of an enamel organ has been found, however. Armadillos always give birth to identical quadruplets from a single fertilized egg.

Tubulidentata

Tubulidentates are another order with few teeth. There is only one living tubulidentate, the insectivorous aardvark from South America. It is a burrowing anteater about 1.5 m (5 feet) long with relatively few coarse hairs, an elongated piglike snout, and a long sticky tongue that is used for capturing termites.

Pholidota

Pholidota is an insectivorous order lacking teeth. Here, again, there is only one pholidotan, the pangolin *Manis* (Fig. 5-24) from Africa and Southeast Asia. Pangolins are also called scaly anteaters

---

*A discussion of this mutation in terms of Lamarckism will be found in Chapter 18.

because they have epidermal scales resembling those of lizards. Between the scales are scattered hairs.

Rodentia

Rodents are a large and diverse group of mammals that have a single pair of upper and lower incisor teeth. These teeth are long, curved, and covered with enamel on their outer surfaces only, which provides a chisel-like edge for gnawing. The incisors grow throughout life. Since canine teeth are absent, there is a diastema, or stretch of jaw devoid of teeth, behind the incisors (Fig. 11-14). At the beginning of the large intestine there is a long, coiled cecum that houses commensal cellulose-digesting microorganisms. Rodents are the most numerous mammals on earth.

Lagomorpha

The order Lagomorpha was established for rabbits and hares, which were once classified as rodents. They differ from rodents in having two pairs of incisors on the upper jaw—a small pair lying immediately back of, rather than alongside of, a much larger pair. The front pair, like those of rodents, are long, sharp, and deeply rooted and grow throughout life. The smaller pair lack a cutting edge. Rabbits differ from hares in having shorter ears and legs, producing naked young, and in other respects. Rabbits and hares have a split upper lip, which gave rise to the term "harelip."

Ungulates and subungulates

It is now necessary to introduce two orders of mammals, **Perissodactyla** and **Artiodactyla,** known as ungulates. They are mostly large herbivores, and all walk on the tips of their toes (Fig. 9-29, deer), which are protected by hoofs (modified claws). Modern ungulates have no more than four toes on each foot, and some such as horses, have only one. Ancestral ungulates probably had five toes. Reduction in the number of toes is illustrated by the familiar example of the horse, the little Eocene ancestors of which had four toes in front and three behind. With successive mutations the number was reduced to one.

The teeth of modern ungulates are also characteristic. They are high crowned, and their grinding surfaces exhibit crosswise ridges separated by deep grooves specialized for grinding grasses. There is little morphological difference between premolars and molars. Ungulates lack a clavicle and as a result probably have more freedom of neck movements in grazing. They are the only mammals with horns, although several models come without them.

In addition to ungulates, three other living orders are thought to have perhaps radiated from early ungulate stock—**Proboscidea, Hyracoidea,** and **Sirenia.** They are called subungulates.

Perissodactyla

Modern perissodactyls occur in three families: horses, tapirs, and rhinoceros. They walk on the hoofed tips of one, three, or occasionally four toes and are distinguished by the fact that the body weight is borne chiefly on a single digit (mesaxonic foot, Fig. 9-31). Perissodactyls are referred to as odd-toed ungulates. However, tapirs and some rhinoceros have four toes on the forelimb.

Artiodactyla

Artiodactyls are ungulates in which the weight of the body is supported by two toes. This is known as a paraxonic foot (Figs. 9-30 and 9-31). Living artiodactyls have an even number of toes, but at least one extinct artiodactyl had five toes on the forelimb. Artiodactyls include pigs, hippopotamuses, peccaries, cows, camels, llamas, deer, antelope, giraffes, goats, and sheep. With the exception of pigs, hippopotamuses, and peccaries, they have stomachs divided into not fewer than three chambers, sometimes four (Fig. 11-20). They bolt their food, which then passes to the rumen, the first segment of the stomach. Such animals are called **ruminants.** At their leisure, they force undigested food balls back up the esophagus and masticate this cud more thoroughly.

Proboscidea

Proboscidea is an order of subungulates that includes elephants, mastodons, and their relatives. They have a proboscis, or trunk, composed of a greatly drawn out upper lip, which is accompanied in its overgrowth by the nostrils (Fig. 11-14, mastodon). They have scanty hair and thick, wrinkled skin. The incisor teeth of one or both jaws are elongated to form tusks, canine teeth are absent, and molars are very large grinders, as in ungulates. Proboscideans are bulky animals, and the limbs are almost vertical pillars of bone and muscle. They have five toes that end in hooves, and on the back of each toe is an elastic pad that bears much of the body weight.

Hyracoidea

Hyracoidea is an order of subungulates containing a single genus, the little *Hyrax,* popularly known as the coney. In some traits coneys resemble rodents and hares (Fig. 3-31). They have short ears, they hunch the body when at rest, the upper lip is split (harelip), and the

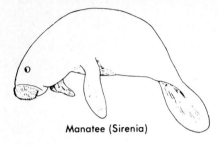

Manatee (Sirenia)

Hyrax (Hyracoidea)

Fig. 3-31. Two subungulates: a sea cow (manatee) and a coney *(Hyrax).* A third subungulate, the mastodon, is illustrated in Fig. 11-14.

incisor teeth grow continuously. Although they are plantigrade, indications are of a closer kinship to ungulates than to other mammals. All digits except one end in small, flat hooves, fingers have been reduced to four and toes to three, the middle toe being the longest, and they have ungulate-like molar teeth.

Sirenia

Sirenians, or sea cows, are the manatees and dugongs. They are stout, clumsy-appearing, freshwater or marine mammals with an overgrown, wrinkled, almost pathetic-looking snout covered with scattered, coarse bristles (Fig. 3-31). The rest of the body is naked except for a few scattered hairs. The forelimbs are paddles, but within them the tetrapod complement of bones is intact. Hind limbs are absent, but there are internal skeletal vestiges of them and of the pelvic girdle. The tail in some is flattened horizontally like that of whales. Although sirenians are aquatic, their breeding grounds (rookeries) are on land. They are considered by authorities to be the most aberrant descendants of very primitive ungulate stock.

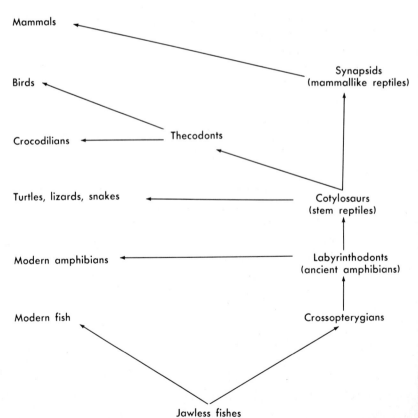

Fig. 3-32. Mainstreams of evolution of living vertebrates based on the monophyletic theory of the origin of tetrapods. See also Fig. 3-10.

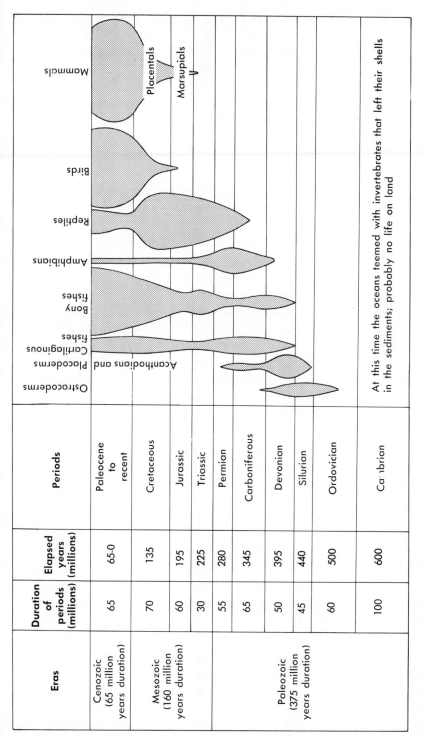

Fig. 3-33. Range and relative abundance of vertebrates through time. Silurian populations include no placoderms. (Modified from Colbert.[11])

Mainstreams of vertebrate evolution

The main lines of evolution from ancient jawless fishes to modern vertebrates may pass through the groups indicated in Fig. 3-32. Note that the lines lead through ancient groups all of which are now extinct except the crossopterygian *Latimeria*. Fig. 3-33 shows the relative abundance of the vertebrate classes through time.

VARIATION, ISOLATION, AND SPECIATION

In this chapter we have had a glimpse of the variety of vertebrate life. But variation is not restricted to differences between species. Variation occurs within populations, and even among littermates. Indeed, no two products of sexual reproduction are identical. The number of kinds of gametes or of homozygous genotypes possible with n pairs of genes is 2^n. The number of different kinds of genotypes possible is 3^n. Even if there were only 100 pairs of genes, 48 digits would be needed for writing the number of possible genotypes. And there are thousands and thousands of pairs of genes. In addition, there may be as many as 400 mutational sites on a single gene. Therefore the number of possible combinations of hereditary traits staggers the imagination. For example, the gastrohepatic artery in a population of *Felis cattus* is sometimes 20 mm long, sometimes 1 mm long, or the gastric and hepatic arteries may arise independently and there is no gastrohepatic artery. The number of variations that actually occurs in arterial channels alone in any interbreeding population is such that one could identify a single shark, or a single human being, from his arterial channels alone. In practice, each of us does better than that! We identify a single human being simply by looking at the face or at a print made from a fingertip. We could, of course, recognize an individual organism by looking at the sequence of nucleotides in its DNA. Genetic variation, coupled with geographical isolation, seems to be the matrix out of which new species evolve.

What happens when a small group of individuals on the periphery of a population wanders sufficiently far from the other members that they establish a new colony out of contact with the original population? Such a geographically isolated group may have one of three fates. If the individuals are not partially preadapted to the newer environment, they may become extinct. Or they may mate with nearby populations of another, closely related species, establishing a zone of hybridization. Or as a result of chance mutations affecting one population and by recombinations and selection pressures, a steady genetic divergence may occur, and the two populations may ultimately become reproductively isolated When reproductive isolation has occurred, a new species will have been produced. The length of time required for the origin of new species by geographical isolation depends on many factors, but the final emergence of new species seems almost inevitable.

Although new animal species may arise other than by geographical isolation, the origin of new species by natural selection *within an existing interbreeding population* is no longer an acceptable concept to most students of evolution.

Not only have new species been *appearing* at different rates during different epochs of the earth's history, depending in part on changes that produce extreme modifications of climate and geography, but species are also *disappearing* at varying rates. Since the start of the twentieth century more than 50 animal species are known to have become extinct. Innumerably more species have come and gone than exist today. Because of the continued rise and demise of species, the biota on earth has been changing since life first appeared on this planet.

CHAPTER SUMMARY

1. The vertebrate classes are Agnatha, Acanthodii, Placodermi, Chondrichthyes, Osteichthyes, Amphibia, Reptilia, Aves, and Mammalia. The first five classes are fishes. The rest are tetrapods.

2. Living agnathans (cyclostomes) lack jaws, paired appendages, typical vertebrae, and scales. Extinct agnathans (ostracoderms) were armored and are the oldest known vertebrates.

3. Acanthodians and placoderms are extinct armored gnathostomes and are the oldest known vertebrates with jaws.

4. Chondrichthyes have cartilaginous skeletons, include elasmobranchs and holocephalans, and are as old as bony fishes with jaws. Elasmobranchs have five to seven naked gill slits and placoid scales. Holocephalans have a fleshy operculum and only a few vestigial placoid scales.

5. Osteichthyes are lobe-finned or ray-finned bony fishes. They have ganoid, cycloid, or ctenoid scales and a bony operculum. The crossopterygian *Latimeria* and ganoids are the oldest living osteichthyes. Teleosts are the most modern. Most lobe fins have internal nares, and the air sacs are often used as lungs.

6. Amphibians probably came from rhipidistian crossopterygians via labyrinthodonts (monophyletic theory). They include anurans and urodeles with glandular skin devoid of scales, and apodans. Most amphibians lay eggs in water and have gill-bearing larvae. A few are viviparous, and some are perennibranchiate.

7. Reptiles, birds, and mammals are amniotes. Their embryos have an amnion, a chorion, an allantois, and a yolk sac. Fishes and amphibians are anamniotes.

8. Reptiles are ectothermic amniotes with epidermal and sometimes dermal scales, and claws. They typically lay large eggs surrounded by a shell (cleidoic eggs). Some are viviparous.

9. Birds are feathered endothermic descendants of archosaurs. Reptilian scales persist on the legs and feet, which bear claws. The

forelimbs are modified for flight except in ratites, in which fore-limbs are usually vestigial or absent. The oldest birds, Archaeor-nithes, had long feathered tails and teeth.

10. Mammals are descendants of therapsid reptiles. They have hair. Prototheria (monotremes) have a cloaca and lay reptilian eggs. Their mammary glands are primitive and there are no nipples. Metatheria (marsupials) and Eutheria (all remaining mammals) give birth to living young. Marsupials use the yolk sac as a pla-centa.

11. Main lines of vertebrate evolution probably pass through groups indicated in Figs. 3-10 and 3-32.

12. Genetic variation coupled with geographical isolation seems to ac-count for most new species.

LITERATURE CITED AND SELECTED READINGS

1. Alexander, R.M.: The chordates, Cambridge, England, 1975, Cambridge University Press.
2. Anderson, H.T., editor: Biology of marine animals, New York, 1969, Academic Press, Inc.
3. Bakker, R.T.: Dinosaur renaissance, Scientific American **232**(4):58, 1975.
4. Bardack, D., and Zangerl, R.: First fossil lamprey: a record from the Pennsylvanian of Illinois, Science **162**:1265, 1968.
5. Barghusen, H.R., and Hopson, J.A.: Dentary-squamosal joint and the origin of mammals, Science **168**:573, 1970.
6. Bond, C.E.: Biology of fishes, Philadelphia, 1979, W.B. Saunders Co.
7. Brodal, A., and Fänge, R., editors: The biology of *Myxine*, Oslo, 1963, Universitetsforlaget (Norway).
8. Brower, K.: Two worlds of the harp seal: above and beneath Arctic ice, Smithsonian **10**(4):44, 1979.
9. Buffetaut, E.: Evolution of the crocodilians, Scientific American **241**(4):16, 1979.
10. Carroll, R.L.: The origin of lizards. In Andrews, S.M., Miles, R.S., and Walker, A.D., editors: Problems in vertebrate evolution, New York, 1977, Academic Press, Inc.
11. Colbert, E.H.: Evolution of the ver-tebrates: a history of the backboned animals through time, ed. 3, New York, 1980, Interscience-Wiley.
12. Daniel, J.F.: The elasmobranch fishes, Berkeley, Calif., 1934, University of California Press.
13. Gans, C., editor: Biology of the reptilia, vol. 1, New York, 1969, Academic Press, Inc.
14. Gans, C., and Tinkle, D.W., editors: Biology of the reptilia, vol. 7, New York, 1977, Academic Press Inc.
15. Gardiner, B.G.: Tetrapod ancestry: a reappraisal. In Panchen, A.L., editor: The terrestrial environment and the origin of land vertebrates, New York, 1980, Academic Press, Inc.
16. Goin, C.J., Goin, O.B., and Zug, G.: Introduction to herpetology, San Francisco, 1978, W.H. Freeman & Co., Publishers.
17. Griffiths, M.: The biology of the monotremes, New York, 1978, Academic Press, Inc.
18. Hardisty, M.W.: Biology of the cyclostomes, London, 1979, Chapman & Hall Ltd.
19. Hopson, J.A., and Crompton, A.W.: Origin of mammals. In Dobzhansky, T., Hecht, M.K., and Steere, W.C., editors: Evolutionary biology, New York, 1969, Appleton-Century-Crofts.

20. Human ancestors. Readings from Scientific American, 1960-1979, San Francisco, W.H. Freeman & Co., Publishers.
21. Hunsaker, D., editor: The biology of marsupials, New York, 1977, Academic Press, Inc.
22. Le Maho, Y.: The emperor penguin: a strategy to live and breed in the cold, American Scientist 65(6):680, 1977.
23. Marcus, H.: Beitrage zur Kenntnis der Gymnophionen. III. Zur Entwicklungsgeschichte des Kopfes. I Teil, Morphologische Jharbuch 40:105, 1909.
24. Nickel, R., Schummer, A., and Seiferle, E.: Anatomy of the domestic birds, New York, 1977, Springer-Verlag.
25. Ørvig, T., editor: Current problems of lower vertebrate phylogeny. Proceedings of the Fourth Nobel Symposium, New York, 1968, Interscience-Wiley.
26. Romer, A.S.: The early evolution of fishes, Quarterly Review of Biology 21:33, 1946.
27. Romer, A.S.: Vertebrate paleontology, ed. 3, Chicago, 1966, University of Chicago Press.
28. Schmalhausen, I.I.: The origin of terrestrial vertebrates (translated from the Russian by Leon Kelso), New York, 1968, Academic Press, Inc.
29. Short, R.V.: The origin of species. In Austin, C.R., and Short, R.V., editors: Reproduction in mammals, book 6, Cambridge, England, 1976, Cambridge University Press.
30. Slijper, E.J.: Whales, New York, 1962, Basic Books, Inc., Publishers.
31. Stahl, B.J.: Vertebrate history: problems in evolution, New York, 1974, McGraw-Hill Book Co.
32. Sturkie, P.D., editor: Avian physiology, ed. 3, New York, 1976, Springer-Verlag.
33. Taylor, E.H.: The caecilians of the world, Lawrence, Kan., 1968, The University Press of Kansas.
34. Thompson, K.S.: The biology of the lobe-finned fishes, Biological Reviews 44:91, 1969.
35. Westoll, T.S.: On the evolution of the Dipnoi. In Jepsen, G.L., Mayr, E., and Simpson, G.G., editors: Genetics, paleontology and evolution, Princeton, N.J., 1949, Princeton University Press.
36. Zimmerman, D.R.: Probing mysteries of how birds can navigate the skies, Smithsonian 10(3):52, 1979.

Symposia in American Zoologist

Evolution and relationships of the amphibia, 5:263, 1965.
Recent advances in the biology of sharks, 17(2):287, 1977.
Behavioral and reproductive biology of sea turtles, 20(3):1980.
Functional-adaptive analysis in systematics, 21(1):3, 1981.

CHAPTER 4

Viviparity, the germ layers, and extraembryonic membranes

THE VERTEBRATE EGG
Egg types

Eggs of vertebrates vary in the amount of yolk they contain and in the distribution of yolk within the egg. Eggs with very little yolk, such as those of the amphioxus and mammals, are **microlecithal.** Eggs with moderate amounts of yolk, such as those of freshwater lampreys, ganoid fishes, lungfishes, and amphibians, are **mesolecithal.** Eggs with massive amounts of yolk, such as those of marine lampreys, elasmobranchs, teleosts, reptiles, birds, and monotremes, are **macrolecithal.**

The yolk in microlecithal eggs is evenly distributed throughout the cytoplasm as fat droplets and small yolk globules. Eggs with an even distribution of yolk are said to be **isolecithal.** In mesolecithal and macrolecithal eggs the large yolk mass tends to be concentrated at one end, the **vegetal pole** (Fig. 4-1). The opposite pole, containing relatively yolk-free cytoplasm, is the **animal pole.** Eggs in which cytoplasm and yolk tend to accumulate at opposite poles are **telolecithal.**

Oviparity

Animals that spawn or lay their eggs are said to be **oviparous.** Eggs of oviparous species contain sufficient nourishment in the form of yolk and, sometimes, albumen to support development into a free-living organism that is soon capable of feeding itself. If the yolk is massive the young may hatch fully formed, as in oviparous amniotes. If there is less yolk, as in frogs, the young hatch in a larval state. When there is very little yolk, as in the egg of the amphioxus, the free-living, self-nourishing state must be achieved very quickly after the egg is deposited. Accordingly, the amphioxus hatches into an externally ciliated, free-swimming embryo 8 to 15 hours after fertilization, at

In this chapter we will look briefly at some varieties of viviparity. We will take a minilook at vertebrate blastulae and gastrulation and see how the coelom forms. The major structures that arise from mesoderm, ectoderm, and endoderm will be summarized (details are in appropriate chapters throughout the book). Finally, we will be introduced to the major extraembryonic membranes and learn what they do for the unhatched or unborn vertebrate.

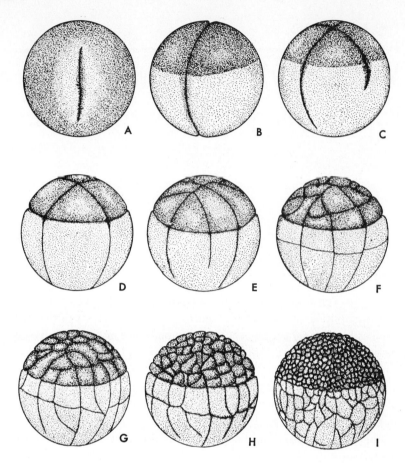

Fig. 4-1. Cleavage and the blastula of amphibian egg. *Dark cells,* animal pole cells containing little yolk; *light cells,* vegetal pole cells containing much yolk. In **I,** gastrulation by epiboly is underway. (After Eycleshymer.)

which time the notochord is a mere ridge in the roof of the primitive gut and there are no gill slits.

Viviparity

In many vertebrates the egg is retained within the mother's body during embryonic development and live young are delivered. Such species are said to be **viviparous.** The relationship between mother and embryos varies from one in which the mother provides protection and little else, as in viviparous sharks, to one in which the embryos depend on the mother for all nourishment, for oxygen, and for carrying away waste products of metabolism, as in viviparous mammals. Many intermediate degrees of dependence have evolved. The term **ovoviviparity** has been coined to designate the condition in which protection, oxygen, and little else are provided, and the term **euviviparity** is used when the embryo cannot develop without nourishment being constantly provided by the mother.

Viviparity in one degree or another has evolved in every class of jawed vertebrates except birds. It has developed independently more than a dozen times in teleost fishes, at least ten times in lizards, and at least six times in snakes. It occurs in 40 families of sharks and rays, and there is fossil evidence for viviparity in holocephalans and chondrosteans. It is thought to have occurred in the extinct *Ichthyosaurus*. There are viviparous urodeles and anurans that give birth to fully metamorphosed young in terrestrial environments, and there are viviparous aquatic apodans.

The dogfish shark, *Squalus acanthias*, is an example of an ovoviviparous organism. The pups are nourished entirely by the yolk from their own yolk sac (Fig. 4-8), but they receive oxygen from greatly enlarged and highly tortuous blood vessels in the uterine lining of the mother. The pups may be removed from the mother 2 to 3 months before birth (the gestation period is 20 to 22 months) and will complete their development, utilizing the nourishment from their yolk sac, as long as they are confined in finger bowls or plastic tubes containing oxygenated seawater.

In viviparous teleosts the egg may be fertilized and the young may develop in the ovarian follicle, there having been no ovulation. The young of *Gambusia* develop in this way. Or the embryos may develop in the ovarian cavity (Fig. 14-32). Among adaptations of the embryo for development in these locations are enlargement of the embryo's pericardial sac, which lies in contact with the maternal tissues of the ovary and absorbs necessary substances; enlargement of the embryonic gut, which lies in contact with maternal tissues; and long villuslike projections (trophotaeniae) of the embryonic gut that protrude through the vent of the embryo into the surrounding nutrient-rich medium. In some teleosts the young develop for a while in the follicular chamber and exhibit an enlarged pericardial sac, then pass into the ovarian cavity and develop absorptive villi. In some species developing eggs or larvae are ingested by other larvae.

Maternal tissues, under the influence of hormones, exhibit adaptations for viviparity. The wall of the ovarian follicle occupied by teleost embryos may develop vascular folds or villi, and these may even project into the mouth or opercular cavity of the embryos. In *Dasyatis americana*, a euviviparous sting ray, the gravid uterus is lined with villi 2 to 3 cm long, which produce a copious secretion that nourishes the embryo. Secretions of uterine glands provide nourishment for unimplanted blastocysts of mammals, and perhaps for implanted blastocysts throughout pregnancy in perissodactyls and artiodactyls. **Histotrophic (embryotrophic) nutrition** is the term applied to nutrition by *glandular secretions* from maternal tissues, as contrasted with nutrition by substances exchanged via a placenta.

INTERNAL AND EXTERNAL FERTILIZATION

In viviparous vertebrates, fertilization takes place within the body of the female. Fertilization is also internal whenever eggs are covered by an impenetrable shell before being extruded.

In oviparous fishes, frogs, and toads external fertilization is the rule. This is possible only because mating takes place in water and very large numbers of sperm and eggs are shed. In apodans and urodeles, however, fertilization is usually internal even though the eggs are subsequently laid. Some male urodeles deposit a sac of sperm embedded in jelly (**spermatophore**) in the immediate vicinity of a female during the mating ritual. The spermatophore is seized by the cloaca of the female or is placed in the cloaca by the male. The sperm then escape from the jelly and migrate up the female reproductive tract to the eggs. Packaging sperm in jelly makes it possible for those few urodeles that live far from water to convey sperm to a female despite lack of a copulatory organ.

Natural selection at work

When eggs are retained within the female or when they are protected by a parent after being laid, the number of eggs produced is small and the mortality is low. When, however, eggs are laid outside the body and are left unprotected, mortality before hatching is high. A naturally high mortality is counterbalanced by production of large numbers of eggs.

An oviparous species that does not conceal or guard its eggs might, as a result of mutations, produce fewer and fewer eggs. Because of the probable destruction of a percentage of eggs, the species would become more rare. The mutations resulting in smaller numbers of eggs, unaccompanied by other mutations providing for protection of the few eggs produced, would finally result in the destruction of the species. **Natural selection** is a term introduced by Charles Darwin to indicate that natural phenomena inexorably determine which organisms will survive. To natural selection may be attributed the following facts: there are very few vertebrates that lay small numbers of eggs in unsheltered locations; there are many vertebrates that lay small numbers of eggs in sheltered or guarded locations; and there are many that lay large numbers of eggs (up to 60 million each season in some fishes) in unguarded locations.

CLEAVAGE AND THE BLASTULA

Early cell divisions of the zygote are referred to as **segmentation,** or **cleavage.** As a result, the zygote becomes subdivided into smaller and smaller cells that form (usually) a hollow sphere, or **blastula.** Each cell of the blastula is a **blastomere** and the cavity is the **blastocoel** (Fig 4-2).

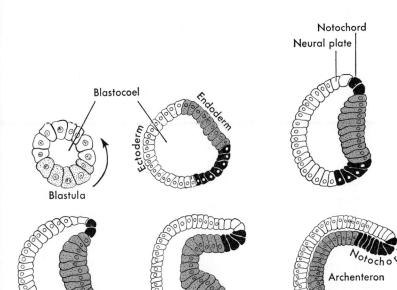

Notochord
Neural plate

Blastocoel

Endoderm

Ectoderm

Blastula

Notochord

Archenteron

Gastrula

GASTRULATION
Amphioxus

Fig. 4-2. Blastula and gastrulation in an amphioxus, sagittal section. Cells in black surround the blastopore (entrance to archenteron) and are the most active, mitotically. Red indicates presumptive endoderm.

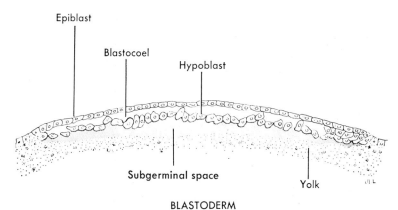

Epiblast

Blastocoel

Hypoblast

Subgerminal space

Yolk

BLASTODERM
Bird

Fig. 4-3. Blastoderm at animal pole of an egg containing a massive yolk, sagittal section. The hypoblast is the roof of the archenteron. Head end is to the left.

When there is very little yolk in an egg, the blastomeres are approximately of equal size (Fig. 4-2, blastula). When cell division is impeded by a moderate amount of yolk, as in amphibian eggs, the cells at the vegetal pole divide more slowly and are larger (Fig. 4-1). When there is a massive yolk, as in the eggs of reptiles and birds, segmentation is confined to the animal pole and results in a **blastoderm** (Fig. 4-3) perched like a skullcap on the massive yolk. The embryo develops from this blastoderm.

The eggs of mammals exhibit an animal-vegetal polarity, just as do the eggs of reptiles, even though mammalian eggs above monotremes have almost no yolk. The first cleavage division divides the egg into two blastomeres, one representing the animal pole, the other, the vegetal pole (Fig. 4-4, cleavage). The descendants of the latter pole rapidly become a nutritional membrane, the **trophoblast,** for absorbing nourishment from the uterine fluids. The animal pole cells become the blastoderm, better known in mammals as the **inner cell mass** and, later, the **embryonic disc.** Because of the cystlike nature of the mammalian blastula, it is called a **blastocyst.**

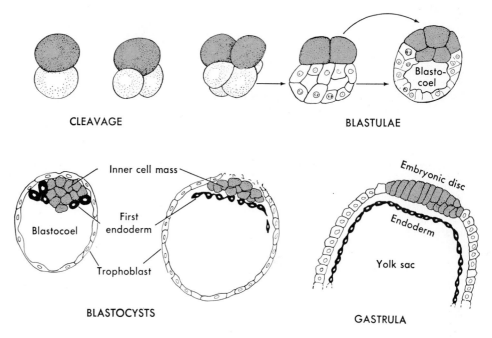

CLEAVAGE   BLASTULAE

Inner cell mass

First endoderm

Blastocoel

Trophoblast

BLASTOCYSTS

Embryonic disc

Endoderm

Yolk sac

GASTRULA

Mammal

Fig. 4-4. Cleavage, blastula, and gastrula-like stage of a mammal. At cleavage (upper left) the red cell at the animal pole gives rise to the embryo. The other cell gives rise to the trophoblast. The first endoderm (hypoblast) comes from the inner cell mass. The yolk sac contains no yolk.

As a result of cleavage, all vertebrates, including human beings, pass through a hollow, spherical stage of development known as the blastula. During this stage, areas of distinctive developmental potential (rudiments of future ectoderm, endoderm, mesoderm, notochord) are established. Presumptive (i.e., future) notochordal cells are intimately associated with presumptive mesoderm for a time. The term **chordomesoderm** designates this undifferentiated dorsal region.

GASTRULATION

Gastrulation is a dynamic process of cellular movements whereby presumptive endoderm, mesoderm, and notochord cells of the blastula reach the interior of the embryo. These displacements, mostly migratory, are referred to as **formative,** or **morphogenetic, movements** because in the process the cells that until then were totipotent (capable of becoming any kind of cell) thereby become restricted with respect to the direction of further differentiation. The restriction is imposed in part by chemical messages from nearby cells; but there are other factors that are not yet known. Rapid cell proliferation pro-

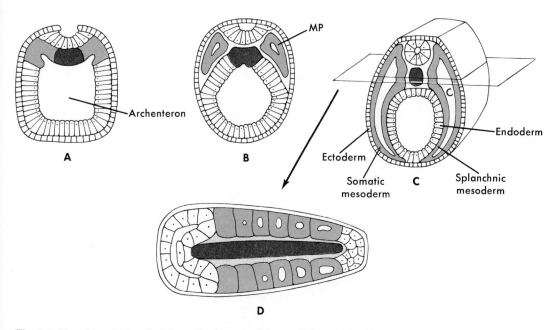

Fig. 4-5. Mesoderm and coelom formation in an amphioxus. **A,** Longitudinal bands of mesoderm (light red) lie in the dorsolateral wall of the archenteron lateral to the notochord (dark red). **B,** Mesodermal pouches (MP) have formed. **C,** The pouches have grown ventrad between ectoderm and endoderm to form a coelom, **C. D,** Early larva in frontal section showing segmented coelom.

vides a continuing supply of additional cells for these formative movements.

In an amphioxus presumptive endoderm folds into the blastocoel (Fig. 4-2). The process, **involution,** produces the earliest gut (**archenteron**). The entrance to the archenteron is the **blastopore.** Soon, presumptive notochord cells flow inward to become the temporary roof of the archenteron (Fig. 4-2, gastrula). Then, presumptive mesoderm cells pass inward to lie in the roof of the gut at either side of the notochord. At this stage the amphioxus embryo consists of an outer tube of ectoderm and an inner tube mostly of endoderm surrounding the archenteron. The roof of the archenteron is future notochord and mesoderm (Fig. 4-5, *A*). Cells proliferated from the rim (lips) of the blastopore result in elongation of the embryo, now a **gastrula.**

In vertebrates, gastrulation is affected by the quantity of yolk. Amphibians manage to tuck the unwieldy yolk inside the embryo, where it becomes the floor of the archenteron. This is accomplished partly when the small cells of the animal pole grow downward over the large cells of the vegetal pole, a process called **epiboly** (Fig. 4-1). Yolk then constitutes the archenteric floor, and the notochord is temporarily in its roof (Fig. 4-6).

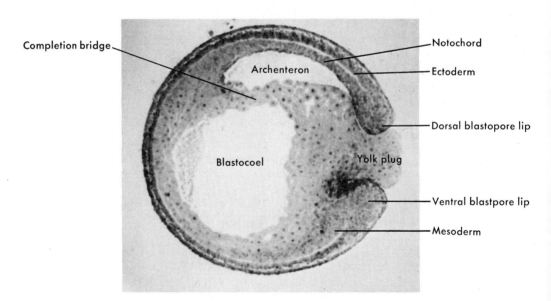

Fig. 4-6. Frog gastrula. The surface layer consists of animal pole cells that have grown downward around the yolk, enclosing it. The notochord is being proliferated from the dorsal lip of the blastopore. This is a later stage than in Fig. 4-1, **I,** and redistribution of weight has rotated the embryo 90 degrees counterclockwise. (From Phillips, J.B.: Development of vertebrate anatomy, St. Louis, 1975, The C.V. Mosby Co.)

In vertebrates with massively yolked eggs, birds for example, the cells of the animal pole do not immediately grow downward around the massive yolk. Instead, the blastoderm splits into an upper sheet of cells, the **epiblast,** and a lower sheet, the **hypoblast** (Fig. 4-3). This process, **delamination,** results in a gastrula in minimum time, hastening formation of mesodermal blood vessels necessary for transporting yolk to the embryo. The epiblast contains chiefly presumptive ectoderm and chordomesoderm. Most of the hypoblast is presumptive endoderm. Later, cells from the hypoblast grow downward around the yolk to become the endodermal lining of a yolk sac, although not in bony fishes. Details will be found in appropriate textbooks of embryology. Delamination eliminates initial infolding of presumptive endoderm into the blastocoel and reduces the archenteron to an insignificant structure.

Mammalian gastrulation commences by delamination of an epiblast and hypoblast from an **inner cell mass** (Fig. 4-4). Then the hypoblast (first endoderm) grows "downward" around a yolk that isn't there!

MESODERM FORMATION AND THE COELOM

The formation of mesoderm is simplest in an amphioxus, in which the first mesoderm arises from a pair of mesodermal folds in the dorsolateral wall of the archenteron (Fig. 4-5, *A*). These bands fold upward, pinch off, and form a series of hollow **mesodermal (coelomic) pouches** (Fig. 4-5, *B*). About the time that two pouches have appeared, the embryo hatches into a free-swimming larva. As the larva elongates, additional pouches form.

After the mesodermal pouches are established, they grow ventrad, pushing between ectoderm and endoderm (Fig. 4-5, *C*). They finally meet underneath the gut and fuse, establishing a temporary ventral mesentery. The outer wall of each pouch lies against the ectoderm and is called **somatic mesoderm.** Together with the ectoderm it forms the **somatopleure,** which is the early **body wall.** The inner wall of each pouch lies against the endoderm and is called **splanchnic mesoderm.** Together with endoderm it constitutes the **splanchnopleure,** which becomes chiefly the digestive tube of the trunk. The cavity between somatic and splanchnic mesoderm is the coelom (Fig. 4-5, *C*).

In the amphioxus the coelom is segmented for a while because of its origin from a series of pouches. Later, the walls between pouches rupture, establishing a single long coelom on each side. Still later, the ventral mesentery ruptures, and the left and right coelomic cavities become confluent underneath the gut.

Vertebrates do not form mesoderm as outpocketings of the archenteron. In those with mesolecithal eggs, chordomesoderm from the surface of the blastula streams over the lips of the blastopore into the interior to establish a notochord (Fig. 4-6) and, lateral to that, **dorsal mesoderm.** The dorsal mesoderm then segments to form mesodermal somites homologous with the mesodermal pouches of the amphioxus (Fig. 1-11). Presumptive mesoderm also flows into what is becoming the lateral body wall to form a thin sheet of unsegmented **lateral-plate mesoderm** that splits into somatic and splanchnic mesoderm containing the coelom. A strand of unsegmented **nephrogenic mesoderm** connects the dorsal mesoderm with lateral-plate mesoderm and gives rise to the kidneys and their ducts (Fig. 1-11).

Mesoderm formation in amniotes with macrolecithal eggs is accomplished by much streaming and migrating of cells laterad and caudad above the huge yolk, resulting in what appears to be a token blastopore at what will become the caudal end of the future embryo. From this site a notochordal process pushes forward beneath the epiblast. Presumptive mesoderm cells push forward alongside the process to establish dorsal mesoderm, while other presumptive mesoderm cells migrate beneath the epiblast forward, outward above the massive yolk sphere, and downward to provide lateral-plate mesoderm. Details are beyond the scope of this text. Placental mammals have a similar pattern of mesoderm formation that bespeaks their reptilian ancestry. The state of knowledge of morphogenetic movements has been reviewed by Ballard.[4]

FATE OF THE MESODERM
Mesodermal somites (epimere)

The somites constitute collectively the **dorsal mesoderm,** or epimere. They are aligned beside the notochord and neural tube the entire length of the trunk and tail, and they form in the head in varying numbers (Fig. 15-6). Typical somites exhibit three regions—**dermatome, sclerotome,** and **myotome** (Fig. 4-7). Myotomes contribute mesenchyme, an aggregation of undifferentiated cells that gives rise to skeletal muscles except those of the visceral arches. Muscles derived from myotomes are **myotomal muscles.** Dermatomes contribute mesenchyme that gives rise to the dermis of the skin of the back. (Most of the dermis arises from lateral-plate mesoderm and, in the head, neural crests.) Sclerotomes give rise to the vertebral column, the proximal portion of ribs, and the posterior part of the neurocranium.

Lateral-plate mesoderm (hypomere)

Lateral mesoderm is confined to the trunk and consists of somatic and splanchnic mesoderm (Fig. 4-7). Somatic mesoderm gives rise chiefly to the connective tissues, blood vessels, and skeleton of the

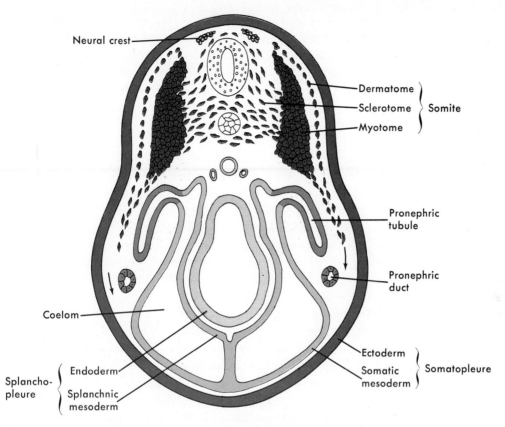

Fig. 4-7. Vertebrate embryo in cross section showing fate of mesoderm. *Dark red,* mesodermal somite (dorsal mesoderm) and its derivatives; *medium red,* derivatives of intermediate mesoderm; *light red,* lateral mesoderm. Sclerotome cells (scleroblasts) are streaming toward notochord and neural tube to form a vertebra; myotomal cells (myoblasts) are streaming into lateral body wall (arrows) to form myotomal muscle; dermatome will form dermis of skin of back.

body wall and limbs. The dermis of the body wall is its outermost product, and the parietal peritoneum is its innermost product. Splanchnic mesoderm gives rise to smooth muscles and connective tissue of the digestive tract and its outpocketings and to the heart. The visceral peritoneum is its outermost derivative. Splanchnic mesoderm migrates into the head fold to give rise to the dermatocranium.

Nephrogenic mesoderm (mesomere)

Nephrogenic mesoderm consists of a pair of long ribbons of mostly unsegmented mesoderm extending the length of the trunk just lateral to the somites. It gives rise to kidney tubules and to most of the urinogenital ducts.

FATE OF THE ECTODERM

A median ventral invagination of the ectoderm of the embryonic head, the **stomodeum,** becomes the anteriormost part of the oral cavity (Fig. 1-1). This part of the oral cavity is therefore ectodermal. Stomodeal ectoderm gives rise to enamel of the teeth and some of the more anterior glands of the oral cavity. An evagination from the roof of the stomodeum, **Rathke's pouch,** becomes the adenohypophysis (Fig. 17-6).

An ectodermal invagination similar to the stomodeum develops in relation to the cloaca. This is the **proctodeum** (Fig. 1-1). It gives rise to the terminal lining of the cloaca in lower vertebrates. No discernible part remains in adult mammals.

Ectoderm gives rise to the epidermis of the skin and all its derivatives, including glands that lie in the dermis but open onto the surface by ducts. The nervous system, olfactory epithelium, retina and lens, membranous labyrinth, neuromast system, and, in the skin, chemoreceptors are ectodermal.

All neural crest contributions (Fig. 4-7) are ectodermal. In the head these include structures usually thought of as mesodermal—dermis, subcutaneous connective tissue, teeth, most of the pharyngeal skeleton, parts of the neurocranium, branchiomeric musculature, and, in amphibians at least, the leptomeninx of the brain and cord. Neural crest derivatives outside the head include chromaffin tissue everywhere, adrenal medulla, calcitonin-producing cells, and all pigment cells wherever located. Neural crests also give rise to certain neurons and neurilemmal cells. The foregoing derivatives illustrate the diverse potentialities of ectoderm.

Mesenchyme of ectodermal origin is **ectomesenchyme.** If it is from the neural tube or neural crests, it is also called **neurectoderm.**

FATE OF THE ENDODERM

Endoderm gives rise to the epithelium of the entire alimentary canal between the stomodeum and proctodeum. Any taste buds or oral glands behind the stomodeal area are endodermal. Since pharyngeal pouches arise as outpocketings of endoderm, the derivatives of the pouches—thymus, parathyroids, ultimobranchial glands, auditory tube, middle ear cavity, and crypts associated with mammalian tonsils—have endodermal components. Any midventral evaginations of the embryonic pharynx, such as thyroid, lungs, or swim bladders, and their ducts are lined with endoderm or have endodermal components. Caudal to the pharynx the endoderm evaginates to form liver, gallbladder, pancreas, and various gastric and intestinal ceca. Most urinary bladders and the urinogenital sinus of mammals are lined with endoderm, since these are derived from the cloaca. Any

other structures that arise as evaginations of the endodermal tube
have endodermal components.

EXTRAEMBRYONIC MEMBRANES

Most embryonic vertebrates are provided with special membranes
that extend beyond the body. These extraembryonic membranes arise
early in ontogeny and perform important services for the embryo until hatching or birth. The chief extraembryonic membranes are the
yolk sac, amnion, chorion, and **allantois.** The last three are found
only in reptiles, birds, and mammals. The yolk sac is the most primitive.

Yolk sac

The yolk sac surrounds the yolk (Figs. 4-8 and 4-9). It empties
into the midgut and is usually lined by endoderm, although not in
bony fishes. The sac is highly vascular, and its vessels (**vitelline arteries** and **veins**) connect with circulatory channels within the embryo.
Yolk particles in the sac are usually digested by enzymes secreted by
the lining of the sac and then transported to the embryo by vitelline
veins. (In sharks, yolk also enters the intestine directly from the sac,
propelled by rapidly beating cilia that line the sac and stalk.) The yolk
sac therefore grows smaller as the embryo grows larger. As it shrivels,
it slowly disappears through the ventral body wall. The intracoelomic
remnant of the yolk sac is finally incorporated into the wall of the
midgut, or it may remain as a small diverticulum.

In embryonic sharks a large diverticulum of the yolk sac develops
within the coelom close to where the sac opens into the duodenum.
In pups ready to be born and with the yolk sac almost completely
retracted, the diverticulum is easily demonstrated. It is distended

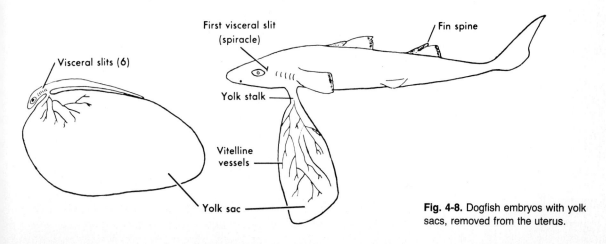

Visceral slits (6)

First visceral slit
(spiracle)

Fin spine

Yolk stalk

Vitelline
vessels

Yolk sac

Fig. 4-8. Dogfish embryos with yolk
sacs, removed from the uterus.

with yolk, which has also spilled over into the spiral intestine. This remaining yolk serves to nourish the newborn pup for several days until it is able to obtain food from the environment.

Despite the fact that there is no yolk in typical mammalian eggs, embryonic mammals develop a yolk sac (Fig. 4-4)—a reminder of their genetic relationship with egg-laying reptiles. In humans a vestige of the yolk sac (Meckel's diverticulum) remains in about 2% of the adult population. Its average position is on the ileum, 1 m before the ileocolic valve, and its average length is about 5 cm.

Since the yolk sac in viviparous vertebrates is highly vascularized and lies close to the maternal tissues, it often serves as a membrane for absorbing oxygen from the parent. After the yolk in the sac is depleted, or if there is none, it may also absorb nourishment from maternal tissues. When functioning in either capacity, it constitutes a **simple yolk sac placenta.**

Amnion and chorion

Embryos developing from eggs exposed to the air would be subject to dessication if they had no protection. Compensating for this in reptiles, birds, and mammals are two almost watertight saccular membranes, the amnion and chorion. These come into existence simultaneously when delicate upfoldings of the somatopleure meet above the embryo (Fig. 4-9, A).

The **amnion** is a sac filled with salty fluid that surrounds the embryo. The source of the fluid is chiefly metabolic water—water produced during cellular respiration when oxygen from the air unites with hydrogen from nutrients. The fluid is secreted by the amnion into the amniotic sac. (Turtle eggs laid in moist sand absorb considerable water from the environment, but this appears to be unusual.) Amniotic fluid buffers the fetus against mechanical injury.

The **chorion** forms a much larger **chorionic sac** surrounding the amniotic sac (Fig. 4-10, pig) and lying in more or less intimate relationship with the eggshell or the lining of the maternal uterus (Fig. 4-9, A).

Allantois

The allantois is an extraembryonic membrane that arises from the embryonic cloaca as a midventral evagination (Fig. 4-9, B).* Typically, it grows until it comes in contact with the chorion to form a **chorioallantoic membrane.**

In oviparous and ovoviviparous reptiles, in birds, and in mono-

---

*In a few mammals, including humans, the allantois arises from the yolk sac before a cloaca has formed and later assumes the usual relationship with the cloaca.

tremes the chorioallantoic membrane comes in contact with the inner surface of the porous eggshell (Fig. 4-9, *B*). There it serves as a respiratory organ for exchange of oxygen and carbon dioxide between fetal organism and environment. In mammals above marsupials the chorioallantoic membrane comes in contact with the lining of the mother's uterus, since there is no eggshell. Here, too, the membrane serves as a respiratory organ, but it performs two additional functions. It serves as a site for transfer of nutrients from mother to young and for transfer of metabolic wastes from young to mother. Thus the chorioallantoic membrane in fetal mammals constitutes a chorioallantoic placenta.

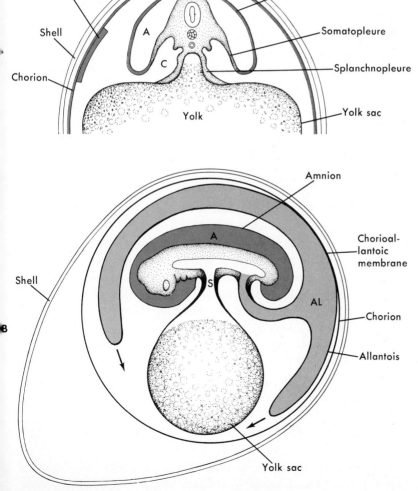

Fig. 4-9. Extraembryonic membranes of an egg-laying amniote. **A,** Cross section of embryo showing amnion and chorion arising from amniotic folds of somatopleure. The position of the allantois, when fully differentiated, is indicated on left of drawing. **B,** Relationships of allantois, which is growing in direction of arrows. *A,* Amniotic cavity; *AL,* allantoic cavity; *C,* intraembryonic coelom; *S,* yolk stalk.

In some mammals, including cats, rabbits, and humans, the allantoic evagination grows only part way out the umbilical cord, then dwindles to terminate as a blind sac. However, its vessels, the **allantoic (umbilical) arteries** and **veins,** continue toward and vascularize the chorion, which is the fetal part of the placenta.

The base of the allantois—the part closest to the cloaca—becomes the urinary bladder (Fig. 13-30). The part of the allantois between the bladder and the umbilicus may remain after birth as a **middle umbilical ligament (urachus).** The portion outside the body is discarded at hatching or birth. It is likely that the allantois is the old amphibian urinary bladder that has acquired an added role during fetal life.

Placentae

The term **placenta** in a broad sense refers to any region in a viviparous species where parental and embryonic tissues of any kind are closely apposed, and which serves as a site for exchange of necessary substances between parent and embryo. In this sense, placentae are exhibited by some viviparous fishes that develop in an ovarian follicle. In a more restricted sense, a placenta is an organ composed of (1) the modified region of an extraembryonic membrane (yolk sac, choriovitelline membrane, chorioallantoic membrane, or chorion alone) that lies in intimate association with the maternal uterine lining and (2) the associated modified lining of the maternal uterus.

The yolk sac frequently serves as a placenta. In viviparous anamniotes—vertebrates lacking amnion, chorion, and allantois—the yolk sac may lie against the lining of the uterus and constitute the fetal part of a **simple yolk sac placenta.** It serves in this capacity in many sharks and rays. In euviviparous reptiles and the lowest placental mammals (marsupials), the yolk sac lies against the chorion and the chorion is in intimate association with the uterine lining. This is a **choriovitelline placenta.** It is more modern than a simple yolk sac placenta. Mammals above marsupials have a **chorioallantoic placenta.**

The intimacy of the anatomical relationship between fetal and maternal tissues in mammals varies greatly. In marsupials and most ungulates the fetal placenta lies in simple contact with the uterine lining, and at birth the fetal membranes simply peel away from the uterus without any shedding of the uterine lining. This is said to be a **contact (nondeciduous) placenta.** In more intimate relationships chorionic villi, which are fingerlike outgrowths of the chorionic sac, become more or less rooted into the uterine lining or even dangle into uterine blood sinuses. When the fetal part of such a placenta disengages from the uterus at parturition (birth), the invaded portion of the uterine lining (decidua) is shed, and some bleeding occurs.

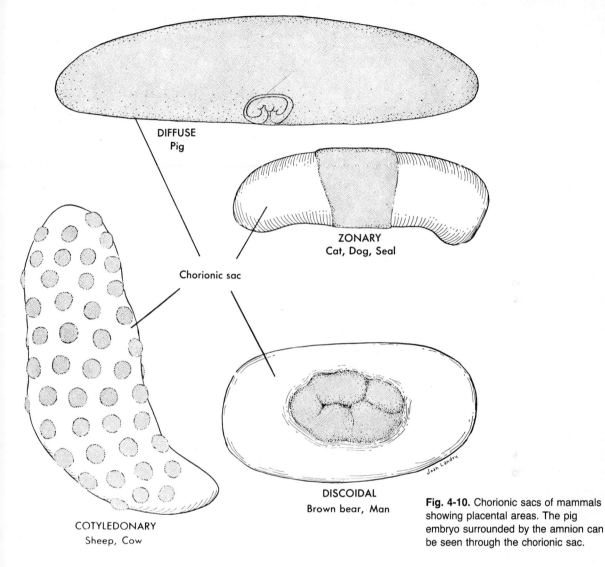

DIFFUSE
Pig

ZONARY
Cat, Dog, Seal

Chorionic sac

COTYLEDONARY
Sheep, Cow

DISCOIDAL
Brown bear, Man

Fig. 4-10. Chorionic sacs of mammals showing placental areas. The pig embryo surrounded by the amnion can be seen through the chorionic sac.

This is said to be a **deciduous placenta.** In any case, the extraembryonic membranes along with any sloughed uterine tissue are delivered as the **afterbirth.**

Chorionic villi (indicating functional placental regions) are distributed on the chorionic sac (Fig. 4-10) in isolated patches (**cotyledonary placenta**), in a band encircling the chorion (**zonary placenta**), in a single, large, discoidal area (**discoidal placenta**), or diffusely over the entire surface of the chorion (**diffuse placenta**). The diffuse placenta is thought to be more primitive. Placentae of mammals, at least, are a source of hormones that assist in maintaining pregnancy.

CHAPTER SUMMARY

1. Oviparous vertebrates deposit eggs that contain enough nourishment to support development of a free-living, self-nourishing organism.

2. Eggs are microlecithal, mesolecithal, or macrolecithal, according to the quantity of yolk. They are isolecithal or telolecithal, depending on the distribution of the yolk within the egg.

3. The amphioxus deposits small eggs with very little yolk that hatch quickly into immature, free-living, ciliated larvae with rudimentary organ systems.

4. Viviparous vertebrates develop in the body of the female parent. In ovoviviparous species the eggs are laden with yolk, and the mother provides oxygen, protection, and little else. In euviviparous species the eggs are practically devoid of yolk, and all nourishment is supplied by the parent.

5. In viviparity special highly vascularized embryonic tissues (pericardial sac, gills, villi, opercular lining, extraembryonic membranes, and other tissues) are sites for absorption of necessary substances.

6. Viviparity is found in every vertebrate class except cyclostomes and birds.

7. Fertilization is internal in viviparous species, in urodeles and apodans, and in species that cover the egg with a shell.

8. As a result of fertilization and cleavage, a blastula with a blastocoel is formed. A blastoderm forms in yolk-laden eggs. An inner cell mass forms in placental mammals.

9. Gastrulation is characterized by notogenesis and formation of three germ layers. Among processes are involution, epiboly, and delamination, accompanied by morphogenetic movements.

10. Embryonic mesoderm consists of dorsal mesoderm (mesodermal somites), nephrogenic mesoderm, and lateral-plate mesoderm.

11. Mesodermal somites consist of sclerotome, dermatome, and myotome. These give rise, respectively, to vertebrae and ribs, dermis of the back, and myotomal muscles.

12. Lateral-plate mesoderm consists of somatic and splanchnic layers. Somatic mesoderm plus ectoderm becomes somatopleure (body wall); splanchnic mesoderm plus endoderm gives rise chiefly to splanchnopleure, which becomes the digestive tube.

13. Nephrogenic mesoderm gives rise to kidneys and urinogenital ducts.

14. The coelom is the cavity between somatic and splanchnic mesoderm. It is initially segmented in the amphioxus, unsegmented in vertebrates.

15. Ectoderm contributes epidermis and its derivatives, nervous system and many special sense organs, and derivatives of the stomodeum and proctodeum. Neural crests contribute much of the neurocranium, pharyngeal skeleton and branchiomeric muscle, chromaffin tissue, pigment cells, adrenal medulla, and miscellaneous tissues.

16. Endoderm gives rise to the epithelium of the digestive tract and its evaginations, to taste buds and oral glands behind the stomodeum, to the epithelial derivatives of the pharyngeal pouches and pharyngeal floor, and to most of the cloaca and its derivatives.

17. The chief extraembryonic membranes are yolk sac, amnion, chorion, and allantois.

18. A yolk sac develops in all vertebrates even though no yolk is present. Vitelline vessels transport digested yolk, when present, to the embryo. The yolk sac sometimes serves as a placenta, either alone (simple yolk sac placenta) or in association with the chorion (choriovitelline placenta).

19. The amnion and chorion are concentric sacs surrounding the amniote fetus. Amniotic fluid helps prevent desiccation of fetuses and mechanical injury. The chorion is applied to the eggshell or to the lining of the maternal uterus. In the latter case it is part of a placenta.

20. The allantois is a midventral evagination of the embryonic cloaca. It comes in contact with the chorion to form a chorioallantoic membrane lying close to the eggshell or to the uterine lining of the mother. In the latter case it is part of a chorioallantoic placenta. The base of the allantois becomes the urinary bladder in amniotes.

21. The most common vertebrate placentae with respect to fetal membrane components are chorioallantoic, choriovitelline, and simple yolk sac placentae. The latter are the most primitive.

22. Placentae may be contact or deciduate. Villi may be arranged in a zonary, cotyledonary, discoidal, or diffuse pattern.

LITERATURE CITED AND SELECTED READINGS

1. Amoroso, E.C.: Viviparity in fishes, Symposium of the Zoological Society of London 1:153, 1960.
2. Arey, L.B.: Developmental anatomy, ed. 7 (revised), Philadelphia, 1974, W.B. Saunders Co.
3. Balinsky, B.I.: An introduction to embryology, ed. 5, Philadelphia, 1981, W.B. Saunders Co.
4. Ballard, W.W.: Morphogenetic movements and fate maps of vertebrates, American Zoologist 21(2):391, 1981.
5. DeHaan, R.I., and Ursprung, H., editors: Organogenesis, New York, 1965, Holt, Rinehart and Winston, Inc.
6. Ham, R.G., and Veomett, M.J.: Mechanisms of development, St. Louis, 1980, The C.V. Mosby Co.
7. Hopper, A.F., and Hart, N.H.: Foundations of animal development, New York, 1980, Oxford University Press, Inc.
8. Keith, L.M.: The developing human, ed. 2, Philadelphia, 1977, W.B. Saunders Co.
9. Matthews, L.H.: The evolution of viviparity in vertebrates. Memoirs of the Society for Endocrinology, no. 4, Cambridge, England, 1955, Cambridge University Press.
10. Oppenheimer, S.B.: Introduction to embryonic development, Boston, 1980, Allyn & Bacon, Inc.
11. Patten, B.M.: Early embryology of the chick, ed. 5, New York, 1971, McGraw-Hill Book Co.
12. Patten, B.M., and Carlson, B.M.: Foundations of embryology, New York, 1974, McGraw-Hill Book Co.
13. Smith, C.C., and Fretwell, S.D.: The optimal balance between size and number of offspring, American Naturalist 108:499, 1975.
14. Wourms, J.P.: Viviparity: the maternal-fetal relationship in fishes, American Zoologist 21(2):473, 1981.

CHAPTER 5

Skin

The skin of all vertebrates is built in accordance with a basic blueprint. It consists of a multilayered **epidermis,** derived from ectoderm, and a **dermis,** derived chiefly from mesoderm. Modifications of the epidermis and dermis involve (1) the relative number and complexity of skin glands, (2) the extent of differentiation and specialization of the most superficial layer (stratum corneum) of the epidermis, and (3) the extent to which bone develops in the dermis. The skin of an amphioxus exhibits epidermis and dermis, but the epidermis is only one cell thick (Fig. 5-1).

SKIN OF THE EFT

As an introduction to the skin, we will examine briefly a skin unencumbered by scales, feathers, or hair—the skin of a red eft, the juvenile land stage of the urodele *Notophthalmus*. It illustrates generalized vertebrate skin with one notable difference: the absence of ossification in the dermis.

The epidermis of an eft is a stratified epithelium (Fig. 5-2). The columnar cells in the deepest layer of the epidermis (**stratum germinativum**) are constantly undergoing mitosis and replacing those lost from the surface. Proliferation from the basal layer causes older cells to be pushed outward. As they approach the surface, they become flattened (squamous) and synthesize **keratin,** a scleroprotein that is insoluble in water. When keratin is synthesized in a cell, the cell is said to be **keratinized,** or **cornified,** and it dies. Thus the outermost layer (**stratum corneum**) of the epidermis is made up of flattened, dead, cornified (keratinized) cells. The stratum corneum is constantly being shed in patches and replaced.

The glands of the skin develop from the epidermis and, in efts, are simple sacs, most of which secrete mucus. As they grow, they invade the dermis, where they are close to capillaries. In addition to the bases of glands and blood vessels, the dermis of efts consists chiefly of collagenous and other connective tissues, small nerves, lymphatics, and pigment cells.

In this chapter we will look at the basic structure of vertebrate skin. We will examine the epidermis of aquatic vertebrates and then see how it has been modified for life in air. We will look also at some of the remarkable structures that form from epidermis. Next we will look at the dermis and discover that in early vertebrates it was loaded with bone, that bone is still present in much modern skin, and that the absence of bone is a specialization. Finally, we will look briefly at skin pigment and some of the things that skin does to help vertebrates survive.

109

Fig. 5-1. Skin of a young amphioxus.

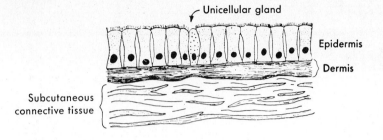

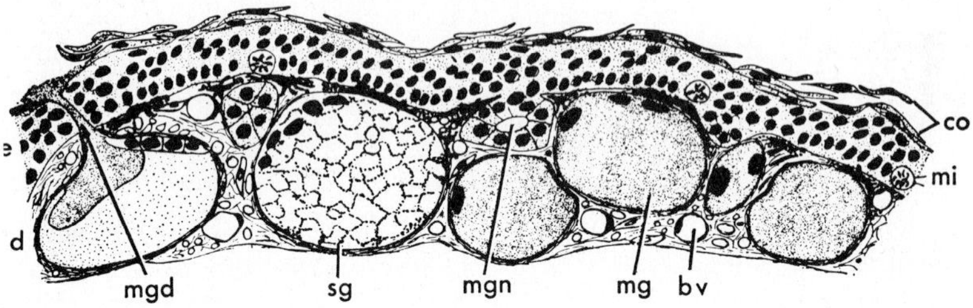

Fig. 5-2. Skin of *Notophthalmus,* land stage (eft). **bv,** Blood vessel; **co,** cells of stratum corneum; **d,** dermis; **e,** epidermis; **mg,** simple alveolar mucous gland; **mgd,** duct of discharging mucous gland; **mgn,** new epidermal gland invading the dermis; **mi,** mitotic figure in the basal layer of the epidermis; **sg,** exhausted mucous gland.

Notophthalmus dramatically illustrates the correlation in vertebrates between a terrestrial existence, lack of a mucous covering, and the presence of a stratum corneum. The larvae live in water and have many mucous glands and no stratum corneum. When the larvae metamorphose into efts and assume life on land, the skin glands become quiescent, and a prominent stratum corneum forms and persists as long as the eft lives on land. As the eft approaches sexual maturity and migrates back to water, the mucous glands again become active, and the stratum corneum is shed and does not reappear. The skin of larvae and adults resembles that of fishes, whereas the skin of efts is like that of terrestrial amphibians.

THE EPIDERMIS

We will study the epidermis separately from the dermis because the two have different roles. The epidermis is the interface between organism and environment, and this is reflected in its structure. The dermis provides physiological support for the interface.

Two kinds of covering overlie the living epidermis of vertebrates. In fishes and most aquatic amphibians it is a thin coat of **mucus** that appears to be secreted by every epidermal cell that reaches the surface. In terrestrial vertebrates it is a layer of dead, water-impervious cells, the stratum corneum (Fig. 5-3). The survival value of the stratum corneum is clear. It minimizes water loss through the skin of vertebrates that live in air. The survival value of the constant mucous

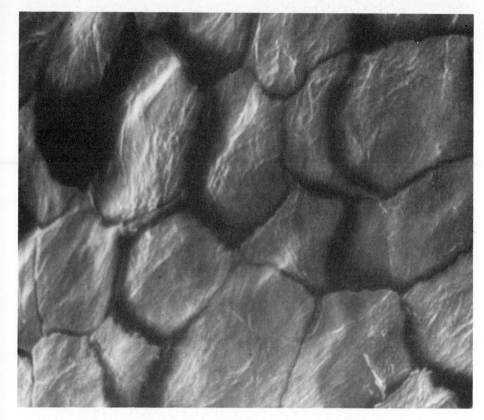

Fig. 5-3. Keratinized (cornified) cells of the stratum corneum on the surface of human skin. (Courtesy Johnson & Johnson Research, New Brunswick, N.J.)

coat is unknown, but it is certain to play as vital a role in survival of fishes as the stratum corneum does in terrestrial vertebrates.

Embryonic skin has a temporary surface layer of flattened epidermal cells, the **periderm,** that protects the underlying actively proliferating stratum germinativum. In mammals it lies on the surface of the embryonic hair (**lanugo**) and is therefore called **epitrichium.** The periderm is lost at the time of hatching or birth, or shortly thereafter, being replaced by the protective mucus or stratum corneum.

The epidermis is glandular, and that of fishes is exceptionally so. Most of the glands of fishes and larval amphibians are unicellular. Multicellular glands are either straight, coiled, or branching tubes (**tubular glands**), or they are composed of one or more sacs (simple, branched, or compound **alveolar glands**). Multicellular glands, as well as feathers and hair, although epidermal, invade the dermis, where they acquire an intimate relationship with capillaries that satisfy their constant need for raw materials.

Epidermis of fishes and aquatic amphibians

Mucous glands abound in fishes and aquatic amphibians. In fishes, most of them are single cells of various shapes, which exude mucus into the surface (Figs. 5-4 to 5-6). A few, usually with an added ingredient that makes the mucus slimy, are multicellular sacs that approach or invade the dermis, as in *Protopterus* (Fig. 5-6, g). In amphibians most mucous glands are multicellular and they expand until they become subcutaneous (Figs. 5-2 and 5-7). Neither unicellular nor multicellular mucous glands are the source of the constant mucous coat of fishes. That coat is a product of typical epidermal cells.

Mucous glands release their secretion in special circumstances, and the survival value of the mucus is sometimes obvious, sometimes speculative. Many fishes and aquatic amphibians threatened with capture exude a slimy mucus in such abundance that they become

Fig. 5-4. Skin of a larval lamprey. The dermis contains very dense collagenous fibers.

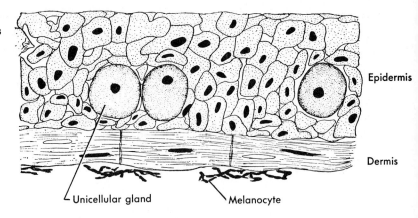

Epidermis

Dermis

Unicellular gland   Melanocyte

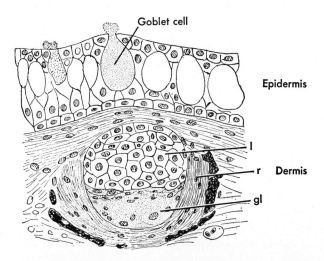

Goblet cell

Epidermis

l

r   Dermis

gl

Fig. 5-5. Skin and light organ (photophore) of a luminous fish. **gl,** Luminous cells; **l,** lens cells; **r,** reflector cells (absent in some species) surrounded by pigment cells (dark). The goblet cells are unicellular glands.

very slippery. This is especially true of hagfishes, whose multicellular slime glands are surrounded by striated muscle fibers. The lungfish *Protopterus* surrounds itself with a slimy cocoon before aestivating in a burrow during the dry season. Some teleost mothers secrete nutritious mucus that is eaten by hatchlings. It can be assumed that mucus keeps the skin moist in species that make short excursions out of water and that this enables the skin to continue to perform its respiratory role until the mucus dries. The role of the mucus secreted by the ampullae of Lorenzini of sharks is purely speculative. Mucus in fishes and aquatic amphibians plays an important role related to maintenance of an appropriate internal environment and in meeting some of the challenges of the external environment.

Serous glands are present in small numbers in fishes, and they are rare in aquatic amphibians. They have a granular cytoplasm, and their

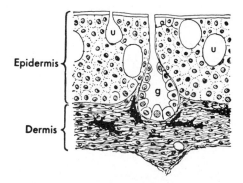

Fig. 5-6. Glandular skin of the dipnoan *Protopterus*. Multicellular, **g,** and unicellular, **u,** glands in the epidermis. Pigment cells are seen in the dermis.

Epidermis

Dermis

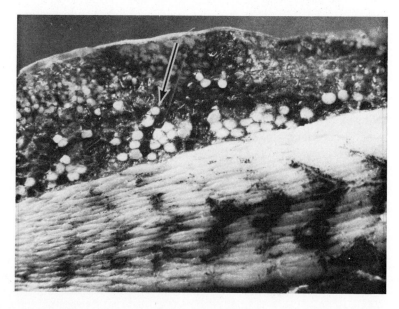

Fig. 5-7. Undersurface of skin from the tail of *Necturus,* an aquatic urodele, showing mucous glands (arrow) projecting into subcutaneous tissue just external to muscle.

Fig. 5-8. Lamprey teeth and buccal funnel. **A,** Cornified tooth (black). The stellate tissue may be the beginning of a replacement tooth. **B,** Buccal funnel. The horny teeth are shown as white against a dark background.

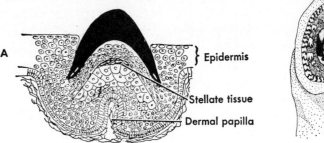
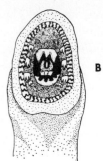

watery secretions are basically protective, being mostly noxious or poisonous, or alarm substances that are released when the population is endangered.

Some of the multicellular glands of fishes, especially deep-water teleosts, have become light-emitting organs, or **photophores.** Like other multicellular skin glands, photophores arise in the epidermis and invade the dermis. In one variety (Fig. 5-5), the basal part of the gland consists of mucous cells that serve as a magnifying lens. Surrounding the base of the photophore are a blood sinus and a concentration of pigment cells. The light emitted by photophores is not intense and is of many hues. Among other roles the light serves for species and sex recognition and sometimes aids in concealment by countershading.

Most fishes synthesize little or no keratin, but aquatic amphibians sometimes have a thin stratum corneum, especially species that venture onto land. However, in a few species of fishes and aquatic amphibians, localized surfaces develop cornified structures. Conical horny epidermal spines and teeth develop in the buccal funnel and on the rasping tongue of cyclostomes (Fig. 5-8); and tadpoles have horny teeth, lips, and jaws that enable them to feed by rasping on vegetation during the larval stage. These are shed at metamorphosis. Calluslike caps develop on the toes of aquatic urodeles subjected to buffeting in mountain streams.

Epidermal glands of terrestrial vertebrates

Mucous glands have all but disappeared from the skin of terrestrial vertebrates, stratum corneum having taken the place of mucus as a universal covering.* Mucous glands could dehydrate a vertebrate lacking drinking water in the immediate environment. Also, terres-

---

*Anurans are semiterrestrial. They inhabit moist environments and require mucus to maintain a skin that can participate in respiration.

trial vertebrates have no unicellular skin glands. They probably lost survival value when they became covered by a continuous sheet of dead cells.

The predominant skin glands of reptiles and, to a lesser extent, terrestrial amphibians, especially toads, are serous glands that secrete irritating or toxic alkaloids, or pheromones (Fig. 5-9). Most of these glands are **holocrine,** that is, the *cells* constitute the secretion instead of simply manufacturing it, as in **merocrine glands. Pheromones** are substances that, when secreted into the environment, have an effect on the behavior or physiology of other organisms, usually members of the same species. As many as four different sets of serous glands, probably pheromonal, encircle the vent of lizards; and pheromones smeared on branches attract insects, which are eaten. Musk turtles exude a yellowish fluid from two glands on each side of the trunk just below the carapace, and a row of glands of unknown function, probably pheromonal, lies along the back in crocodilians. Femoral glands on the medial side of the hind limb of male lizards secrete a substance that hardens to form temporary spines that help to restrain the female during copulation.

Only two integumentary glands have been described in birds, and both are oil glands. The **uropygial gland** is a prominent swelling at the rump. It is best developed in aquatic birds, but it is readily located in domestic fowl. Its oily secretion is transferred to feathers during preening. The other variety is smaller **oil glands** that line the outer ear canal and encircle the vent in some birds.

The skin glands of mammals are variations of two basic types, sebaceous, which are oil glands, of which mammary glands appear to be a variant; and sudoriferous glands, the most common of which secrete sweat.

Sebaceous glands are alveolar glands of varying complexity with a holocrine, lubricatory, oily exudate. They are present wherever there are hairs, and the **sebum** is usually exuded into a hair follicle (Fig. 5-10). Fur and human hair glisten after brushing because of the oil. In the outer ear canal they are called **ceruminous glands;** and their waxy grease (cerumen), along with the hairs, traps insects that might otherwise go deeper into the canal and touch the painfully sensitive eardrum. **Tarsal,** or **meibomian, glands** secrete onto the conjunctiva of the eye. These glands are embedded within the tarsus, a plate of dense connective tissue in each eyelid. The glands open in a single row on the inner surface of the lids just internal to the row of eyelashes. Sebaceous glands open independently of hairs on the lips, glans penis, and labia minora; but most of the lubricatory reproductive fluids of mammals are produced by mucous glands. Marine mammals are practically devoid of hair and lack sebaceous glands.

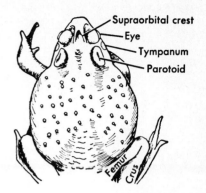

Fig. 5-9. Warty skin of toad *(Bufo).* A serous (granular) gland, the parotoid, is seen behind the eye.

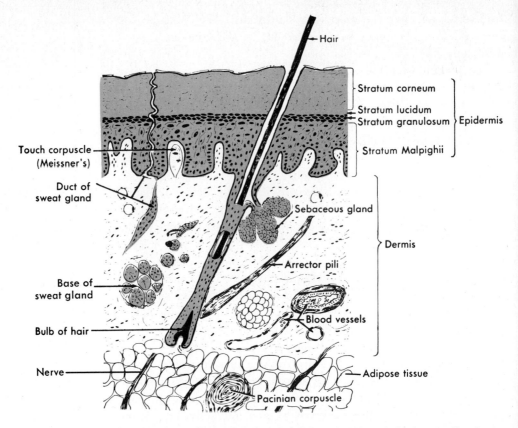

Hair

Stratum corneum

Stratum lucidum
Stratum granulosum
Stratum Malpighii

Epidermis

Touch corpuscle
(Meissner's)

Duct of
sweat gland

Sebaceous gland

Dermis

Arrector pili

Base of
sweat gland

Bulb of hair

Blood vessels

Nerve

Adipose tissue

Pacinian corpuscle

Fig. 5-10. Mammalian skin, with hair follicle and epidermal glands extending deep into the dermis. Supporting the constituents of the dermis are dense bundles of collagenous connective tissue. Epidermal derivatives are red.

Sudoriferous, or **sweat, glands** are long, slender, coiled tubular glands that extend deep into the dermis of mammals (Fig. 5-10). Their secretion oozes onto the surface through tortuous channels that open as pores. The glands appear to be principally thermoregulatory, with evaporation of sweat having a cooling effect. Humans, with less hair than most mammals, have the largest number of sweat glands per surface area. In many mammals sweat glands are confined to the feet (cats, mice, for instance), lips, ears, or back of the head. Pangolins, whose skin is scaly (Fig. 5-24), and marine animals, whose environment precludes cooling by evaporation, have none. Sudoriferous glands that open into the follicles of eyelashes and along the lid margins are **ciliary glands.**

Sebaceous and sudoriferous glands produce a variety of scents, most of which are pheromonal or defensive. Glands on the feet of goats leave odoriferous trails that other members of the species can

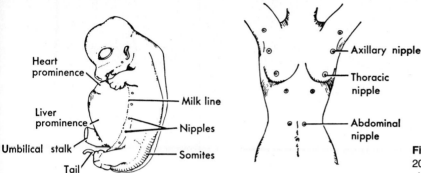

Fig. 5-11. A, Milk line and nipples in a 20-mm pig embryo. **B,** Supernumerary nipples in human female.

recognize; anal glands of skunks drive away enemies, and those of male musk deer signal the sex. Kangaroo rats have sebaceous glands on the back, where they are exposed when the back is arched in defense. Male elephants have a temporal gland that swells during breeding seasons. Natives say that it signals danger. A gland above the eye of a peccary looks like a navel. Some male lemurs have a hardened patch of skin on the forearm, under which is a gland the size of an almond. Most of the odors at a well-maintained mammalian zoo are caused by scent glands, not by unhygienic conditions in the pens and cages. One species, *Homo sapiens,* takes the pheromone from the anal gland of a musk deer, adds other odorants, and dabs it behind the ears. It is called perfume, but it performs the role of a pheromone.

Mammary glands develop in both sexes from a pair of elevated ribbons of ectoderm called **milk lines,** which extend along the ventrolateral body wall of the fetus from axilla to groin (Fig. 5-11, *A*). Patches of future mammary tissue develop at one or more sites along each milk line, depending on the species, and invade the dermis (Fig. 5-12). They later spread beneath the dermis, and a nipple forms above each patch. As females approach sexual maturity, rising titers of female hormones cause the juvenile duct system to spread and branch. Later, during pregnancy, a battery of hormones causes the formation of alveoli at the ends of the duct system. Like sebaceous glands, they are holocrine glands with a fatty secretion.

The number and location of mammary glands, and hence nipples, depend on the number of young that is typical of the species and on the survival value of one location as opposed to another. Cats, dogs, pigs, rodents, edentates, and many other mammals have axillary, thoracic, abdominal, and inguinal nipples that develop along most of the milk line. During pregnancy in these species adjacent glands may

Fig. 5-12. Successive stages of mammary gland development. **A,** Equivalent to a human embryo at 6 weeks; **B,** equivalent to a human embryo at 9 weeks and to a mouse embryo at 16 days; **C,** intermediate stage; **D,** at birth. Gray area represents dermis.

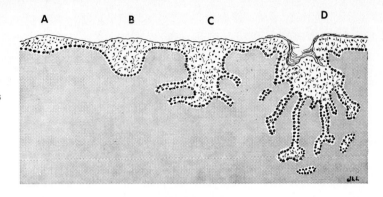

MAMMARY GLAND
Morphogenesis

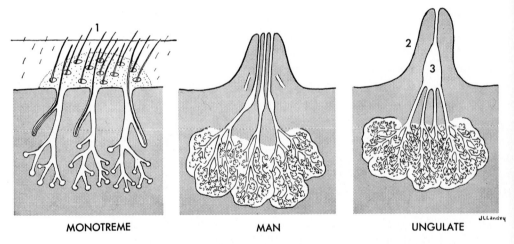

MONOTREME   MAN   UNGULATE

Fig. 5-13. Mammary glands, ducts, and nipples. The monotreme lacks nipples, and the glands resemble modified sweat glands. **1,** Hairs. **2,** Nipple. **3,** Cistern.

expand toward each other until they have formed two long continuous masses of considerable weight. Species with smaller litters have fewer nipples. Insectivores and some lemurs have one thoracic and one inguinal pair. Flying lemurs and marmosets have a single pair, and they are in the armpits. Monkeys, apes, and humans have one pair located where the nursing baby can be protected in the mother's arms while she monitors the environment for enemies. Cetaceans have a single pair near the groin, where the baby porpoise or whale can hold on and nurse while the mother feeds, surfaces, and dives. Nutrias, which are at home in water, have four nipples on the back, and the babies ride along above the water line while nursing. Supernumerary nipples may form in any individual (Fig. 5-11, *B*).

Monotremes do not develop typical mammary glands or nipples. Instead, in both sexes modified sweat glands produce a nutritious secretion, which is lapped off a convenient tuft of hairs by the young (Fig. 5-13, monotreme). Nipples would probably be useless in the duckbill, since it appears doubtful whether the young, hindered by horny beaks and lacking muscular cheeks and lips, could nurse. Except during lactation, the nipples of the opossum are hygienically stored in depressions within the skin.

The stratum corneum of terrestrial vertebrates

Keratinization provides protection against desiccation, the minimal requirement, along with aerial respiration, for life on land. This is what the stratum corneum does for amphibians, who must return to the water to breed. The evolution of an amnion completed the liberation of vertebrates from an aquatic environment and the stratum corneum became scaly, protecting reptiles against abrasion. Thereafter, the stratum corneum became increasingly specialized in advantageous locations on the body for offense, defense, and, finally, thermoregulation. Early specializations—scutes, claws, horny protuberances—were followed by hair and feathers, the latter being the most remarkable cornified appendages of all.

EPIDERMAL SCALES

Epidermal scales, found only in amniotes, are more or less regular overlapping thickenings of stratum corneum. They are most evident in lizards and snakes, which earned these reptiles the name "squamates" (Figs. 5-14 and 5-15). Thinning of the stratum corneum at scale "joints" permits mobility of the skin. Large quadrilateral or roughly polygonal scales are **scutes.** Snakes have them on the belly, where they are used for locomotion (Chapter 9). Turtles have smooth, tough scutes on the plastron, which slides along the ground, thinner ones on the carapace (Fig. 5-16), and more typical scales elsewhere. Scales sometimes assume bizarre shapes (Figs. 5-17 and 16-10).

In birds, epidermal scales are found where there are no feathers— the facial area, legs, and feet. In armadillos, hair and scales are regularly interspersed over the entire body (Fig. 5-18); but in most mammals when scales are present they are confined to the legs and tail, as in rodents. Pangolins have scales that appear to be composed of agglutinated hairs (Fig. 5-24). Their scales and perhaps those of armadillos are **cenogenetic,** that is, of recent origin rather than remnants of reptilian scales.

Lizards and snakes have two distinct layers of stratum corneum: an

Fig. 5-14. Squamate scales. **A,** Collared lizard. The outer ear canal is seen behind the angle of the jaws. **B,** Diagrammatic section of skin of a snake or lizard. **1,** Dermis; **2,** actively mitotic layer of epidermis; **3,** newly cornified layer of epidermis; **4,** older cornified layer to be shed at next molt. **C,** Scales from the banded water snake, *Nerodia fasciata.* (**A** courtesy F.W. Schmidt, naturalist photographer, La Marque, Tex. **C** courtesy T.P. Forks, University of Southern Mississippi, Hattiesburg.)

Fig. 5-15. Epidermal scales on head of milk snake *Lampropeltis triangulum.* **1,** Rostral; **2,** nasal; **3,** internasal; **4,** prefrontal; **5,** preocular; **6,** supraocular; **7,** postoculars; **8,** parietal; **9,** anterior temporals; **10,** fifth of seven infralabials; **L,** loreal; **S,** first and last supralabials. (Courtesy Kenneth L. Williams.)

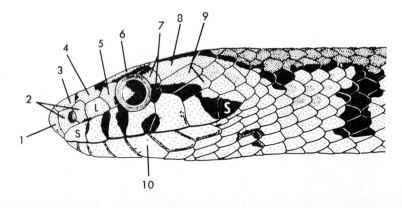

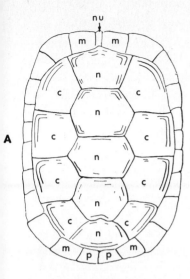

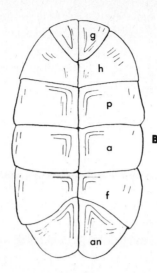

Fig. 5-16. Epidermal scales of the turtle *Chrysemys.* **A,** Carapace. **B,** Plastron. On the carapace the scutes shown are, **c,** costals; **m,** marginals all around the periphery, including the nuchal **(nu),** and pygals **(p); n,** neurals. On the plastron the scutes shown are, **g,** gulars; **h,** humerals; **p,** pectorals; **a,** abdominals; **f,** femorals; **an,** anals.

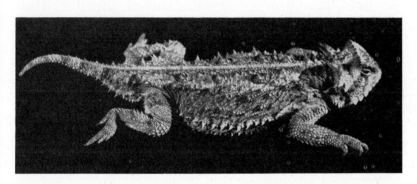

Fig. 5-17. Warty and spiny skin of horned toad, a lizard. (Courtesy Carolina Biological Supply Co., Burlington, N.C.)

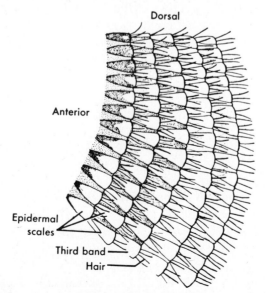

Fig. 5-18. Armadillo skin showing epidermal scales and hair.

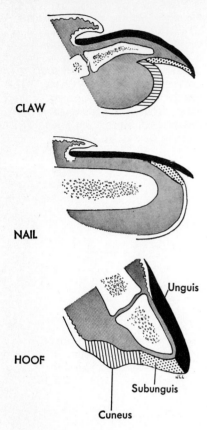

CLAW

NAIL

HOOF

Unguis

Subunguis

Cuneus

Fig. 5-19. Claw, nail, hoof, and terminal phalanx diagrammed in sagittal section.

inner layer in the process of being deposited and an outer one that will be shed at the next molt (Fig. 5-14, *B*). In lizards the outer layer flakes off in large patches, but in snakes the outer layer of the entire body, including the spectacle (thick lenslike conjunctiva) is shed in one piece. Crocodilians and turtles do not molt; their stratum corneum wears off gradually, like that of human beings.

CLAWS, NAILS, AND HOOFS

Claws, nails, and hoofs are modifications of the stratum corneum at the ends of digits. Claws first appeared in reptiles and have persisted in birds and most mammals. (The "claws" of the African clawed toad are not comparable to reptilian claws.) Claws evolved into nails in primates and into hoofs in ungulates. Claws, nails, and hoofs have the same basic structure. They consist of two curved parts, a horny dorsal plate, the **unguis,** and a softer ventral plate, the **subunguis** (Fig. 5-19). The two plates wrap partially around the terminal phalanx, which is usually pointed when associated with a claw, blunt when associated with a hoof or nail. A still softer calluslike, cornified pad, the **cuneus** (called the "frog" by horsemen), is frequently present in ungulates, partially surrounded by the subunguis. The thick, hard unguis of a hoof is U or V shaped, and, since it consists of dead cells, a shoe can be nailed into it. The unguis of a nail has become flattened, and the subunguis is much reduced. As a result, nails cover only the dorsal surfaces of digits; but, if permitted to grow, nails become clawlike.

Although claws in birds are often thought of as associated only with the feet (Fig. 5-20), sharp claws are frequently borne on one or more digits of the wings (ostriches, geese, some swifts, and others). *Young hoatzins use claws on the wings for climbing about on the bark of trees, but the claws cease growing and disappear at maturity. Archaeopteryx* had three claws on each wing. Only squamate claws are shed. Claws, nails, and hoofs of other animals are worn down by friction.

FEATHERS

Feathers are remarkably complicated cornified outgrowths of the epidermis. There are three morphological varieties: contour feathers, down feathers (plumules), and hairlike feathers (filoplumes). The roles of feathers are described in Chapter 3.

Contour feathers (Fig. 5-21, *A*) are the conspicuous feathers that give the bird its contour, or general shape. A typical contour feather consists of a horny, hollow **shaft** and two flattened **vanes.** The base of the shaft devoid of vanes is the **calamus (quill).** The vane-bearing segment of the shaft is the **rachis.** Each vane consists of a row of **barbs,** which in turn have **barbules** and **flanges** (Fig. 5-21, *B*). The

Fig. 5-20. Claw on the middle toe of a great blue heron. (From Atwood, W.H.: Comparative anatomy, ed. 2, St. Louis, 1955, The C.V. Mosby Co.)

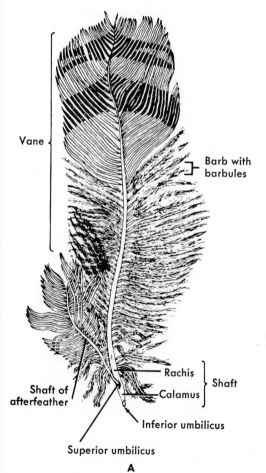

Vane

Barb with barbules

Shaft of afterfeather

Rachis
Calamus] Shaft

Inferior umbilicus

Superior umbilicus

A

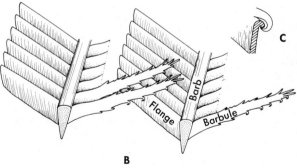

Flange

Barb

Barbule

B

C

Fig. 5-21. A, Contour feather from a grouse. **B,** Two successive barbs showing two barbules interlocked by hooklets with flanges. **C,** Cross section of a flange showing interlock.

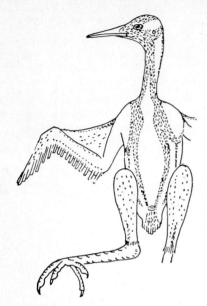

Fig. 5-22. Feather tracts.

barbules have **hooklets,** which interlock with the flanges of adjacent barbs and stiffen the vane (Fig. 5-21, *B* and *C*). When a contour feather is ruffled, the barbules have become unhooked. Preening rehooks the hooklets, returning the feather to its tailored state. During preening the oily secretion of the uropygial gland is applied to the barbs. On the smaller contour feathers of the wings (covert feathers), the lower barbules lack hooklets, and this region of the feather is fluffy. In ostriches and some other birds all feathers are fluffy.

Arising from a notch (**superior umbilicus**) on the shaft of a contour feather at the base of the rachis is an **afterfeather.** Usually the aftershaft is much smaller than the main shaft; but in emus and cassowaries the afterfeather is of the same length, which results in double feathers.

Although contour feathers cover most of the body, the follicles from which they grow are usually disposed in feather tracts, or **pterylae** (Fig. 5-22). A few birds, including ostriches and penguins, lack these.

Inserting on the walls of the feather follicles in the dermis are smooth erector muscles (**arrectores plumarum**), which, along with extrinsic integumentary muscles, enable a bird to fluff its feathers.

Down feathers are small, fluffy feathers lying underneath and between contour feathers. Very young birds lack contour feathers and are covered with down. Down feathers may be ancestral to contour feathers. They have a short calamus, with a crown of barbs arising from the free end. Hooklets are lacking. Eiderdown, used in pillows, is the down feathers of the eider duck.

Filoplumes are hairlike feathers familiar to housewives who singe hens before cooking them. Filoplumes consist chiefly of a threadlike shaft. They are usually scattered throughout the skin among the contour feathers. They are the very long colorful feathers of a peacock.

Feathers arise from feather follicles lined by epidermis (Fig. 5-23). The feather primordium (**pinfeather**) is covered by an epidermal feather sheath and contains a core of dermis, the dermal papilla. The mitotic layer of epidermis at the base of the follicle proliferates as tall columns of epidermal cells that push toward the tip of the growing feather just under the epidermis. These columns separate from one another, cornify, and develop into barbs with barbules. When the feather sheath splits open, the fluffy barbs stretch out of their cramped quarters, and the quill elongates.

When a feather is full grown, the dermal papilla in the shaft dies and becomes the pulp. The living basal portion of the papilla withdraws from the base of the shaft leaving an opening, the **inferior umbilicus.** New feathers develop from reactivated dermal papillae that have already given rise to feathers. In many birds—perhaps in

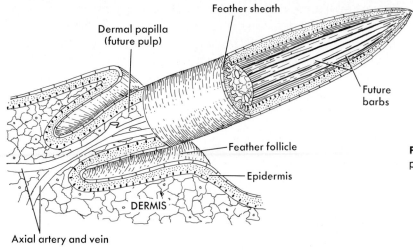

Dermal papilla
(future pulp)

Feather sheath

Future barbs

Feather follicle

Epidermis

DERMIS

Axial artery and vein

Fig. 5-23. Developing down feather, or pinfeather.

all—old feathers are passively pushed out of the follicles by incoming feathers.

HAIR

Hairs, like feathers, are keratinized appendages of the skin. They may form a dense, furry covering over the entire body, or there may be only one or two bristles on the upper lip, as in some whales. Where fur is dense, there are usually short, fine hairs (underfur) as well as long, coarse ones.

Hairs have an insulating effect when dense enough and are also sensitive tactile organs. The root of each is surrounded by a basketlike network of sensory nerve endings, and displacement of the root initiates a train of sensory impulses to the brain. Disturb a single hair on the back of your hand and note the sensation evoked. Vibrissae (stiff long whiskers on the face of many mammals) perform this role exclusively.

Hairs grow in isolated groups of two to a dozen or more, and linearly between scales when the latter are present. Some monkeys have groups of three, apes have groups of five, and humans have groups of three to five. A glance at the side of your own hand, near the base of the thumb, will reveal the linear arrangement of hairs in that location. The phylogenetic origin of hair is not known, and existing theories are speculative.

Hairs grow from hair follicles (Fig. 5-10). The **bulb** of the hair is a swelling at the base of the follicle that contains a vascular dermal papilla. It is an area of rapid mitosis that is constantly contributing

Fig. 5-24. Pangolin showing epidermal scales. (From Flower and Lydekker: Introduction to the study of mammals, London, A. & C. Black, Ltd.)

new cells that make the hair longer. The **root** is the portion within the follicle where the hair has not yet separated from the surrounding epidermal cells of the follicular wall. Here the cells are becoming cornified and are dying. The **shaft** commences just below the openings of the one or more sebaceous glands into the follicle and extends beyond the skin. Within the follicle it is surrounded by sebum. Beyond the root, coarse hairs may contain a **medulla** composed chiefly of air spaces previously occupied by pulp.

Inserting on the wall of each hair follicle is a tiny smooth muscle, the **arrector pili,** or "elevator of the hair" (Fig. 5-10). When the arrectores pilorum contract, the hairs are drawn toward a vertical position and the skin around the base of each hair is pulled into a tiny mound, causing (in humans) "gooseflesh," or "chill bumps." Elevation of the hairs in many mammals causes the animal to look ferocious. It also increases the insulating effect of the fur.

The scales of pangolins (Fig. 5-24) and, perhaps, the horns of rhinos (Fig. 5-25) may be evolutionary products of agglutinated hairs. Other modifications of hair include bristles, the spines of spiny anteaters, and porcupine quills.

Hair follicles first develop as cylindrical ingrowths of the epidermis into the dermis (Fig. 5-26). Beneath the epidermal ingrowth and indenting its base, a dermal papilla organizes. With continued proliferation of epidermal cells, the hair primordium grows deeper and deeper into the dermis, nourished by vessels within the papilla.

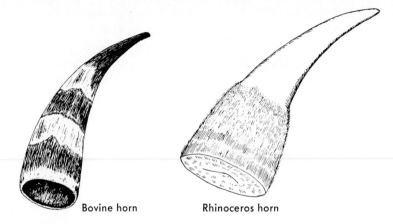

Fig. 5-25. Mammalian horns.

Bovine horn   Rhinoceros horn

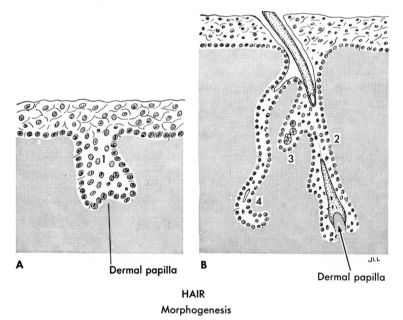

Fig. 5-26. Successive stages in the development of hair and associated glands. **1,** Initial epidermal ingrowth into dermis; **2,** hair follicle; **3,** developing sebaceous gland; **4,** sweat gland. *Gray area,* dermis.

A   Dermal papilla   B   Dermal papilla

HAIR
Morphogenesis

When the bulb at the base of the primordium is sufficiently differentiated, cornified cells start to appear, and a hair shaft rises out of the follicle.

HORNS

Most artiodactyls of the bovine family (cattle, antelope, sheep, goats) have true horns that are offensive or defensive weapons. They consist of a core of dermal bone covered by a horny epidermal sheath and are never shed. The sheath is the actual horn, and when removed it is hollow (Fig. 5-25, bovine horn). It is a product of the stratum corneum. Horns usually occur in both sexes, although not always. Polled cattle have lost their horns by selective breeding. Male pronghorn antelopes have true horns that branch, and the horny part, but not the bony core, is shed annually.

The horns of a rhinoceros differ from bovine horns. They are composed of agglutinated keratinized hairlike epidermal fibers that form a solid structure perched on a roughened area of the nasal bone. Both sexes have them, and they are not shed. Some African rhinos have two horns, one behind the other. Horns are not limited to mammals. Some dinosaurs had them; and the male Jacksonian chameleon has three large horns with bony cores, and these are not shed.

Antlers and giraffe horns are not cornified structures but dermal bone that is at first covered by soft skin containing velvety hair that is permanent only in giraffes. In deer, usually at the approach of autumn, the blood supply to the "velvet" is cut off at the base of the antler, and the skin, unable to be maintained, sloughs off, leaving bare bone. Later, at the end of the rutting season when male territory no longer needs to be defended and when testosterone is declining in the circulation, the antlers are lost.

BALEEN AND OTHER CORNIFIED STRUCTURES

Toothless whales have from 100 to 400 broad, thin, horny sheets of oral epithelium called baleen, or whalebone (Fig. 5-27), that hang into the oral cavity from the palate along its length. Each sheet is fringed along the edge, and the fringes act like combs or sieves that strain food out of the water passing between them. The sheets of the huge right whale exceed 3 m in height. Differences in the arrangement and configuration of the sheets are correlated with feeding habits. A blue whale swims up to a dense swarm of small fish or crustaceans, opens its mouth, and takes in water and food until a huge pouch under the tongue, pharynx, and chest wall is filled with about

Fig. 5-27. Sheets of baleen (whalebone) removed from the oral cavity of a whalebone whale. The sheets may be from 2 to 12 feet long. (Courtesy General Biological Supply House, Inc., Chicago.)

70 tons of food and water. The mouth is then closed, and the pouch is emptied by forcing the water through the sieve and back into the sea. The collected food is swallowed at a leisurely pace through a very small throat. Other whales skim the surface for plankton with the mouth open or feed near the bottom. Baleen is continually being worn away and replaced, like hair or fingernails.

Rattlesnake **rattles** are rings of horny stratum corneum that remain attached to the tail after each molt (Fig. 5-28). **Beaks** are covered with a horny sheath, and roosters' **combs** are covered with a thick, warty stratum corneum. Monkeys and apes sit on thick **ischial callosities,** and camels kneel on **knee pads. Tori** are epidermal pads that most mammals other than ungulates walk on (Fig. 5-29). Cats "pussyfoot" by retracting their claws and walking stealthily on tori. At the ends of digits, tori are called **apical pads. Corns** and **calluses** are temporary thickenings of the stratum corneum that develop where the skin has been subjected to unusual friction.

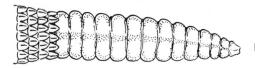

Fig. 5-28. Rattles from a rattlesnake.

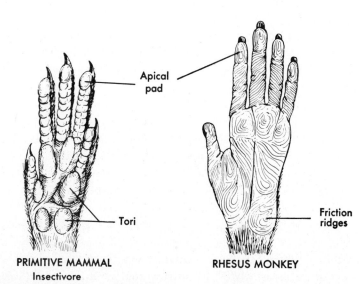

Apical pad

Tori

Friction ridges

Fig. 5-29. Tori and friction ridges.

PRIMITIVE MAMMAL
Insectivore

RHESUS MONKEY

THE DERMIS

The basic constituent of dermis, whether of fishes or human beings, is collagenous connective tissue (Fig. 6-2). Other constituents are the structures listed on p. 109, encapsulated receptors for temperature and touch in amniotes, and feather and hair follicles in endotherms. In addition, the dermis has an ancient and persistent potential to form bone, and bone is a constituent of the dermis in at least some members of every vertebrate class except Aves. Early fishes had so much bone in the skin that they are called armored fishes. When bone is lacking in the dermis, it is because bone salts were not deposited on the collagenous matrix. Cowhide, from which leather is made, the dermis of leatherback turtles, the skin of cyclostomes—all these are exceptionally tough because the collagen bundles are densely packed as though prepared for a shower of bone salts that, for lack of an enzyme or some other reason, never materialized.

Bony dermis of fishes

The armor of ancient fishes varied in histological details, but a generalized pattern consisted of lamellar bone, spongy (vascular) bone, dentin, and a surface layer of enamel or enameloid (Fig. 5-30, ancient armor). Frequently, the surface was roughened by **denticles,** which were knobby enameloid-covered elevations of dentin. The armor was disposed as broad bony plates or small bony scales that covered much of the body (Fig. 2-1). The armor was protective, but it may have also served as a storage site for calcium and phosphates. In time, the large plates on the trunk and tail gave way to smaller and thinner scales, those on the head contributed to the skull, and those on the "shoulder" contributed dermal bone to the otherwise endochondral endoskeleton of the pectoral girdle.

Dermal plates and scales on living fishes are classified as cosmoid, ganoid, placoid, and modern fish scales, the latter being cycloid or ctenoid. **Cosmoid scales** and **plates** were present on early lobe-finned fishes and resembled ancient armor; remnants are still present in living dipnoans. The dentin in these is sometimes called cosmine, which accounts for their name. **Ganoid scales** and **plates** covered ganoid fishes when ganoids were at their zenith. The earliest ganoid scales, called **paleoniscoid** (Fig. 5-30), are found today only on *Polypterus,* on *Calamoichthyes,* and on the surviving crossopterygian, *Latimeria;* but on the latter the dentin layer has been reduced. Today's garfish scales (Fig. 5-30, **lepidosteoid** scales) have lost the spongy bone, but they still form a continuous shiny armor on the entire trunk and tail (Fig. 5-31, *A*). On the head there are small bony plates (Fig. 8-8, *A*). Other surviving ganoids have reduced the bony layer even more, the bones are broad plates, as on sturgeons, and ganoin is lacking. In

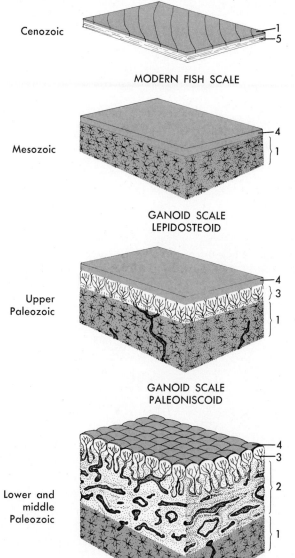

Cenozoic

MODERN FISH SCALE

Mesozoic

GANOID SCALE
LEPIDOSTEOID

Upper
Paleozoic

GANOID SCALE
PALEONISCOID

Lower and
middle
Paleozoic

ANCIENT ARMOR

Fig. 5-30. Dermal bone and dermal scales through the ages, diagrammatic. **1,** Lamellar bone; **2,** spongy bone; **3,** dentin; **4,** enameloid of one kind or another, including ganoin; **5,** fibrous plate characteristic of modern fish scales. The surface elevations in ancient armor are denticles consisting of layers **3** and **4.** The lamellar bone in modern fish scales is acellular. Cosmoid scales (not illustrated) resemble ancient armor.

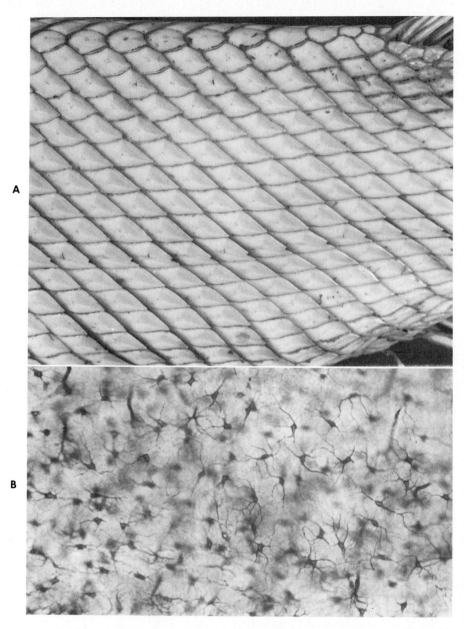

Fig. 5-31. Ganoid scales. **A,** Scales on trunk of a garfish. The tail is at the right. **B,** Canaliculi and lacunae within a single scale (microscopic).

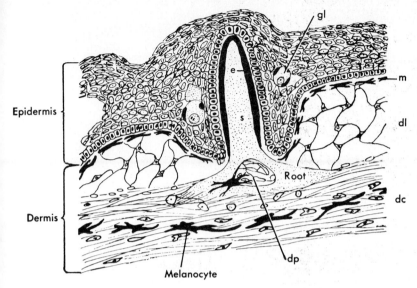

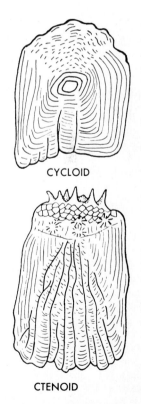

Fig. 5-32. Developing placoid scale in skin of embryonic shark. Dermis consists of compact layer, **dc**, and loose layer, **dl; dp,** dermal pulp within root and spine; **e,** enamel; **gl,** unicellular epidermal gland; **m,** melanocyte; **s,** spine, composed of dentin, enamel, and a core of pulp.

bowfins, bony plates are confined to the head, and modern cycloid scales cover the rest of the body.

Placoid scales are bony denticles found only on elasmobranchs, ancient and modern. They have the same structure as paleoniscoid scales but consist of a flat **basal plate** or **root** (lamellar bone) and a **spine** (dentin and enamel), and the spines erupt through a glandular epidermis (Fig. 5-32). Placoid scales become teeth at the edges of the jaws.

Cycloid scales are found on teleosts and modern lobe-finned fishes, and **ctenoid scales** are found on some teleosts (Fig. 5-33). These modern scales consist of a very thin layer of *acellular* lamellar bone underlaid by a plate of dense collagen (Fig. 5-30, modern fish scale). As a result, they are very flexible. The overlying epidermis becomes thin and may even rub off. Cyclostomes, catfish, eels, and some other recent fishes have lost the ability to form scales. Nevertheless, scale anlagen form transitorily in embryos. On the other hand, sea horses and pipefishes have dense bony plates in the dermis of much of the body.

Dermal ossification in tetrapods

When the first tetrapods lumbered onto land, they brought with them versions of cosmoid scales of their lobe-finned ancestors. Some labyrinthodonts, and even some cotylosaurs, had large bony plates in their skin; others had minute bony scales. These ossifications, often called **osteoderms** in tetrapods, still form in a few amphibians, most reptiles, and armadillos.

CYCLOID

CTENOID

Fig. 5-33. Modern flexible fish scales. The upper edges are caudal free borders.

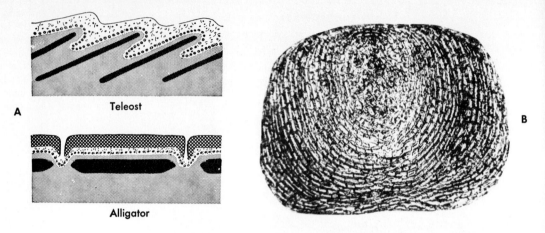

Fig. 5-34. A, Site of dermal scales (black) in a teleost and of osteoderms in an alligator. Gray represents dermis. **B,** A single bony scale from an apodan.

Fig. 5-35. Alligator skin. **A,** From dorsum of neck, showing epidermal scales. **B,** Same section turned upside down to show osteoderms (dermal scales) embedded in skin beneath the tall crests. The middorsal line may be used as a reference point.

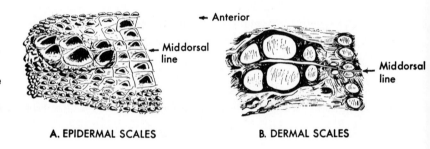

Fig. 5-36. Dermal plates of the carapace, **A,** and plastron, **B,** in the turtle *Chrysemys,* from an internal view. On the carapace the plates shown are **c,** costals, united with ribs; **n,** nuchal; **p1** and **p2,** precaudals; **v,** vertebrals (six of the eight are labeled). Marginals encircle the periphery and include the pygal, **py.** On the plastron the plates shown are **e,** epiplastrons; **en,** entoplastron; **h,** hyoplastrons; **hp,** hypoplastrons; **xi,** xiphiplastrons.

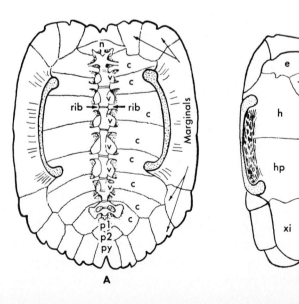

Caecilians and some tropical toads have dermal scales. Those between furrows in apodans are microscopic, are perpendicular to the surface, and lie in circumferential bands separated by glandular skin. Those in furrows are just large enough to be seen with the naked eye when loosened with a scalpel (Fig. 5-34, *B*). Crocodilians have oval osteoderms, especially along the back, where they are often associated with cornified crests (Fig. 5-35, *B*). A few lizards have similar but smaller scales under their epidermal scales. Turtles other than leatherbacks are truly armored, being boxed in by large bony plates that meet in immovable sutures (Fig. 5-36). The carapace and plastron are united by bony lateral bridges that must be sawed through to expose the viscera.

Among mammals armadillos alone have dermal armor as a normal condition. It consists of identical small polygonal bones immovably united and extending almost to the midventral line. The bone is covered by epidermal scales (Fig. 5-18). The bone and scales are probably cenogenic. Bone forms in the skin of other mammals, including human beings, as a pathological condition (dermostosis). An earlier observation is worth repeating: the dermis of vertebrates has an ancient and persistent potential to form bone.

DERMAL INDUCTION OF EPIDERMAL DIFFERENTIATION

Whether an epidermis produces feathers, scales, hair, or ciliated, striated, glandular, or simple squamous epithelium is determined by instructions in the form of specific amino acids exported during embryogenesis by the underlying dermis at that specific site. Feathers can be induced to grow on the feet of chicks if dermis from a potential feathered area is transplanted under the epidermis of the embryonic foot at the critical time during embryonic development, that is, when the controlling genes in the dermis are "turned on." Even the chorionic epithelium can be made to produce feathers or scales by carefully timed transplants of appropriate dermis.

INTEGUMENTARY PIGMENTS

Chromatophores are cells that contain pigment granules. They have permanent branched processes extending from the cell, and, although located at many deep sites including meninges and even within striated muscles, they are most common in the skin, where they account for skin color. They arise from cells that migrate from neural crests.

Chromatophores are identified by the color of their granules. **Melanophores** and **melanocytes** contain melanin granules (melanosomes), which are varying shades of brown. Only melanophores participate in physiological color changes (see next paragraph). **Xantho-**

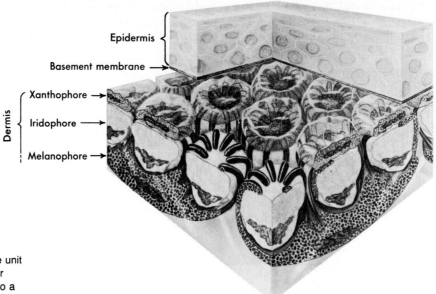

Epidermis {

Basement membrane →

Dermis {

Xanthophore →

Iridophore →

Melanophore →

Fig. 5-37. Dermal chromatophore unit responsible for physiological color changes in anurans. Adaptation to a dark background is illustrated, with processes of melanophores overlying iridophores. (Modified from Bagnara, J.T., Taylor, J.D., and Hadley, M.E.: The Journal of Cell Biology **38**:67, 1968.)

phores contain yellow granules, and **erythrophores** contain red granules. (The two latter are sometimes called lipophores because the granules are soluble in lipid solvents.) **Iridophores** contain a prismatic substance, guanine, which reflects and disperses light, producing silvery or iridescent skin.

Dermal chromatophores are responsible for rapid color changes (**physiological color changes**), such as are seen in chameleons. Physiological color changes occur only in ectotherms and are induced reflexly by neurotransmitters and by hormones, such as intermedin and melatonin. The color change results from dispersal of granules into the processes of pigment cells, or aggregation of granules to a position close to the nuclei.* Dispersal of granules forms a blanket that masks underlying pigments; aggregation exposes them. Since not all varieties of chromatophores respond alike to the same stimulus, various color combinations result. A functional association of dermal chromatophores is illustrated in Fig. 5-37.

Some vertebrates—sharks, birds, mammals, for instance—cannot change color reflexly because the granules in their chromatophores cannot aggregate and disperse. These animals change color only as pigment granules are synthesized in response to long-term stimuli such as exposure to sunlight ("getting a tan," for example) or when

---

*Blushing and blanching of human skin result from reflex vasodilation and vasoconstriction and do not involve chromatophores.

hairs, feathers, or epidermis is shed and replaced with new hairs, feathers, or epidermis with different color combinations or densities. These are **morphological color changes.**

The pigment in hair and feathers is not in pigment cells. Electron microscopy has shown that pigment cells with branched processes that extend among the epidermal cells of the growth zone of feather and hair follicles actively *inject* pigment into the cells that are being added to the growing feather or hair. Hairs receive only melanin granules, and hair color is attributable to the specific distribution and density of the granules and to the number of air vacuoles in the medulla of the hairs. Gray hair and white hair are the result of large numbers of air vacuoles and little melanin. Feathers receive brown, yellow, and red pigments.

Despite what appear to be blue feathers, vertebrates have no blue granules. When viewed under a microscope by *transmitted* light, the "blue" feather is seen to be brown, the color of the melanin granules beneath the prismatic layer. The blue color observed in *reflected* light is a dispersion phenomenon, like the blue of the sky. A red feather is red even when viewed in transmitted light because of red pigment. The iridescence of feathers is also a dispersion phenomenon.

MISCELLANEOUS FUNCTIONS OF SKIN

Dermal armor provides protection from attack and protects the brain and special sense organs from mechanical injury. Even in the absence of armor a leathery dermis provides some protection against penetration of foreign objects. Skin glands secrete obnoxious or poisonous substances that ward off enemies. Glands keep skin moist and the conjunctiva of the eye free of irritants. Integumentary pigments provide protective coloration and, in naked skin, absorb excess solar radiation. The bristling coat of an angry mammal and the ruffled plumage of a frightened bird make them ominous. Claws, nails, horns, spines, barbs, needles—all confer advantages in the struggle for existence.

Temperature regulation is effected largely by the skin. Fur and feathers insulate against heat and cold, sweat cools through evaporation, and dilation of blood vessels within the dermis increases heat loss by radiation. When heat conservation is necessary, the vessels constrict. Fat deposits in the dermis insulate deep tissues from icy waters or frigid air or provide energy stores for hibernation, migration, or periods of seasonal famine.

The skin assists in maintaining homeostasis. Bony scales are reservoirs for calcium and phosphate storage. Chloride-secreting glands excrete salts, and stratum corneum conserves water. Aquatic amphibians excrete carbon dioxide through the skin. Mammary glands provide nourishment. Adhesive pads and claws assist in climbing, scutes assist in slithering, and feathers provide an airfoil for aerial locomotion. The distribution of pigment and pheromonal secretions signal species and sex and serve as alarms. Nerve endings in skin alert vertebrates against inimical forces, brood pouches house developing young, and vitamin D is synthesized in some skin. You will be able to think of other roles that the integument performs.

CHAPTER SUMMARY

1. Vertebrate skin consists of a stratified, nonvascular epidermis and a vascular dermis.

2. The epidermis of fishes and aquatic amphibians is covered with a thin basic coat of mucus of unknown significance. The surface of terrestrial vertebrates is covered with a stratum corneum that inhibits dehydration.

3. The basic mucous coat of fishes is produced by otherwise undifferentiated cells at the surface of the epidermis. Stratum corneum results from keratinization of epidermal cells as they approach the surface.

4. Epidermal glands are mucous or serous (granular), unicellular or multicellular, and the latter are tubular or alveolar. The glands of one vertebrate class or another produce mucus, slime, noxious substances, oils, fats, sweat, nourishment for new offspring, and pheromones. Photophores are light-emitting glands of fishes. Birds have only oil glands. Mammals have sudoriferous and sebaceous glands.

5. The epidermis of fishes has many mucous glands, many unicellular glands, and no stratum corneum. Semiterrestrial (semiaquatic) amphibians have fewer mucous glands, fewer unicellular glands, and a thin covering of cornified cells. Terrestrial vertebrates have very few mucous glands, no unicellular glands, and a well-defined stratum corneum.

6. The stratum corneum of amniotes forms epidermal scales, scutes, crests, claws, nails, hoofs, horns, baleen, rattles, horny teeth, beak coverings, feathers, hair, and miscellaneous structures.

7. Feathers consist of a shaft (calamus and rachis), and vanes (barbs, and barbules that usually have hooklets). They are elevated by smooth arrectores plumarum. There are contour feathers, down feathers, and filoplumes.

8. Modifications of hair include spines, quills, bristles, vibrissae, scales of anteaters, and perhaps rhinoceros horns. Hairs are elevated by smooth arrectores pilorum.

9. The principal component of dermis is collagen. It supports blood vessels, lymphatics, nerves, chromatophores, encapsulated cutaneous receptors, the bases of multicellular epidermal glands, hair and feather follicles, and their erector muscles. It also contains other connective tissues including, as a widespread condition, bony scales or plates. Invasion of the dermis by epidermal structures puts the latter in the midst of capillaries from which they obtain nutrients.

10. Bone in the dermis is a primitive and generalized condition; absence is a specialization. It was the chief component of the dermis of the earliest fishes and tetrapods and is still present in nearly all fishes and in caecilians, some toads, most reptiles, and armadillos, forming broad plates, smaller bony scales, flexible modern fish scales, osteoderms, or shells. Bony scales and plates are cosmoid (ancient), ganoid (paleoniscoid or lepidosteoid), placoid (elasmobranchs), ctenoid (teleosts), or cycloid (teleosts and modern lobe fins). It forms pathologically in human beings.

11. Chromatophores are pigment-containing cells of neural crest origin with permanent branching extensions of the cell body. Physiological color changes are rapid and result from movement of pigment granules into or out of the processes. Morphological color changes are slow, depend on melanin synthesis, and are generally related to molting, shedding, or aging.

12. Some of the functions of skin are listed on pp. 137 and 138.

LITERATURE CITED AND SELECTED READINGS

1. Appleby, L.G.: Snakes shedding skin, Natural History **89**(2):64, 1980.
2. Birch, M.C., editor: Pheromones, New York, 1974, Elsevier/Excerpta Medica/North-Holland.
3. Ling, J.K.: Adaptive functions of vertebrate molting cycles, American Zoologist **12**:77, 1972.
4. Lucas, A.M., and Stettenheim, P.R.: Avian anatomy: integument. Parts I and II. Agriculture Handbook 362, Washington D.C., 1972, United States Government Printing Office.
5. Modell, W.: Horns and antlers, Scientific American **220**(4):114, 1969.
6. Montagna, W., and Parakkal, P.F.: The structure and function of the skin, ed. 3, New York, 1974, Academic Press, Inc.
7. Moss, M.L.: The origin of vertebrate calcified tissues. In Ørvig, T., editor: Current problems in lower vertebrate phylogeny, New York, 1968, Interscience-Wiley.
8. Ørvig, T.: The dermal skeleton: general considerations. In Ørvig, T., ed-

itor: Current problems in lower vertebrate phylogeny, New York, 1968, Interscience-Wiley.

9. Quay, W.B.: Integument and the environment: glandular composition, function, and evolution, American Zoologist **12:**95, 1972.

10. Sengel, P.: Morphogenesis of skin, Cambridge, England, 1976, Cambridge University Press.

11. Spearman, R.I.C.: The integument: a textbook of skin biology, Cambridge, England, 1973, Cambridge University Press.

Symposium in American Zoologist

The vertebrate integument, **12:**12, 1972.

CHAPTER 6

Mineralized tissues: an introduction to the skeleton

In this chapter we will examine mineralized tissues, meet some common varieties, see how these are formed, and look briefly at their phylogeny. We will discover that the skeleton has a role in homeostasis, and we will find out why it is necessary that a skeleton undergo continual remodeling.

Collagen
Bone
Dentin
Preskeletal blastemas, membrane bone, and replacement bone
Dermal bone
Cartilage
Calcium regulation and skeletal remodeling
Tendons, ligaments, and joints
Heterotopic bones
Mineralized tissues and the invertebrates
Regional components of the skeleton

The skeleton is composed of hardened (mineralized) connective tissues and of ligaments, tendons, and bursae. The hardened tissue for the most part is bone, but there is also dentin (often considered a kind of bone), cartilage (often a precursor of bone), and enamel or enamel-like substances. Osteoblasts produce bone, chondroblasts produce cartilage, odontoblasts produce dentin, and ameloblasts produce enamel. These specialized cells arise from less differentiated scleroblasts that arise from mesenchyme (Fig. 6-1). **Mesenchyme** is an aggregation of undifferentiated cells. A preliminary step in formation or repair of skeletal tissues is the synthesis of collagen by fibroblasts. Adults retain islands of mesenchyme that have the potential to repair or replace bone and other connective tissues throughout life.

COLLAGEN

Collagen is a proteinaceous **fibril** demonstrable only by high-power electron microscopy. Fibrils aggregate to form collagen **fibers** that are visible with light microscopy. The fibers form dense bundles that are woven into a compact network found in dermis, tendons, and ligaments (Fig. 6-2). It is on this network that minerals are deposited to form hard connective tissues.

BONE

Bone is composed of a matrix of collagenous fibers, the spaces between which have been impregnated with **hydroxyapatite crystals** that are composed of calcium, phosphate, and hydroxyl ions $[3Ca_3(PO_4)_2 \cdot Ca(OH)_2]$. The crystals are deposited under the influence of osteoblasts. **A cementing substance** composed of water and mucopolysaccharides binds the crystals to the collagen matrix. In most bone the osteoblasts ultimately become trapped in tiny pools of interstitial fluid called **lacunae** (Fig. 6-3), thereby becoming bone cells

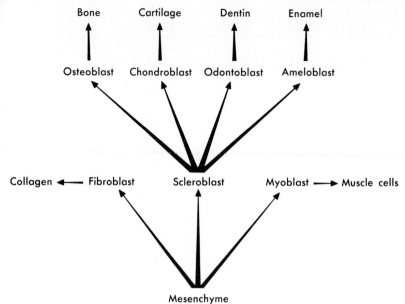

Bone   Cartilage   Dentin   Enamel

Osteoblast   Chondroblast   Odontoblast   Ameloblast

Collagen ◄—— Fibroblast   Scleroblast   Myoblast ——► Muscle cells

Mesenchyme

Fig. 6-1. Some differentiated products of mesenchyme.

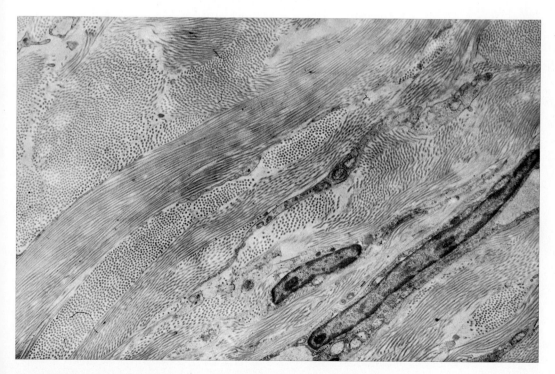

Fig. 6-2. Collagen bundles in tendon. The fibers appear as dots in cross section. The cells are fibrocytes. (Courtesy H.J. Werner, Baton Rouge, La.)

Fig. 6-3. Section of one osteon (haversian system) in compact bone to show lacunae (black) and canaliculi (canals radiating from the lacunae). (From Bevelander, G., and Ramaley, J.A.: Essentials of histology, ed. 7, St. Louis, 1974, The C.V. Mosby Co.)

(**osteocytes**). The process of bone formation is known as **osteogenesis.** Lacunae contain calcium and phosphate ions. Some of these will be converted into crystals and others result from dissolution of crystals, since calcium and phosphate deposit and withdrawal are constantly taking place. Interconnecting the lacunae are tiny fluid-filled canals, or **canaliculi.**

In **osteon bone** the collagen bundles are deposited in concentric layers, or lamellae, surrounding an artery and vein. This results in haversian systems, or **osteons** (Fig. 6-3). On the surface of all bones the collagen bundles are deposited as flat lamellae instead of concentrically, and there are no haversian systems. Osteon and surface bone are **compact bone,** also called **lamellar bone.** The interior of many bones is spongy because of bony trabeculae that separate spaces filled with bone marrow. This is **spongy,** or **cancellous, bone.** The haversian systems of osteon bone and the trabeculae and spaces of spongy bone are arranged in directions that afford maximum rigidity when the usual stresses are applied.

In some bones the osteoblasts retreat as they deposit bone, leaving behind no canaliculi or lacunae. This is **acellular bone,** also called aspidin. The flexible scales of modern fishes contain acellular bone.

DENTIN

Dentin has the same constituents as bone, and it will be referred to as bone in this chapter. It is confined to the skin and teeth. The odontoblasts that deposit dentin are not trapped in lacunae. Instead, they retreat as they deposit it and are located at the inner border of the dentin (Fig. 6-4). The canaliculi are delicate canals called **dentinal**

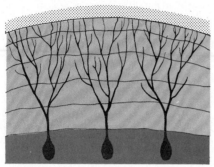

Enameloid
substance

Dentin

Odontoblasts

Fig. 6-4. Dentin covered with enameloid. The canaliculi (dentinal tubules) contain processes of odontoblasts.

tubules that extend from the odontoblasts all the way to the surface of the dentin. The tubules contain processes of the odontoblasts. Dentin, when present, forms only in the outer layer of the dermis just beneath the epidermis, and it is frequently coated on its surface by enamel or enameloid substances (Fig. 5-30, ancient armor). Some enamels appear to be produced by ameloblasts derived from ectoderm. Others may possibly be a very hard variety of dentin.

PRESKELETAL BLASTEMAS, MEMBRANE BONE, AND REPLACEMENT BONE

A blastema is any aggregation of embryonic mesenchyme cells, which, given the appropriate stimulus, differentiate into some tissue such as muscle, bone, or cartilage. Before bone or cartilage can be deposited, a preskeletal mesenchymal blastema must develop. The mesenchyme that produces preskeletal blastemas is chiefly of mesodermal origin. However, in the head and pharyngeal arches it is neurectoderm.

Once the blastema has aggregated, some of the mesenchyme cells become fibroblasts and secrete collagen. Others become osteoblasts or chondroblasts and secrete bone or cartilage. The capacity to deposit either one depends in part on inheritance of appropriate enzyme systems.

Bone deposited directly in a blastema is **membrane bone.** The process of membrane bone formation is known as **intramembranous ossification.** It gives rise to certain bones of the lower jaw, skull, and pectoral girdle; to dentin and other bone that arises in the skin; to vertebrae in a few vertebrates (teleosts, urodeles, apodans); and to bones in a few other locations. Periosteal bone (bone deposited by the periosteal membrane) is membrane bone.

Some bone is deposited in preexisting cartilage, and this is called **replacement bone.** The cartilage is first removed, then bone is deposited where cartilage previously existed. The process is known as **endochondral ossification.** The processes of endochondral and intramembranous ossification are the same in that they consist of impregnation of a collagenous matrix with hydroxyapatite crystals. However, in endochondral ossification, cartilage must be removed before bone may be deposited.

DERMAL BONE

Bone that forms within the dermis of the skin is dermal bone. It arises by intramembranous ossification and may be dentin, spongy bone, or lamellar bone, depending on the species and locations. All three contributed to the dermal armor of ancient fishes (Fig. 5-30). Somewhere in geological time and along phylogenetic pathways leading from armored fishes, some fibroblasts from the skin evidently were exported to membranes beneath the skin, where they now produce the matrix on which osteoblasts deposit membrane bone. Many membrane bones appear to have such a phylogenetic origin and to represent bones that, at one time, formed *in*, rather than *under*, the dermis. They include some of the bones alongside and above the brain, some bones of the lower jaw, and certain bones of the pectoral girdles. Only those membrane bones that arise phylogenetically or ontogenetically from skin should be called **dermal bones.**

CARTILAGE

Cartilage resembles bone in that the cells (**chondrocytes**) lie in pools of fluid surrounded by a collagenous matrix. The matrix, however, contains a sulfated mucopolysaccharide. Unlike bone, cartilage has no canaliculi demonstrable by light microscopy, and no blood vessels penetrate it except those en route to other organs. Therefore the cells are supplied with oxygen and nutrients by diffusion.

Cartilage is formed within a prechondral mesenchymal blastema by the deposit of chondroitin sulfate. The process is known as **chondrogenesis.** Once cartilage has formed, it may remain throughout life, or it may be resorbed and replaced by bone. The latter is more likely, since cartilage in vertebrates, especially hyaline cartilage, appears to be primarily an embryonic or juvenile tissue. As long as cartilage is present, endochondral bone formation may continue.

Hyaline cartilage is a translucent cartilage found in many locations. In vertebrate embryos it is abundant, constituting a temporary skeleton to be replaced later by bone. Cartilage with thick, dense collagenous bundles in the interstitial matrix is **fibrocartilage.** The intervertebral discs of mammals are fibrocartilage. **Elastic cartilage** contains elastic fibers. In mammals it occurs in the pinna of the ear, in the walls of the outer ear canal, in the epiglottis, and elsewhere. Cartillage may have calcium salts deposited within the interstitial substance. This **calcified cartilage** is often mistaken for bone. The jaws of sharks contain much calcified cartilage.

Cartilaginous fishes appear to be unable to give expression to the genetic code necessary for ossification except for formation of dentin in scales and teeth.

CALCIUM REGULATION AND SKELETAL REMODELING

Bone and cartilage not only serve as mechanical supports for the vertebrate body but, with scales and teeth, constitute important storage places for calcium and other mineral salts. They therefore participate in maintaining homeostasis. Calcium is constantly being deposited and withdrawn. When serum calcium levels are rising, calcium is usually deposited in bone or cartilage, along with inorganic phosphate, as hydroxyapatite crystals. When serum calcium levels are falling, calcium may be withdrawn from the skeleton and other depots to maintain a normal serum calcium level.

In addition to bone resorption in response to lowered blood calcium levels, cartilage and bone are constantly being resorbed for another reason. Consider the skull of a newborn human being (Fig. 6-5). Can one envision any way this skull can become that of a 21-year-old human being unless cartilage and bone are being constantly resorbed and replaced day by day as the individual grows? A 21-year-old human brain would never fit into the cranial cavity of a newborn baby! Skeletal remodeling is a necessary and continuous process. Although it is a more active process in growing skeletons, it is characteristic of all (Fig. 6-6).

Remodeling also occurs in response to continuing mechanical stress resulting from muscle contraction or weight bearing. Bone becomes thicker where stress is high, thinner where stress is low. Roughened areas, bony ridges, and prominences to which muscles attach enlarge with muscle use. The clearly defined lattice structure of cancellous bone bears a striking resemblance to the lines of stress generated by the bone's natural load.

TENDONS, LIGAMENTS, AND JOINTS

Tendons and ligaments are made of thick, closely packed bundles of collagen (Fig. 6-2). **Tendons** connect muscles with bone. When a muscle contracts, the pull on the bone is exerted through the tendon. In accordance with this mechanical requirement the collagen is in

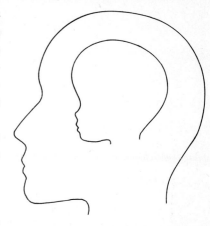

Fig. 6-5. Comparative size of skull of newborn and 21-year-old human being.

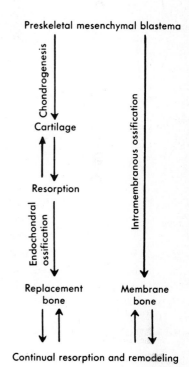

Fig. 6-6. Steps in osteogenesis and remodeling.

parallel bundles and fibrocytes lie in rows between them. **Ligaments** connect bone to bone, and the collagen bundles have a less regular arrangement. Ligaments and tendons that become flat and very wide are **aponeuroses.** The longest ligament in mammals is the nuchal ligament in the back of the neck of grazing mammals. Extending between the skull and the neural spines of some of the thoracic vertebrae, it provides mechanical support for the head. It is least well developed in short-necked mammals.

The term "ligament" is sometimes applied to fibrous connective tissue membranes or cords that hold visceral organs in place as, for example, the falciform ligament and round ligament of the ovary. However, these are not skeletal structures.

In some species tendons and ligaments normally become mineralized in one or more locations. Turkeys, for example, have ossified tendons in their legs, and ornithischian dinosaurs had them millions of years ago. **Sesamoid bones** or cartilages (so named because they reminded early anatomists of sesame seeds) are nodules of bone or cartilage that form in tendons or ligaments. Best known is the patella, or kneecap, which is endochondral in some species, intramembranous in others.

A **joint** is the site where two bones (or cartilages) meet. If the joint is movable in one or more planes, it is a **diarthrosis.** The articular surfaces of the bones in a movable joint are usually covered with a layer of hyaline cartilage, which is readily replaceable with wear. Ligamentous bands hold the bones together and form a fluid-filled joint capsule, or **bursa,** around the joint. A lubricatory **synovial fluid** is secreted by a synovial membrane that lines the bursa.

In some joints movement is not possible. These are **synarthroses.** The suture between the frontal and parietal bones (Fig. 8-25) is an example of a synarthrosis. Sometimes bones meet and become united by collagen and hydroxyapatite crystals that obliterate the suture. This condition is said to be an **ankylosis.** The premaxillary and maxillary bones of the human embryo ankylose and, as a result, the premaxillary cannot be distinguished as a separate bone in adults. A **symphysis** is a joint in the midline, in which two bones are separated by fibrocartilage and movement is severely limited. The pubic symphysis of female mammals becomes a bit more movable by hormonal dissolution of the fibrocartilage shortly before labor begins.

HETEROTOPIC BONES

In addition to the usual cartilages and bones that make up the axial and appendicular skeleton, miscellaneous heterotopic bones develop in aberrant locations by endochondral or intramembranous ossification. They are usually missing from routine skeletal preparations.

Among heterotopic bones are the **os cordis** in the interventricular septum of the heart of deer and bovines, and the **baculum (os penis)** embedded between the spongy bodies in the penis of bats, marsupials, carnivores, insectivores, bovines, rodents, and lower primates (Fig. 6-7). The baculum reaches a length of nearly 60 cm in walruses. An **os clitoridis** is embedded in the clitoris in otters, several rodents, rabbits, and numerous other female mammals.

Bone or cartilage forms in the gizzard in some doves. The syrinx of birds often develops an internal skeletal element, the **pessulus**. At least one species of bat has bone in the tongue. Bone develops in the gular pouch of a South American lizard, in the muscular diaphragm of camels, and in the upper eyelid of crocodilians (**adlacrimal, or palpebral, bone**). A similar plate of connective tissue, the **tarsus**, develops in human beings. A **rostral bone** develops in the snout of a number of mammals including pigs, and a **cloacal bone** develops in the ventral wall of the cloaca of some lizards.

MINERALIZED TISSUES AND THE INVERTEBRATES

Mineralized tissues are not unique among vertebrates. In fact, two thirds of the living species of animals that contain mineralized tissues are invertebrates.[2] The matrix is collagen, and it goes back as far as the sponges; but the inorganic crystals in invertebrates are more often calcium carbonate than calcium phosphate. Cartilage is found among invertebrates, including squids, some gastropods, and protochordates; and bone, dentin, cartilage, and enameloid were all well developed in Ordovician ostracoderms. For that reason, we cannot say that any one of these is phylogenetically older.

REGIONAL COMPONENTS OF THE SKELETON

The skeleton may be divided regionally into the following parts, which include associated ligaments and tendons:

Axial skeleton
    Notochord and vertebral column
    Ribs and sternum
    Skull and visceral skeleton
Appendicular skeleton
    Pectoral and pelvic girdles
    Skeleton of paired fins or limbs
    Skeleton of median fins of fishes
Heterotopic bones

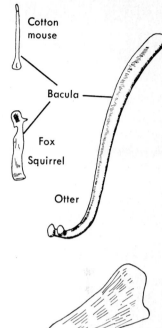

Fig. 6-7. Heterotopic bones.

CHAPTER SUMMARY

1. The chief mineralized tissues are bone (from osteoblasts), dentin (from odontoblasts), cartilage (from chondroblasts), and enamel (from ameloblasts).

2. Bone consists of collagen, inorganic salts, cementing substance, and osteocytes that usually occupy lacunae interconnected by canaliculi.

3. Bone is compact (lamellar) or spongy (cancellous). Lamellar or osteon bone is compact bone with haversian systems. Acellular bone lacks canaliculi and lacunae.

4. Membrane bone forms directly in mesenchyme. Endochondral bone forms in preexisting cartilage.

5. Dermal bone is membrane bone that arises ontogenetically or phylogenetically from skin.

6. Dentin is a form of bone with peripheral odontoblasts, long canaliculi, and no lacunae. It is confined to the skin and teeth.

7. Cartilage consists of a matrix of collagen and chondroitin sulfate, and of chondrocytes. It may be hyaline, fibrocartilage, or elastic and is sometimes calcified.

8. Bone and cartilage are constantly being deposited and resorbed, thereby maintaining homeostasis and orderly growth.

9. Tendons attach muscles to bone. Ligaments connect bone to bone. Both may be calcified.

10. Joints are diarthroses, synarthroses, or symphyses. Bursae are ligamentous and contain synovial fluid if the joint is movable.

11. Heterotopic bones form in miscellaneous locations by endochondral or intramembranous ossification.

12. Many invertebrates have mineralized tissues consisting of collagen, inorganic salts, and cementing substances. Among vertebrates, cartilage, bone, dentin, and enamel may be equally old.

LITERATURE CITED AND SELECTED READINGS

1. Burt, W.H.: Bacula of North American mammals, University of Michigan Museum of Zoology Miscellaneous Publications 113:1 76, 1970.
2. Hall, B.K.: Evolutionary consequences of skeletal differentiation, American Zoologist 15:329, 1975.
3. Halstead, L.B.: Calcified tissue in the earliest vertebrates, Calcified Tissue Research 3:107, 1969.
4. Hancox, N.M.: Biology of bone, Cambridge, England, 1972, Cambridge University Press.
5. Moss, M.L.: The origin of vertebrate calcified tissues. In Ørvig, T., editor: Current problems of lower vertebrate phylogeny, New York, 1968, Interscience-Wiley.
6. Moss, M.L.: Skeletal tissues in sharks, American Zoologist 17:335, 1977.
7. Ørvig, T.: The dermal skeleton: general considerations. In Ørvig, T.: editor: Current problems of lower vertebrate phylogeny, New York, 1968, Interscience-Wiley.
8. Patterson, C.: Cartilage bones, dermal bones and membrane bones, or the exoskeleton versus the endoskeleton. In Andrews, S.M., Miles, R.S., and Walker, A.D., editors: Problems in vertebrate evolution, New York, 1977, Academic Press, Inc.
9. Todd, J.T., and others: The perception of human growth, Scientific American 242(2):132, 1980.

CHAPTER 7

Vertebrae, ribs, and sterna

The vertebral column, skull, ribs, and tetrapod sternum, along with their ligaments, constitute the major components of the **axial skeleton.** The vertebral column forms around and within the notochord during ontogeny; the ribs and sternum form in the lateral and ventral body wall.

VERTEBRAL COLUMN

The vertebral column is the keystone of the skeleton. It is a usually flexible arch to which the head is attached and from which all the rest of the body is suspended in fishes, and all of the trunk between appendages in most tetrapods. It provides a protective bony tunnel for the spinal cord and, in the absence of an adult notochord, it is an essential participating skeletal structure for locomotion. In no vertebrate is its locomotor importance more readily demonstrated than in fishes and limbless tetrapods.

Fishes are surrounded by an environment that offers a degree of resistance to forward progress and a buoying effect on the body. During locomotion, resistance is overcome by pushing laterally on the water with rhythmical, undulating, side-to-side movements of the trunk and tail. These movements are brought about by muscles attached to vertebrae and myosepta. The architecture of the vertebral column of most fishes permits only the necessary side-to-side flexibility of the column. When vertebrates ventured onto land they brought with them the fishlike method of locomotion, but it was an awkward way to move about. Unlike water, land is beneath the animal rather than around it, it is not level, and it is littered with obstacles that must be avoided or clambered over. Eventually, selective forces altered the vertebral column to provide the dorsoventral flexibility more suited to locomotion on land, while at the same time providing a strong skeletal arch for suspending the trunk above the ground between forelimbs and hind limbs. These changes were achieved at the expense of some side-to-side flexibility of the column, and they ultimately resulted in regional specialization of trunk vertebrae in tetrapods.

Centra, arches, and processes

Most vertebrae have a **centrum, neural arch,** and one or more processes, or **apophyses,** that project from the arches or centra (Figs. 7-1 and 7-2). Centra occupy the position occupied earlier by the notochord. Neural arches are perched on the centra, and the successive arches and their interconnecting ligaments enclose a long **vertebral,** or **neural, canal** occupied by the spinal cord. In fishes, urodeles, most reptiles, some birds, and many long-tailed mammals **hemal arches,** or **chevron bones** as they are called in amniotes, are inverted beneath the centra of the tail and house the caudal artery and vein (Figs. 7-1, C and D, and 7-2).

Transverse processes, or **diapophyses,** are the most common apophyses. They extend varying distances laterad into the horizontal septum between the epaxial and hypaxial muscles (Fig. 1-2). They serve as attachments for some of the muscles that operate the vertebral column for locomotion. **Zygapophyses** are paired processes at the cephalic end of trunk vertebrae (**prezygapophyses),** and at the caudal end (**postzygapophyses),** chiefly in tetrapods (Fig. 7-2). The articular facets of prezygapophyses articulate with facets of the postzygapophyses immediately ahead in such manner as to restrict dorsoventral flexion of the column. The tail of tetrapods is highly flexible because zygapophyses are lacking. **Parapophyses** articulate with the ventral head of two-headed ribs (Fig. 7-19). **Basapophyses** are paired ventrolateral projections from centra. In some species the two meet beneath the centrum in the tail to form hemal arches. Hemal arches in other species seem to be modified ventral ribs. **Hypapophyses** (Fig. 7-2, trunk) are midventral projections from centra, to which muscles attach. Other processes are found in occasional species.

Morphogenesis of vertebrae

A typical vertebra arises from mesenchyme cells that stream out of the sclerotomes of mesodermal somites, surround the notochord and neural tube, and produce the blastema for a future vertebra (Fig. 4-7). Then, some of the blastemal cells, chondroblasts, deposit within the blastema a cartilaginous centrum and neural arch and, in the tail, a hemal arch. The temporary result is a cartilaginous vertebra with the notochord constricted within each centrum. Later, the cartilage is removed and bone is deposited where cartilage previously existed. By this process a vertebra consisting of replacement bone is formed. In chondrichthyeans, cartilaginous vertebrae are deposited, but they are never replaced by bone. Presumably, the enzyme systems needed for ossification are missing.

The process of vertebral formation is modified in teleosts, apodans, and urodeles. In these, bone is deposited directly in the mesenchy-

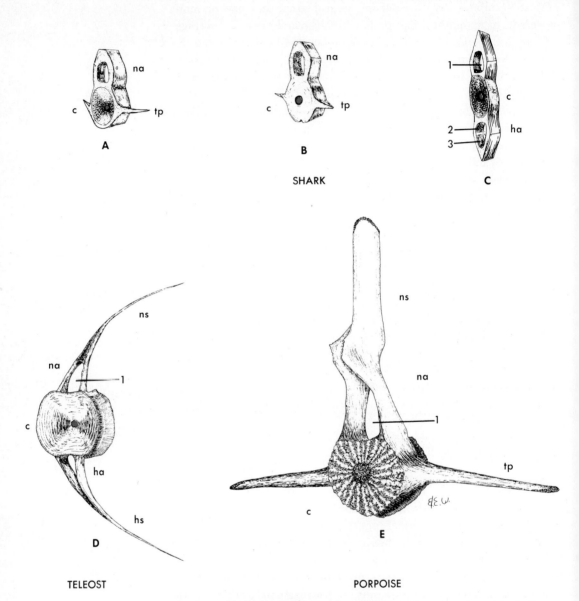

TELEOST

PORPOISE

Fig. 7-1. Selected vertebrae from cephalic view. **A,** Trunk vertebra of shark. **B,** Cross section of trunk vertebra near middle of centrum. **C,** Tail vertebra of shark. **D,** Tail vertebra of teleost. **E,** Lumbar vertebra of porpoise. The fish vertebrae are amphicelous, the porpoise vertebra is acelous. **c,** Centrum; **ha,** hemal arch; **hs,** hemal spine; **na,** neural arch; **ns,** neural spine; **tp,** transverse process. **1,** Vertebral canal housing spinal cord; **2** and **3,** canals for caudal artery and caudal vein, respectively. *Red,* site of notochord.

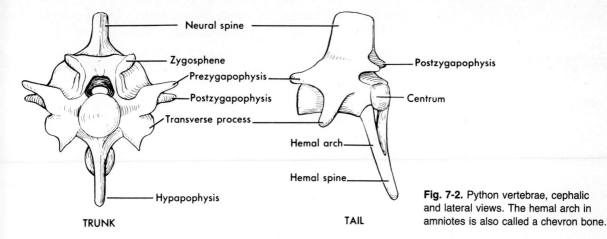

Fig. 7-2. Python vertebrae, cephalic and lateral views. The hemal arch in amniotes is also called a chevron bone.

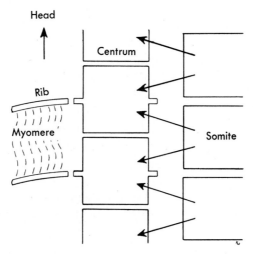

Fig. 7-3. Relationship of centra and their joints to myomeres. Somites and myomeres are segmental. Ribs, myosepta, and centra are intersegmental. Arrows show source of scleroblasts that contribute to each centrum.

mal blastema without an intermediate cartilage stage. These verte-brae are therefore membrane bone.

In many fishes and urodeles cartilage or membrane bone is depos-ited not only *around* the notochord (**perichordal cartilage** or **bone**), but chondroblasts penetrate the notochord sheath and deposit carti-lage—not bone—*within* the sheath and notochord. Thus the centra of these vertebrates, including those with perichordal membrane bone, contain a core of chordal cartilage that may or may not ossify. The contrasting results are seen among amphibians: urodeles and apodans have centra composed of membrane bone with a core of chordal cartilage and, inside that, remnants of the original notochord tissue, whereas the entire centrum is replacement bone in anurans.

The difference in these amphibian classes inspires questions concerning the monophyletic origin of amphibians (Chapter 3).

In the formation of vertebrae, scleroblasts from the caudal half of one somite and the cephalic half of the next stream to an intersegmental location around the notochord to establish the blastema for a centrum (Fig. 7-3). As a result, intervertebral joints are *intrasegmental;* and fish myomeres, pulling on two successive myosepta or ribs, cause lateral undulation of the column for swimming. The joints in fishes, however, are not as freely movable as those in tetrapods.

Vertebral columns of fishes

The vertebrae of fishes exhibit remarkable variety. Modern lungfishes, sturgeons, spoonbills, and *Latimeria* have no centra (Fig. 7-4). The notochord is present and unconstricted. Chordal cartilage within the thickened notochord sheath provides rigidity. Associated with the notochord in each body segment are paired basidorsal, basiventral, interdorsal, and interventral cartilages. The condition resembles an arrested developmental state in which centra were never completed.

Agnathans have an even stranger column if, indeed, they may be said to have one. The only skeletal elements are **lateral neural cartilages** (Fig. 1-4), one or two pairs per body segment, depending on the species. Caudally, the lateral neural cartilages fuse to form a single dorsolateral cartilaginous plate perforated by foramina for spinal nerves. In hagfishes, lateral neural cartilages are limited to the tail. These cartilages may be vestigial vertebrae, primitive vertebrae, or they may bear no phylogenetic relationship to vertebrae. Whether or not you call them vertebrae depends on how you wish to define "vertebra." How would you define the term?

In holocephalans, chordal cartilage is deposited in the notochord sheath, which thickens greatly. Thereafter, calcification converts the sheath into calcified cartilaginous rings that are much more numerous than body segments (Fig. 7-5).

In sharks the notochord is present throughout the length of the vertebral column and is constricted within each centrum (Fig. 7-6). As a result, the centra, composed of chordal and perichordal cartilage, are concave at each end (Fig. 7-1, *A*). Each neural arch consists of bilateral dorsal plates; between arches are intercalary plates. Therefore the spinal cord is enclosed in a continuous cartilaginous tunnel perforated only by foramina for spinal nerves and blood vessels. Hemal arches in the tail have similar plates. A centrum that is concave at each end is said to be **amphicelous** (Fig. 7-7).

Teleosts have well-ossified amphicelous vertebrae (Fig. 7-1, *D*). The centra and neural arches of successive vertebrae are interconnected by a complex system of collagenous and elastic ligaments that permit lateral undulation of the body for swimming. The core of each centrum is a dumbbell-shaped vacuole where the notochord previously existed, and the space between two centra is occupied by a porous cartilage-like material that probably includes embryonic notochordal tissue. Neural spines are often elongated, and in the tail and posterior trunk successive spines are sometimes interconnected by a delicate bony rod formed by ossification of interspinous liga-

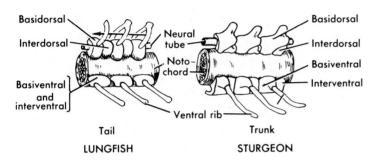

Fig. 7-4. Vertebral components in adult lungfish *(Neoceratodus)* and sturgeon. Arrow in lungfish indicates canal occupied by a supportive longitudinal ligament.

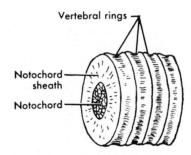

Fig. 7-5. Calcified cartilaginous notochordal rings of an extinct holocephalan. The rings are more numerous than the somites. The neural and hemal arches have been removed.

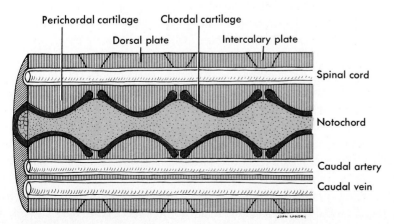

Fig. 7-6. Caudal vertebral column of *Squalus,* sagittal section. Bilateral dorsal plates lie above each centrum and constitute a neural arch. Chordal cartilage has been deposited in the notochord sheath (dark red).

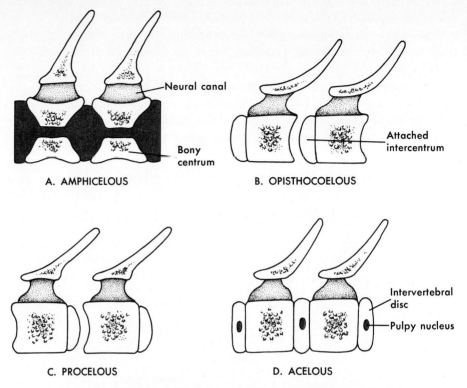

Fig. 7-7. Vertebral types based on articular surfaces. Midsagittal sections, head to the left. Amphicelous vertebrae are found in fishes, generalized urodeles, caecilians, and primitive lizards, opisthocelous in salamanders, procelous in anurans and modern reptiles, and acelous in mammals. The condition in birds is discussed on p. 164. Color indicates notochordal tissue.

ments. In lower teleosts the spines are sometimes surmounted by **supraneural bones.** A variety of processes, mostly unlike those of tetrapods, protrude from the arches and centra.

Many fishes have two centra and two sets of arches in each body segment in the tail, and a few have duplication of centra and arches in the trunk also. The condition is known as **diplospondyly.** *Amia* has what look like two centra per body segment (Fig. 7-8), but only one bears arches, so the other is called an **intercentrum.** Diplospondyly was also present in some fossil amphibians. The advantage of this condition is speculative.

Flexion of the vertebral column of bony fishes is pretty much restricted to lateral displacement of the column. This is facilitated by elasticity of the ligaments that interconnect vertebrae, rather than by freely movable intervertebral joints such as those of tetrapods. The joint between the first vertebra and the skull is immovable, the two being united by cartilage or collagenous connective tissue.

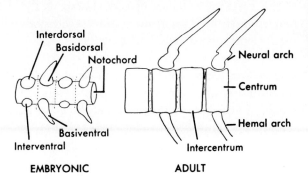

Fig. 7-8. Tail vertebrae of *Amia*. A centrum and intercentrum develop in each body segment. Embryonic basidorsal and basiventral cartilages contribute to each centrum, and interdorsal and interventral cartilages contribute to each intercentrum.

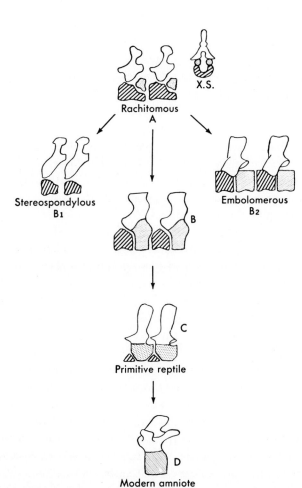

Fig. 7-9. Modifications of tetrapod vertebrae leading to modern amniotes. The rachitomous type (shown also in cross section, X.S.) occurred in crossopterygians and in the earliest amphibians. **B** is from a labyrinthodont thought to be in the reptile line. **B₁** and **B₂** are from other labyrinthodonts. *Diagonal lines,* hypocentrum; *stippled,* pleurocentrum. An interpretation of the phylogeny of amphibian vertebrae will be found in Schmalhausen.[9]

Evolution of tetrapod vertebrae

The vertebral columns of early tetrapods did not consist of one bony unit per body segment, as in most tetrapods today. A "vertebra" in crossopterygians and early amphibians (Fig. 7-9, *A*) consisted of a **hypocentrum (intercentrum)**, which was a large, anterior, median, wedge-shaped element that was incomplete dorsally, and two **pleurocentra,** which were smaller, posterodorsal, intersegmental elements. A vertebra of this kind is **rachitomous.** All later tetrapod vertebrae are probably modifications of the rachitomous variety. Changes leading to modern amniotes appear to have been characterized by increased prominence of pleurocentra (Fig. 7-9, *B* to *D*). The rachitomous variety was also modified in other directions (Fig. 7-9, B_1 and B_2). Whether the centra of modern amphibians represent hypocentra or pleurocentra is not known.

Even in modern tetrapods, each centrum commences ossification at several symmetrical loci around the notochord; and, as the separate centers expand, they coalesce. The typical tetrapod vertebra is, therefore, a composite structure. The findings of embryology, comparative anatomy, and paleontology all point to the same conclusion: an adult tetrapod vertebra composed of a centrum and neural arch in each body segment is not primitive. Primitively, several skeletal components occupied each body segment.

Rachitomous vertebrae were amphicelous, and amphicelous vertebrae are still present in generalized urodeles such as *Necturus*, in caecilians, *Sphenodon*, and primitive lizards such as geckos, all of which retain vestiges of notochord in the intervertebral joints. In other tetrapods the notochord is obliterated in adults; and the centra become flattened at one or both ends and separated by intercentra or, in mammals, intervertebral discs of variable and debatable homologies (Fig. 7-7, *B* to *D*). These provide intervertebral joints that are more freely movable than joints between amphicelous vertebrae. A vestige of the notochord, the **pulpy nucleus,** remains in the intercentra or intervertebral discs of crocodilians and mammals (Fig 7-7, *D*).

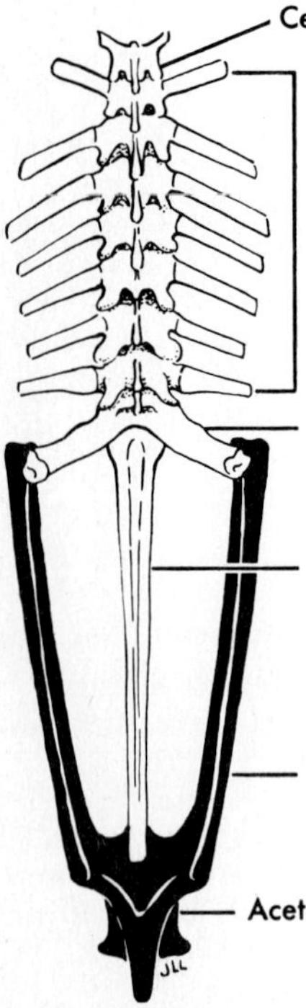

Regional specialization in tetrapod columns

Tetrapod limbs push against the earth, and the reaction, or opposing force, is transmitted through the ilia of the pelvic girdle to one or more of the hindmost trunk vertebrae. These are appropriately modified and are described as **sacral** (Fig. 7-10). Survival on land required increased mobility of the head with its sense organs, especially eyes that scan the horizon. This was accomplished by freeing the craniovertebral joint for movement and by formation of a neck by shortening or eliminating ribs just behind the head. This resulted in **cervical vertebrae** (Figs. 7-10 and 7-11). In crocodilians, lizards, birds, and

Cervical (1)

Dorsals (2-8)

Sacral (9)

Urostyle

Pelvic girdle

Acetabulum

Fig. 7-10. Vertebral column and pelvic girdle (black) of an anuran. The transverse processes include short ribs. The pelvic girdle is braced against the sacral vertebra.

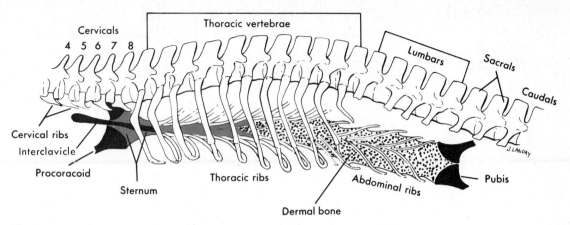

Fig. 7-11. Vertebrae and ribs of an alligator. Abdominal ribs are also called gastralia.

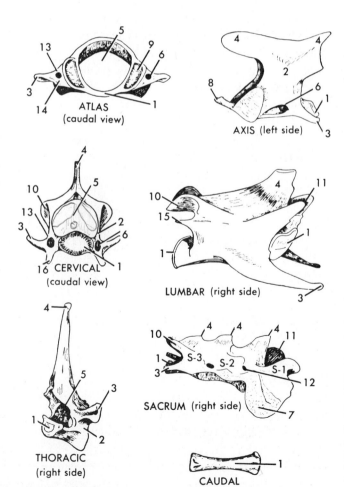

Fig. 7-12. Cat vertebrae. **1,** Centrum; **2,** pedicle; **3,** transverse process; **4,** neural spine; **5,** vertebral canal; **6,** transverse foramen; **7,** site of articulation with ilium; **8,** odontoid process; **9,** articular facet for axis; **10,** postzygapophysis; **11,** prezygapophysis; **12,** intervertebral foramen; **13,** diapophysis; **14,** parapophysis; **15,** accessory process; **16,** vestige of a cervical rib with two heads, one fused with a diapophysis; the other with a parapophysis to form a transverse foramen; **S-1, S-2, S-3,** sacral vertebrae.

mammals long ribs are restricted to the anterior region of the trunk. Vertebrae that bear these are **thoracic,** and the remaining trunk vertebrae are **lumbar** (Fig. 7-11). Among tetrapods, snakes have the longest columns with as many as 400 or more vertebrae. This provides snakes with an elongated, multijointed body that can be twisted into loops or sinuous curves for locomotion without limbs. Caecilians, also limbless, have as many as 250 or more vertebrae, and some urodeles have 100. The awkward leaping anurans have the shortest columns.

THE CRANIOVERTEBRAL JUNCTION AND NECK VERTEBRAE

The craniovertebral joint of living amphibians is only a little more movable than that of fishes, and there is only one cervical vertebra. This permits little movement of the head independently of the trunk. Amniotes have more cervical vertebrae, which results in a flexible neck; and the first two are modified in such a manner as to allow movement of the head independently of the neck. The first vertebra, or **atlas,** is ringlike (Fig. 7-12, atlas) because its centrum is no longer attached. The atlas articulates with the skull in a condyloid joint (one occipital condyle in reptiles, two in mammals) in which the skull rocks as in nodding "yes." The centrum of the atlas is attached to the second vertebra, or **axis,** as an odontoid process that projects forward

Fig. 7-13. First two vertebrae of a cat, sagittal sections. The centrum of the atlas is attached to the axis as an odontoid process.

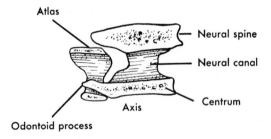

Atlas

Neural spine

Neural canal

Axis

Centrum

Odontoid process

Fig. 7-14. The eight cervical vertebrae, eight cervical ribs (red), and proatlas, **P,** of an alligator, left lateral view. **1,** Atlas and attached first rib. Immediately behind the first rib is the rib of the axis. The ribs are fused to transverse processes.

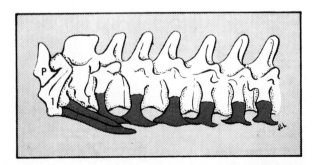

to rest on the floor of the atlas (Figs. 7-12, axis, and 7-13). The skull and atlas pivot as a unit on the odontoid process as in shaking the head "no." This rotation of the head is possible because of reduction or absence of the prezygapophyses and postzygapophyses on these two vertebrae. The degree of rotation is maximal in mammals. In some reptiles and a few mammals an additional neural arch of unknown homology, the **proatlas,** is interposed between skull and atlas (Fig. 7-14). In the lizard *Lacerta* there is a membranous gap at that location.

A long neck is advantageous in feeding, as well as in scanning the horizon. It enables long-legged tetrapods to reach food and water on the ground while standing, rather than having to get on their knees or belly to do so. The latter posture would endanger the species in a habitat that includes stealthy carnivores. Birds have the largest number of neck vertebrae, 12 or more in common species, 25 in swans.

Mammals almost always have seven cervical vertebrae (Table 7-1). This is as true in the stubby, rigid neck of whales as in the neck of the tallest giraffe. The only exceptions are edentates with six, eight, or nine and manatees with six. In moles several cervical vertebrae ankylose, perhaps strengthening the neck for burrowing. In cetaceans and armadillos there is no external evidence of a neck, and all cervical vertebrae are shortened and more or less fused together.

Table 7-1. Number of vertebrae in selected tetrapods

	Cervical	Thoracic	Dorsal	Lumbar	Sacral	Caudal
Anura	1		7		1	Urostyle
Salamander	1		10		1	24
Lizard *(Lacerta)*	8		22		2	Numerous
Painted turtle	8		10		2	25 to 30
Alligator	9*	10*		5 to 6	2	34 to 40
Pigeon	12 to 14	5		6	2	15†
Mammals	6 to 9	9 to 25		5 to 8	2 to 5‡	3 to 50
Horse	7	18 to 20		6	5	15 to 21
Opossum	7	13		6	2	19 to 35
Hamster	7	13		6	4	13 to 14
Sheep	7	13		6 to 7	4	16 to 18
Dog	7	12 to 13		7	3	19 to 23
Rabbit	7	12		7	4	16+
Human being	7	12		5	5	3 to 5
Bat	7	11		5	5	9
Sperm whale	7	11		8	0	24

*Or 8 C and 11 T, depending on the definition of thoracic.
†Includes four in the pygostyle.
‡Except cetaceans with none.

Flexibility of the neck is exceptional in birds and turtles because of the way their neck vertebrae articulate. The caudal ends of the centra in the neck of birds are saddle shaped with a convexity in the right-left axis and a concavity in the dorsoventral axis; and the cephalic end of the next centrum is shaped to accommodate this configuration. These vertebrae are **heterocelous.** The joints permit much side-to-side flexion of the neck as well as much dorsoventral flexion. Because of the atlas-axis complex and the length and flexibility of the neck, birds can turn their head 180 degrees to the rear. Turtles have ball-and-socket joints in the neck, so most turtles can completely retract their head and neck into the protection of the shell by folding the neck dorsoventrally or, in side-necked turtles, sidewise.

Cervical vertebrae in birds and mammals have a **transverse foramen** between the two heads of the vestigial cervical ribs (Fig. 7-12, cervical). Successive foramina provide a **vertebrarterial canal** that transmits the vertebral artery and vein to the brain.

BRACING THE HIND LIMBS: SACRUM AND SYNSACRUM

Sacral vertebrae bear short, stout transverse processes that are strong enough to take the thrust of the pelvic girdle as the limbs push

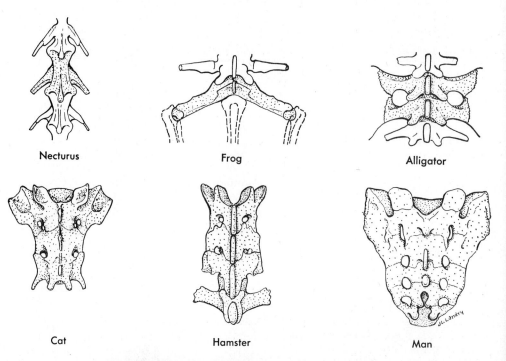

Necturus   Frog   Alligator

Cat   Hamster   Man

Fig. 7-15. Sacral vertebrae (stippled) of selected vertebrates, dorsal views. They have ankylosed to form a sacrum in the amniotes illustrated.

against the earth in locomotion (Fig. 7-10). Amphibians have one sacral vertebra, living reptiles and most birds have two, and most mammals have three to five. When there are more than one, the sacral vertebrae usually ankylose to form a single bony complex, the **sacrum** (Fig. 7-15). No sacrum forms in caecilians, limbless reptiles, or cetaceans, all of which lack hind limbs.

In birds the last thoracic vertebra, all lumbars, the two sacrals (three in ostriches), and the first few caudals unite to form one adult bone, the **synsacrum** (Figs. 7-16 and 7-17, *B*); and the latter becomes more or less fused with the ilia of the pelvic girdle (Fig. 7-17, *A*). The synsacrum provides a rigid framework for the teeter-totter–like two-legged stance of birds. The thoracic vertebrae anterior to the synsacrum also unite more or less completely so there is little flexibility in the avian backbone behind the neck. This axial rigidity reduces the number of muscles needed to keep the body streamlined during flight. However, the historical selective forces responsible for this condition may have been quite different from what seem to be the current advantages.

Armadillos also have a synsacrum. It consists of up to 13 fused sacral and anterior caudal vertebrae. In addition, there is extensive fusion of neck vertebrae in these armored animals.

TAIL VERTEBRAE

UROSTYLE, PYGOSTYLE, AND COCCYX

Caudal vertebrae in early tetrapods may have numbered 50 or more, but in modern ones the number is much reduced. Toward the end of the tail all arches and processes become progressively shorter until finally the members of the series consist of small cylindrical centra only (Fig. 7-18).

Anurans have a unique **urostyle** at the end of the vertebral column (Fig. 7-10). It arises from a continuous elongated perichordal cartilage

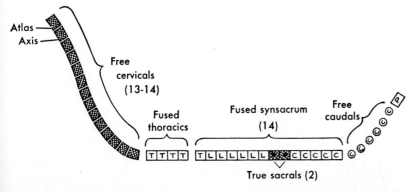

Fig. 7-16. Vertebral column of pigeon, diagrammatical. **T**, Thoracic; **L**, lumbar; **C**, caudal; **P**, pygostyle, composed of four fused vertebrae.

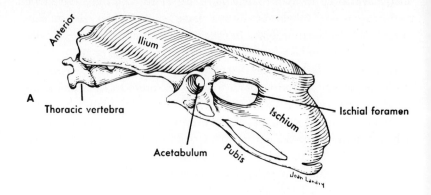

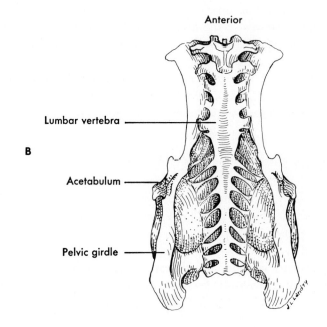

Fig. 7-17. Synsacrum and pelvic girdle of the guinea hen. **A,** Left lateral view. **B,** Ventral view.

Fig. 7-18. Complete set of tail vertebrae from a hamster, left lateral view.

at the base of the larval tail, and it remains and ossifies when the tail is lost at metamorphosis. That it is composed of ancestral postsacral vertebrae is evident from the one or more coalesced centra, vestigial arches, transverse processes, and nerve foramina that are part of the cranial end of the urostyle in some species. The urostyle accounts for the small number of vertebrae in anuran vertebral columns.

Birds have remnants of a tail, and some have more caudal vertebrae than some mammals. Pigeons have 15. Five are ankylosed with the synsacrum, the next six or so are free, and the last four or five are fused to form a pygostyle, which is the skeleton of the stumpy externally visible tail (Fig. 7-16). (The pygostyle develops as four or five independent cartilaginous centra.)

Apes and human beings have four or five vestigial tail vertebrae. These are separate in the young and lack neural arches and prominent processes; but with age, two or three of them at least unite to form a rigid **coccyx.** The centra are still identifiable.

When captured by the tail, many lizards break it proximal to the site of capture and scurry away. This **autotomy** is implemented by a zone of soft tissue that divides each caudal centrum into cephalic and caudal halves, the location being at the level of a myoseptum. At this site the break occurs and regeneration of the tail begins.

RIBS

Ribs articulate with vertebrae and extend into the body wall. A few fishes, *Polypterus* and salmon, for instance, have dorsal and ventral ribs associated with each trunk vertebra (Fig. 7-19, *A*). **Dorsal ribs** pass laterad into the horizontal septum; **ventral ribs** arch ventrad in myosepta. At the level of the vent the ventral ribs of the two sides meet beneath the centrum in some species to form hemal arches. In other species, ribs are formed from basapophyses. A dorsal and ventral rib in each segment of the trunk may be primitive.

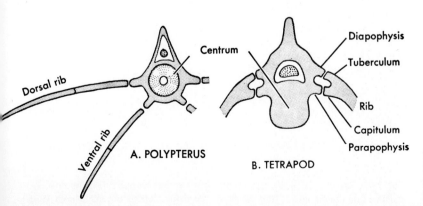

Fig. 7-19. Relationship of ribs to vertebral column. **A,** Dorsal and ventral ribs of *Polypterus* and some teleosts. **B,** Bicipital rib of tetrapods.

Fig. 7-20. Cervical ribs of a cobra, a "spreading adder." The first three ribs, associated with the atlas, axis, and third vetebra, are short and hidden by the jaws. **C4,** Neural spine of the fourth cervical vertebra.

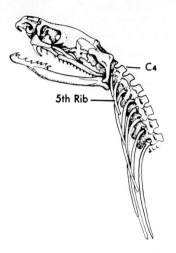

Fig. 7-21. Skeleton of trunk, tail, and pectoral girdle of a pigeon. Bones of the pectoral girdle are black. The ventral keel of the sternum is the carina. The clavicles and interclavicle form the furcula, or wishbone.

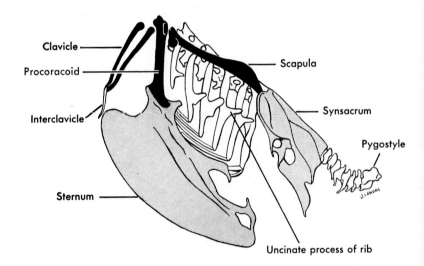

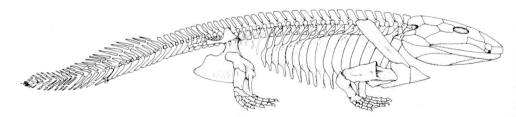

Fig. 7-22. Skeleton of *Ichthyostega,* the oldest known tetrapod. Missing ribs indicated by dotted lines. (After Jarvik, E.: Scientific Monthly **80:**152, March 1955.)

Most fishes have only ventral ribs; sharks and a few other fishes have only dorsal ones. The teleost *Hippocampus* (sea horse) has none. Neither do cyclostomes, but here it is probably correlated with absence of centra.

In early tetrapods, ribs were present in every body segment from the atlas to the end of the tail; but, as tetrapod limbs became reoriented to hold the trunk well above the ground, long movable ribs became confined mostly to the thorax. The remaining ribs grew shorter and, especially in the neck, ankylosed with transverse processes (Fig. 7-14). Snakes and apodans, however, have long ribs the entire length of the body, and these are used in locomotion. A half dozen or more of the more posterior ribs of the flying lizard *Draco* are prolonged and rotate outward to elevate the skin, which forms a patagial membrane on which the animal glides from tree to tree. The long cervical ribs of cobras can be rotated outward to cause the neck to "spread" (Fig. 7-20). Human beings not infrequently have a cervical or lumbar rib as an anomaly.

Thoracic ribs usually have a bony dorsal segment, the **vertebral rib,** and a cartilaginous ventral segment, the **sternal rib,** or **costal cartilage.** In birds, the sternal ribs are bony. There is frequently a movable joint between the dorsal and ventral segments that provides flexibility for breathing, during which the ribs are rotated upward and outward, which increases the size of the pleural cavity. Most sternal ribs connect to the sternum, either directly or via other ribs; those that do not are **"floating" ribs.** The thoracic ribs of birds and some lizards have flat **uncinate processes** that overlap the next rib and serve for attachment of some of the scapular muscles (Fig. 7-21). Early tetrapods also had uncinate processes (Fig. 7-22). The ribs of turtles are fused with the carapace and are useless (Fig. 5-36, *A*).

The head of each rib, along with transverse processes, is formed by scleroblasts from somites. The remainder of the rib arises from the somatopleure. Most ribs are replacement bone, but in the ventral abdominal wall of crocodilians and some lizards there are bony ribs of intramembranous origin. These **gastralia** may be remnants of dermal scales (Fig. 7-11).

STERNUM

The sternum is a tetrapod structure, and primarily amniote. There is little evidence that stem amphibians had one, and among modern amphibians it is well differentiated only in anurans (Fig. 9-5). It is absent in the limbless caecilians and is either flimsy or absent in urodeles (Fig. 7-23). In lizards it is a large shield-shaped plate of cartilage or replacement bone that the pectoral girdle is braced against ventrally (Fig. 7-24, lizard). It is missing in snakes, some limbless lizards,

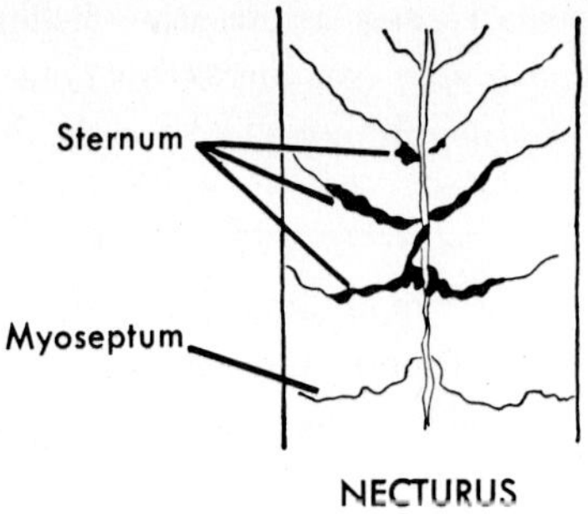

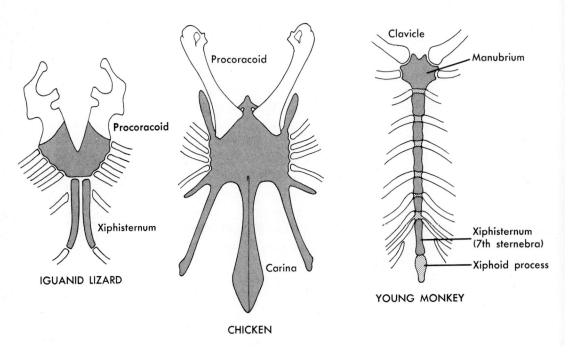

Fig. 7-23. The "sternum" of a necturus.

Fig. 7-24. Sternum (gray) of a reptile, bird, and mammal. Stipple indicates cartilage. The sternum articulates anteriorly with a component of the pectoral girdle and laterally with ribs.

and turtles. A varying number of ribs articulate with the sternum, and these, along with the sternum and vertebral column, provide a bony enclosure for the thoracic viscera.

The sternum of birds that can fly has developed an enormous keel, or **carina,** where the massive pectoral flight muscles attach (Fig. 7-21). Pterosaurs also had a carina. The mammalian sternum is composed of bony segments, or **sternebrae,** except in cetaceans and sirenians (Fig. 7-24, monkey). The posteriormost sternebra, the xiphisternum, bears a cartilaginous or bony xiphoid process.

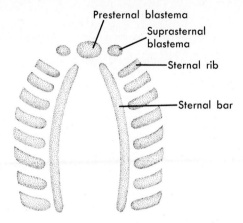

Fig. 7-25. Mesenchymal blastemas that contribute to the amniote sternum. Presternal and suprasternal blastemas develop in mammals only. The ventral ends of developing ribs are also shown.

The amniote sternum arises as paired mesenchymal bars that later unite and undergo chondrogenesis, and in many mammals **presternal** and **suprasternal** blastemas also develop (Fig. 7-25). The presternal blastema contributes to the manubrium, and the suprasternal centers sometimes do. In a few mammals (insectivores, edentates, rodents, and a few others) the suprasternal centers give rise to independent **suprasternal ossicles** that lie between the clavicle and the manubrium. Some human beings have suprasternal ossicles, but they are not found unless there is an occasion to do an x-ray examination of the sternoclavicular joint. One might speculate that the presternal and suprasternal centers are vestiges of the median interclavicle and paired coracoids of the pectoral girdle of reptiles.

CHAPTER SUMMARY

1. Typical vertebrae consist of centra, neural arches, one or more processes, and, in many tails, hemal arches.

2. Transverse processes (diapophyses) are present in most vertebrates. Tetrapods of one species or another have basapophyses, hypapophyses, parapophyses, and zygapophyses.

3. Fishes swim by lateral undulation of trunk and tail and have only trunk and tail vertebrae. Tetrapods locomote by pushing down against the substrate, and their trunk vertebrae are subdivided into cervical, dorsal, and sacral vertebrae. Dorsals are further subdivided into thoracic and lumbar when long curved ribs are limited to the anterior trunk.

4. In fishes the notochord persists within the adult vertebral column from skull to tip of tail. It is constricted within centra, expanded between centra, producing an hourglass-shaped amphicelous vertebra.

5. The notochord sheath and notochord of fishes and primitive urodeles are infiltrated with chordal cartilage, and the sheath is surrounded by perichordal cartilage (elasmobranchs), replacement bone (most fishes), or membrane bone (teleosts, apodans, urodeles).

6. The sole axial skeleton of holocephalans consists of rings of calcified cartilage deposited in the notochord sheath around an unconstricted notochord.

7. Modern lungfishes have no centra. Paired basidorsal, interdorsal, basiventral, and interventral cartilages are aligned along the unconstricted notochord.

8. The centra of elasmobranch fishes consist of chordal cartilage, perichordal cartilage, constricted notochord, and no bone.

9. Cyclostomes have no centra. Lateral neural cartilages are perched above the notochord.

10. Some fishes and primitive tetrapods exhibit diplospondyly.

11. The vertebral columns of crossopterygians and stem amphibians consisted of arches, a hypocentrum, and two pleurocentra per body segment. The notochord was persistent, and the vertebrae were amphicelous. These are rachitomous vertebrae and are probably ancestral to all modern tetrapod vertebrae.

12. Generalized urodeles, caecilians, and primitive lizards have amphicelous vertebrae and retain much notochordal tissue. In mammals, notochord persists in intercentra as pulpy nuclei.

13. More or less vertical flexibility of the vertebral column in tetrapods is provided by opisthocelous (specialized urodeles), procelous (anurans and modern reptiles), heterocelous (birds), and acelous (most mammals) vertebrae.

14. Amphibians have one cervical vertebra. The number is higher in reptiles, and still higher in birds, which have long, flexible necks. The first two vertebrae in amniotes are the atlas and axis. Mammals typically have seven cervicals. A proatlas is found in some reptiles and mammals.

15. Sacral vertebrae bear stout transverse processes that brace the hind limbs and pelvic girdle against the vertebral column. Amphibians have one, reptiles and birds two, and mammals three to five sacral vertebrae.

16. Sacral vertebrae in amniotes usually unite to form a sacrum. The sacrum of birds unites with adjacent lumbar and caudal vertebrae to form a synsacrum.

17. Caudal vertebrae often bear hemal arches or chevron bones. The vertebrae are reduced to archless centra near the end of the tail. Caudal vertebrae in anurans form a urostyle; in birds, a pygostyle; in hominoids, a coccyx.

18. Most vertebrae and the proximal parts of ribs are endochondral bone. Those of teleosts, urodeles, and apodans are membrane bone.

19. Some fishes have dorsal ribs, most have ventral ribs, and a few have both. Agnathans have none.

20. Most tetrapod ribs are bicipital. They are mostly confined to the thorax except in limbless amphibians and reptiles that use them for locomotion. Short ribs are often fused with transverse processes.

21. Gastralia are abdominal ribs of crocodilians and some lizards. They are dermal bone.

22. Sterna are limited to tetrapods. They are absent in limbless tetrapods and turtles and are small or absent in urodeles. Flying birds have a carina, and mammals have sternebrae.

23. Amniote sterna arise in part as paired sternal bars that later unite. Embryonic suprasternal ossicles in mammals may contribute to the sternum or remain as separate bones.

LITERATURE CITED AND SELECTED READINGS

1. Alexander, R.M.: Functional design in fishes, London, 1967, Hutchinson University Library.
2. Evans, F.G.: The morphology and functional evolution of the atlas-axis complex from fish to mammals, Annals of the New York Academy of Sciences **39:**29, 1930.
3. Goodrich, E.S.: Studies on the structure and development of vertebrates, London, 1930, The Macmillan Co., Ltd. (Reprinted by Dover Publications, Inc., New York, 1958.)
4. Hoffstetter, R., and Gasc, J.-P.: Vertebrae and ribs of modern reptiles. In Gans, C., Bellairs, A. d'A., and Parsons, T.S., editors: Biology of the reptilia, vol. 1, New York, 1969, Academic Press, Inc.
5. Laerm, J.: The development, function, and design of amphicelous vertebrae in teleost fishes, Journal of the Linnean Society of London, Zoology **58:**237, 1976.
6. Panchen, A.L.: The origin and early evolution of tetrapod vertebrae. In Andrews, S.M., Miles, R.S., and Walker, A.D., editors: Problems in vertebrate evolution, New York, 1977, Academic Press, Inc.
7. Romer, A.S.: Osteology of the reptiles, Chicago, 1956, University of Chicago Press.
8. Schaeffer, B.: Osteichthyan vertebrae, Journal of the Linnean Society of London, Zoology **47:**185, 1967.
9. Schmalhausen, I.I.: The origin of terrestrial vertebrates (translated from the Russian by Leon Kelso), New York, 1968, Academic Press, Inc.
10. Wake, D.B., and Lawson, R.: Development and adult morphology of the vertebral column in the Plethodontid salamander *Eurycea bislineata,* with comments on vertebral evolution in amphibia, Journal of Morphology **139:**251, 1973.
11. Williams, E.E.: Gadow's arcualia and the development of tetrapod vertebrae, Quarterly Review of Biology **34:**1, 1959.

CHAPTER 8

Skull and visceral skeleton

The word "skull" is seldom misunderstood by the layman. To him, it is the bony structure that Hamlet held in his hand and gazed at dolefully as he spoke his now famous words, "Alas, poor Yorick." To the morphologist, however, the term poses a problem because of the intimate relationship in fishes between the skeleton that protects the brain and special sense organs of the head and the skeleton of the jaws and branchial arches. The latter has been inherited in modified form by higher vertebrates including, alas, poor Yorick. For this reason, the morphologist may avoid the term "skull" and refer instead to (1) the **neurocranium,** or **primary braincase;** (2) the **dermatocranium;** and (3) the **visceral skeleton,** or **splanchnocranium.** In this chapter, for practical purposes, "skull" will mean what the layman probably thinks it means, but without the lower jaw. We can then classify the parts of the cranial skeleton of vertebrates as follows.

Skull

   Neurocranium

   Dermatocranium

Visceral skeleton

   Embryonic upper jaw cartilage (palatoquadrate) and its replacement bones

   Embryonic lower jaw cartilage (Meckel's) and its replacement and investing bones

   Skeleton of the branchial arches

The upper jaw is visceral skeleton because it is part of the first visceral arch (Fig. 8-1). However, in bony vertebrates it becomes incorporated into the skull as development progresses.

THE NEUROCRANIUM

The neurocranium (sometimes called endocranium or primary braincase), is the part of the skull that (1) protects the brain and certain special sense organs, (2) arises as cartilage, and (3) is subsequently partly or wholly replaced by bone except in cartilaginous

In this chapter we will see that vertebrates from fishes to man form their head skeleton out of three components: a cartilaginous braincase, ancient dermal armor, and contributions from the branchial skeleton. We will see how these components are assembled in cartilaginous and bony skulls and note the new functions achieved by the old branchial skeleton when vertebrates took up life on land.

175

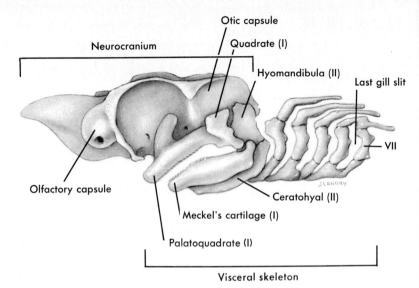

Fig. 8-1. Skull and visceral skeleton of the shark *Squalus acanthias.* **I, II,** and **VII,** Skeleton of first, second, and seventh pharyngeal arches. Labial cartilages, gill rakers, and gill rays are omitted.

fishes. The neurocranium in all jawed vertebrates develops in accordance with the basic pattern described below.

The cartilaginous stage

Parachordal and prechordal cartilages and notochord. The neurocranium commences as a pair of parachordal and prechordal cartilages (Fig. 8-2, *A*) underneath the brain. Parachordal cartilages parallel the anterior end of the notochord beneath the midbrain and hindbrain. Prechordal cartilages (also called **trabeculae cranii**) develop anterior to the notochord underneath the forebrain. The parachordal cartilages expand across the midline toward each other and unite. In the process, the notochord and parachordal cartilages are incorporated into a single, broad, cartilaginous **basal plate.** The prechordal cartilages likewise expand and unite across the midline at their anterior ends to form an **ethmoid plate.**

Sense capsules. While parachordal and prechordal cartilages are forming, cartilage also appears in two other locations: (1) as an **olfactory (nasal) capsule** partially surrounding the olfactory epithelium and (2) as an **otic capsule** completely surrounding the otocyst, which is the developing inner ear (Fig. 8-2, *A* and *B*). The olfactory capsules are incomplete anteriorly, since water (in fishes) or air (in tetrapods) must have access to the olfactory epithelium. The walls of the olfactory and otic capsules are perforated by foramina that transmit nerves and vascular channels.

An **optic capsule** forms around the retina but it is not the orbit, or

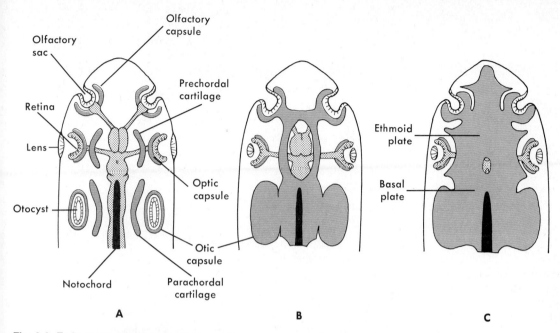

Fig. 8-2. Early stages in development of a cartilaginous neurocranium, as seen from a ventral view. In **A** the notochord is seen underlying the midbrain and hindbrain. In **B** the notochord has been incorporated into the caudal floor of the neurocranium (basal plate). In **C** a cartilaginous floor has been completed beneath the entire brain. The optic capsule will later become the sclerotic coat of the eyeball.

skeletal socket, in which the eyeball lies. It is the **sclerotic coat** of the eyeball. Although this capsule is fibrous in mammals, cartilaginous or bony plates often form within the sclerotic coat (Fig. 16-13). This is an ancient condition, having been present in crossopterygians and extinct amphibians and reptiles. Because the optic capsule does not fuse with the rest of the neurocranium, the eyeball is free to move independently of the skull. Therefore the sclerotic coat is not conventionally considered part of the neurocranium.

Completion of floor, walls, and roof. The expanding ethmoid plate unites anteriorly with the olfactory capsules, and the expanding basal plate unites with the otic capsules that lie lateral to the hindbrain. The ethmoid and basal plates also expand toward one another until they meet to form a floor on which the brain rests (Fig. 8-2, *C*). Further development of the cartilaginous neurocranium involves construction of cartilaginous walls alongside the brain and, in lower forms only, a partial or complete cartilaginous roof over the brain. The cranial nerves and blood vessels are already present by this time, and

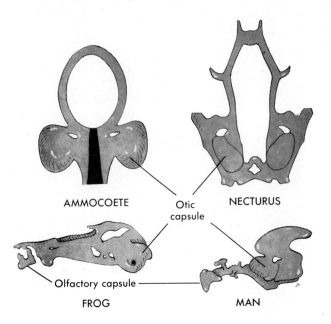

Fig. 8-3. Cartilaginous neurocrania from selected embryonic, larval, or immature vertebrates. Dorsal view of ammocoete and *Necturus;* lateral view of frog and man.

AMMOCOETE

Otic capsule

NECTURUS

Olfactory capsule

FROG

MAN

the cartilage is deposited in a manner that leaves foramina for these structures. The largest is the foramen magnum in the rear wall of the neurocranium.

In cartilaginous and lower bony fishes the brain is completely covered by a cartilaginous roof. But in teleosts and tetrapods the brain is never completely roofed over by cartilage.

The preceding pattern of development recurs throughout the vertebrate series and produces a cartilaginous neurocranium that protects much of the embryonic brain, the olfactory epithelia, and the inner ear (Fig. 8-3). The blastema that gives rise to the cartilaginous neurocranium is a contribution chiefly of neural crest ectoderm with sclerotomal contributions to the basal plate and occipital regions.

Adult cartilaginous neurocrania

Cartilaginous fishes retain a cartilaginous neurocranium thoughout life. The neurocranium in these fishes (Fig. 8-1) completely encloses the brain, and the otic and olfactory capsules are fused into it along with the notochord. Dorsally, an endolymphatic fossa is perforated by endolymphatic and perilymphatic ducts and there is a dorsal opening, the pineal (epiphyseal) foramen, that is occupied by the pineal body in life.

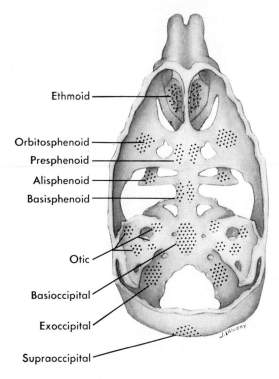

Ethmoid

Orbitosphenoid

Presphenoid

Alisphenoid

Basisphenoid

Otic

Basioccipital

Exoccipital

Supraoccipital

Fig. 8-4. Cartilaginous neurocranium of a fetal pig with chief endochondral ossification centers of mammals superimposed (dots). The neurocranium is complete as shown, there being no cartilage above the brain. The ethmoid center will become the cribriform plate perforated by olfactory foramina. The alisphenoid center is thought to be in the palatoquadrate cartilage in mammals. The otic centers are in the otic capsule.

Among bony fishes, lungfishes and most ganoids retain a highly cartilaginous neurocranium throughout life. In order to see it, the membrane bones that overlie it must be stripped away (Fig. 8-7).

In cyclostomes the several cartilaginous components of the embryonic neurocranium remain in adults as more or less independent cartilages (Fig. 8-32). An olfactory capsule, otic capsules, a basal plate, a notochord (not fused with the basal plate), and other cartilages not homologizable with those of gnathostomes can be identified. The roof above the brain remains fibrous.

Neurocranial ossification centers

In bony vertebrates the embryonic cartilaginous neurocranium is mostly replaced by replacement bone. The process of endochondral ossification occurs more or less simultaneously at numerous separate ossification centers (Fig. 8-4). Although the specific number of such centers varies in different species, four regional groups are universally involved. These groups—occipital, sphenoid, ethmoid, and otic—will be discussed next.

Occipital centers. The cartilage surrounding the foramen magnum may be replaced by as many as four bones. One or more endochondral ossification centers ventral to the foramen magnum produce a

Fig. 8-5. Endochondral ossification centers (dots) and intramembranous ossification centers (black networks) superimposed on the occipital and right temporal bones of an adult cat. **A,** Caudal view. **B,** Medial view. The bulla arises from new cartilage not associated with the earlier neurocranium. The mastoid portion is an outgrowth of the petrous portion.

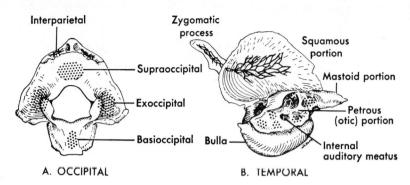

basioccipital bone underlying the hindbrain (Fig. 8-5). Centers in the lateral walls of the foramen magnum produce two **exoccipital bones.** Above the foramen a **supraoccipital bone** may develop. In mammals all four occipital elements usually fuse to form a single **occipital bone.** In modern amphibians, one or more of these may remain cartilaginous, although they were bony in stem amphibians.

The neurocranium of tetrapods articulates with the first vertebra via one or two **occipital condyles.** Stem amphibians had a single condyle borne chiefly on the basioccipital bone. Living reptiles and birds still have a single condyle. Modern amphibians and mammals diverged from the early tetrapod condition, gradually shifting the condyles from the median basioccipital to the two exoccipitals. The selective factors in the environment that caused this shift are unknown, and what the survival value might have been is purely speculative.

Sphenoid centers. The embryonic cartilaginous neurocranium underlying the midbrain and pituitary gland ossifies to form a **basisphenoid bone** (anterior to the basioccipital) and a **presphenoid.** Thus a bony platform consisting of occipital and sphenoid bones underlies the brain. The side walls above the basisphenoid and presphenoid ossification centers form lateral sphenoid elements (**orbitosphenoid, pleurosphenoid,** and others*), and these may remain separate or unite with the basisphenoids and presphenoids to form a single adult **sphenoid bone** with "wings" (Fig. 8-6). The pituitary rests in the sella turcica of the basisphenoid region. No replacement bones develop above the brain.

Ethmoid centers. The ethmoid region lies immediately anterior to the sphenoid and includes the ethmoid plate and olfactory capsules. Of the four major ossification centers in the cartilaginous neurocranium (occipital, sphenoid, ethmoid, otic), the ethmoid more than the

---

*The alisphenoid of at least some mammals evidently forms in the palatoquadrate cartilage rather than in the neurocranium.

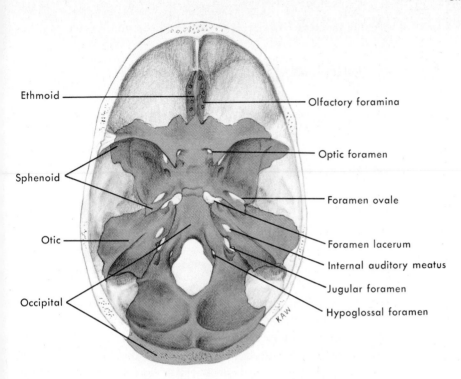

Ethmoid — Olfactory foramina

Optic foramen

Sphenoid

Foramen ovale

Otic — Foramen lacerum

Internal auditory meatus

Jugular foramen

Occipital — Hypoglossal foramen

KAW

Fig. 8-6. Bony neurocranium (red) of human skull. The calvarium (roof) of the skull has been sawed off, and view is looking down into skull from above. Major endochondral ossification centers are labeled at left. The sphenoid bone exhibits an anterior (lesser) wing enclosing the optic foramina and a posterior (greater) wing between the two label lines for the sphenoid bone. The olfactory foramina are in the cribriform plate of the ethmoid.

others tends to remain cartilaginous. Ossification centers in this region become the **cribriform plate** of the ethmoid, perforated by olfactory foramina (Fig. 8-6), and several of the **conchae,** or turbinal bones (**ethmoturbinals**) in the nasal passageways of crocodilians, birds, and mammals. **Mesethmoid** bones ossify in some mammals and contribute to the otherwise cartilaginous median nasal septum. In anurans the **sphenethmoid** is the sole bone arising in the sphenoid and ethmoid regions.

Otic centers. The cartilaginous otic capsule is replaced in lower vertebrates by several bones with such names as **prootic, opisthotic,** and **epiotic.** One or more of these may unite with adjacent replacement or membrane bones. For example, in frogs and most reptiles the opisthotics fuse with the exoccipitals and in birds and mammals the prootic, opisthotic, and epiotics all unite to form a single **periotic,** or **petrosal bone.** The petrosal, in turn, may unite with the squamosal, a membrane bone, to form a **temporal bone** (Fig. 8-5, *B*). Six ossification centers have been described in the otic capsule of a human fetus.

THE GENERALIZED DERMATOCRANIUM

The membrane bones of the skull constitute collectively the dermatocranium. After considering how the dermatocranium probably originated, we will examine its basic architecture in generalized vertebrates. The insight thus gained will enable us to relate the dermatocranium to the rest of the skull in modern tetrapods. Because the skulls of modern fishes are highly specialized and vary widely, we will mention them only occasionally.

How it may have begun

Much of the body of the earliest vertebrates was encased in bony dermal armor. As far back as ostracoderms this armor varied widely in the extent to which it covered the body—head and anterior trunk only, head and entire trunk, or head, trunk, and tail; in the relative size of the bones or scales making up the armor—large shields, smaller plates, minute scales; and in the relative size of the plates or scales on the head contrasted with those on the rest of the body. There is also evidence that some ostracoderms—cephalaspids, at least—passed through one or more cycles of expansion and reduction of their dermal armor, going from tiny scales to increasingly larger plates, then more or less reversing the trend; and that the reduction

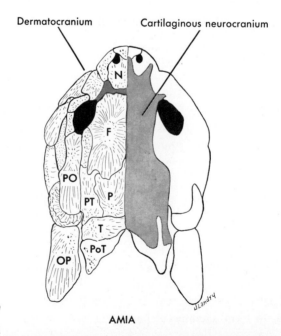

Fig. 8-7. Skull of *Amia calva,* dorsal view. Dermal bones have been removed on the right side to reveal underlying cartilaginous neurocranium. **F,** Frontal bones; **N,** nasal; **OP,** operculum; **P,** parietal; **PO,** postorbital; **PoT,** posttemporal; **PT,** pterotic; **T,** tabular. The bones anterior to the nasals are ethmoids. Premaxillae are not visible in this view.

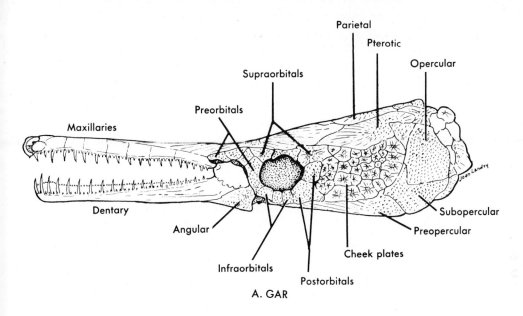

A. GAR

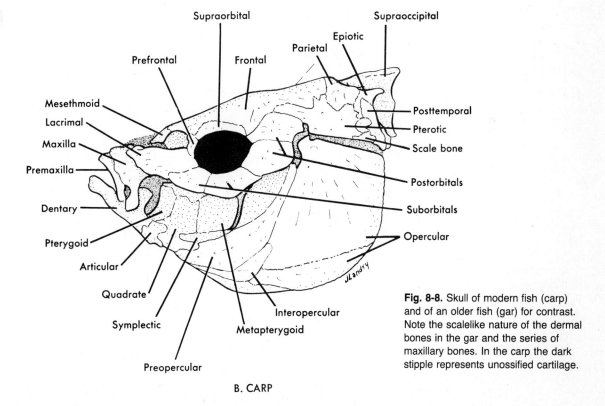

B. CARP

Fig. 8-8. Skull of modern fish (carp) and of an older fish (gar) for contrast. Note the scalelike nature of the dermal bones in the gar and the series of maxillary bones. In the carp the dark stipple represents unossified cartilage.

came earlier and was more complete on the trunk than on the head.[15] Among jawed fishes, too, there have been those that lost most or all their dermal plates or scales except in the skin overlying the neurocranium and pectoral girdle. Even today, in the relict *Amia* and gars,* the membrane bones on the top and sides of the head are still in the skin, where they overlie (invest, ensheath) the neurocranium (Fig. 8-7). The small cheek plates of gars (Fig. 8-8, *A*) are either skull bones or scales, whichever you prefer to call them. It is as though natural selection has been preserving the armor that protected the brain and the sense organs of the head.

In modern vertebrates, these membrane bones of the head no longer ossify from mesenchyme *within* the dermis but from subdermal mesenchyme that is continuous with that of the developing dermis. It is as though scleroblasts responsible for these bones differentiated deeper and deeper in the mesenchyme underlying the epidermis until the bones became part of the skull. *It is these bones that constitute the dermatocranium.* The embryonic mesenchyme that gives rise to them migrates into the embryonic head fold from lateral-plate mesoderm of the trunk.

Its basic structure

For convenience of discussion the generalized dermatocranium can be divided into (1) bones that form above and alongside the brain and neurocranium (roofing bones), (2) dermal bones of the upper jaw, (3) bones of the primary palate, and (4) opercular bones.

Roofing bones. The primitive pattern for roofing bones is seen in crossopterygian fishes and labyrinthodonts (Fig. 8-9). Roofing bones in these vertebrates provided a protective shield over the brain and special sense organs with openings only for the nares and eyes, including the parietal eye. In crossopterygians a series of paired and unpaired bones extended along the middorsal line from the nares to the occiput, overlying the brain, olfactory capsules, and any other neurocranial cartilage that developed in the area. In labyrinthodonts the unpaired bones were missing and a series of paired nasals, frontals, parietals, and postparietals (dermoccipitals) took their place. The postparietals disappeared, perhaps by coalescence with the supraoccipital, in phylogenetic lines diverging from the earliest reptiles. A parietal foramen housing the parietal eye is still present in many fishes, amphibians, and lizards.

Forming a ring around the orbit in the generalized skull were a lacrimal, prefrontal, postfrontal, postorbital, and infraorbital (jugal). At the posterior angle of the skull were intertemporal, supratemporal,

---

*A relict is a survivor of a vanishing group.

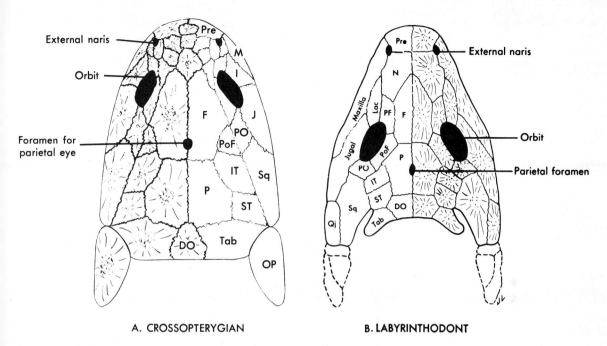

A. CROSSOPTERYGIAN   B. LABYRINTHODONT

Fig. 8-9. Early dermal bone patterns from which tetrapod dermatocrania probably evolved. **A,** Skull of the crossopterygian fish *Eusthenopteron.* Note midline bones and small, scalelike bones in the rostral region. The location of the parietal foramen is in dispute. **B,** Skull of a Carboniferous labyrinthodont, representing the primitive tetrapod condition. Broken lines indicate deleted opercular bones.
DO, Dermoccipital (postparietal); **F,** frontal; **I,** infraorbital; **IT,** intertemporal; **J,** jugal; **Lac,** lacrimal; **M,** maxilla; **N,** nasal; **OP,** opercular; **P,** parietal; **PF,** prefrontal; **PO,** postorbital; **PoF,** postfrontal; **Pre,** premaxilla; **Sq,** squamosal; **ST,** supratemporal; **Qj,** quadratojugal; **Tab,** tabular. (Modified from numerous sources.)

tabular, and, lower down, squamosal and quadratojugal bones. Labyrinthodonts developed a longer facial area, or snout, than is seen in crossopterygians by elongating the bones between the external nares and orbits. This could have been correlated with altered methods of capturing food or manipulating it in the mouth.

Dermal bones of the upper jaw. The earliest embryonic upper jaw, the palatoquadrate cartilage, is not a dermatocranial element but part of the visceral skeleton. It is the only upper jaw that cartilaginous fishes develop, and in many of these fishes it moves independently of the neurocranium (Fig. 8-1). In bony vertebrates this cartilage becomes overlaid, or invested, by tooth-bearing dermal bones, including premaxillae and maxillae, and these become sutured to some of the marginal bones of the dermatocranium, including the jugals (Figs. 8-9 and 8-10). Thus the upper jaw, a part of the visceral skeleton, becomes incorporated into the dermatocranium. This does not hap-

Fig. 8-10. Skull of small sea turtle, lateral view, lower jaw removed. **1,** Premaxilla; **2,** maxilla; **3,** jugal; **4,** quadratojugal; **5,** quadrate; **6,** prefrontal; **7,** frontal; **8,** postfrontal; **9,** parietal; **10,** squamosal; **11,** supraoccipital; **12,** middle ear cavity. (From Kent, G.C.: Systemic dissections of vertebrates: a laboratory guide, St. Louis, 1975, The C.V. Mosby Co.)

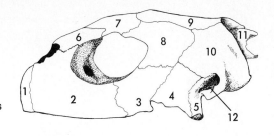

Fig. 8-11. Primary palates of a crossopterygian and labyrinthodont. Note similarity of structure. The basisphenoid and quadrate are not part of the palate.

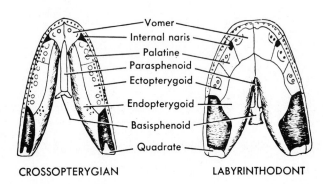

pen to the lower jaw; therefore the dermal bones of the mandible will be discussed under "The visceral skeleton."

The primary palate. The primary palate is the roof of the oral cavity or pharynx. In sharks its skeleton is cartilaginous because it is the floor of the neurocranium on which the brain rests. In bony vertebrates membrane bones are applied to the underside of the neurocranium and to any of the palatoquadrate cartilage extending into the area, and these bones become the major constituents of the primary palate. In crossopterygians and early tetrapods these were an unpaired **parasphenoid** beneath the sphenoid region of the neurocranium, paired **vomers** beneath the ethmoid region, and paired **palatines, endopterygoids,** and **ectopterygoids** laterally (Fig. 8-11). Primitively, teeth formed on all these palatal bones, and some of these teeth persist today in many lower vertebrates. Internal nares pierced the anterolateral margins of the primary palate in lung breathers, and unossified areas (palatal vacuities) separated the endopterygoid and parasphenoid bones. A primary palate is present with modifications in all tetrapods (Figs. 8-12, *B,* and 8-13); but in those that also develop a secondary palate the primary palate ends up in the roof of the nasal passageway (Figs. 8-17 and 11-3).

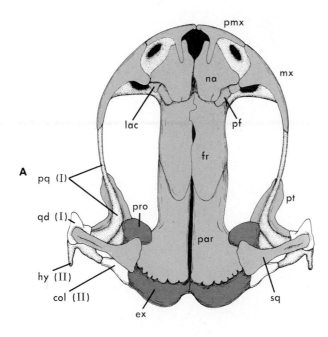

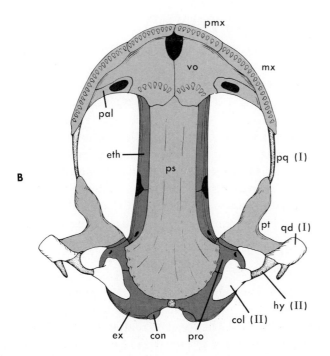

Fig. 8-12. Skull of *Ranodon,* a primitive urodele in the family Hynobiidae. **A,** Dorsal view; **B,** palatal view. Light red indicates dermal bones; dark red, neurocranial bones; stipple, cartilage. **col,** Columella; **con,** occipital condyle; **eth,** sphenethmoid; **ex,** exoccipital; **fr,** frontal; **hy,** dorsal process of hyoid; **lac,** lacrimal; **mx,** maxilla; **na,** nasal; **pal,** palatine; **par,** parietal; **pf,** prefrontal; **pmx,** premaxilla; **pq,** palatoquadrate cartilage; **pro,** prootic; **ps,** parasphenoid; **pt,** pterygoid; **qd,** quadrate; **sq,** squamosal; **vo,** vomer. I and II indicate origin from first or second visceral arch. (After Schmalhausen,[18] courtesy Academic Press, Inc. From Lebedkina.)

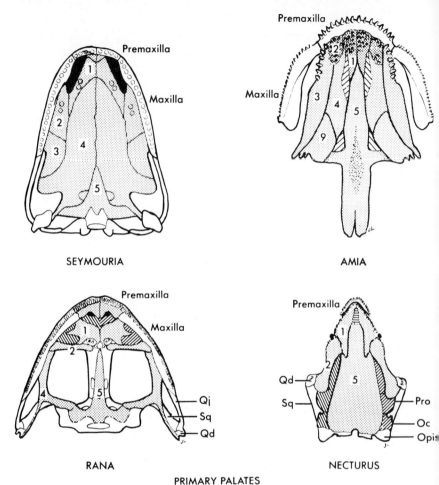

Fig. 8-13. Primary palates of a reptilelike amphibian *(Seymouria),* a ganoid fish *(Amia),* and two amphibians *(Rana* and *Necturus).* Cartilage is indicated by diagonal lines; internal nares are black, and palatal bones are stippled. **1,** Vomer; **2,** palatine (in *Necturus,* palatopterygoid); **3,** ectopterygoid; **4,** endopterygoid; **5,** parasphenoid; **9,** epipterygoid (of endochondral origin). **Oc,** Cartilaginous portion of otic capsule; **Opis,** opisthotic; **Pro,** prootic; **Qd,** quadrate; **Qj,** quadratojugal; **Sq,** squamosal.

Opercular bones. The operculum is a fleshy flap of the hyoid arch of bony fishes. It extends backward over the gill slits (Fig. 12-2), stiffened by opercular bones (Fig. 8-8). Although present in crossopterygian fishes, the operculum was lost along with the gills in the evolution of labyrinthodonts, and no vestiges remain in tetrapods.

THE NEUROCRANIAL-DERMATOCRANIAL COMPLEX IN MODERN TETRAPODS

We can now look briefly at the neurocranial-dermatocranial complex as it has evolved in modern tetrapods. A disproportionate amount of time will be spent on reptiles because they have diversified more than the other tetrapods and because during the Mesozoic the skulls of some of them underwent architectural changes that were incorporated into the skulls of birds and mammals.

Amphibians

The skulls of modern amphibians are considerably modified from those of labyrinthodonts, although they are still **platybasic** (flattened) compared with the vaulted **tropibasic** skulls of higher amniotes. Much of the neurocranium remains cartilaginous, except in apodans. The only replacement bones in anurans and urodeles are a sphenethmoid, two prootics, and two exoccipitals that now bear occipital condyles. In perennibranchiate urodeles even the sphenethmoid fails to ossify. The rigid bony neurocranium of apodans may be correlated with burrowing.

The dermatocranium consists of fewer membrane bones than that of labyrinthodonts. The bones that once surrounded the orbit have been lost except for the lacrimals and prefrontals that are still present in primitive urodeles (Fig. 8-12, *A*). Also missing are the primitive bones of the temporal region from the orbit caudad (intertemporals, supratemporals, tabulars, postparietal). This leaves the otic capsule exposed dorsally and laterally. Only the squamosal and, sometimes, quadratojugal remain in this region. Premaxillae and maxillae are usually represented in the upper jaw (the lower margin of the dermatocranium), but in perennibranchiates even maxillae fail to develop.

The primary palate has been altered. Ectopterygoids have been lost, and the remaining pterygoids have been reduced to a pair of bipartite bones that form braces between the upper jaw and the braincase posteriorly (Fig. 8-12, *B*). In anurans the palatines have been reduced to transverse splinters that brace the upper jaw against the palate anteriorly, and enormous palatal vacuities have developed (Fig. 8-13, *Rana*). As a result, the large eyeballs, which monitor the environment just above the water line when the frog is nearly submerged, can be retracted into the roof of the oral cavity. In urodeles, on the contrary, the parasphenoid has become exceptionally broad (Fig. 8-13, *Necturus*).

The hyomandibula, a bone of the second pharyngeal arch that is inherited from fishes (Fig. 8-1), has become the **columella,** a bone of the middle ear. This and other changes associated with loss of gills are discussed under "The visceral skeleton."

Reptiles

The skulls of cotylosaurs were little changed from those of labyrinthodonts, and some of the primitive features are still present in modern reptiles. Among these are a full complement of neurocranial bones, a single occipital condyle, a larger complement of membrane bones than remains in other modern tetrapods (Fig. 8-14, alligator), and, in many lizards, a parietal foramen housing a third eye. Among

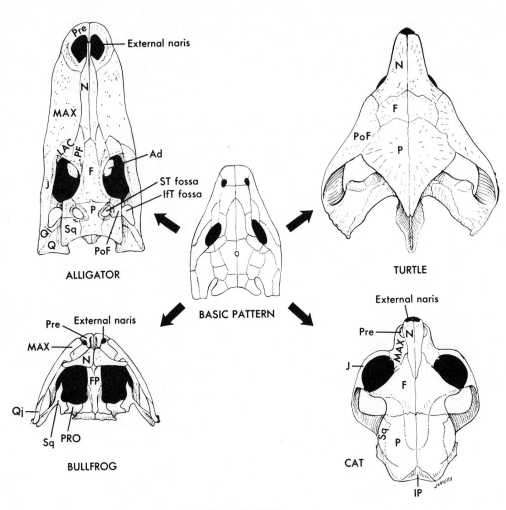

ROOFING BONES

Fig. 8-14. Roofing area and associated bones in selected tetrapods, dorsal views. The basic pattern represents a labyrinthodont. The turtle is an alligator snapping turtle, *Macroclemys temminckii.* **F,** Frontal; **LAC,** lacrimal; **N,** nasal; **P,** parietal; **PF,** prefrontal; **PoF,** postfrontal; **Pre,** premaxilla; **Sq,** squamosal; **ST,** supratemporal fossa; **Qj,** quadratojugal; **Ad,** adlacrimal; **FP,** frontoparietal; **IfT,** infratemporal fossa; **IP,** interparietal; **J,** jugal; **MAX,** maxilla; **PRO,** prootic; **Q,** quadrate. As a study aid you may wish to color homologous bones on the different skulls with the same colors.

major modifications that developed are temporal fossae, a partial or complete secondary palate, and, in therapsid reptiles, two occipital condyles and increased prominence of the dentary bone. Fossae and a partial secondary palate have been transmitted to birds through archosaurs, and all four modifications have been transmitted to mammals through therapsid reptiles.

TEMPORAL FOSSAE AND A NEW JAW JOINT

A temporal fossa is a hollowed-out region bounded by one or more bony arches in the temporal region of the amniote skull (Fig. 8-15). Stem reptiles had none, and so their skulls are **anapsid**—lacking an arch. Today, only turtles among living amniotes lack temporal fossae. Synapsida, the extinct mammal-like reptiles, developed a single tem-

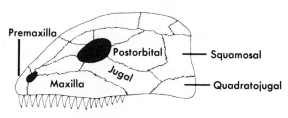

A. ANAPSID (stem reptile)

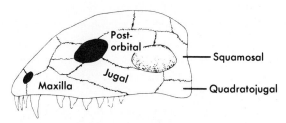

B. SYNAPSID (mammal stock)

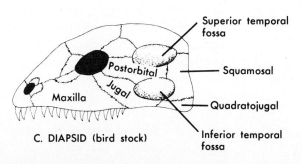

C. DIAPSID (bird stock)

Fig. 8-15. Temporal fossae in reptiles leading to birds and mammals. The squamosal and postorbital bone in the diapsid skull form the superior temporal arch. The squamosal and jugals form the zygomatic arch in the synapsid skull.

poral fossa surrounded by the postorbital, squamosal, and jugal bones, the last two forming an underlying **zygomatic arch.** This **synapsid skull** was transmitted to mammals.

Some reptiles developed superior and inferior temporal fossae (Fig. 8-15, *C*). When there are two fossae there are two arches, hence the term, **diapsid skull.** The lower arch corresponds to the zygomatic arch of synapsids. The upper arch, beneath the superior temporal fossa, is formed by the postorbital and squamosal bones. Birds arose from diapsid reptiles and, like crocodilians, have diapsid skulls. Lizards and snakes have modified diapsid skulls, lizards having lost the lower arch and snakes both arches.

Ichthyosaurs and plesiosaurs had one dorsally located fossa, which may have been equivalent to the superior fossa of diapsids, since the postorbital bone met the squamosal below the fossa. This **euryapsid** condition no longer exists.

The temporal region of a turtle skull is an enigma. It has no fossa, which suggests a primitive condition. Yet, there seems to have been considerable excavation at the rear. Supratemporal, tabular, and postparietal bones are missing, the postorbital bone has united with the postfrontal bone, and parietal and squamosal bones have receded from the rear, leaving a wide gap in the temporal region (Fig. 8-14, turtle). Therefore it cannot be said with assurance that the turtle skull is a true anapsid condition.

Temporal fossae provide space and surfaces in functionally necessary positions for accommodating the powerful adductor muscles that raise the lower jaws of amniotes. In labyrinthodonts and cotylosaurs the adductor mandibulae was confined to cramped quarters just internal to the roofing bones of the temporal region. (In cartilaginous fishes it lies just under the skin of the head because there is no dermatocranium [Fig. 10-16, *A*].) At best this muscle enabled primitive fishes and tetrapods to seize food, bite off pieces of large prey, and close the mouth to prevent return of the food to the environment. The food was swallowed whole. Temporal fossae provided the adductor with relatively cavernous spaces in which to thicken during contraction, opened an exit that enabled the muscle to spread upward to acquire an attachment on the surface of the dermatocranium for better leverage, and provided one or more bony arches for the anatomical origin of a masseter muscle, which separated from the primitive adductor mandibulae along with a temporalis and pterygoid muscle. (Fig. 10-16, *C*, shows the masseter and temporalis. The pterygoid lies medial to the masseter in the primitive position.) These powerful adductors, assisted by hyoid arch muscles, produce the complex side-to-side, forward-backward, and rotatory chewing movements seen in herbivores that grind grasses or chew their cuds and in carnivores that crush bones.

The increased mass of the chewing muscles resulted in broader surfaces on the lower jaw for their insertion and necessitated stronger bracing of the lower jaw against the skull. These changes can be followed in successively later Triassic synapsid reptiles. A ramus developed on the dentary bone and extended increasingly farther upward in the temporal fossa toward the temporal region (Fig. 8-16, *B* and *C*). Meanwhile, the fossa was moving lower and farther caudad, as if to accommodate the ramus. The ramus provided a broad lateral surface area for insertion of the growing masseter and a broad medial surface for the pterygoid. In addition, a rugged coronoid process developed high on the ramus where the temporalis was inserting. At the same time, the remaining bones of the reptilian mandible were being reduced, which culminated in mammals in loss of all lower jaw bones except the dentary (Fig. 8-16, *D*).

Expansion of the dentary bone brought it close to, and finally in contact with, the squamosal (now part of the temporal bone), against which it established a site of bracing and articulation. For a while, therefore, the lower jaw articulated at two places with the skull on each side. The articular bone formed a joint with the quadrate of the upper jaw, as in generalized reptiles, and the dentary formed a joint with the squamosal, as it does in today's mammals. The two joints existed side by side in *Eozostrodon*, one of the oldest known mammals of the Late Triassic. Soon, however, the articular and quadrate (bones of the visceral skeleton, and not dermal bones), were captured by the middle ear cavity and became ear ossicles. Mammals had achieved a new jaw joint between dentary and squamosal! The shape, slant, and relationships of the condyle on the ramus of the dentary bone where it articulated with the skull differed with the demands made on it by the feeding habits of different mammals.

SECONDARY PALATES

A secondary palate is a horizontal partition that divides the primitive oral cavity, the roof of which is the primary palate, into separate oral and nasal passageways, thereby displacing the internal nares caudad (Fig. 11-3, cat). Embryonic development of a secondary palate in a mammal is illustrated in Fig. 8-17. A secondary palate appears first in reptiles. In crocodilians, medially directed shelflike palatal processes of the premaxillae, maxillae, palatine, and pterygoid bones meet in the midline to form a completely bony secondary palate with internal nares far to the rear (Fig. 8-18, alligator). In other reptiles and in birds most palatal processes, if formed, do not reach the mid-

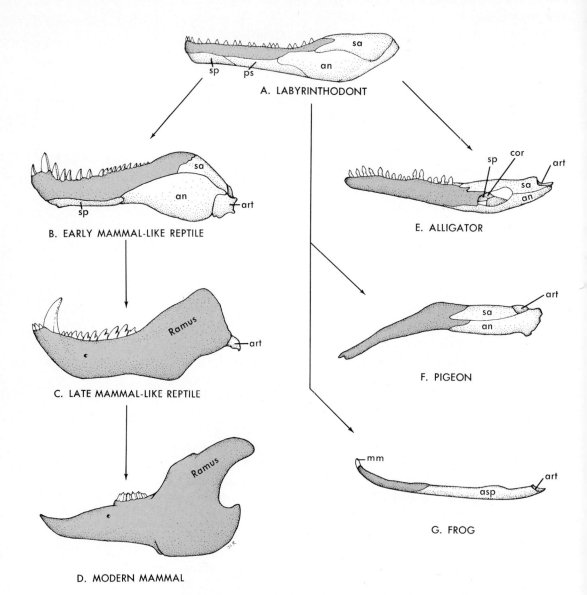

Fig. 8-16. The mandibles of tetrapods. **A** to **D**, Probable evolutionary stages leading to modern mammals. The dentary (red) became increasingly larger, whereas other bones were reduced and finally lost. Arrows indicate phylogenetic pathways. **E** to **G**, Lower jaws of three modern tetrapods for comparison with primitive pattern. All are dermal bones except the mentomeckelian and articular. **an,** Angular; **art,** articular (cartilage in frog); **asp,** angulosplenial; **cor,** coronoid; **mm,** mentomeckelian; **ps,** postsplenial; **sa,** surangular; **sp** splenial. **B,** Pelycosaur; **C,** late therapsid; **D,** rabbit. Left lateral views.

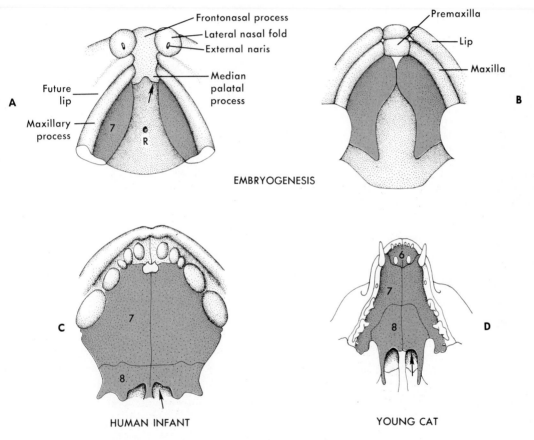

EMBRYOGENESIS

HUMAN INFANT   YOUNG CAT

SECONDARY PALATES

Fig. 8-17. A to **C,** Formation of secondary palate in humans. **D,** Secondary palate
of young cat for comparison. Arrows indicate nasal passageways. **6,** Palatine
process of premaxilla; **7,** palatine process of maxilla; **8,** palatine process of
palatine bone. In **A** (fetus approximately 18 weeks old) the palatine processes of
the maxillae are growing toward the midline, forming a secondary roof (red) in the
oral cavity. **R,** Rathke's pouch in primary roof. In **B** the palatine processes of the
maxillae have met anteriorly. In **C** the palate is complete. Failure of palatine
processes to meet in midline results in a cleft palate.

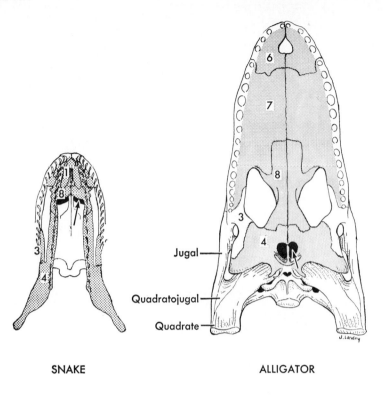

Fig. 8-18. Long secondary palate of alligator (gray) and short secondary palate of water snake (represented by palatine process of palatine bone). Compare location of internal nares (arrows). **1,** Vomer of primary palate; **3,** ectopterygoid; **4,** pterygoid; **6,** palatine process of premaxilla; **7,** palatine process of maxilla; **8,** palatine process of palatine. The palatines continue caudad as palatal ridges bounding a palatal fissure and articulating with the pterygoid.

SNAKE   ALLIGATOR

line, and the secondary palate is shorter, or incomplete (Figs. 8-18, snake, and 8-19). In mammals the pterygoid bone does not participate in forming the secondary palate and the caudal part of the palate is fleshy (soft palate). Failure of one or more of the processes to reach the midline results in a cleft palate. Some turtles may be said to have a cleft palate as a normal condition. In vertebrates with a secondary palate the primary palate remains in the roof of the nasal passageway underlying the neurocranium, usually with a reduced complement of membrane bones. For example, no parasphenoid is present in crocodilians.

The secondary palate of crocodilians and mammals separates the respiratory airstream from the food pathway all the way to the glottis (crocodilians), or most of the way (mammals), enabling the mouth to be occupied with food without breathing being interrupted. The advantage to a terrestrial mammal that masticates its food is easily demonstrable. Try eating a hamburger while holding your nose closed!

Although squamates and birds have a very short secondary palate, they channelize the respiratory airstream in a palatal fissure bounded by longitudinal ridges on the palatine bones (Figs. 8-18, snake, and 11-4). The ridges resemble the palatal processes that give rise to secondary palates.

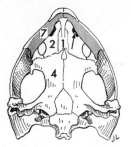

A. COMMON SNAPPER

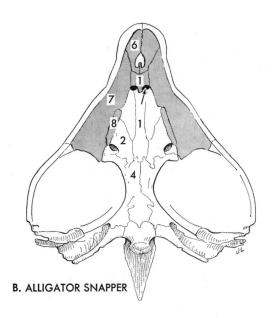

B. ALLIGATOR SNAPPER

Fig. 8-19. Species differences in the secondary palate (gray) of turtles. **A,** *Chelydra serpentina.* **B,** *Macroclemys temminckii.* **C,** *Lepidochelys olivacea* Ridley, the posterior part of the quadrate and the squamosal and supraoccipital regions omitted. In **A** only the maxilla, **7,** participates in formation of the rudimentary secondary palate. In **B** and **C** additional bones participate. **1,** Vomer; **2,** palatine bone of primary palate; **4,** pterygoid; **6,** palatine process of premaxilla; **7,** palatine process of maxilla; **8,** palatine process of palatine bone. Arrows indicate position of internal nares. You may wish to color homologous bones with the same colors.

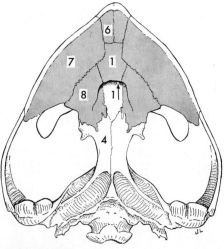

C. SEA TURTLE

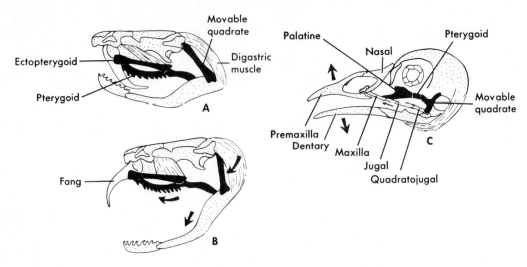

Fig. 8-20. A and **B,** One kind of kinetism in the palate of a snake; **C,** kinetism in a bird's skull. Note the hinge in front of the orbit between nasal bone and braincase. Arrows indicate direction of movement as the mouth opens.

Table 8-1. Skulls of early tetrapods contrasted with those of modern amphibians and reptiles with reference to a few selected characteristics

	Early tetrapods	Modern reptiles	Modern amphibians
Neurocranium	Well ossified	Well ossified	Mostly cartilage
	One condyle	One condyle	Two condyles
	Platybasic	Tropibasic	Platybasic
Primary palate	Complete complement of dermal bones	Relatively complete	Fewer
	Parasphenoid small	Small	Large in urodeles
	Vacuity small	Small	Large in anurans
	Internal nares lateral	Medial	Lateral
Secondary palate	None	Partial or complete	None
Dermal roofing bones	Complete complement	Some reduction	Extensive reduction
Parietal foramen	Present	Present in some	Confined to larvae
Marginal bones	Complete complement	Usually complete	Fewer
Bones ensheathing Meckel's cartilage	Numerous	Numerous	Fewer

Kinetism. The palates of caecilians, snakes, most lizards, and birds have movable hingelike joints within the complex and, along with the upper jaw in some species, are movable independently of the rest of the skull. The complex in amniotes usually pivots on a movable quadrate that shoves the entire complex forward and upward, raising the upper jaw (Fig. 8-20). This enables snakes to open their mouth wide enough to take in animals larger than their own head. Mechanical details differ among the orders. **Cranial kinesis** was present in one form or another in crossopterygians, some labyrinthodonts, and some extinct reptiles. In Table 8-1 the skulls of early tetrapods and modern amphibians and reptiles are contrasted with respect to the palates and a few other traits.

Birds

Differences between birds' skulls and those of their archosaurian ancestors are largely associated with altered feeding habits, a larger brain, reduction in thickness of the bones, loss of sutures in adult carinates, and large orbits (Fig. 8-20, *C*). The neurocranium is well ossified, incomplete dorsally, and bears a single occipital condyle. There is a reptilian complement of dermal bones, but these have become thin and lightweight, which shifted the bird's center of gravity caudad and reduced the energy needed to balance on two legs. Despite this the skull is sturdy. The ethmoid region of the neurocranium and a narrow arch of roofing bones between the orbits bear the shocks generated when woodpeckers drill in solid wood. The enlarged brain has resulted in a vaulted skull with the frontal and parietal bones bulging outward and arching upward alongside the brain. The foramen for the parietal eye was lost as alternative mechanisms for synchronizing gonadal cycles with day lengths evolved. The skull is diapsid, but the arch between the superior and inferior temporal fossae has been lost. The lacrimal bones are pierced by a lacrimal duct that drains excess tears from the surface of the eyeball into the nasal canal. Premaxillae and dentaries and, sometimes, maxillae and nasals form elongated beaks adapted for a variety of feeding habits (Fig. 18-1).

Elongated forward-directed processes of the palatine bones of the primary palate support palatal folds in the roof of the oral cavity (Fig. 8-21). These channelize the respiratory airstream in a deep groove (the **palatal fissure**) between internal nares and glottis (Fig. 11-4). The palate and upper jaw complex exhibit several varieties of kinetism in the different orders (Fig. 8-20, *C*). The parasphenoid does not participate in the kinetic movements, being fused with the basisphenoid. It encloses auditory tubes that extend between the middle ear cavity and pharynx. As in reptiles, there is a single ear ossicle, the **columella**.

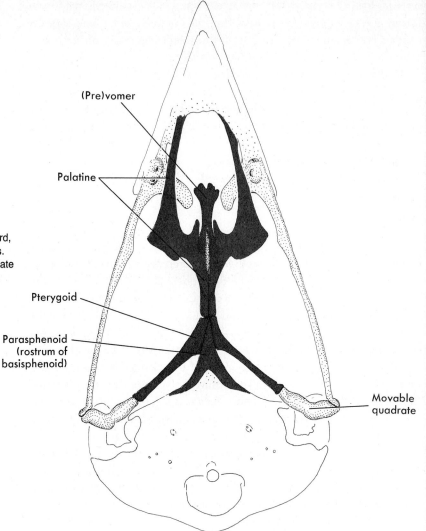

Fig 8-21. Primary palate (red) of a bird, the cotinga. Birds lack ectopterygoids. (Courtesy J.J. Moroney, Louisiana State University Natural Science Museum, Baton Rouge.)

(Pre)vomer

Palatine

Pterygoid

Parasphenoid
(rostrum of
basisphenoid)

Movable
quadrate

Mammals

The major features that differentiate mammalian skulls from those of reptiles other than synapsids have been described in earlier discussions of *temporal fossae, enlargement of the dentary bone,* the *altered site of articulation of the lower jaw with the braincase,* and *secondary palates.* The mammalian skull has also become increasingly domed as the cerebral hemispheres ballooned dorsally, laterally, and caudad. The skull of modern man is rounder and higher than that of as recent an anthropoid as Neanderthal man.

The neurocranium does not form above the brain, and soft spots

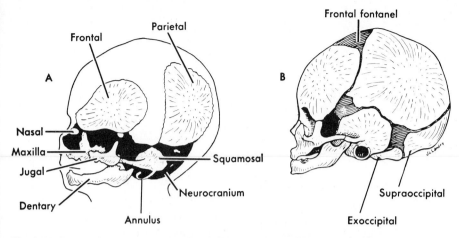

Fig. 8-22. Two stages in the development of the human skull. **A,** Intramembranous ossification is under way. The neurocranium (black) is incomplete lateral to and above the brain. **B,** Intramembranous ossification has progressed, but "soft spots" (fontanels) remain where there is no cartilage or bone. The exoccipital and supraoccipital are neurocranial bones.

can be felt in the heads of newborn babies until ossification of the roofing bones is complete (Fig. 8-22). Soft spots, or **fontanels,** enable the fetal skull to be molded appropriately during delivery through the narrow birth canal. A small bregmatic bone ossifies in the frontal fontanel in some species and occurs as an anomaly in human beings. Paracelsus called it the "antiepileptic bone" because he believed it served as a pop-up valve for relieving pressure in the head. Occipital bones bear two occipital condyles inherited from therapsid reptiles. The basioccipital and sphenoid bones form a floor on which the brain stem rests, and ethmoid cartilages or bones underlie the olfactory bulbs, house the olfactory epithelium, and transmit olfactory nerve bundles. Ossification centers in the otic capsules form a pair of periotic (petrosal) bones that lie buried beneath the overgrown temporal lobes of the cerebral hemispheres. The endoskeletal components of a typical mammalian skull are diagramed in Fig. 8-23.

The dermatocranium is usually represented in mammals by paired premaxillae, maxillae, jugals (malars), nasals, lacrimals, and squamosals; by paired or unpaired frontals and parietals; and by an unpaired interparietal, all of which are paired in embryos and, in some species, in neonates. A postparietal was found in *Homo erectus* and is still present in some human populations, chiefly Mongolians. It is sometimes called an Inca bone because it was common among Inca Indians (Fig. 8-24). Premaxillae are not identifiable in human skulls because

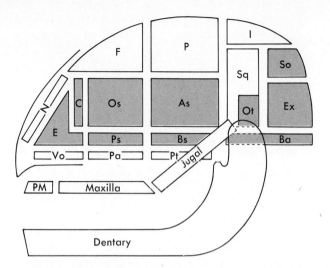

Fig. 8-23. Chief endochondral (red) and dermatocranial (white) components in a typical mammalian skull. The vomer, palatine, and pterygoid are parts of the primary palate. The premaxilla and maxilla contribute horizontal processes to the secondary palate. The dentary is a membrane bone of the visceral skeleton. The alisphenoid is said to be derived from the palatoquadrate cartilage or, occasionally, to be intramembranous in origin.

As, Pleurosphenoid (alisphenoid)
Ba, Basioccipital
Bs, Basisphenoid
C, Cribriform plate of ethmoid
E, Ethmoid, perpendicular plate
Ex, Exoccipital
F, Frontal

I, Interparietal
N, Nasal
Os, Orbitosphenoid
Ot, Otic (petrous)
P, Parietal
Pa, Palatine

PM, Premaxilla
Ps, Presphenoid
Pt, Pterygoid
So, Supraoccipital
Sq, Squamosal
Vo, Vomer

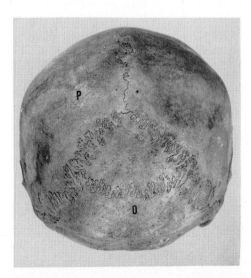

Fig. 8-24. Inca bone in a human skull from the Aleutian Islands. **P,** Parietal; **O,** occipital. (Courtesy William S. Laughlin.)

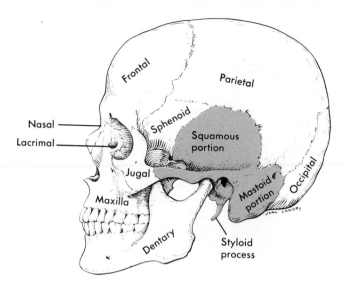

Fig. 8-25. Skull of modern man. The temporal bone is red.

they unite with the maxillae early in embryonic life, a discovery made by the poet-biologist Goethe, much to his "unspeakable joy." The zygomatic arch varies from massive to slender, depending on the power exerted by the masseter muscle. It has become extremely delicate, or even incomplete, in insectivores that do little chewing of their food.

Some mammals have a temporal bone (Fig. 8-25). When present as an entity, it consists of numerous components that are separate in other mammals (Fig. 8-26). The **squamous portion** is the squamosal bone of other mammals. The **petrosal component** is the ossified otic capsule. The **tympanic portion** surrounds the middle ear cavity and sometimes expands to form a tympanic bulla (Fig. 8-27). Associated with the tympanic portion is a bony ring, the **annulus tympanicus** (Fig. 8-34), derived, according to evidence from embryonic opossums, from the angular bone of reptiles.* The tympanic membrane, or eardrum, is attached to it. A **mastoid portion** of endochondral origin is new in mammals. A **styloid process** from the hyoid arch sometimes coalesces with the temporal bone ventrally (Fig. 8-25).

Air-filled cranial sinuses are often found within the maxilla, sphenoid, and ethmoid bones. The frontal sinuses of sheep and goats extend into the horns; and when male goats butt heads at speeds of up to 35 miles (60 km) per hour as part of the mating ritual, the walls of the sinus act as a bony brace that shunts the shock waves away from the brain to the vertebral column via bones of the skull.[16]

---

*The annulus of anurans is thought to be derived from the palatoquadrate cartilage.

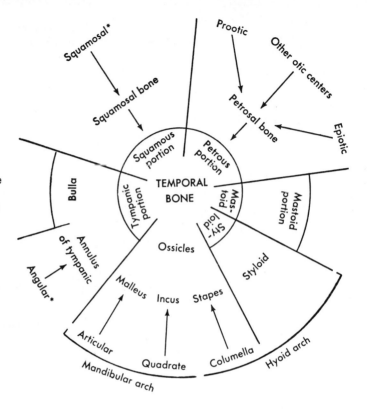

Fig. 8-26. Schematic representation of the multiple nature of the temporal bone of mammals. Note reduction in number of separate elements from the condition in reptiles (outer circle) to mammals (other circles). The two dermal elements have asterisks. The mastoid portion and tympanic bulla are mammalian innovations. The ossicles are within the temporal bone but not part of it.

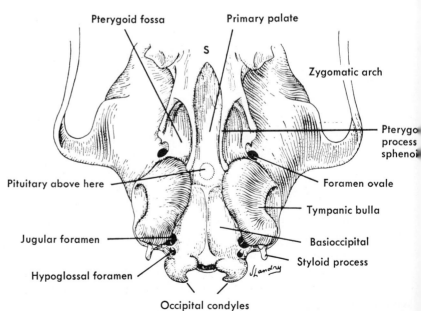

Fig. 8-27. Hamster skull, caudal part, ventral view. **S**, Secondary palate. The primary palate is the roof of the nasopharynx.

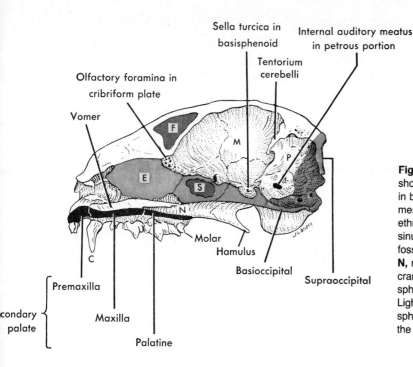

Olfactory foramina in
cribriform plate

Vomer

Sella turcica in
basisphenoid

Internal auditory meatus
in petrous portion

Tentorium
cerebelli

F

M

P

E

S

N

C

Molar

Hamulus

Basioccipital

Supraoccipital

Premaxilla

Maxilla

Palatine

condary
palate

Fig. 8-28. Sagittal section, cat skull, showing bony part of secondary palate in black. **C,** Canine tooth; **E,** mesethmoid (perpendicular plate of ethmoid) in nasal septum; **F,** frontal sinus in frontal bone; **M,** middle cranial fossa housing cerebral hemispheres; **N,** nasal passageway; **P,** posterior cranial fossa housing cerebellum; **S,** sphenoidal sinus in presphenoid bone. Light gray designates ethmoid, sphenoid, and occipital components of the neurocranium.

Of the primary palate inherited from reptiles, the vomer, now unpaired, lies at the base of the nasal septum (Fig. 8-28), and the palatines are in the lateral wall of the nasopharynx where they contribute to the orbit. The pterygoids are reduced to small winglike pterygoid processes of the sphenoid complex (Fig. 8-27). The parasphenoid and ectopterygoids have been lost.

Mammals have three pairs of scroll-like turbinal bones, or conchae, extending into the nasal passageway from the nasal, ethmoid, and maxillary bones (Fig. 12-21). Inspired air en route to the lungs is moistened and warmed by venous plexuses beneath their nasal epithelium. Most reptiles other than turtles have one pair of turbinals and birds have two, but these may not all be homologous. Ethmoturbinals are high in the nasal cavity of mammals and are covered with olfactory epithelium. Their turbinal structure traps some of the inspired air so that weak or highly diluted odorants coming from food or enemies are more likely to be detected.

Unique in mammals is the presence of the articular and quadrate bones in the middle ear cavity, where they serve as ear ossicles along with the columella.

Reduction in number of bones during phylogeny

The number of individual bones, especially membrane bones, has tended to be reduced during phylogeny. With reference to Fig. 3-32, any group at the end of an arrow has fewer bones in the skull than the group preceding it in the phylogenetic line. Labyrinthodonts had fewer than crossopterygians, cotylosaurs had fewer than labyrinthodonts, modern reptiles have fewer than cotylosaurs, and mammals have fewer than mammal-like reptiles. Modern amphibians have fewer than their ancestors, the labyrinthodonts. This generalization does not mean that *modern* reptiles have fewer bones than *modern* amphibians. In fact, reptiles have more. But then, modern reptiles were not derived from modern amphibians.

The reduction is a result of fusion of adjacent embryonic ossification centers, phylogenetic loss of ossification centers, and obliteration of sutures in young animals. Reduction in the number of membrane bones in the mandible during phylogeny illustrates this trend (Fig. 8-16 and Table 8-2).

Membrane bones often unite with adjacent replacement bones, giving rise to a single bone with a dual history. Postfrontals and su-

Table 8-2. Reduction in number of dermal bones investing Meckel's cartilage when early vertebrates are contrasted with later ones

Fishes			Tetrapods				
			Primitive	Modern			
Primitive	Crossopterygians	Modern	Labyrinthodonts	Reptiles and birds	Amphibians	Mammals	
Dentary	Dentary	Dentary*	Dentary	Dentary	Dentary	Dentary	
Angular	Angular	Angular†	Angular	Angular	Angular‡		
Surangular	Surangular		Surangular	Surangular			
Infradentary§	Splenial		Splenial	Splenial	Splenial‡		
Infradentary	Coronoid		Coronoid	Coronoid			
Infradentary	Prearticular	Derm-articular‖	Prearticular				
Infradentary			Intercoronoid				
Infradentary			Precoronoid				
Infradentary			Postsplenial				
Infradentary							

Primitive forms had a larger number of bones than modern ones. Reptiles have retained more of the primitive elements than other modern tetrapods.

*Dentary incorporates mentomeckelian of endochondral origin in some teleosts.
†May be absent. Sometimes named surangular.
‡Sometimes incorporated in an angulosplenial.
§Variable number.
‖May include articular of cartilage origin.

pratemporals sometimes unite with replacement bones of the otic capsule to form sphenotic and pterotic bones; the squamosal unites with otic and other elements to contribute to a temporal bone. The mammalian interparietal, a membrane bone, may unite with the supraoccipital. Unions such as these have reduced the number of bones in the skulls of recent tetrapods.

THE VISCERAL SKELETON

The visceral skeleton, or splanchnocranium, is the skeleton of the pharyngeal arches. In fishes, therefore, it is the skeleton of the jaws and gill arches. In tetrapods this skeleton has become modified to perform new functions on land.

The blastemas that give rise to the visceral skeleton come from neural crests, and they first secrete cartilage. Later, the cartilage may be partly or wholly replaced by bone. Only in the first arch is it ensheathed by dermal bone. We will look first at a shark, in which no bone forms and in which we can see the visceral skeleton in its primitive capacity, that of supporting the jaws and gills.

Sharks

Squalus acanthias is a generalized vertebrate that, however, lacks ensheathing and replacement bones. The visceral skeleton consists of cartilages in each pharyngeal arch (Fig. 8-1) and median **basihyal** and **basibranchial cartilages** in the pharyngeal floor (Fig. 8-29). The skeleton in each arch conforms fairly closely to a basic pattern (Fig. 8-30,

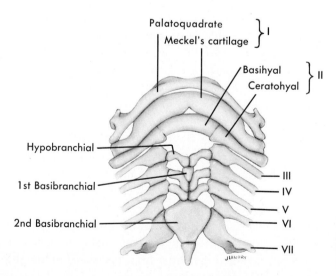

Fig. 8-29. Visceral skeleton of *Squalus acanthias,* ventral view. **III** to **VII,** Ceratobranchial cartilages of the third to seventh pharyngeal arches.

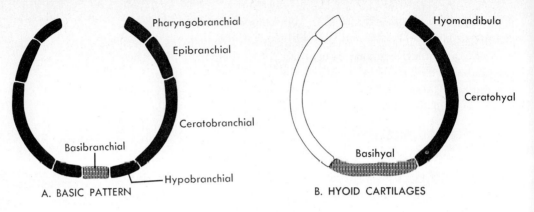

A. BASIC PATTERN

B. HYOID CARTILAGES

Fig. 8-30. Skeletal components of a typical branchial arch, **A,** and modifications in the hyoid and mandibular arches of *Squalus acanthias,* **B** and **C.** Midventral elements in the pharyngeal floor are shown in white on black. The basihyal is paired in embryos.

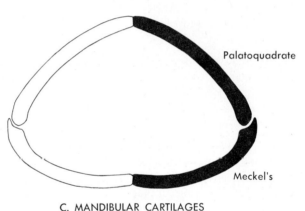

C. MANDIBULAR CARTILAGES

A), and all but the first and last support gills. The first arch and, to a degree, the second, are modified for feeding.

The skeleton of the first (mandibular) arch consists of two cartilages on each side, a **palatoquadrate cartilage** dorsally and **Meckel's cartilage** ventrally (Fig. 8-30, *C*). The left and right cartilages meet in the midline to form the upper and lower jaws. Slender labial cartilages of unknown significance (not illustrated) extend from the angles of the mouth into a position where lips would be. The skeleton of the second (hyoid) arch consists of paired **hyomandibular cartilages** dorsally and gill-bearing **ceratohyals** laterally (Figs. 8-1 and 8-30, *B*).

At the angle of the mouth, Meckel's cartilage and the palatoquadrate cartilage articulate with one another and with the hyomandibula in a movable joint united by ligaments (Fig. 8-1). The other end of the hyomandibula is bound by ligaments to the otic capsule and suspends the jaws and the entire branchial skeleton from the neurocranium. This is **hyostylic jaw suspension.**

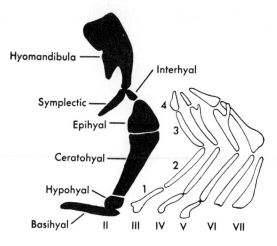

Hyomandibula

Interhyal

Symplectic

4

Epihyal

3

Ceratohyal

2

Hypohyal

1

Basihyal

II III IV V VI VII

BRANCHIAL SKELETON

Salmon

Fig. 8-31. Visceral skeleton of a salmon, upper and lower jaws removed. Hyoid cartilages are in black. The basihyal is unpaired. **1** to **4,** Hypobranchial, ceratobranchial, epibranchial, and pharyngobranchial elements of the third arch.

Bony fishes

The visceral skeleton of bony fishes resembles that of sharks in general morphology (Fig. 8-31). The chief differences are that the embryonic palatoquadrate and Meckel's cartilages become invested by dermal bones, the hyoid arch consists of more segments that enable it to assume additional roles in feeding, and the remaining arches consist of replacement bone instead of cartilage.

The palatoquadrate cartilages ossify at their caudal ends to become **quadrate bones,** the palatal portions of these cartilages usually ossify to become palatine,* epipterygoid, and metapterygoid bones; and the entire upper jaw complex acquires a new relationship to the skull by becoming invested by membrane bones. The membrane bones vary in number and relationships, and similarly named bones are often of doubtful homology or clearly not homologous. One bone is usually named **maxilla** in all species (Fig. 8-8, *B*).

Meckel's cartilages ossify at their caudal ends to become **articular bones,** and the remainder of these cartilages becomes invested by a variety of membrane bones, one of which is usually named **dentary** (Fig. 8-8, *B*). In some fishes a short segment of Meckel's cartilage at the mandibular symphysis ossifies to become a mento-meckelian bone. (The mentomeckelian of some amphibians is a membrane bone.)

Fig. 8-31 shows the replacement bones of the hyoid arch of a salmon. The hyomandibula articulates with the otic capsule, as in sharks, and the symplectic articulates with the quadrate of the upper jaw.

---

*Not homologous with the palatine of tetrapods, which is membrane bone.

Feeding and jaw suspension in fishes

Early voracious jawed fishes had wide mouths, the hinge of the jaws was far back under the skull, and the membrane bones of the upper jaw were solidly fused with the braincase and unable to move independently. As a result, in feeding, the mandible was simply lowered and then snapped shut on prey in the manner of modern sharks. Whatever portion of the prey was inside the orobranchial chamber was swallowed (see discussion of procuring food in Chapter 11).

Ray-finned fishes underwent modifications in the relationships of the hyoid arch to the jaws, of the upper jaw to the palate and braincase, and of the jaws to each other. The premaxilla and, often, the maxilla became movable independently of the rest of the skull and hinged together, and one process of the maxilla became attached by a ligament to the dentary bone so that movement of one displaced the other (Fig. 8-8). Accompanying these changes the large adductor muscle of the lower jaw inserted farther and farther forward on the mandible and the mouth became smaller and more rounded. The effect of the changes has been that the upper and lower jaws of the most highly specialized teleosts can be thrust forward independently of the skull, gently or rapidly according to the diet, and retracted once the food is within the orobranchial chamber. While the jaws are protruded and the mouth is open, suction created in the orobranchial chamber draws food into the mouth. The specific details of these new relationships and the mechanics of their operation are as numerous as the taxa that exhibit them.[1,13]

Feeding by inertial suction in the freshwater teleost *Petrotilapia tridentiger* has been described by Liem.[13] In its natural habitat this fish feeds on algae attached to submerged rocks; in an aquarium it feeds equally well on other foods. Abduction of the hyomandibula expands the orobranchial chamber, the lower jaw falls open, the opercular cavity expands, in that sequence, and zooplankton in the water immediately ahead are slowly drawn into the mouth. The lower jaw is then raised, the upper jaw remains briefly protruded, and then the hyomandibula is adducted, which compresses the chamber. The two phases, expansion and compression, together occupy about 600 milliseconds. Activity of the muscles was recorded by electromyography. By manipulating the hyoid skeleton and jaws appropriately the protruded jaws can be directed upward for collecting food on the surface of the water or downward for food on the substrate. Fish of appropriate size can also be taken in by rapid operation of the mechanism; and old-fashioned biting or snapping can also be employed. Teleosts that pursue prey have fewer operational options in their feeding repertoire.

The jaw-hyoid complex, whether of a shark or teleost, must be braced against some support, and the nearest is the braincase. In *Squalus* the hyomandibular cartilage is braced against the otic capsule and the jaws are braced against the hyomandibula. This is a fairly recent arrangement and is seen in modern actinopterygians. The condition is known as **hyostyly** (Fig. 8-1). A more primitive condition is seen in some older sharks in which jaws and hyoid are both braced directly against the braincase, a condition known as **amphistyly.** Still another variant is seen in lungfishes and chimaeras, in which the hyomandibula plays no role in bracing the jaws against the skull. This condition, "self-bracing" of the jaws, is **autostyly.** More sophisticated terminologies are employed by specialists.

ARE JAWS MODIFIED GILL ARCHES?

Many years ago it was proposed that the upper and lower jaws represent a gill arch that became modified for predatorial feeding when filter feeding was abandoned. There is circumstantial evidence for this, in that the innervation, blood supply, and muscles of the first arch are the first of a series of homologizable structures that are repeated in the gill arches. However, circumstantial evidence is not proof, and the question can be answered only by speculation.

Cyclostomes

The visceral skeleton of cyclostomes (Fig. 8-32) is quite unlike that of jawed fishes. For example, *Myxine* has no identifiable palatoquad-

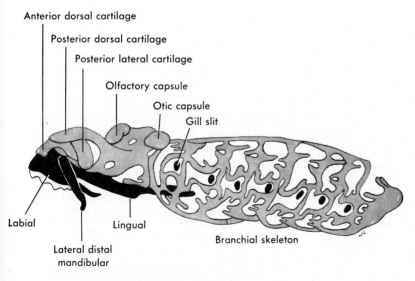

Anterior dorsal cartilage
Posterior dorsal cartilage
Posterior lateral cartilage
Olfactory capsule
Otic capsule
Gill slit
Labial
Lingual
Branchial skeleton
Lateral distal mandibular

NEUROCRANIUM and VISCERAL SKELETON
Lamprey

Fig. 8-32. Neurocranium and visceral skeleton of a lamprey. Black elements may represent vestiges of jaws. Olfactory capsule is a midline structure, otic capsules are paired. The lingual cartilage is also called basal plate cartilage.

rate or Meckel's cartilages. It does have a "dental plate," or lingual cartilage, that forms a V-shaped trough in the floor of the oral cavity, and, beneath this, an immovable basal plate to which the muscles of the dental plate are attached. There is evidence that these may be derived from the first visceral arch; if so, the rasping tonguelike structure of which they are a part may be considered a type of lower jaw. With regard to an upper jaw, a careful study of the visceral skeleton of a hagfish led to the conclusion that a rudimentary upper jaw is fused with the neurocranium.[3] The rest of the visceral skeleton of cyclostomes consists of cartilages of unknown homology, including a basketlike cartilaginous framework immediately under the skin surrounding the gill slits.

Tetrapods

With pulmonary respiration and life on land, the visceral skeleton, so necessary in gill-bearing vertebrates, underwent profound modifications. Some previously functional parts were deleted, and those that persisted perform new and, sometimes, surprising functions.

Not only have changes in the visceral skeleton taken place during the *evolution* of tetrapods; they occur also during *ontogeny* of every gill-bearing amphibian that undergoes complete metamorphosis. For example, larval frogs have six pairs of visceral cartilages, and the last four (III to VI) support gills. These branchial cartilages unite ventrally in a hypobranchial plate (Fig. 8-33, *A*). During metamorphosis (Fig. 8-33, *B* and *C*) visceral cartilages V and VI regress and disappear, the hypobranchial plate enlarges, and, along with the first basibranchial, becomes incorporated into a broad plate (body of the hyoid) in the buccal and pharyngeal floor. The ceratohyal cartilage (arch II) is reduced to a slender anterior horn (cornu) of the hyoid, and the cartilage of arch IV becomes a posterior horn. Other changes take place with the result that a visceral skeleton initially adapted for branchial respiration becomes converted, in the span of a few short days, to one suitable for life on land. Perennibranchiate amphibians, on the other hand, retain a branchial skeleton throughout life. In the sections that follow, we will examine the changes in the visceral skeleton of tetrapods.

EAR OSSICLES FROM HYOMANDIBULAE AND JAWS

It will be recalled that the hyomandibular cartilages of sharks are interposed between the quadrate bone of the upper jaw and the otic capsule housing the inner ear. In autostyly the hyomandibula could be dispensed with, and that is what happened in the modern lungfishes *Lepidosiren* and *Protopterus*. The hyomandibula persisted in amphibians but lost its articulation with the quadrate and became

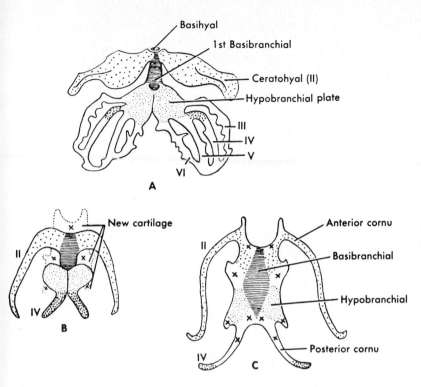

Fig. 8-33. Metamorphosis of visceral skeleton of a frog, jaws omitted. **A,** Branchial skeleton of larva. **B,** Condition in late metamorphosis. **C,** Hyoid of a young frog. Coarse and fine stipple and cross hatching indicate homologous areas. **x,** Cartilage added at metamorphosis. **II to VI,** Skeleton of second through sixth pharyngeal arches.

attached to the eardrum. The other end continued to abut against the otic capsule. The hyomandibula thereby became a bone conducting sound waves from the eardrum to the inner ear. It was the only ear ossicle in tetrapods for 150 million years, until the advent of the first mammals. The evolution of the hyomandibula to become a **columella,** or stapes, has been described by Schmalhausen.[18] That the columella is indeed the dorsal segment of the hyoid arch skeleton can be seen in the skull of the primitive urodele *Ranodon* (Fig. 8-12, A).

The articular and quadrate bones that ossify in the posterior ends of the lower and upper jaw cartilages of amphibians, reptiles, and birds serve as the site of articulation of the jaws. In synapsid reptiles the lower jaw achieved a new articulation directly against the skull (dentary against the squamosal, p. 193), and this freed the articular and quadrate bones to perform a new function. Gradually they became detached from the jaws and isolated within the middle ear cavity. The articular, now called **malleus,** became attached to the eardrum. The relationships of these bones are the same as in fishes with hyostylic jaw suspension: the articular (malleus) forms a joint with the quadrate (**incus**), the quadrate articulates with the hyomandibula (**stapes**), and the stapes articulates with the otic capsule containing the

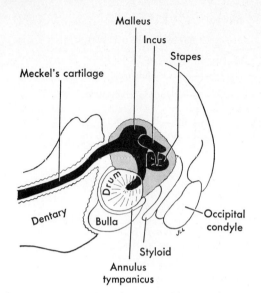

Fig. 8-34. Posterior lip of Meckel's cartilage surrounded by the developing middle ear cavity (gray) in a mammalian embryo.

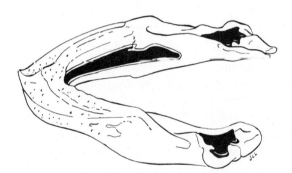

Fig. 8-35. Mandible of an adult sea turtle, from the left and above, showing core of Meckel's cartilage (black) ensheathed by membrane bone.

inner ear. The capture of the malleus by the first pharyngeal pouch is repeated during the ontogeny of most mammals (Fig. 8-34).

The lower jaw evidently was used for conducting sound long before the quadrate and articular bones were isolated in the middle ear cavity. By resting their lower jaw on the substrate urodeles, anurans, apodans, and probably some snakes and lizards that lack eardrums and, sometimes, even columellae, hear substrate-conducted sound by bone conduction through the lower jaw and skull. Mammals achieved greater acuity of hearing airborne sounds with the evolution of three ear ossicles.

THE FATE OF MECKEL'S CARTILAGE IN TETRAPODS

The embryonic Meckel's cartilage may continue to grow and become a prominent core of cartilage within the adult mandible as in turtles and crocodilians (Fig. 8-35), but more often it disappears with few or no remnants. Occasionally it gives rise to a mentomeckelian bone. In early tetrapods it was invested by a number of membrane bones, chiefly the dentary, angular, surangular, splenial, coronoid, and, sometimes, a prearticular. This condition is little changed today in living reptiles and birds. Modern amphibians have a reduced number, and mammals have only the dentary.

THE TETRAPOD HYOID AND A WOODPECKER'S TONGUE

When speaking of tetrapods the term "hyoid" or "hyoid apparatus," designates the skeletal derivatives of the hyoid arch other than the stapes, and those of the more caudal arches other than the larynx. The hyoid consists of a median plate (**body of the hyoid**) at the base of the tongue in the pharyngeal floor just anterior to the larynx, and two or three horns, or **cornua,** in the pharyngeal wall (Figs. 8-36, *B* to *H,* and 8-37). The body is derived from basihyal and basibranchial cartilages. The anterior horns arise from the second pharyngeal arch and are homologous with the ceratohyals of fishes. The more caudal horns arise from the third and, frequently, fourth arches.

In lizards and birds the body of the hyoid is narrow, and an elongated process extends forward into the tongue as an **entoglossal bone** (Fig. 8-36, *C* and *E*). Special accelerator muscles attach to the entoglossus in lizards and birds with long darting tongues. In some male lizards (anoles and related genera) a similar process extends caudad into the gular pouch, or dewlap. In snakes the entire branchial skeleton is vestigial.

The hyoid of mammals has two paired horns, an anterior pair from arch II and a posterior pair from arch III. In cats the anterior horns are longer (**greater horns**) and are composed of four segments (Fig. 8-36, *G*). The dorsalmost, or **tympanohyal,** ends in a notch in the tympanic bulla. In humans the anterior horns are shorter (**lesser horns**), a **stylohyoid ligament** represents the middle segment, and the **styloid process** of the temporal bone is equivalent to the tympanohyal (Figs. 8-25 and 8-38). In rabbits, too, the anterior horn is shorter (Fig. 8-37), and a slender **stylohyal bone** embedded in the tendon of the stylohyoideus minor muscle close to the skull is equivalent to the tympanohyal of cats. These are examples of the variations found among mammals.

The hyoid anchors the highly mobile tongue of tetrapods, provides attachment for some of the extrinsic muscles of the larynx, is the skeleton for the buccopharyngeal pressure pump used in respiration in anurans, has subtle effects on lower jaw movements, and is the attachment for muscles that participate in swallowing. The associated hypobranchial and branchiomeric muscles approach the hyoid from

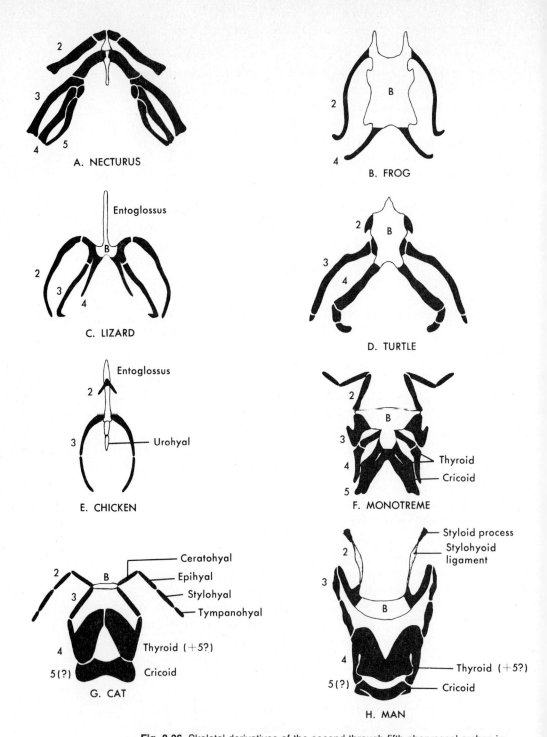

Fig. 8-36. Skeletal derivatives of the second through fifth pharyngeal arches in selected tetrapods. **B,** Body of hyoid. **2** to **5,** Derivatives of arches 2 through 5. The projections from the body in **B** to **H** are the horns of the hyoid. In **E,** the body of the hyoid extends forward into the tongue as an entoglossus to which are attached two paraglossals (2).

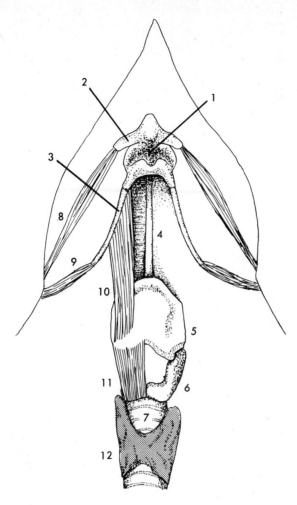

Fig. 8-37. Hyoid, larynx, and associated structures of a rabbit, ventral view. **1,** Body of hyoid; **2,** anterior horn of hyoid; **3,** caudal horn of hyoid; **4,** median thyrohyoid ligament; **5,** thyroid cartilage; **6,** cricoid cartilage; **7,** trachea; **8,** stylohyoideus minor; **9,** stylohyoideus major; **10,** thyrohyoideus; **11,** cricothyroideus; **12,** thyroid gland. The stylohyoidei and cricothyroideus are branchiomeric muscles; the thyrohyoideus is hypobranchial.

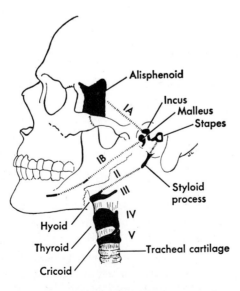

VISCERAL SKELETON

Fig. 8-38. Visceral skeleton of man. **IA,** Broken line connects derivatives of palatoquadrate cartilage; **IB,** broken line connects vestiges and derivatives of Meckel's cartilage; **II,** stylohyoid ligament; **III to V,** derivatives of third, fourth, and fifth arches. **III,** Greater (posterior) horn of hyoid bone (illustrated also in Fig. 12-10).

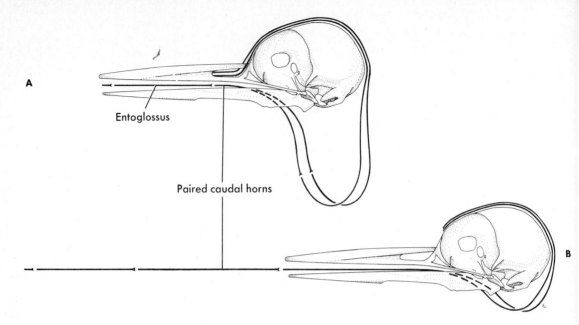

Fig. 8-39. Hyoid of a hairy woodpecker with, **A,** tongue retracted and, **B,** tongue extended. Although paired, the horns lie close together and appear as one when extended. Broken lines indicate position of horns medial to the jaw.

many directions—lower jaw, larynx, sternum, clavicle, styloid process of skull, and elsewhere. These muscles stabilize the hyoid in a single position or move it forward, backward, up, or down.

The hyoid of woodpeckers is a remarkable tool for impaling grubs (Figs. 8-39 and 11-6). From the entoglossal bone, which is embedded in the barbed tongue, two exceptionally long flexible posterior horns extend toward the temporal region of the skull and beyond. When the tongue is in a retracted position, they loop from the base of the tongue backward into the neck, then arch dorsally and forward under the skin on top of the head, reaching all the way to the beak. In impaling a grub they are straightened by an accelerator muscle that shoots the tongue into the prey. Elastic recoil of the horns immediately returns the tongue to the mouth with the impaled food.

THE LARYNGEAL SKELETON

Nearly all tetrapods have cricoid and arytenoid cartilages (or replacement bones), and mammals have thyroid bones as well (Figs. 12-9 and 12-10). Thyroid cartilages arise from mesenchyme of the fourth pharyngeal arch and, perhaps, the fifth. Cricoid and arytenoid cartilages appear to be products of the fifth arch. Since the caudal end of the pharyngeal arch series has been subject to reduction dur-

Table 8-3. Skeletal derivatives of pharyngeal arches in sharks and *approximate* homologues in bony vertebrates

Arch	Shark	Teleost	Necturus	Frog	Reptile and bird	Mammal
I	Meckel's cartilage Pterygoquadrate	Articular* Quadrate Epipterygoid Metapterygoid	Articular Quadrate Palatal cartilage	Articular Mentomeckelian† Quadrate Annulus tympanicus (?)	Articular Quadrate Epipterygoid	Malleus Incus Alisphenoid
II	Hyomandibula Ceratohyal Basihyal	Hyomandibula Symplectic Interhyal Epihyal Ceratohyal Hypohyal Basihyal	Rudimentary Ceratohyal Hypohyals	Columella (stapes) Anterior horn of hyoid Body of hyoid	Columella (stapes) Anterior horn of hyoid Entoglossus in reptiles and birds	Columella (stapes) Styloid process in mammals
III	Pharyngobranchial Epibranchial Ceratobranchial Hypobranchial	Pharyngobranchial Epibranchial Ceratobranchial Hypobranchial	Epibranchial Ceratobranchial	Body of hyoid	2nd horn of hyoid Body of hyoid	2nd horn of hyoid
IV	Branchial skeleton	Branchial skeleton	Branchial skeleton	Last horn and body of hyoid Laryngeal cartilages (?)		Thyroid cartilages
V	Branchial skeleton	Branchial skeleton	Branchial skeleton	Laryngeal cartilages (?) (precise homologies unknown)		Thyroid cartilages
VI	Branchial skeleton			Not present		
VII	Branchial skeleton					

*Sometimes part of derm-articular.
†Of intramembranous origin in some species.

ing evolution, it is not surprising that problems are encountered in relating the caudalmost laryngeal cartilages to specific arches.

Perspective

It is evident that the visceral skeleton is an ancient mechanism associated originally with feeding and branchial respiration. In tetrapods it has been modified for transmission of airborne sound (malleus, incus, stapes), for attachment of tongue muscles, and for support of vocal cords. These adaptations illustrate how mutations alter ancient structures for new functions. Some of the skeletal derivatives of the visceral arches in representative living vertebrates are listed in Table 8-3.

CHAPTER SUMMARY

1. During ontogeny the neurocranium is constructed of prechordal and parachordal cartilages, notochord, and cartilaginous olfactory and otic capsules knit together and completed by cartilaginous walls and, in lower vertebrates, a roof above the brain. An optic capsule remains independent of the rest of the neurocranium and sometimes forms scleral rings.

2. In agnathans and cartilaginous jawed fishes the neurocranium remains cartilaginous throughout life. In agnathans the components are loosely articulated.

3. The chief centers of ossification in the neurocranium of bony vertebrates are occipital, sphenoid, ethmoid, and otic. Basic replacement bones are exoccipital, basioccipital, supraoccipital; basisphenoid, presphenoid, orbitosphenoid, pleurosphenoid; mesethmoid, cribriform plate, ethmoturbinals; prootic, opisthotic, epiotic, or petrosal. These may be reduced in number by fusion.

4. A single occipital condyle is found in ancient tetrapods and in modern reptiles and birds. Modern amphibians, synapsid reptiles, and mammals have two.

5. The membrane bones of the skull constitute the dermatocranium. They are vestiges of ancient dermal armor.

6. The chief dermal bones of primitive tetrapod skulls were (a) **roofing bones**—nasal, frontal, parietal, postparietal; intertemporal, supratemporal, tabular, squamosal, quadratojugal; lacrimal, prefrontal, postfrontal, postorbital, infraorbital (jugal); (b) **upper jaw bones**—premaxilla and maxilla; (c) **primary palatal bones**—parasphenoid, vomer, palatine, endopterygoid, ectopterygoid; and (d) **opercular bones.** A parietal foramen was present.

7. Modern amphibian skulls have lost many membrane bones, and much of the neurocranium remains unossified. Anurans have large palatal vacuities. Apodan skulls have diverged the least.

8. Modern reptiles retain extensive ossification of the neurocranium, a single occipital condyle, numerous membrane bones, and a parietal foramen in lizards. Among specializations are temporal fossae, a partial or complete secondary palate in turtles, some lizards, and crocodilians, increased prominence of the dentary bone in therapsids, a turbinal bone, and mandibular fenestrae in archosaurs.

9. Temporal fossae result in diapsid (two-arch) and synapsid (one-arch) skulls and variants. The former were transmitted to birds, the latter to mammals. Turtles have anapsid skulls. Euryapsid skulls were found in ichthyosaurs and plesiosaurs.

10. Cranial kinesis is found in crossopterygians, some labyrinthodonts, caecilians, some extinct reptiles, snakes, some lizards, and birds.

11. Bird skulls are diapsid and reptilian. The dermal bones are numerous, but sutures have been obliterated except in ratites and the skulls are very thin. The skull is highly domed to accommodate the expanded brain. Jaws are elongated to form a beak.

12. The mammalian skull has a single temporal fossa bounded by a zygomatic arch. The dentary is the sole bone of the mandible and it articulates with the squamosal portion of the temporal complex. The quadrate and articular bones have joined the columella as middle ear ossicles. The braincase is greatly expanded and dermatocranial bones are reduced in number. There is a full complement of neurocranial bones and some obliteration of neurocranial sutures during ontogeny. A temporal bone often combines numerous separate components and includes a mastoid region and, often, a tympanic bulla. The primary palate lacks parasphenoid and ectopterygoids, and the secondary palate is complete. There are three pairs of turbinal bones.

13. The visceral skeleton of cyclostomes consists of a branchial basket not readily homologizable with the visceral skeleton of other vertebrates. There are no recognizable palatoquadrate or Meckel's cartilages.

14. The visceral skeleton of dogfish sharks consists of palatoquadrate and Meckel's cartilages, hyoid cartilages including a dorsal hyomandibula, a series of additional branchial cartilages, and median ventral basihyal and basibranchial cartilages, all suspended from the otic capsule by the hyomandibula (hyostylic jaw suspension).

15. The visceral skeleton of bony fishes resembles that of sharks except that it ossifies. The embryonic upper jaw cartilages are invested by membrane bones and their caudal ends become quadrate bones. Meckel's cartilages are invested, and the caudal ends become articular bones.

16. Jaw suspension in fishes is mostly hyostylic, amphistylic, or autostylic.

17. Meckel's cartilage in all tetrapods except mammals gives rise to the articular bone at the hinge of the lower jaw. The remainder is invested by one or more membrane bones including dentary, angular, surangular, splenial, coronoid, and prearticular. The cartilage remains as a core within the mandible of adult crocodilians and turtles, becomes vestigial or disappears in other adult mandibles.

18. In tetrapods commencing with amphibians the hyomandibula becomes the columella, or stapes, of the middle ear. The remainder of the second arch, the third arch, and sometimes part of the fourth arch give rise to horns of the hyoid. Basihyal and basibranchial cartilages give rise to the body of the hyoid. The remainder of the fourth arch and the fifth arch give rise to the skeleton of the larynx.

19. In mammals the posterior ends of the embryonic lower and upper jaw cartilages become malleus and incus bones in the middle ear cavity.

20. The neurocranium arises chiefly from neurectoderm and sclerotomal mesoderm, the splanchnocranium arises from neurectoderm, and the dermatocranium arises from lateral-plate mesoderm that migrates into the embryonic head fold from farther back.

LITERATURE CITED AND SELECTED READINGS

1. Alexander, R.M.: The functions and mechanisms of the protrusible upper jaws of some acanthopterygian fish, Journal of Zoology (London) **151**:43, 1967.
2. Allin, E.F.: Evolution of the mammalian ear, Journal of Morphology **147**:403, 1975.
3. Ayers, H., and Jackson, C.M.: Morphology of the Myxinoidei. I. Skeleton and musculature, Journal of Morphology **17**:185, 1901.
4. Bock, W.J.: Kinetics of the avian skull, Journal of Morphology **114**:1, 1964.
5. Brodal, A., and Fänge, R., editors: The biology of *Myxine*, Oslo, 1963, Norway Universitetsforlaget.
6. Carroll, R.L.: The hyomandibular as a supporting element in the skull of primitive tetrapods. In Panchen, A.L., editor: The terrestrial environment and the origin of land vertebrates, New York, 1980, Academic Press, Inc.
7. Crompton, A.W., and others: The movement of the hyoid apparatus during chewing, Nature **258**:69, 1975.
8. Crompton, A.W., and Parker, P.: Evolution of the mammalian masticatory apparatus, American Scientist **66**(2):192, 1978.
9. De Beer, G.R.: The development of the vertebrate skull, Oxford, England, 1937, The Clarendon Press.
10. Frezzetta, T.H.: Adaptive problems and possibilities in the temporal fenestration of tetrapod skulls, Journal of Morphology **125**:145, 1968.
11. Gans, C., and Parsons, T.S., editors: Biology of the reptilia, vol. 4, New York, 1973, Academic Press, Inc.
12. Goodrich, E.S.: Studies on the structure and development of vertebrates, London, 1930, The Macmillan Co., Ltd. (Reprinted by Dover Publications, Inc., New York, 1958.)
13. Liem, K.F.: Adaptive significance of intra- and interspecific differences in the feeding repertoires of cichlid fishes, American Zoologist **20**(1):295, 1980.
14. Lombard, R.E., and Bolt, J.R.: Evolution of the tetrapod ear: an analysis and reinterpretation, Biological Journal of the Linnaean Society **11**:19, 1979.
15. Ørvig, T.: The dermal skeleton: general considerations. In Ørvig, T., editor: Current problems in vertebrate phylogeny, New York, 1968, Interscience-Wiley.
16. Reed, C.A., and Schaffer, W.: Evolutionary implications of cranial morphology in the sheep and goats, American Zoologist **6**:565, 1966.
17. Romer, A.S.: Osteology of the reptiles, Chicago, 1956, University of Chicago Press.
18. Schmalhausen, I.I.: The origin of terrestrial vertebrates (translated from the Russian by Leon Kelso), New York, 1968, Academic Press, Inc.
19. Stahl, B.J.: Vertebrate history: problems in evolution, New York, 1974, McGraw-Hill Book Co.

CHAPTER 9

Girdles, fins, limbs, and locomotion

The pectoral and pelvic girdles and the skeleton of the fins and limbs make up the **appendicular skeleton.** Girdles brace the fins and limbs against the force that these appendages transmit from the substrate. These forces are strongest and most continual in amniotes, since their limbs elevate the body well above the ground. The pectoral girdle, in turn, is braced against the skull in many bony fishes and against the sternum in tetrapods; and the pelvic girdle in tetrapods is braced against the vertebral column.

Some vertebrates lack one or both pairs of fins or limbs, and most of these are aquatic or live in burrows. The list includes agnathans (no paired fins), eels and a number of other teleosts (no pectoral fins), and cetaceans, sirenians, and urodeles in the family Sirenidae (no hind limbs), all of whom are aquatic or primarily so. It includes caecilians, snakes, and amphisbaenians, all limbless, all with some aquatic species, and otherwise mostly burrowers. The list also includes a lizard without hind limbs *(Bipes)*, lizards without forelimbs, and completely limbless lizards. Limbless aquatic species swim with lateral undulation of the trunk and tail; terrestrial species have evolved compensatory locomotor movements that will be discussed later. Loss of limbs is correlated with an elongated trunk, although not universally, and in some instances in which one limb is missing an embryonic limb bud appears transitorily.

PECTORAL GIRDLES

In its basic form a pectoral girdle is a U-shaped skeletal complex in the body wall that articulates with the anterior fins or limbs. It is stabilized by the multidirectional forces exerted on it by muscles that originate on the axial skeleton and insert on the girdle, and by other muscles that arise on the girdle and insert on the fin or limb.

Pectoral girdles in all vertebrates are modifications of a basic pattern seen in early jawed fishes. In these vertebrates the girdle consisted of three pairs of replacement bones that constituted an endo-

In this chapter we will focus on skeletal structures that, along with the axial skeleton, participate in locomotion. We will find that fins vary widely but that all tetrapod limbs reflect a basic pattern. We'll note examples of how that pattern has been modified for diverse activities such as hopping, swimming, running, and flying, and we will learn how snakes propel themselves without limbs. We'll see how the pelvic girdle has been altered to facilitate laying massive avian eggs or the birth of a mammal. We'll examine some far-out ideas of how the first paired fins arose and finally, a plausible theory of the origin of tetrapod limbs.

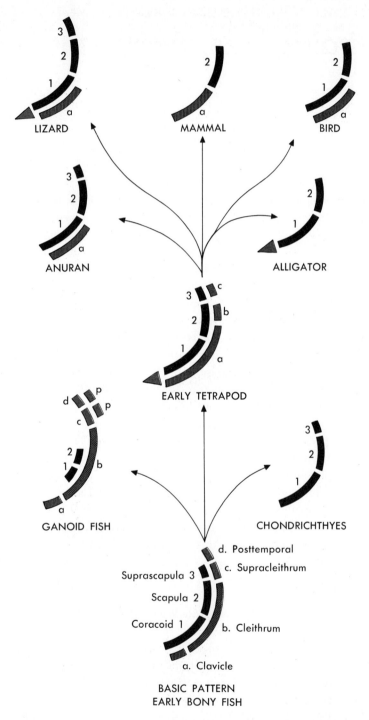

Fig. 9-1. Pectoral girdle in selected phylogenetic lines. Dermal bones are red, and cartilage and replacement bones are black. Triangles represent interclavicle. **1,** In alligator and bird, procoracoid; **p,** postcleithrum. Only one half of each girdle is illustrated, and relationships have been distorted when necessary to emphasize homologies. The basic pattern is based on *Eusthenopteron*.

skeleton and at least four pairs of investing bones derived from dermal armor (Fig. 9-1, basic pattern). As in today's fishes, it was located immediately behind and directly in line with the branchial skeleton, resembling in this respect the skeleton of a gill. (This inspired the hypothesis that the pectoral girdle is a modified gill arch.) The replacement bones were, on each side, a ventral **coracoid,** a **scapula** that receives the force transmitted to the body by the fin or limb, and a **suprascapula.** The dermal bones were a small ventral **clavicle** that met the opposite clavicle in a midventral symphysis, a large **cleithrum** overlying the scapula, a smaller **supracleithrum,** and a **posttemporal** that anchored the girdle to the tabular region of the skull. **Postcleithral** bones sometimes accompanied the supracleithrum (Fig. 9-1, ganoid fish).

In later bony fishes the coracoid and scapula were reduced in size and the cleithrum became the major bone of the girdle (Fig. 9-2). In teleosts the embryonic coracoid and scapula unite to form an adult coracoscapula (Fig. 9-3). A full complement of dermal bones has remained except in holosteans and teleosts, who lost the clavicle. Cartilaginous fishes deposit bone in the skin and teeth only. Therefore they have no dermal bones in their girdle, and the coracoid, scapula, and suprascapula remain cartilaginous throughout life (Fig. 9-4).

The pectoral girdles of early tetrapods were remarkably similar to those of early jawed fishes except that a new midventral dermal bone, the **interclavicle,** had appeared (Fig. 9-1), and the girdle was no longer anchored to the skull.

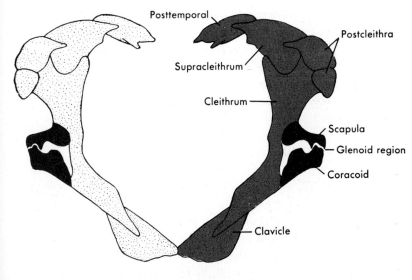

PECTORAL GIRDLE

Fig. 9-2. Pectoral girdle of the ganoid fish *Polypterus*. Dermal bones are red, replacement bones are black.

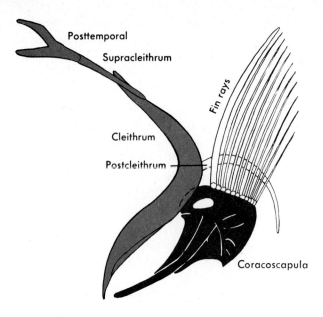

Posttemporal

Supracleithrum

Fin rays

Cleithrum

Postcleithrum

Coracoscapula

Fig. 9-3. Pectoral girdle and fin skeleton of ribbonfish, a teleost. Dermal bone is red, replacement bone is black.

MODERN FIN SKELETON

Among adaptations that were converting early, relatively weak, tetrapod appendages into sturdy ones, the coracoids or procoracoids began to brace the forelimbs against the newly acquired sternum (Figs. 7-11; 7-24, iguanid lizard; and 9-5). In some tetrapods the clavicle assisted or even replaced the coracoids (Figs. 7-24, monkey; and 9-5). In others the clavicle was lost (some lizards, turtles, some mammals, crocodilians), although in crocodilians it appears temporarily in embryos. The fishlike cleithra and supracleithra have been lost in all living tetrapods, and urodeles have lost all dermal bones of the girdle. In general, *in bony fishes there was a reduction in the number of replacement bones,* whereas *in tetrapods it is the membrane bones that have been reduced or lost.*

In the embryonic coracoid region (coracoid plate) tetrapods have more than one potential chondrification center, including an anterior and posterior center on each side. Bones that arise from the anterior center can be called more precisely **procoracoids, precoracoids,** or **anterior coracoids.** Bones arising from the posterior centers are then called coracoids. Monotremes have procoracoids and coracoids; but all that is left of this center in placental mammals is a coracoid process of the scapula derived from the posterior ossification center.

Monotremes have a reptilian girdle, but above monotremes only a scapula and, sometimes, a clavicle remain. The clavicle has been lost

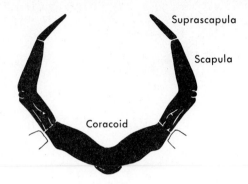

Fig. 9-4. Cartilaginous pectoral girdle of the shark *Squalus,* anterior view.

PECTORAL GIRDLE

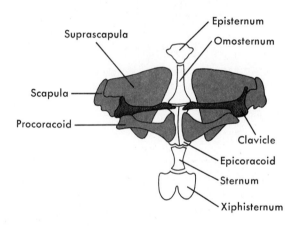

Fig. 9-5. Sternum and pectoral girdle of frog, ventral view. Membrane bone is red, and replacement bones except epicoracoid are gray.

in ungulates and in aquatic mammals whose forelimbs have become paddles. In other carnivores the clavicle has been reduced to a slender splinter reaching neither the sternum nor the scapula. Loss or reduction of the clavicle is not limited to the mammalian orders mentioned. The smaller the clavicle, the more freedom of movement is afforded the shoulder and, consequently, the forelimb. Cats, which are notably agile, have only a splinter for a clavicle, whereas mammals with strong forelimbs that are used for digging, climbing, or flying have a large clavicle that braces the scapula against the sternum. The clavicle is also large in generalized mammals such as insectivores and primates.

A scapula is always present in mammals. It has a broad flat lateral surface divided by a scapular spine into supraspinous and infraspinous fossae that are the origin of strong muscles that insert on the humerus. The pectoral girdles of a few tetrapods are illustrated in Fig. 9-6.

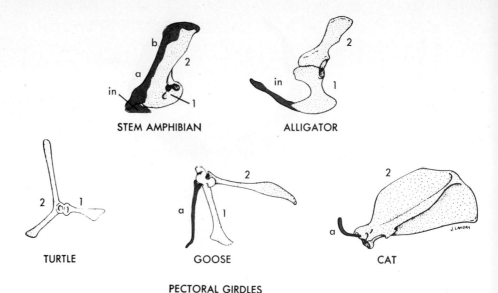

PECTORAL GIRDLES

Fig. 9-6. Left half of the pectoral girdle of selected tetrapods, lateral views. Dermal bones are red, replacement bones are stippled. **1,** Coracoid or procoracoid; **2,** scapula. **a,** Clavicle; **b,** cleithrum; **in,** interclavicle. In turtles the clavicles and interclavicle are fused with the shell.

PELVIC GIRDLES

Pelvic girdles in most fishes consist of two cartilaginous or bony **pelvic,** or **ischiopubic, plates** that meet in a midventral **pelvic symphysis** and brace the pelvic fins (Fig. 9-7, herring). In cartilaginous fishes and lungfishes, two embryonic cartilages unite to form one adult plate (Figs. 9-7, shark; and 9-8). In teleosts that have a short trunk the pelvic plate lies immediately behind or, sometimes, below the pectoral girdle and is often attached to it. Because of this, pelvic fins may project below or even anterior to pectorals. There are no dermal bone components in the pectoral girdles of either fishes or tetrapods.

Tetrapod embryos also develop cartilaginous pelvic plates. Thereafter, each plate ossifies at two centers to form a **pubic bone,** or **pubis,** and a more posterior **ischial bone,** or **ischium** (Fig. 9-9). In the perennibranchiate *Necturus* no pubis ossifies, and the ischia are rudimentary ossification centers in the caudal end of the cartilaginous pelvic plate (Fig. 9-9, *Necturus*). Dorsal to the pelvic plate an additional blastema gives rise to an **ilium.** At the junction of the pubis, ischium, and ilium a socket, the **acetabulum,** accomodates the head of the femur.

Dorsally, the ilium is braced against the stout transverse processes

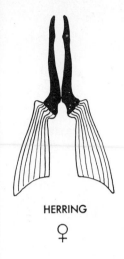

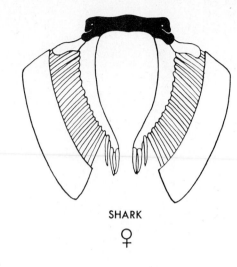

Fig. 9-7. Pelvic plates (black) of a bony and cartilaginous fish.

HERRING
♀

SHARK
♀

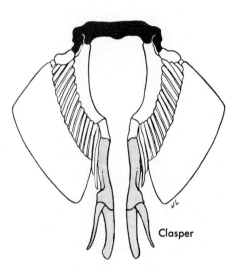

Fig. 9-8. Pelvic plate (black) and fin of a male shark, showing basal fin cartilages modified as claspers (gray). Compare female shark, Fig. 9-7.

Clasper

of sacral vertebrae, with short sacral ribs intervening. The ribs are usually ankylosed to the transverse processes and are not evident except in embryos or larvae (Fig. 9-9, *Necturus*). Ventrally, except in birds, there is a symphysis between either the two pubic bones (**pubic symphysis**), the two ischia (**ischial symphysis**), or both (**ischiopubic symphysis**) (Fig. 9-10). The symphysis is in the midventral coelomic wall immediately anterior to the cloaca. The architecture of the region is such that the force transmitted to the two acetabula as a result of gravity (weight bearing) or locomotion is distributed in two directions: to the sacrum dorsally and to the symphysis ventrally. The proportion distributed in each direction depends on the posture of

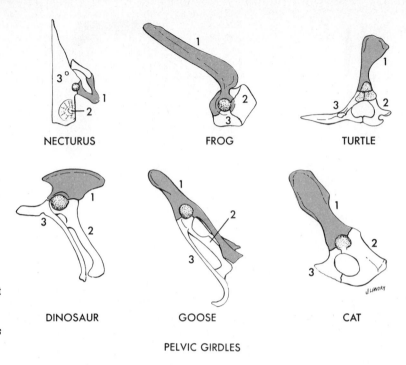

PELVIC GIRDLES

Fig. 9-9. Left halves of pelvic girdles of selected tetrapods, lateral views, except *Necturus,* which is a ventral view. **1,** Ilium (red); **2,** ischium; **3,** pubis. The acetabulum is stippled. In *Necturus* the ischium is an ossification center in the caudal part of the pelvic plate, and the bony ilium has a sacral rib attached dorsally. The dinosaur girdle is of *Camptosaurus,* an ornithischian.

the animal at rest and in motion. The joint between the head of the femur and the girdle is stabilized by muscles that approach the femur from opposing directions. The sacrum and the girdle form a bony enclosure, the **pelvis,** that encircles the caudal end of the coelom. The resulting **pelvic cavity** contains the urinogenital organs and the terminal portion of the large intestine.

Posture and mode of locomotion are correlated with the shape of the ilium, ischium, and pubis, the anatomical relationships of these bones, and their proportional size. A squatting, jumping frog has a different set of vectors affecting the pelvic girdle than does a bird, deer, kangaroo, or marine turtle. In frogs the ilia are slender and greatly elongated, and they extend from the sacral vertebra to the end of the urostyle where they meet the ischia and pubes and where the acetabulum is located (Fig. 7-10). The joint between ilium and sacral vertebra is free to move when a frog pushes off at the start of a leap. As the frog lands, the joint, along with others in the leg, helps dissipate the force of the impact. In many tetrapods this **sacroiliac joint** is not freely movable.

Urodeles have limbs that can scarcely lift the sagging belly off the substrate without the buoying effect of water. The limbs, therefore, bear only part of the weight, whether the animal is resting motionless on the bottom of a pond or is on land. Most of the force exerted

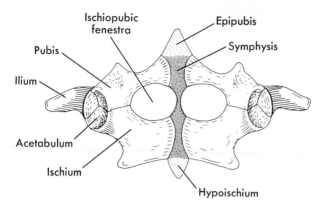

Ischiopubic
fenestra

Epipubis

Symphysis

Pubis

Ilium

Acetabulum

Ischium

Hypoischium

Fig. 9-10. Pelvis of *Sphenodon,*
ventral view, showing ischiopubic
symphysis.

against the girdle of a urodele is a result of pushing against the substrate when moving about, not when resting. The pelvic girdle of urodeles differs little from that of fishes, except that small ilia are braced against the sacral vertebra. A median cartilage, the **prepubic,** or **ypsiloid,** extends from the girdle forward in the ventral body wall.

A variety of pelvic girdle architecture are found among reptiles, which is correlated with their divergent body structure, stances, and modes of locomotion. An expanded ilium accommodates the additional hind limb muscles necessary for more efficient locomotion on land than is seen in amphibians. In expanding, the ilium has become braced against an additional vertebra. In most reptiles the pubis is directed cephalad and the ischium caudad; and because the ilium is directed dorsad the girdle is triradiate (Fig. 9-11). In ornithischian dinosaurs, however, the pubis was directed caudad, paralleling the ischium, as in birds (Fig. 9-9, dinosaur and goose). Turtles and the generalized *Sphenodon* have an ischiopubic symphysis, but some of the more specialized reptiles have only an ischial symphysis. A wide **ischiopubis fenestra** develops on each side between the ischium and pubis in *Sphenodon,* turtles, and lizards (Fig. 9-10). It had not yet evolved in early reptiles. It is called the **obturator fenestra (or foramen)** in synapsid reptiles and mammals because in these it transmits the obturator nerve that supplies some of the hind limb muscles. In other reptiles the nerve passes through a small foramen near the ischiopubic fenestra. An **epipubic bone** and a **hypoischial bone** usually develop in association with the pelvic girdle of reptiles (Fig. 9-10), and one or both are present in monotremes and marsupials. In the latter it is also called **marsupial bone** because it supports the marsupial pouch.

The ilia and ischia of birds are enormously expanded, providing a broad site for attachment of the muscles used in bipedal locomotion, and the girdle is braced against lumbar as well as sacral vertebrae

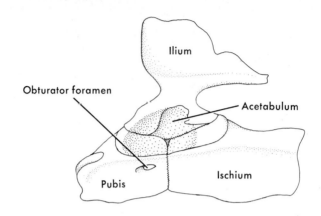

A. PRIMITIVE TETRAPOD

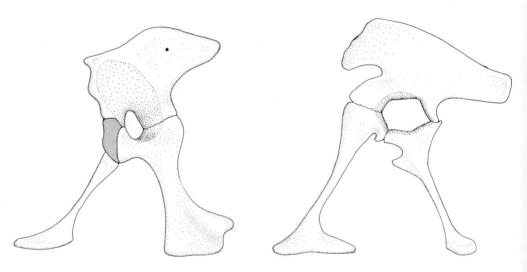

B. ALLIGATOR   C. SAURISCHIAN DINOSAUR

Fig. 9-11. Left pelvic girdles of selected reptiles, lateral view. **A,** *Seymouria,* a borderline reptilelike amphibian. **B,** *Alligator.* **C,** *Allosaurus.* **D,** *Varanus.* **E,** *Ophiacodon,* a primitive reptile in the mammalian line. In **B,** the anterior acetabular wall is partly fibrocartilaginous (gray), and in **B** and **C** the medial wall of the acetabulum is incomplete. Turtle and ornithischian girdles are shown in Fig. 9-9. (**A** after White; **C** after Gilmore; **D** after Bütschli; **E** redrawn from Osteology of the reptiles by A.S. Romer by permission of the University of Chicago Press [copyright 1956 by the International Copyright Union].)

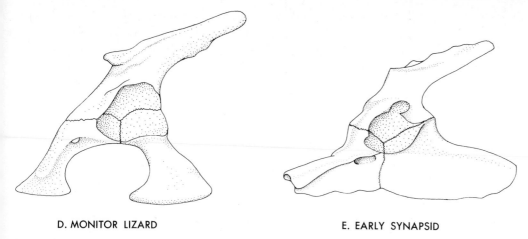

D. MONITOR LIZARD   E. EARLY SYNAPSID

Fig. 9-11. For legend see opposite page.

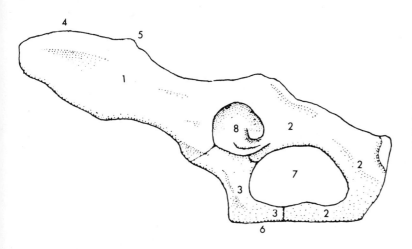

Fig. 9-12. Left coxal (innominate) bone of cat, lateral view. **1,** ilium; **2,** ischium; **3,** pubis; **4,** crest of ilium; **5,** posterior inferior iliac spine; **6,** site of ischiopubic symphysis; **7,** obturator foramen; **8,** acetabulum.

(Fig. 7-17). The pubic bones are reduced to long splinters that are directed caudad (Fig. 9-9, goose). The absence of a pelvic symphysis provides a large pelvic outlet for laying the massive eggs.

In mammals the ilium, ischium, and pubis ankylose early in postnatal life to form a left and right **innominate (coxal) bone** (Fig. 9-12). Dorsally, each innominate joins the sacrum in an almost immobile sacroiliac joint. Ventrally, the two innominates meet in a symphysis to complete the bony pelvis. The ischium does not always contribute to the symphysis. In some species a small **acetabular (cotyloid) bone** ossifies in the acetabular wall.

Mammalian young are delivered through a pelvic outlet bounded ventrally by the pubic symphysis and dorsally by the first few caudal vertebrae (coccyx in human beings). In late pregnancy the fibrocartilage separating the bones at the symphysis is softened by hormones, which permits expansion of the pelvic outlet for delivery. In mice 6 days pregnant the gap between the two bones at the symphysis was shown by x-ray films to be only 0.25 mm. Thirteen days later, on the day of birth, the gap had widened to 5.6 mm.

PAIRED FINS

Most fins are simply steering devices that control direction of movement, or stabilizers that prevent rolling (as a result of torque), side-to-side wobbling (yaw), and unregulated inclination (pitch) of the body, all of which are wasteful of energy if not life threatening. Paired fins also serve as brakes to slow or halt forward motion, but they play little role in propulsion. Locomotion in fishes is principally by lateral undulation of the trunk and of the tail with its vertical fin. The locomotor skeletomuscular complex of fishes is the jointed vertebral column and the metameric body wall muscles. These structures are discussed in Chapters 7 and 10.

It should be mentioned that a few fishes fly, although not as far as did the Wright brothers. Characins, which are primitive voracious teleosts inhabiting fresh tropical waters, get an initial thrust out of the water with the caudal fin and, beating winglike pectoral fins, fly several yards using appendicular muscles that, for a fish, are exceptionally large. This behavior is said to take place only when the fish is alarmed. If so, it's a fishy method of performing a disappearing act.

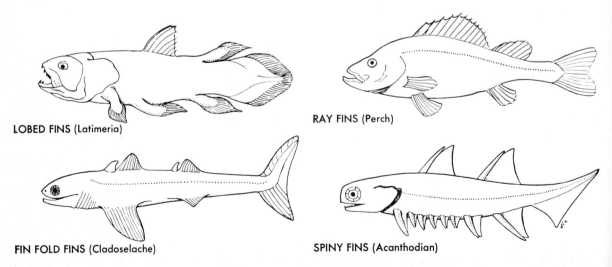

LOBED FINS (Latimeria)

RAY FINS (Perch)

FIN FOLD FINS (Cladoselache)

SPINY FINS (Acanthodian)

Fig. 9-13. External appearances of some fins (not to scale).

Paired fins have diverged greatly in structure since the Devonian. The fins of today's fishes may be grouped in three categories, **lobed fins, fin fold fins,** and **ray fins** (Fig. 9-13). Fin rays, which are flexible filaments in the dermis on both sides of a fin, stiffen the fins (Fig. 9-3). In cartilaginous fishes they are horny fibers, or **ceratotrichia.** In bony fishes they are jointed bony dermal scales, or **lepidotrichia,** aligned end to end.

Lobed fins have a fleshy muscular lobe containing the endoskeleton at their base. They are found with many variations among sarcopterygians. In the modern lungfish *Neoceratodus* the endoskeleton of the fin consists of a long axis of jointed bones, or **axials,** and a series of **preaxial** and **postaxial radials,** or **pterygiophores** (Fig. 9-14, *A*). A fin such as this is said to be biserial because of the two series of radials. It has been called an **archipterygium** because it is very ancient. Whether it was a precursor to any of the known fin types is uncertain.

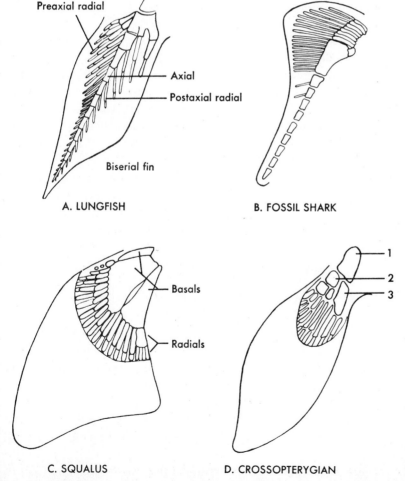

Fig. 9-14. Selected fin skeletons, reoriented. Fin rays are not shown. **A,** Biserial pelvic fin of *Neoceratodus,* a living lobe-finned fish. **B** and **C,** Pectoral fins of the Paleozoic shark *Cladodus* and the modern shark *Squalus.* **D,** Pectoral fin of an ancient crossopterygian, *Eusthenopteron.* **1** to **3** are equivalent by position to the humerus, ulna, and radius of a tetrapod limb.

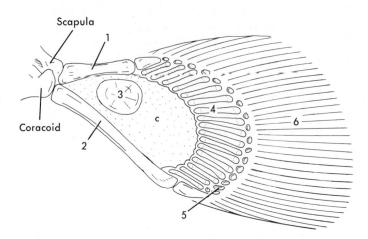

Fig. 9-15. Right pectoral fin of the ganoid fish *Polypterus*. **1** to **3,** Basalia; **4** and **5,** radialia, the small distal ones being cartilage; **6,** fin rays. **c,** Cartilage. The relationships of scapula and coracoid are illustrated in Fig. 9-2.

Fin fold fins are characteristic of Chondrichthyes. The fins of living sharks have a broad base, but the base was even broader in Paleozoic sharklike fishes (Fig. 9-13, *Cladoselache*). Early sharks had what appear to be modified biserial fins (Fig. 9-14, *B*), but the fin skeleton of modern sharks consists of one to five **basal cartilages** and one or several rows of **radials** (Fig. 9-14, *C*). The pelvic fin of males is modified as an intromittent organ (Fig. 9-8).

Ray fins are found in actinopterygians. The endoskeleton of these in some ganoids is not unlike that of modern sharks, having basals and radials (Fig. 9-15). Teleosts, however, have lost the basals and most of the radials and, as a result, fin rays commence at or close to the girdle (Fig. 9-3).

MEDIAN FINS

Most fishes have one or two dorsal fins, an anal fin just behind the vent or anus, and a caudal fin at the end of the tail (Fig. 9-13, perch). The endoskeleton of dorsal and anal fins consists of one or several rows of radials from which fin rays project. Below teleosts the proximal radials of the dorsal fins may rest on the vertebral column, and several may coalesce to form an elongated basal cartilage or bone. Anal fins are sometimes missing in bottom dwellers. In males of some viviparous species the anal fin is modified as an intromittent organ, or **gonopodium**. Median fins are moved by striated muscles that insert on the radials.

There are several varieties of caudal fins classified on the basis of

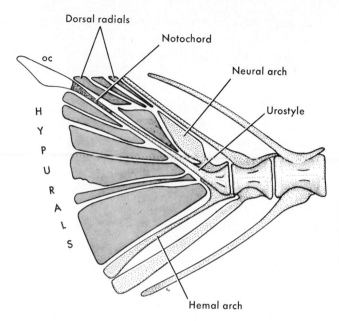

Dorsal radials

Notochord

oc

Neural arch

Urostyle

H
Y
P
U
R
A
L
S

Hemal arch

Fig. 9-16. Skeleton of the homocercal caudal fin of the primitive teleost *Clupea.* The bony urostyle encloses all but the terminal segment of the upturned notochord. Dorsal radials tend to disappear in more specialized teleosts. Fin rays are present but not shown. **oc,** Opisthoural cartilage.

their shape and whether the vertebral column within the fin continues straight or is bent up or down. In **diphycercal** tails, the column or notochord ends without bending, and the tail is symmetrical externally. The condition is seen in cyclostomes (Fig. 3-2), *Polypterus* (Fig. 3-6), and living lobe-fins (Fig. 3-9). In **heterocercal tails** a long section of the vertebral column bends upward into a dorsal lobe unequal in size to the lobe below it, so the tail is asymmetrical in the sagittal plane (Fig. 3-6, *Acipenser* and *Polyodon*). Heterocercal tails are characteristic of sharks. **Homocercal tails** are symmetrical from external appearance (Fig. 9-13, perch), but the vertebral column turns up within the fin (Fig. 9-16). Homocercal tails are found in teleosts and some ganoids. Innumerable gradations exist between heterocercal and homocercal tails, and there is a rare condition (**hypocercal**) in which the vertebral column turns downward.

The endoskeleton of caudal fins provides a base from which fin rays radiate and on which tail muscles insert. In teleosts the upturned notochord is surrounded by a bony sheath, the **urostyle,** that extends upward beyond the last centrum (Fig. 9-16). Several **hypural bones** are braced against the underside of the urostyle and last centrum, and fin rays extend from these, there being no ventral radials. Some hypurals appear to be hypertrophied hemal arches. Specialized teleosts have only two hypurals and no dorsal radials. In heterocercal fins, dorsal radials rest directly on or come close to the vertebral column; and ventral radials, when present, rest on hemal arches. The endoskeleton of a variety of caudal fins is discussed by Goodrich.[6]

Attempts have been made to use the morphology of caudal fins in unraveling phylogenetic relationships among fishes. The approach has been thwarted by tremendous diversity, an incomplete fossil record, and the realization that similarities may be the result of convergent evolution and bear false witness. Comparative embryological studies show that fishes with homocercal tails pass through an ontogenetic heterocercal stage. Applying Baer's law, which may or may not be applicable, would lead to the conclusion that heterocercal tails may be more primitive than homocercal ones.

THE ORIGIN OF FINS

What was the nature of structures that might have given rise to paired fins? This is one of the more puzzling questions in the study of vertebrate phylogeny. To answer it requires more specific knowledge than we have of prevertebrate ancestors. This being so, the best we can do to satisfy our curiosity (which is the motivation for basic science) is to look among the protochordates, ostracoderms, and early bony fishes and speculate.

The **fin fold hypothesis** states that paired fins are derived from a pair of hypothetical continuous fleshy folds of lateral body wall analogous to the metapleural folds of the amphioxus. If such a structure were to become interrupted in the middle of the trunk, remain immediately behind the gills and in front of the tail, and become invaded by body wall muscles and endowed with an endoskeleton, the result would be paired fin fold fins such as those of *Cladoselache* (Fig. 9-13). However, there is no evidence that this happened.

According to the **gill arch hypothesis** of Gegenbaur, pectoral and pelvic girdles are modified gill arches and the fin endoskeleton is an expansion of gill rays. It is true that many comparative anatomy students, seeing a shark skeleton suspended in a museum jar for the first time, think that the pectoral girdle is part of the pharyngeal skeleton because of its location immediately behind the last pharyngeal arch and its **U** shape. It looks as though it could have been a gill. Asserting that it was is speculation.

The most recent hypothesis is the **fin spine hypothesis** proposed near the middle of the twentieth century by Gregory and Raven.[8] In early acanthodians (Fig. 9-13, spiny fins) pectoral and pelvic appendages were the largest of a series of lateral spiny appendages that extended the length of the trunk. Evidently, they were practically immobile. Associated with each spine was a fleshy membrane. In later acanthodians weak fin rays were present in the membrane of one pair of these at the pectoral and pelvic level only, and small radial elements supported the membrane at its base. In time, acanthodians tended to lose all except the pairs containing fin rays. This may be a clue to the origin of paired fins, but it is not known that acanthodians were ancestral in a direct line to cartilaginous and later bony fishes. Among placoderms, arthrodires had a pair of fixed spines projecting behind the head (Fig. 3-4, *Coccosteus*), and antiarchs had jointed, spiny, armor-covered pectoral appendages (Fig. 3-4, *Bothriolepis*).

No known prechordate or protochordate has structures that conceivably could have given rise to vertebrate fins, even allowing free reign to the imagination. Reliable clues to the origin of paired fins are probably hidden forever in the obscurity of time.

TETRAPOD LIMBS

Although tetrapods typically have four limbs, some have lost one or both pairs and in others the forelimbs have been modified as wings or paddles. By employing limbs with appropriate modifications, tetrapods swim, crawl, walk, run, hop, jump, dig, climb, glide, or fly to avoid enemies, seek food and shelter, and find a mate.

Tetrapod limb skeletons consist of five segments: **propodium, epipodium, mesopodium, metapodium,** and **phalanges.** In the forelimb these correspond to the bones of the upper arm, forearm, wrist, palm, and digits, the last three constituting the **manus,** or hand (Fig. 9-17). Table 9-1 lists these segments and their corresponding parts in

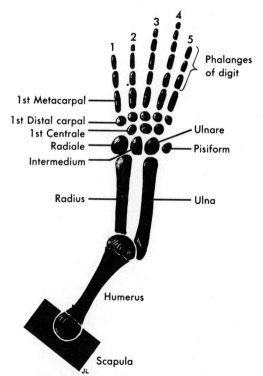

Fig. 9-17. Generalized pattern of a right anterior limb, viewed from above, palm down. **1** to **5,** First to fifth digits.

Table 9-1. Homologous segments in anterior and posterior limbs of tetrapods

Anterior limb		Posterior limb	
Name of segment	Skeleton	Name of segment	Skeleton
Upper arm (brachium)	Humerus	Thigh (femur)	Femur
Forearm (antebrachium)	Radius and ulna	Shank (crus)	Tibia and fibula
Wrist (carpus) ⎫	⎧ Carpals	Ankle (tarsus) ⎫	⎧ Tarsals
Palm (metacarpus) ⎬ Manus	⎨ Metacarpals	Instep (metatarsus ⎬ Pes	⎨ Metatarsal
Digits ⎭	⎩ Phalanges	Digits ⎭	⎩ Phalanges

the hind limb by common names. The skeleton within homologous segments in the various tetrapods is remarkably similar despite outward appearances; it is the orientation of the bones, the relative mobility of the joints, and the complexity of the appendicular muscles as much as the skeleton per se that makes possible the variety of locomotor activities of tetrapods. The most striking differences in skeletons are at the distal ends of the appendages.

The limbs of early tetrapods were short, the first segment extended nearly horizontally from the trunk, and the second segment was perpendicular to the first, directed downward. The bones of the hand and foot were parallel to the substrate (Fig. 3-15, A). This posture persists to a considerable degree in urodeles and primitive lizards; but in most reptiles and in mammals there has been a rotation of the appendages toward the body so that the long axes of the humerus and femur more nearly parallel the vertebral column. To a marked degree the elbow is directed backward and the knee forward (Fig. 9-28, A). Limbs oriented in this fashion are good shock absorbers. They also permit greater leverage between axial skeleton and appendage, which increases speed and agility. Such reorientation was an essential step toward bipedalism.

Generally, hind limbs have stouter muscles, are used to a greater degree in powering locomotion, and are statistically longer than forelimbs. The hind limbs of fleet amniotes such as cursorial lizards and deer are considerably longer than the forelimbs, and in leaping species such as frogs and kangaroos hind limbs may be twice as long. An optional bipedal posture is usually associated with short arms and a stout muscular tail that is used for a prop (Fig. 3-17, *Tyrannosaurus*). Brachiating primates (primates that swing from branch to branch) have exceptionally long arms. The ability of any of these species to survive depends partly on these and other adaptations. Accounts of how appendages are used in varied locomotor activities will be found in references at the end of the chapter.

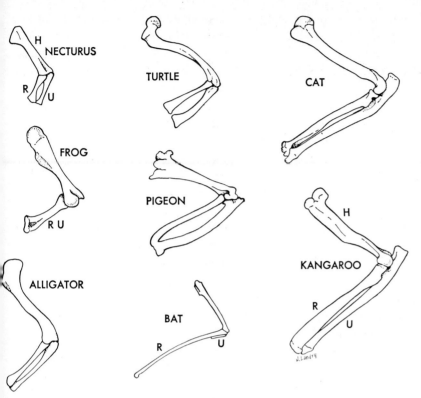

Fig. 9-18. Humerus, radius, and ulna of the left forelimb, lateral views. **H**, Humerus; **R**, radius; **U**, ulna. In the frog the radius and ulna have united to form a radioulna, **RU**. In the bat the ulna is vestigial.

Propodium and epipodium

The humerus is the bone of the upper arm. The similarity of the humeri of all tetrapods is more striking than any differences (Fig. 9-18). Variations in length, diameter, and shape are adaptive modifications. The odd humerus of the mole (Fig. 9-19), for example, has expansions for insertion of massive shoulder muscles for digging. The humeri of carinate birds have a slender central cavity containing diverticula from the lungs.

The radius and ulna are bones of the forearm. The radius is a preaxial (anterior) bone articulating proximally with the humerus and distally with wrist bones on the thumb side of the hand. The radius bears most of the force being transmitted from wrist to humerus. The ulna is a longer, postaxial bone articulating proximally with the humerus and radius and distally with wrist bones on the side opposite the thumb. The ulna sometimes fuses with the radius, or it may be vestigial (Fig. 9-18, frog and bat).

The femur is the bone of the thigh, and the tibia and fibula are bones of the lower leg (shank). The three bones differ relatively little

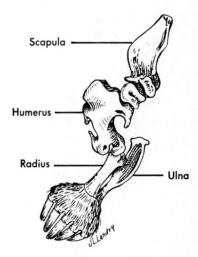

Fig. 9-19. Right anterior limb of a mole, which has been modified for digging. This is a medial view! The palms of a mole turn outward from the body.

from one tetrapod to another. A sesamoid bone, the **patella,** or kneecap, develops in birds and mammals. It ossifies in the tendon of insertion of the powerful extensor muscle of the thigh where the tendon passes over the complicated knee joint to insert on the tibia. The patella protects the joint from the abrasive action of the tendon. The fibula may unite partially or completely with the tibia (Fig. 9-20, mole and frog), it may be reduced to a splinter, as in birds, or it may be lost, as in ungulates (Fig. 9-20, deer). In birds the tibia fuses with the proximal row of tarsals to form a **tibiotarsus.**

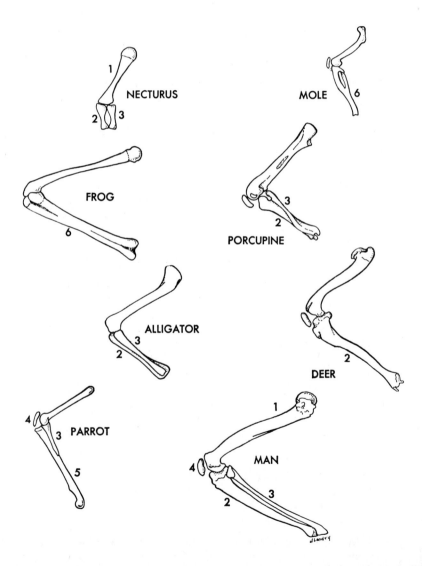

Fig. 9-20. Left thigh and shank bones of representative tetrapods, lateral views. **1,** Femur; **2,** tibia; **3,** fibula; **4,** patella; **5,** tibiotarsus; **6,** tibiofibula.

Manus: the hand

Wrist, palm, and digits constitute a functional unit, the hand, or manus. Considering the wide variety of modifications that have appeared since the labyrinthodonts, the hands of tetrapods are remarkably alike.

In generalized hands the wrist consists of three more or less regular rows of carpal bones (Fig. 9-17). The proximal row has a radial carpal (**radiale**) at the end of the radius, an ulnar carpal (**ulnare**) at the end of the ulna, and an **intermedium** between the two. At the ulnar end of the proximal row in most reptiles and mammals is a sesamoid bone, the **pisiform.** The middle row of carpals in a generalized hand consists of **centralia**—three or four in early tetrapods, two in early reptiles— one of which is sometimes displaced to the proximal or distal row of carpals. The distal row is composed of five **distal carpals** numbered 1 to 5 commencing on the thumb side. Table 9-2 lists the names of the carpal bones.

The metacarpals are the skeleton of the palm. Primitively, there were probably as many distal carpals and metacarpals as there were digits.

Each digit consists of phalanges. The generalized phalangeal formula commencing with the thumb is thought to have been 2-3-4-5-3, the formula in generalized reptiles. In late therapsids it had become 2-3-3-3-3, which is the formula for today's opossums and human beings.

Modifications of the manus with few exceptions involve *reduction in the number of bones by evolutionary loss or fusion.* A less common modification is the *disproportionate lengthening or shortening of*

Table 9-2. Synonymy of carpal bones

Terms preferred by comparative anatomists	Nomina anatomica*	Anglicized names and synonyms
Radiale	Os scaphoideum	Scaphoid, navicular
Intermedium	Os lunatum	Lunate, lunar, semilunar
Ulnare	Os triquetrum	Triquetral, cuneiform
Pisiform	Os pisiforme	Pisiform, ulnar sesamoid
Centralia (0 to 4)	Os centrale	Central carpal(s)
Distal carpal 1	Os trapezium	Trapezium, greater multangular
Distal carpal 2	Os trapezoideum	Trapezoid, lesser multangular
Distal carpal 3	Os capitatum	Capitate, magnum
Distal carpal 4 ⎫ Distal carpal 5 ⎭	Os hamatum	Hamate, unciform, uncinate

*Terms approved by the Eighth International Congress of Anatomists at Wiesbaden in 1965.

some of the bones. Least common is an *increase in the number of phalanges*. Centralia frequently unite with one of the proximal carpals or disappear. As a result, most reptiles and numerous mammals have a single centrale, and it is sometimes found among the proximal row of carpals. Fusion of distal carpals 4 and 5 is common and results in a **hamate bone.** Phalanges or entire digits may be lost. In the latter event the corresponding metacarpal becomes vestigial or lost.

Most modern amphibians have lost one digit in the manus while retaining five in the foot, and the corresponding metacarpal has been reduced or lost (Fig. 9-21). Several wrist bones in amphibians have been lost as independent bones because the embryonic intermedium and ulnare often unite, a proximal carpal often unites with an adjacent one, and fusion between centralia and proximal or distal carpals is common, as observed in embryos. Members of the urodele genus *Amphiuma* have one to three fingers (Chapter 3). The three distal carpals of *Necturus* have been considered to be, commencing on the radial side (Fig. 9-21), carpal 2, carpal 3, and hamate (fused carpals 4 and 5). However, it could be that the fifth finger rather than the

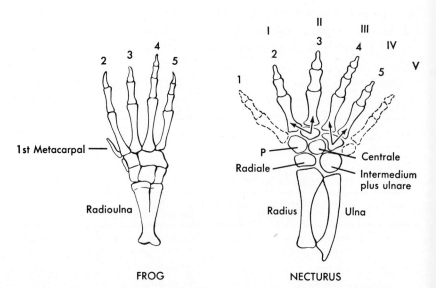

FROG NECTURUS

Fig. 9-21. Hands of *Rana catesbeiana* and *Necturus,* dorsal views. Which finger is missing in *Necturus?* Arabic numerals suggest that in a necturus the thumb, **1,** is missing and the little finger, **5,** is present. Roman numerals suggest that the thumb, **I,** is present and the little finger, **V,** and last distal carpal and metacarpal are missing. Arrows indicate existing muscle attachments. Broken lines represent nonexistent elements, one of which has been lost. **P,** Distal carpal number two or prepollex, depending on interpretation. In the frog shown, the bone at the base of the first metacarpal is probably a displaced centrale.

thumb is missing. The three distal carpals would then represent a prepollex (an extra bone that sometimes occurs near the thumb, or pollex), carpals 1 + 2, and carpals 3 + 4. Carpal 5 would be missing. This interpretation takes into account the fact that the bone labeled *P* in Fig. 9-21 has no muscle connecting it with a finger, and the muscle from the first and second digits attaches to the second of the three distal carpals. This carpal also frequently has double ossification centers. This is one of several approaches employed in attempting to determine homologies of the hand or foot in the absence of other conclusive date.

The muscles that insert on the hands and feet of urodeles are neither strong nor well differentiated, and the joints between the epipodia and wrists or ankles, and between the latter and the metapodia, are capable of little mobility. Thus neither the hands nor the feet of urodeles generate locomotor thrust. They are chiefly platforms, or podia, which, pressing on the substrate, provide friction while muscles higher on the limbs extend the legs. The same is true of the hands, but not the feet, of anurans.

The hands of living reptiles and primitive mammals such as insectivores and primates tend to remain pentadactyl and to have five metacarpals and a nearly full complement of carpals except centralia (Fig. 9-22, turtle and man). In crocodilians, however, the wrist has been reduced to five adult bones (Fig. 9-22, alligator), and in birds the entire manus has been reduced (Fig. 9-23). When present in mammals, the centrale may lie in the distal row of carpals, as in rabbits, or it may unite with the radiale and intermedium to form a bone (scapholunar) of triple origin, as in cats. Human fetuses have a centrale that remains as an independent center of ossification until the third fetal month. Among major modifications of the hand are those for flight, life in the ocean, swift-footedness, and grasping.

Adaptations for flight. In many birds the hand has little independent role in propulsion in air but, being at the end of an airfoil, it has an aerodynamic effect. Loss and fusion of bones have reduced the hand to a rigid, tapering structure (Fig. 9-23). Despite this, most of the basic components of tetrapod hands are identifiable in embryos. Two carpals (radiale and ulnare) form in the proximal row and three in the distal row. As development progresses the three distal carpals unite with the three metacarpals to form a rigid **carpometacarpus.** Three fingers are usually present, and the number of phalanges has been reduced. (Terns often develop four embryonic digits, but only three persist.) The fingers often bear claws that are used in nonaerial locomotion, and, like the rest of the hand, they are covered by feathers.

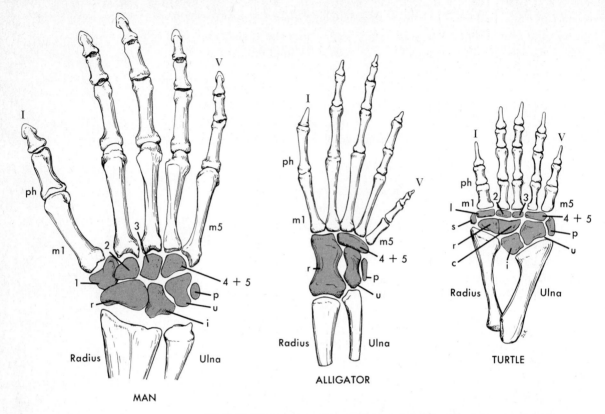

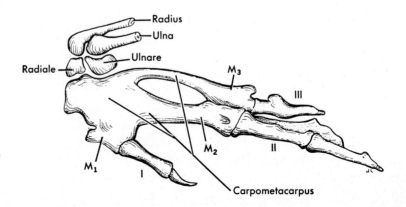

Fig. 9-22. Right manus of man, alligator, and turtle, dorsal views. **c,** Centrale; **i,** intermedium; **m1** and **m5,** first and fifth metacarpals; **p,** pisiform; **ph,** proximal phalanx; **r,** radiale; **s,** radial sesamoid; **u,** ulnare; **1** to **5,** distal carpals; **I** and **V,** first and fifth digits. The alligator has an additional carpal that cannot be seen from this view. Wrist bones are red.

Fig. 9-23. Left manus of a bird. **I** to **III,** Digits; M_1 to M_3, metacarpals fused with three distal carpals to form a carpometacarpus.

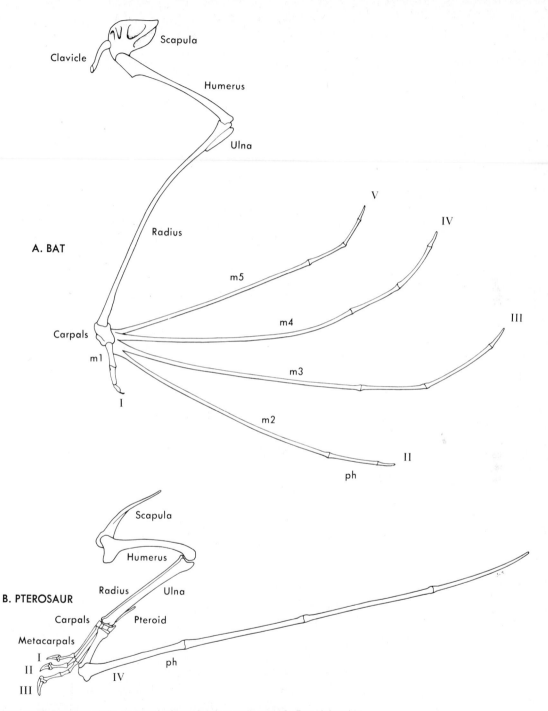

Clavicle

Scapula

Humerus

Ulna

A. BAT

Radius

V

IV

m5

III

m4

Carpals

m3

m1

I

m2

II

ph

B. PTEROSAUR

Scapula

Humerus

Radius   Ulna

Carpals   Pteroid

Metacarpals

I

II

III

IV

ph

Fig. 9-24. Pectoral girdle and limb of two flying vertebrates. **A,** Bat, right wing. **B,** Jurassic pterosaur, left wing. **m1** to **m5,** First through fifth metacarpals; **ph,** proximal phalanx; **I** to **V,** digits.

The first finger of birds that maneuver, alight, and take off in limited spaces is elongated, prominent, and independently movable and is called an **alula.** Songbirds have short, broad wings, and the feathered alula serves as an accessory airfoil at the leading edge of the wing as the bird flits among tree branches. Carnivorous birds have moderately long, broad wings adapted for slow speed flight and quick landings in limited spaces. When these birds are braking, the alula is moved away from the rest of the wing, which creates a slot through which air rushes, making it possible to maintain stable low-speed headway until additional braking is applied with the main wings and tail feathers. There is a joint with considerable flexibility at the elbow and another between the forearm and wrist, except in birds that hover. When flexed at the wrist, the hands exert a strong braking effect for landing, especially in birds with a large wingspread. Birds that hover have high-speed wings (up to 50 strokes per second in hummingbirds), the hand is as long as the arm or longer, and the entire wing is quite rigid.

Contrary to the condition in birds, the hand in pterosaurs and bats was, or is, the main part of the wing (Figs. 3-17, pterosaur; and 9-24). Pterosaurs had four fingers, three of which were normal and bore claws. The fourth was embedded in the wing membrane (**patagium**) and consisted of four enormously elongated phalanges that made this finger as long as the entire body. The associated metacarpal was not elongated, but it was much enlarged. Bats have five fingers. The thumb is normal and bears a claw. The other four fingers are elongated and are associated with four greatly elongated metacarpals. These, and the phalanges, constitute the skeleton of the patagium. The three proximal carpals are united in a single bone. Movement of the hand is responsible for takeoff and true flight in bats. No one has ever seen a pterosaur take off!

Flying lemurs have a patagium, but it is less well developed and the fingers, although embedded in it, are not elongated. Flying lemurs soar but are not capable of true flight. Patagiums in such unrelated animals as pterosaurs, bats, lemurs, and even flying lizards are instances of convergent evolution.

Adaptations for life in the ocean. The hands of ichthyosaurs (Figs. 9-25 and 9-26), plesiosaurs, some sea turtles, penguins, cetaceans, sirenians, seals, and seal lions have become paddlelike flippers. They are flattened, short, and stout, and in several groups the number of phalanges has greatly increased. In some ichthyosaurs there were as many as 26 phalanges per digit, or over 100 in a single hand. Dolphins show the same modification (Fig. 9-26). Within the flippers of most of the other swimmers, however, the bones conform closely to

Ichthyosaurus

Fig. 9-25. Jurassic and Cretaceous ocean-dwelling reptile, ranging up to 3 m in length. (From Colbert, E.H.: Evolution of the vertebrates, ed. 2, New York, 1969, John Wiley & Sons, Inc.)

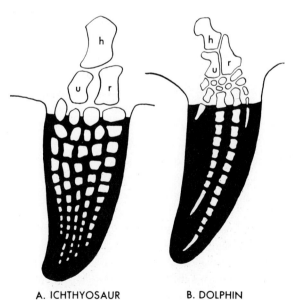

A. ICHTHYOSAUR   B. DOLPHIN

Fig. 9-26. Convergent evolution in anterior limbs. **A,** Extinct, water-dwelling reptile. **B,** Water-dwelling mammal. **h,** Humerus; **r,** radius; **u,** ulna.

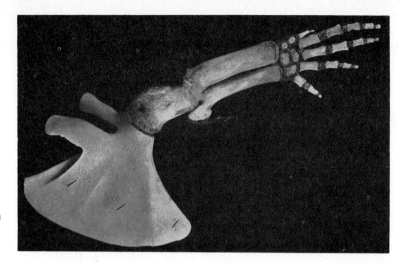

Fig. 9-27. Forelimb and pectoral girdle of a beaked whale. A remarkable resemblance to basic pattern remains, despite the fact that the limb has become paddlelike. (Courtesy American Museum of Natural History, New York.)

the generalized tetrapod pattern (Fig. 9-27). Some aquatic mammals have lost all traces of hind limbs (Fig. 9-28, *C*).

Adaptations for swift-footedness. Mammals with pentadactyl hands and feet are usually **plantigrade,** which means that the wrists, ankles, and digits all rest on the ground. This is a primitive tetrapod stance not associated with fleetness (Fig. 3-15). Generalized mammals— monotremes, marsupials, insectivores, primates—are plantigrade, and so are some specialized ones such as bears and the arboreal raccoons (Fig. 9-29, monkey). Mammals in which only the first digit has been reduced or lost tend to be **digitigrade,** which means that they bear their weight on digital arches with wrist and ankle elevated (Fig. 9-29, dog). Among digitigrade mammals are rabbits, rodents, and most carnivores. These mammals run faster, walk more silently, and are more agile than plantigrade species; and some, such as cats of various kinds, are the fastest runners of all (Fig. 10-10). Cheetahs, for instance, can sprint at an estimated 70 miles (112 km) per hour.[9] To a carnivore, speed makes eating more likely; to a herbivore such as a hare it may mean reaching a burrow instead of being eaten.

The extreme modification of reducing the number of digits and walking on the tips of the remaining ones is seen in **ungulates,** the hoofed mammals. Unguligrade mammals walk on four, three, two, or even one digit (Fig. 9-29, deer), with wrists and ankles elevated well above the ground. The claws have become thick hoofs that bear the body weight and protect the living tissues of the toes from the abrasive action of the substrate (Fig. 5-19). The metacarpals and metatarsals that correspond to the missing digits are vestigial or lost, and those that remain are much elongated and frequently united to form

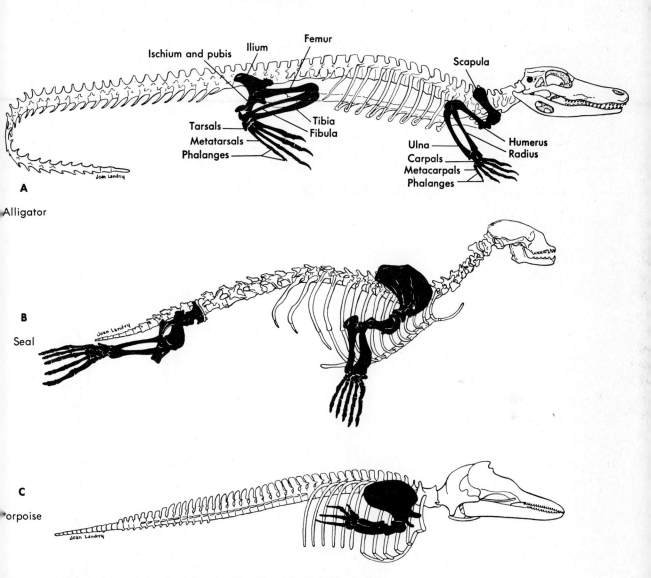

Fig. 9-28. A, Skeleton of a land-dwelling amniote. **B** and **C,** Skeletal adaptations for life in the water. Appendicular skeleton is shown in black. **B** is a "wriggling seal" *(Phoca).* In the seal and porpoise the hand is a paddle in which the phalanges are embedded.

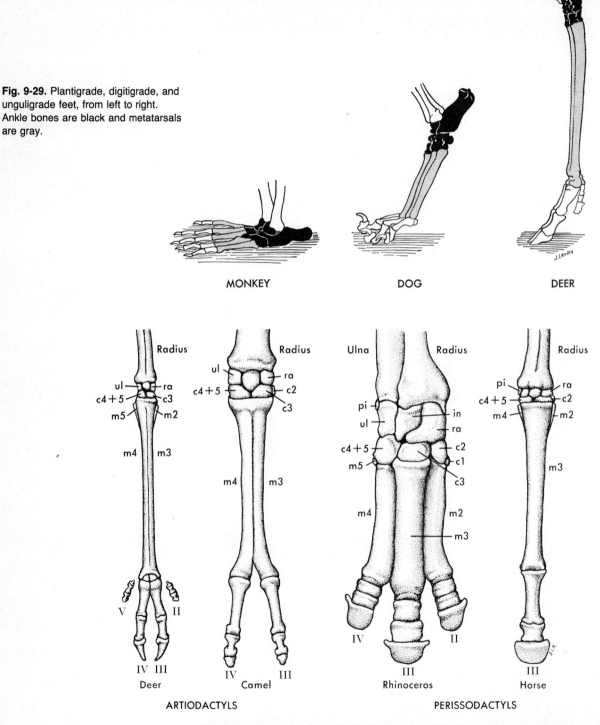

Fig. 9-29. Plantigrade, digitigrade, and unguligrade feet, from left to right. Ankle bones are black and metatarsals are gray.

MONKEY

DOG

DEER

Radius

ul — ra
c4+5 — c3
m5 — m2

m4 — m3

V — II

IV III
Deer

Radius

ul — ra
c4+5 — c2
— c3

m4 — m3

IV — III
Camel

ARTIODACTYLS

Ulna — Radius

pi
ul — in
— ra
c4+5 — c2
m5 — c1
— c3

m4 — m2

— m3

IV — II

III
Rhinoceros

Radius

pi — ra
c4+5 — c2
m4 — m2

m3

III
Horse

PERISSODACTYLS

Fig. 9-30. Right manus of several ungulates as seen from in front. **c2** to **c5**, Distal carpals 2 to 5; **in**, intermedium; **m2** to **m5**, metacarpals 2 to 5; **pi**, pisiform; **ra**, radiale; **ul**, ulnare; **II** to **V** digits.

a "cannon bone" (Fig. 9-30, horse, deer, camel). This had the effect of providing an additional slender distal segment to the limb. Although excelled in sprinting speed by some carnivorous digitigrade mammals, ungulates can sustain their speed for a much longer period of time. Not only are the feet of ungulates well suited for running, but also they function extremely well in rugged mountainous terrains. However, specialization has made their fingers and toes useless for anything else. This is the price of specialization.

Sequential evolutionary steps leading to the most specialized unguligrade stance may be illustrated by placing the fingers and palm flat on a tabletop with the forearm perpendicular to the surface. This represents roughly the plantigrade position. Raising the palm off the table while keeping the fingers flat on the table illustrates roughly the digitigrade position. Unguligrade conditions may be illustrated by placing only the fingertips on the table and then raising the thumb, the little finger, the second finger, and finally the fourth finger, leaving only the third finger to bear the body weight, as in modern horses. Those fingers that fail to reach the table represent digits that have been successively reduced or lost in ungulates.

The horse underwent these successive changes commencing with the early *Eohippus*, which had four digits on the manus, and culminating in the modern *Equus*, which has a single digit. Despite extreme specialization of the manus of the modern horse, the proximal row of carpals (Fig. 9-31) is intact, and the distal row lacks only the first carpal. With the loss of digits, I, II, IV, and V, metacarpals 1 and 5 have been lost, and 2 and 4 have been reduced to splinters. Metacarpal 3, associated with digit III, has elongated (Fig. 9-30).

Evolution among the ungulates seems to have progressed along two independent lines. In the line leading to **artiodactyls,** the weight of the body tended to be distributed equally between digits III and IV. Thus arose the "cloven" hoof (Fig. 9-32). Such a foot is said to be **paraxonic** because the body weight is borne on two parallel axes (Fig. 9-31, camel). Artiodactyls of today have an even number of digits. In the evolutionary line leading to **perissodactyls,** the body weight increasingly tended to be borne on digit III, the middle digit. This is a **mesaxonic** foot (Figs. 9-30 and 9-31, horse). Most perissodactyls have an odd number of digits; tapirs, however, have a small fourth digit on the front feet, three on the rear. It is the mesaxonic foot and not the number of digits that defines the perissodactyls.

Adaptations for grasping. Many mammals are able to flex their hand at the joint between palm and fingers. Rodents, for example, sit on their haunches and nibble on food held between *two hands,* which are flexed in this manner and *which face one another.* A further specialization is the ability to wrap the fingers (but not the thumb)

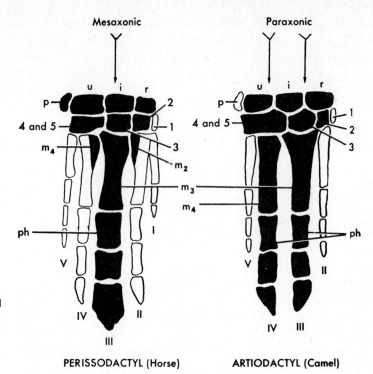

Fig. 9-31. Mesaxonic and paraxonic manus of representative ungulates, showing bones lost (white) and retained (black) and indicating distribution of body weight through wrist and digits. The horse and camel are used as specific examples, and the number of bony elements is correct for these animals. **i,** Intermedium; **m₂** to **m₄,** second, third, and fourth metacarpals; **p,** pisiform; **ph,** first phalanx; **r,** radiale; **u,** ulnare; **1** to **5,** distal carpals; **I** to **V,** digits.

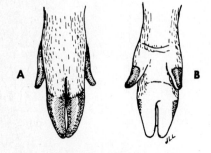

Fig. 9-32. Foot of fetal pig. There is a cleft between digits. Thus the hoof is "cloven." **A,** As seen from in front; **B,** as seen from behind.

around an object such as a pencil so that it is held securely in *one hand*. This is accomplished by flexing the fingers at each interphalangeal joint. Only primates can do that.

Another step in the evolution of the mammalian hand was development of an opposable thumb—one that can be made to touch the tips of each of the other digits. This was accomplished by formation of a saddle joint at the base of the thumb where it meets the palm, by setting the thumb at increasingly wider and wider angles to the index finger, and by the evolution of strong adductor pollicis (thumb) muscles. True opposability is found in Old World monkeys, but even there the hand does not have the full range of functional capability that has evolved in human beings. Neither New World monkeys nor anthropoid apes have a perfectly opposable thumb. With such a hand, humans were able to fashion increasingly sophisticated instruments, commencing with rocks chipped by design and continuing to the electronic computer. As John Napier[16] has said, "The implements of early man were as good (or as bad) as the hands that made them." Of course, evolution of the brain was an essential concomitant; still it seems impossible that any species on the planet earth lacking a prehensile hand, even having the brain, could evolve so sophisticated an existence.

Table 9-3. Comparison of skeletal elements of manus and pes

Manus*	Pes, with synonyms	
Radiale	Tibiale	Talus or astragalus†
Intermedium	Intermedium	
Ulnare	Fibulare	Calcaneus
Pisiform		
Centralia (0 to 4)	Centralia (0 to 4)	Navicular
Distal carpal 1	Distal tarsal 1	Entocuneiform
Distal carpal 2	Distal tarsal 2	Mesocuneiform
Distal carpal 3	Distal tarsal 3	Ectocuneiform
Distal carpal 4 } Hamate Distal carpal 5 }	Distal tarsal 4 } Distal tarsal 5 } Cuboid	
Metacarpals (1 to 5)	Metatarsals (1 to 5)	
Digits (I to V)	Digits (I to V)	

*For synonyms, see Table 9-2.
†Often incorporates the intermedium and a centrale.

Pes: the hind foot

The pes is comparable bone for bone with the manus except that there is no consistent equivalent of the pisiform bone (Table 9-3). Tetrapods primitively had four centralia in the pes. The number was reduced to one or two in primitive reptiles and to one in primitive mammals.

The pes of three amphibians is illustrated in Fig. 9-33. In anurans two stout proximal tarsals, tibiale and fibulare, are firmly united at each end to provide a strong mechanical brace terminating at an intratarsal joint. At the joint are two or three small distal tarsals, one of which may be a displaced centrale. This architecture provides a broad plantigrade foot for pushing off when jumping, the sole means of anuran locomotion on land.

Living reptiles display considerable phylogenetic loss and embryonic fusion of ankle bones, turtles to a lesser degree than others. The proximal row of tarsals is reduced to a single bone in *Sphenodon* and most lizards and has been given the name **astragalocalcaneus** (Fig. 9-34). It incorporates all proximal tarsal bones and a centrale. A highly flexible intratarsal joint between proximal and distal tarsals helps bipedal lizards to run rapidly in a digitigrade manner, the long tail maintaining balance by trailing on the ground. The primitive joint between leg and ankle in these lizards is immobilized by ligaments. Most reptiles have five toes, although alligators and some lizards have four and some freshwater turtles have three. The phalangeal formula for *Sphenodon*, 2-3-4-5-4, is the generalized formula for reptiles. Alligators have reduced it to 2-3-4-4-0 and turtles to 2-3-3-3-2.

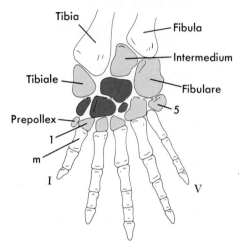

A. LABYRINTHODONT

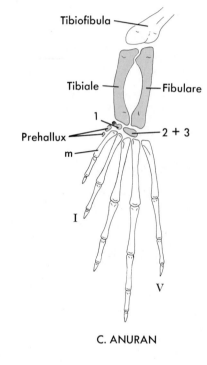

C. ANURAN

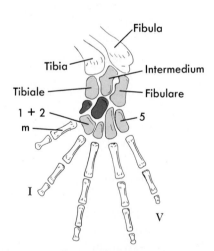

B. SALAMANDER

Fig. 9-33. Left pes of amphibians. **A,** Rachitomous labyrinthodont *Trematops.* **B,** Generalized plethodontid salamander *Hydromantes.* **C,** *Rana catesbeiana.* Tarsal bones are red, and centralia are darker. **I** and **V,** First and fifth digits; **1** to **5,** distal tarsals; **m,** metatarsal. (A after Schaeffer[14]; B after Wiedersheim.)

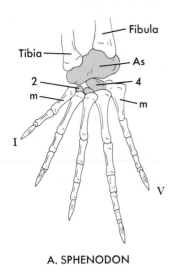

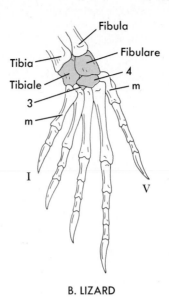

Fig. 9-34. Left pes of *Sphenodon* and the lizard *Uromastix*. **I** and **V,** First and fifth digits; **2** to **4,** distal tarsals; **As,** astragalocalcaneus; **m,** metatarsal.

A. SPHENODON

B. LIZARD

A bird's foot is highly modified (Fig. 9-35). The proximal tarsals are united with the lower end of the tibia to form a **tibiotarsus,** there are no centralia, and the distal tarsals are united with the second, third, and fourth metatarsals to form a long, rigid **tarsometatarsus.** A first metatarsal remains in some species. There is an intratarsal joint between the tibiotarsus and tarsometatarsus, and a joint between the tarsometatarsus and the toes. The latter permits a digitigrade stance. Because of the direction in which the head of the femur approaches the acetabulum, the femur is horizontal when a bird is standing, so it is actually resting on its thighs much like a person when squatting. This stance keeps the bird in a "ready" position for takeoff, since extending the leg at the knee and intratarsal joint gives the initial thrust for becoming airborne. The thigh of a standing bird is not visible because it is quite short and, along with the knee, it is tucked away under the feathers.

Most birds have four toes, a few have three; ostriches alone have two. The phalangeal formula is the same as that for the first four toes of *Sphenodon*. Usually, three toes are directed radially forward and one comes off the back of the foot; but a few birds, including woodpeckers and parrots, have two toes at the back, the four forming an **X (zygodactyly).** The arrangement, plus exceptionally stiff tail feathers, enables woodpeckers to prop themselves against a vertical tree trunk and brace themselves while drilling. Birds can sleep while on a perch because the long tendons of the muscles of the shank pass along the posterior aspect of the ankle to insert on the claw-bearing

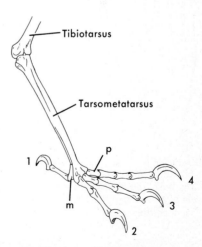

Fig. 9-35. Left ankle and digits of a passerine bird, medial view, head to the right. **1** to **4,** Digits; **m,** first metatarsal; **p,** phalanx.

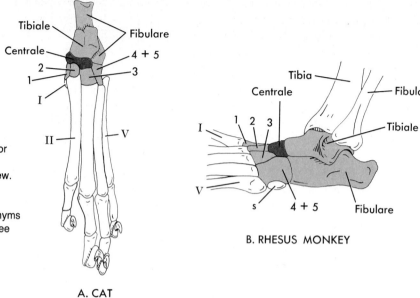

Fig. 9-36. **A,** Left pes of cat, anterior view. **B,** Left ankle and associated bones of rhesus monkey, lateral view. **1** to **5,** Distal tarsals; **I, II,** and **V,** metatarsals; **s,** sesamoid in the peroneus longus muscle. For synonyms for mammalian ankle bones (red) see Table 9-3.

A. CAT

B. RHESUS MONKEY

MONKEY   MAN

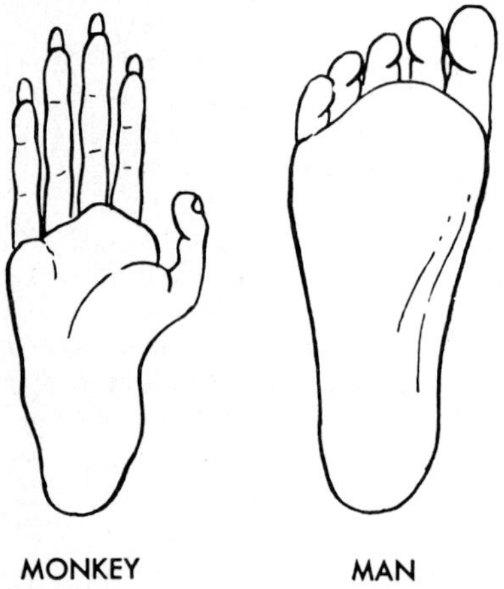

Fig. 9-37. The partially opposable big toe of an Old World monkey and the nonopposable toe of man.

digits. The weight of the body stretches the tendons and keeps the claws flexed around the perch.

Mammals, like their therapsid ancestors, lack an intratarsal joint but have a large hinge joint between tibia and tibiale (**astragalus**), which is the weight-bearing articulation between leg and ankle (Fig. 9-36, *B*). The other proximal tarsal, the fibulare (**calcaneus**), is elongated upward in digitigrade and unguligrade mammals and backward in plantigrade mammals (Fig. 9-29) to become the heel on which the postaxial gastrocnemius muscle of the calf inserts via Achilles tendon. Most of the primitive tarsal bones are retained (Fig. 9-36, *A*). In hominoids a metatarsal arch, or instep, distributes the body weight over four solid bases, the heel and ball of each foot. DuBrul[3] has compared this with the four-pedestal architecture of the Eiffel Tower. The arch also absorbs some of the shock generated by bipedal locomotion and provides "spring" for walking and running.

The phalangeal formula for early mammals was 2-3-3-3-3, and this is still the formula for opossums. The big toe as well as the thumb are opposable in many primates but not in human beings (Fig. 9-37). An opposable first digit is correlated with brachiation.

LOCOMOTION WITHOUT LIMBS

Limbs provide traction and leverage for locomotion on land. Snakes and limbless lizards cannot gain traction in this manner; yet they are highly successful on land because modifications of the vertebral column, ribs, body wall muscles, and skin, among others, have provided them with alternative methods of moving about.

The most common method of locomotion in snakes, and also in limbless lizards, is by forming irregular loops that become propped against, and push against, any available stationary object on their path, such as a clump of vegetation, a rock, a root, or simply an irregularity of the surface. The process is illustrated in Fig. 9-38 and explained in the accompanying legend. While the animal is moving, the eyes, which are close to the ground, constantly scan the substrate for the next contact point. When one looms, the head is thrust in that direction. Upon contact a wave of muscular contraction commences at the head and travels to the last segment of the tail, which is pulled forward in its turn. A minimum of three contact sites are necessary for this mode of locomotion, and no appreciable force is exerted downward against the ground. This mode of locomotion, referred to as **serpentine,** or **lateral undulation,** is a modification of the swimming movements of fishes. A basic necessity is a body that is metameric with respect to the skeletomuscular system.

Some snakes glide—seemingly flow—forward while keeping the entire body in a straight line, a spectacle that some viewers find unnerving! The ventral skin acts like a conveyor belt, sections of which stop and go. This has been termed **rectilinear locomotion,** and it depends on generating friction between sections of the ventral skin and the substrate. Unlike snakes that press laterally against contact points for leverage, these snakes press against the ground, using bunched groups of belly scutes as intermittent holdfasts. After a brief interval of holding, during which time the next more caudal group of scutes is catching up, the downward pressure exerted by the first group is released, and the group flows forward, stretched out and elevated from the substrate, until it catches up with the group ahead. Meanwhile, the group immediately behind is holding fast. Thus rhythmical waves of forward flowing and resting scutes sweep along the body from head to tail. The skin, like that of many other snakes, is only loosely attached to the underlying tissues, there is much elastic tissue in the dermis, and the scutes, approximately one body segment long, overlap and are connected to the next by a pleat of cutaneous membrane that unfolds during movement. This combination of factors enables each scute to be released from the ground and commence its forward movement an instant before the next. Two sets of striated muscles are responsible for rectilinear locomotion. A pair of slender costocutaneus muscles extends downward and backward from high on each rib to the dermis at the edges of each scute. When these contract they lift the scute off the substrate so that it no longer serves as a holdfast, and they draw it forward while stretching the interscutal

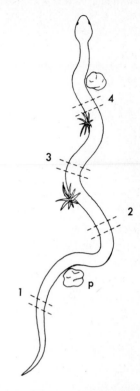

Fig. 9-38. Serpentine locomotion. Forward progression is achieved by exerting pressure against contact points, or props, **p**, on the path. The head moves forward to a new contact point, and the rest of the body follows the established looping path, the segment at position 1 moving successively to positions 2, 3, and 4 while the loops remain stationary with reference to the contact points. Eventually, each loop will be at the end of the tail and new loops will have formed anteriorly. Any track consists of sinuous waves.

membrane. A second pair, more powerful, extends less obliquely from a scute to the lower end of a more caudal rib. Contraction of the latter maintains the forward movement of the body mass within the skin envelope. Amphisbaenians use rectilinear progression, but the entire skin moves, not just the ventral skin. Amphisbaenians resemble crawling earthworms.

Sidewinding, illustrated in Fig. 9-39 and described in the legend, enables rattlesnakes and other snakes to occupy sandy deserts, where the ground offers too few stationary contact points for lateral undulation and is too unstable to provide sustained friction for rectilinear locomotion. Sidewinding is also used by many snakes in other environments when they are temporarily in a situation, probably infrequent, where, because of the nature of the surface, other methods of locomotion would be clumsy or ineffectual. In sand, the body usually occupies two or three tracks at a time, and more or less of the anterior quarter of the snake is thrust forward to start a new one.

Burrowing snakes propel themselves in the burrow by modified lateral undulation, bracing S-shaped loops against the burrow wall and exerting horizontal force against the wall as contraction waves sweep from head to tail, propelling the body mass forward. From the first brace the head is thrust forward, after which it establishes a new brace. Successive sections then move forward from succeeding braces and new loops are established anteriorly. The process, reminiscent of the operation of the bellows when a concertina (accordion) is being

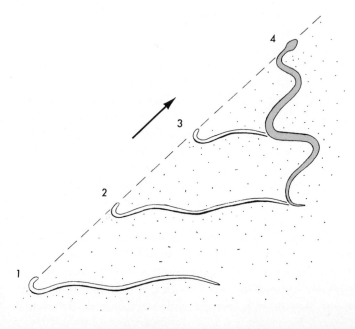

Fig. 9-39. Locomotion in sidewinder snakes. **1** to **4,** Successive tracks in sand left when the head and neck are lifted from the ground, thrust forward, and set down firmly at the next position. The body does not touch the ground between tracks. The rest of the body is "flowing" above ground to the new position. Dotted lines and arrow indicate direction of movement.

played, has been called **concertina** movement. The method in combination with constrictor movements and others is used in climbing trees, especially when following channels in the bark. A long snake often combines lateral undulation with concertina movement in appropriate habitats as a common method of going from place to place.[16]

All the foregoing methods of locomotion are made possible by vertebral columns consisting of up to 400 or more highly flexible intervertebral joints; by exceptional ribs that extend from the atlas to the tip of the tail and reach almost to the midventral line; by the unusually large number of muscle bundles that interconnect vertebrae and connect vertebrae with ribs; by wide, smooth, overlapping horny ventral scutes interconnected by pleated membranes; by the exceptional elasticity of the dermis; and by loose skin that allows independent movement of skin and enclosed body mass. These are the more obvious features that facilitate locomotion without limbs on land. Most systems had to undergo modification in one way or another for the foregoing adaptations to be effective.

THE ORIGIN OF LIMBS

Although the problem of the origin of paired fins may never be satisfactorily resolved, this is not true of the origin of tetrapod limbs. All evidence points to the origin of tetrapods from fishes, and so the paired fins of some ancient fish must have been the precursors of tetrapod limbs. The question then arises: Did the skeleton of the fin of any known Devonian fish evince the potentiality of becoming a limb? For an answer we turn to the lobe-finned crossopterygians, which resembled the first tetrapods in many respects.

The skeleton in the basal lobe of rhipidistian crossopterygian fins bears a striking resemblance to that in a tetrapod limb (Fig. 9-40). In crossopterygians a single bone (we will call it a "humerus") articulates proximally with the scapula and distally with a pair of bones (we will call them "radius" and "ulna"). Loss of the fin rays and relatively minor modifications of the fin distal to the radius and ulna could have produced the first tetrapod limb. Westoll[18] has proposed that the first two rows of carpals and tarsals may be modified radials and the more distal bones may have evolved from new ossification centers; that is, they are cenogenic. Meanwhile, the girdles of the labyrinthodonts remained fishlike, except that the pelvic girdle acquired an ilium.

It is possible that crossopterygian fins were used sometimes as props for resting on the water bottom, without bearing any appreciable weight. Minor modifications would have permitted "walking" on the muddy or sandy bottoms close to shore. Several hundred living species of fishes do this, including the Australian lungfish. Some liv-

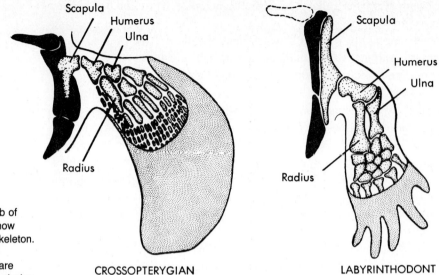

CROSSOPTERYGIAN

LABYRINTHODONT

Fig. 9-40. Pectoral fin of crossopterygian fish and forelimb of primitive tetrapod, oriented to show similarity of proximal bones of skeleton. Dermal bones are black, and replacement bones or cartilage are stippled. Dotted line represents missing girdle bone. The "ulna" and "radius" of the crossopterygian are enlarged radials.

ing fishes move several feet inland nightly. Some climb inclined planes with little fins that have a remarkable resemblance to hands.

The pressures that drove vertebrates onto the land must, of necessity, be conjectural. It may be that there were fewer predators on land, that there was less competition for food, or simply that food was abundant on land. Or perhaps it was simply a manifestation of the tendency of organisms to invade a contiguous environment whenever nothing prevents the invasion. Whatever the explanation, it seems that it was almost inevitable that a limb more suitable for life on land would evolve sooner or later from the fin of a fish.

CHAPTER SUMMARY

1. The appendicular skeleton consists of pectoral and pelvic girdles and the skeleton of the fins or limbs.

2. All pectoral girdles are modifications of a basic architectural pattern seen in early bony fishes. Three of the components are cartilages or endochondral bones derived from the endoskeleton. The other components are membrane bones derived from dermal armor.

3. Coracoids, scapulae, and suprascapulae are endoskeletal. Coracoids are absent above monotremes. Scapulae are almost universal.

4. Clavicles, cleithra, supracleithra, posttemporals, and postcleithra are dermal bones. Cleithra and supracleithra are confined to fishes. Clavicles occur in most classes and are best developed in tetrapods. A midventral interclavicle of intramembranous origin is found in reptiles, birds, and monotremes.

5. Recent bony fishes have tended to lose the replacement bones. Tetrapods have tended to lose dermal bones.

6. The pelvic girdle of fishes consists of two pelvic (ischiopubic) plates. These usually meet ventrally in a pelvic symphysis and articulate laterally with a pelvic fin. The two plates unite to form a median bar in sharks and lungfishes.

7. In tetrapods two ossification centers in each pelvic plate become ischial and pubic bones that may form symphyses. An ilium braces the girdle against the vertebral column. There is no dermal armor in the pelvic girdle.

8. Additional small bones commonly associated with the pelvic girdle include epipubics and hypoischials.

9. The ilium, ischium, and pubis unite to form an innominate bone (coxa) in mammals. It encloses an obturator foramen. The sacrum and pelvic girdle constitute a pelvis that encloses a pelvic cavity.

10. Excepting sesamoids, appendicular bones distal to the girdles arise by endochondral ossification.

11. Paired fins are of three types: lobed fins (Sarcopterygii) with a central jointed axis and preaxial and postaxial radials; fin fold fins (Chondrichthyes) with a proximal row of basals and distal rows of radials; and ray fins (Actinopterygii), reduced to a few short radials or none and supported chiefly by fin rays.

12. Median fins have a skeleton of radials and rays. The caudal fins of teleosts also contain a urostyle and hypural bones. Caudal fins include diphycercal, heterocercal, homocercal, and hypocercal varieties.

13. The origin of fins is unknown. Fin fold, gill arch, and fin spine hypotheses have been proposed.

14. Tetrapod limb skeletons consist of a propodium, epipodium, mesopodium, metapodium, and phalanges. The last three constitute the manus or pes.

15. The orientation of the bones, relative mobility of the joints, and complexity of the muscles determine the nature of the locomotor activities of the various tetrapods.

16. Structural modifications of the manus and pes involve reduction in the number of bones, disproportionate lengthening or shortening of segments, and, in some aquatic tetrapods, increase in number of phalanges.

17. Digits have been reduced to four or fewer in modern amphibians, three in birds, and as few as one in some ungulates. Loss of digits is accompanied by loss or reduction of associated carpals and metacarpals or tarsals and metatarsals.

18. The most striking modifications of the manus are in flying tetrapods (pterosaurs, birds, bats), water-adapted reptiles and mammals (ichthyosaurs, plesiosaurs, cetaceans, sirenians), and ungulates. A few species lack one or both pairs of limbs.

19. Mammalian stances are plantigrade, digitigrade, and unguligrade. Ungulate feet are hoofed and either mesaxonic (perissodactyls) or paraxonic (artiodactyls).

20. Birds have no free ankle bones, one free metatarsal, and two to four toes, and they are digitigrade. Some swift lizards are digitigrade while running.

21. Snakes move by lateral undulation, sidewinding, or rectilinear or concertina movements.

22. Tetrapod limbs appear to be modifications of a lobed fin resembling that of rhipidistian crossopterygians.

LITERATURE CITED AND SELECTED READINGS

1. Alberch, P.: Convergence and parallelism in foot morphology in the neotropical salamander genus *Bolitoglossa*. I. Function, Evolution **35**:84, 1981.
2. Alexander, R.M., and Goldspink, G., editors: Mechanics and energetics of animal locomotion, London, 1977, Chapman & Hall Ltd.
3. Du Brul, E.L.: Biomechanics of the body. BSCS Pamphlet, no. 5, Boston, 1965, D.C. Heath & Co.
4. Elder, H.Y., and Trueman, E.R., editors: Aspects of animal movement, Cambridge, England, 1980, Cambridge University Press.
5. Gans, C.: Tetrapod limblessness: evolution and functional corollaries, American Zoologist **15**:455, 1975.
6. Goodrich, E.S.: Studies on the structure and development of vertebrates, London, 1930, The Macmillan Co., Ltd. (Reprinted by Dover Publications, Inc., New York, 1958.)
7. Goslow, G.E., Reinking, R.M., and Stuart, D.G.: The cat step cycle: hind limb joint angles and muscle lengths during unrestrained locomotion, Journal of Morphology **141**: 1, 1973.
8. Gregory, W.K., and Raven, H.C.: Studies on the origin and early evolution of paired fins and limbs, Annals of the New York Academy of Sciences **42**:273, 1941.
9. Hildebrand, M.: The adaptive significance of tetrapod gait selection, American Zoologist **20**:255, 1980.
10. Lande, R.: Evolutionary mechanisms of limb loss in tetrapods, Evolution **32**:73, 1978.
11. Ostrom, J.H.: Bird flight: how did it begin? American Scientist **67**(1):46, 1979.
12. Rackoff, J.S.: The origin of the tetrapod limb and the ancestry of tetrapods. In Panchen, A.L., editor: The terrestrial environment and the origin of land vertebrates, New York, 1980, Academic Press, Inc.
13. Romer, A.S.: Osteology of the reptiles, Chicago, 1956, University of Chicago Press.
14. Schaeffer, B.: The morphological and functional evolution of the tarsus in amphibians and reptiles, Bulletin of the Museum of Natural History **78**:395, 1941.
15. Snyder, R.C.: Adaptations for bipedal locomotion of lizards, American Zoologist **2**:191, 1962.
16. Vertebrate structures and functions: readings from Scientific American with introductions by Norman K. Wessells, San Francisco, 1955-1974, W.H. Freeman and Co., Publishers. Includes Gray, J.: How fishes swim; Hildebrand, M.: How animals run; Gans, C.: How snakes move; Napier, J.: The antiquity of human walking; Napier, J.: The evolution of the hand; and Welty, C.: Birds as flying machines.
17. Walker, A.D.: Evolution of the pelvis in birds and dinosaurs. In Andrews, S.M., Miles, R.A., and Walker, A.D., editors: Problems in vertebrate evolution, New York, 1977, Academic Press, Inc.
18. Westoll, T.S.: The origin of the primitive tetrapod limb, Proceedings of the Royal Society of London, Series B **131**:373, 1943.

19. Westoll, T.S.: The lateral fin-fold theory and the pectoral fins of ostracoderms and early fishes. In Westoll, T.S., editor: Studies on fossil vertebrates, London, 1958, University of London Press.

20. Wu, T.Y.-T., Browkaw, C.J., and Brennen, C., editors: Swimming and flying in nature, New York, 1975, Plenum Press.

CHAPTER 10

Muscles

Muscle is a tissue specialized to do one thing, and to do it well: to shorten when stimulated. Shortening is a result of chemical changes in two muscle proteins, actin and myosin. Shortening of a sufficient number of fibers causes a corresponding shortening and fattening of the entire muscle mass. If the muscle surrounds a lumen, the lumen is compressed. If it extends between two structures, one of these is drawn toward the other. The usual stimulus for muscle contraction is a nerve impulse (Fig. 10-1).

CLASSIFICATION OF MUSCLES

Muscles may be classified according to several criteria. When classified histologically, muscles may be **striated** or **smooth.** Striated muscle tissue is composed of long multinucleate muscle fibers (Fig. 16-20), each fiber containing bundles of myofibrils, which, in turn, are composed of filaments of the contractile protein, actinomyosin. Because of the chemical structure of actinomyosin, myofibrils have dark bands that, when aligned, give the muscle fiber a striated appearance (Fig. 10-1). Striated muscle fibers are usually assembled to form an organ (a striated muscle). However, wisps of them are found among other tissues in numerous locations. A muscle fiber contracts when stimulated by a neurotransmitter released at a motor end-plate by a motor nerve fiber (Fig. 10-1). Unlike striated muscle, smooth muscle occurs most often in sheets as part of an organ. The cells are spindle shaped and uninucleate and lack striations (Fig. 10-2). **Cardiac muscle** is a special type of striated muscle found in the heart wall.

Muscles may be either **voluntary** or **involuntary** according to whether they can be operated at will. Voluntary muscles contract at will unless they are fatigued. This does not mean that they may not be operated unintentionally (reflexly) if the body is endangered, as when the skin comes in contact unexpectedly with a pin. Involuntary muscles, on the contrary, are not ordinarily contracted at will, being predominantly under reflex control.

In this chapter we will study chiefly the skeletal muscles. We will classify muscles from several viewpoints and then examine them in major functional groups, observing the generalized vertebrate pattern and seeing how the pattern was modified as vertebrates became increasingly adapted for life on land.

Muscles attached to the skeleton are **skeletal muscles** and are striated and voluntary. Skeletal muscles are disposed in accordance with a generalized pattern evident in fishes but recognizable in higher vertebrates. Evolutionary modifications of the basic pattern are correlated chiefly with assumption of life on land. Muscles not attached to the skeleton must be referred to as **nonskeletal,** since no other term (smooth, involuntary, etc.) is the exact opposite of the word skeletal. Nevertheless, most nonskeletal muscles are smooth and involuntary.

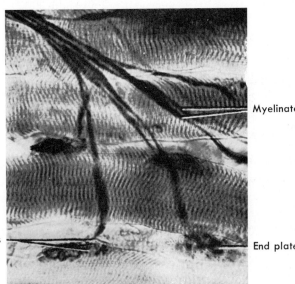

Fig. 10-1. Striated muscle fibers innervated by myelinated nerve fibers that end on motor end-plates. (From Bevelander, G., and Ramaley, J.A.: Essentials of histology, ed. 8, St. Louis, 1979, The C.V. Mosby Co.)

Myelinated fibers

Naked fibers

End plate

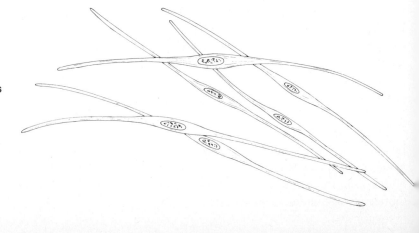

Fig. 10-2. Isolated smooth muscle cells from intestine.

If one uses the foregoing criteria, most of the muscles could be classified according to the following scheme:

Skeletal, striated, voluntary muscles
    Axial
        Body wall and tail
        Hypobranchial and tongue
        Extrinsic eyeball
    Appendicular
    Branchiomeric
    Integumentary
Nonskeletal, smooth, involuntary muscles
    Muscles of tubes, vessels, and hollow organs
    Intrinsic eyeball muscles
    Erectors of feathers and hairs
Cardiac muscle
Electric organs

The foregoing categories are not mutually exclusive and no such scheme can be devised. Some branchiomeric muscles have become secondarily associated with the appendages, the intrinsic ciliary muscles of the eyeball of reptiles and birds are often striated, and erectors of feathers and hairs are smooth integumentary muscles.

It is sometimes convenient or appropriate to classify muscles as somatic or visceral. In general, **somatic muscles** orient the animal (its body, or soma) with respect to the external environment. They enable an animal to go deeper into an environment to pursue food or a mate and to withdraw from an environment that is hazardous. Therefore skeletal muscles, other than those of the visceral arches (branchiomeric muscles), are somatic.

The chief role of **visceral muscle** is to maintain an appropriate internal milieu. It is the muscle of hollow organs, vessels, tubes, and ducts; the intrinsic muscle of the eyeball (iris diaphragm, ciliary body, campanula); the erectors of hairs and feathers; and the striated muscles of the jaws and remaining visceral arches. Visceral muscle compresses lumens as in emptying bladders or heart; causes peristalsis, which propels substances within tubes; and serves as sphincter and dilator muscles in such diverse locations as the iris diaphragm, pyloric sphincter, and gill pouches.

If one wishes to classify musculature on the basis of whether it is somatic or visceral, a scheme somewhat like the following would be useful:

Somatic muscles
    Muscles of the body wall and tail
    Hypobranchial and tongue muscles
    Extrinsic eyeball muscles
    Appendicular muscles

Table 10-1. Some contrasts between somatic and visceral muscles

Somatic muscles	Visceral muscles except branchiomeric
Striated, skeletal, voluntary	Smooth, nonskeletal, involuntary
Primitively segmented	Unsegmented
Arise primitively from somites (**myotomal muscle**)	Arise mostly from lateral mesoderm*
Mostly in body wall and appendages	Mostly in splanchnopleure†
Primarily for orientation in external environment	Regulate internal environment
Innervated directly by spinal nerves and cranial nerves III, IV, VI, XII	Innervated by postganglionic fibers of autonomic nervous system‡

*Branchiomeric muscles arise from ectomesenchyme.
†Those in the body wall erect hairs or feathers or constrict blood vessels.
‡Branchiomeric muscles are innervated by cranial nerves V, VII, IX, and X.

Visceral muscles
    Branchiomeric muscles
    Muscles of tubes, vessels, hollow organs
    Intrinsic eyeball muscles
    Erectors of feathers and hairs
    Cardiac muscle

As in the preceding classification, the above categories are not mutually exclusive. A few appendicular muscles are branchiomeric, erectors of feathers and hairs are in the body wall, and electric organs have been omitted because some are somatic and some are visceral.

Except for branchiomeric muscles, visceral muscles exhibit few evolutionary changes throughout the vertebrate series and will receive little attention in this chapter. Some contrasts between somatic and visceral muscles are presented in Table 10-1.

INTRODUCTION TO SKELETAL MUSCLES
Skeletal muscles as organs

A skeletal muscle is an organ just as the stomach is, and the organs constitute a **skeletal muscle system.** Skeletal muscles consist of **muscular** and **tendinous portions.** The tendinous portions are part of the muscle and are extensions of its tough connective tissue sheath (**muscle fascia,** or **epimysium**) and of the connective tissue within the muscle. The tendinous portions anchor the muscle to its origins and insertions.

The **anatomical origin** of a muscle is the site of attachment that,

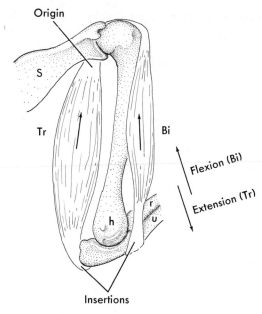

Origin

S

Tr

Bi

Flexion (Bi)

Extension (Tr)

r

u

h

Insertions

Fig. 10-3. Origin, insertion, and direction of tensile force exerted by two muscles of the right upper arm of a rabbit, lateral view. Arrows within muscles indicate direction of pull on the forearm; arrows at right indicate direction of displacement of forearm when muscles contract. **Bi,** biceps brachii (preaxial); **h,** humerus at elbow; **r,** radius; **s,** scapula; **Tr,** long head of triceps brachii (postaxial); **u,** ulna. **Tr** provides the motive power for a first class lever and **Bi** for a third class lever. The two muscles must operate synergistically, monitored by proprioceptive feedback to the central nervous system to effect smooth operation of the forearm against a load.

under most functional conditions, remains fixed; that is, the structure on which it originates is not displaced when the muscle contracts. For example, when the biceps muscle of the upper arm contracts, the forearm is drawn toward the upper arm. The origin is, therefore, somewhere above the elbow (Fig. 10-3). The **insertion** of a muscle is the site of attachment that is normally displaced by contraction of the muscle. The biceps referred to above inserts on a bone of the forearm. A muscle may cause displacement of the origin instead of the insertion if the latter becomes immobilized by other muscles. For example, the geniohyoid muscle, which is attached to the hyoid bone and to the lower jaw at the chin, either lowers the jaw or draws the hyoid forward, depending on which one is immobilized at the time.

Muscles with a pronounced bulge in the middle are said to have a **belly.** Some muscles are straplike, or broad and flat, and have no belly. Broad, flat muscles usually have broad tendons. Such a tendon is an **aponeurosis.** Broad muscles that insert on connective tissue raphes (seams) such as the linea alba or the raphe in the floor of the buccal cavity may compress a cavity and the organs within it.

During dissection of adult mammals, students frequently notice that skeletal muscles vary in size in the two sexes. Androgens, the predominant gonadal hormones of males, cause amino acids to be linked together into polypeptides and proteins. Since muscle is 80% protein, androgen results in statistically demonstrable larger muscles in males. This confers on the male an added advantage during mating, which increases the likelihood of impregnation of all ovulated eggs in a population and therefore the probability of survival of the species.

Actions of skeletal muscles

Skeletal muscles may be grouped according to their function. **Flexors** bend and **extensors** straighten a structural complex, such as an arm or leg. **Adductors** draw a part toward the midline; **abductors** cause displacement away from the midline. **Protractors** cause a part, such as the tongue or hyoid, to be thrust forward or outward; **retractors** pull it back. **Levators** raise a part; **depressors** lower it. **Rotators** cause rotation of a part on its axis. **Supinators** are rotators that turn the palm upward, **pronators** make it prone (turn it downward). **Tensors** make a part such as the eardrum more taut. **Constrictors** compress internal parts. **Sphincters** are constrictors that make an opening smaller; **dilators** have an opposite effect. Most sphincter and dilator muscles are nonskeletal.

It is exceptional for a single skeletal muscle to act independently of other muscles. Instead, muscles nearly always cooperate in functional groups. While one functional group is contracting, another group ("antagonistic muscles") must relax simultaneously, or a stalemate would result. In order that muscles may act cooperatively (synergistically), they must be reflexly directed by the nervous system, just as the musicians in a symphony orchestra must be directed by a conductor. The reflex control of skeletal muscles comes chiefly from the cerebellum, which sends motor impulses to appropriate muscles after receiving incoming information. The information is in the form of feedback over sensory fibers from muscle spindles, from tendons, and from the bursae of affected joints. The sensory phenomenon is known as proprioception (Chapter 16).

Names and homologies of skeletal muscles

Skeletal muscles have been named for the direction of their fibers (oblique, rectus), location or position (thoracis, supraspinatus, superficial), number of divisions (triceps), shape (deltoid, teres, serratus), origin and/or insertion (xiphihumeralis, stapedius), action (levator scapulae, risorius), size (major, longissimus), and for still other reasons including a combination of these. Insight into the significance of a muscle's name should aid in recalling more information about a muscle.

Names were given to human muscles several hundred years ago, and many of these names are still used. Frequently, these names were applied later to the corresponding muscles of animals, especially tetrapods. But the fact that two muscles in two different vertebrate groups bear the same name is no assurance that the two are homologous, and the less related the animals, the more likely it is that they may not be. One reason is that some muscles have apparently shifted their attachments from time to time, and so similarity of origin and insertion is not a highly reliable criterion for homology. An example is the genioglossus muscle, which inserts on the mammalian tongue. The probable homologue in some birds inserts on the sublingual seed pouch. Embryonic origin and nerve supply are considered more reliable criteria; yet these too, may sometimes lead to false assumptions. On the other hand, homologies between *functional groups* of muscles of vertebrates may be deduced with a much greater degree of reliability.

AXIAL MUSCLES

Axial muscles are the skeletal muscles of the trunk and tail. They extend forward beneath the pharynx as hypobranchial muscles and muscles of the tongue and are present in the orbits as extrinsic muscles of the eyeballs.

The immediately evident gross feature of axial muscles in generalized vertebrates is their metamerism (Fig. 10-4). This primitive condition along with a flexible vertebral column enables fishes and many aquatic tetrapods to propel themselves in water by rhythmical lateral undulatory movements that sweep from head to tail, which is how fishes swim (Fig. 10-5). These muscles perform the same function for limbless tetrapods living on land. In higher tetrapods some of the metamerism became obscured when paired appendages took over responsibility for locomotion on land; nevertheless, much of the axial musculature is metameric, even in humans.

The axial muscles are segmental because of their embryonic origin: they arise from segmental mesodermal somites (Figs. 10-6 and 15-6). Mesenchyme cells from the myotome of each somite stream into the embryonic lateral body wall and migrate ventrad while undergoing repeated cell division (Fig. 10-7). Ultimately, they reach the midventral line, where a longitudinal connective tissue raphe, the **linea alba,** forms. These myotomal cells (cells whose lineage can be traced to myotomes) form blastemas for body wall muscles; and because the somites are metameric, the blastemas are metameric. Several blastemal cells, now myoblasts, unite to form multinucleate striated muscle fibers, and the body wall muscles take shape. The metamerism of the embryonic somites is expressed in adults as **myomeres** wherever myosepta separate the muscle of one body segment from the next.

Myosepta do not form in the abdominal region of higher tetrapods (Fig. 10-4, *E*). As a result their abdominal musculature consists of broad sheets rather than serially repeated myomeres. Nevertheless, these sheets are innervated by as many spinal nerves as there were

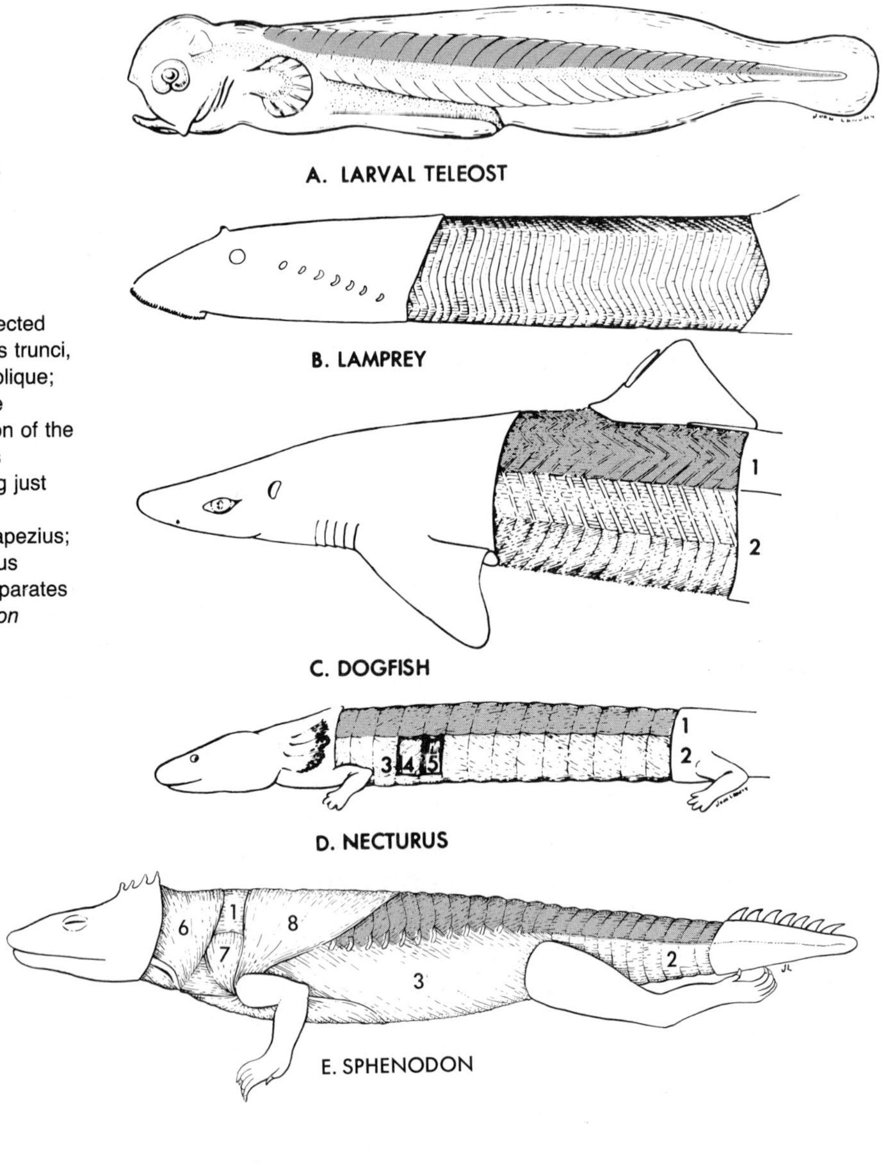
A. LARVAL TELEOST
B. LAMPREY
1
2
C. DOGFISH
1
2
3
4
5
D. NECTURUS
6
1
8
7
3
2
E. SPHENODON

Fig. 10-4. Trunk muscles of selected vertebrates. **1,** Epaxials (dorsalis trunci, red); **2,** hypaxials; **3,** external oblique; **4,** internal oblique; **5,** transverse muscle of abdomen. The location of the notochord in the larval teleost is indicated by stipple commencing just behind eye. In *Sphenodon* the appendicular muscles are, **6,** trapezius; **7,** dorsalis scapulae; **8,** latissimus dorsi. The horizontal septum separates *1* and *2* in **C** and **D.** (*Sphenodon* modified from Byerly.[6])

Fig. 10-5. Lateral undulation in a fish.

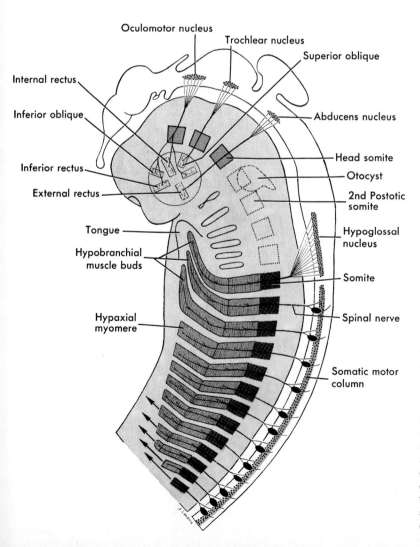

Oculomotor nucleus

Trochlear nucleus

Superior oblique

Internal rectus

Inferior oblique

Abducens nucleus

Inferior rectus

External rectus

Head somite

Otocyst

2nd Postotic somite

Tongue

Hypobranchial muscle buds

Hypoglossal nucleus

Somite

Spinal nerve

Hypaxial myomere

Somatic motor column

Fig. 10-6. Axial muscle origins and innervation in a generalized vertebrate embryo (diagramatic). The eyeball muscles arise from three preotic head somites associated with the oculomotor, trochlear, and abducens nuclei, respectively. Segmental muscles of the trunk arise from trunk somites and are supplied by corresponding segmental nerves. Hypobranchial musculature migrates forward into the floor of the pharynx accompanied by a nerve supply. Motor fibers innervating myotomal muscle have their cell bodies in the somatic motor column of the cord and brain. The postotic somites (dotted outlines), which vary in number in different species, make no contribution to the musculature. The central nervous system has been projected above the embryo for clarity.

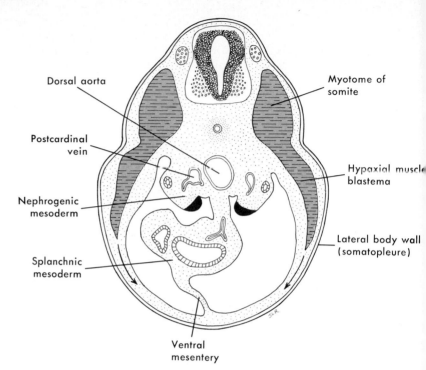

Dorsal aorta

Myotome of somite

Postcardinal vein

Hypaxial muscle blastema

Nephrogenic mesoderm

Lateral body wall (somatopleure)

Splanchnic mesoderm

Ventral mesentery

Fig. 10-7. Cross section of mammalian embryo showing invasion of myotomal cells (red) into lateral body wall to form hypaxial muscles.

somites that contributed to the blastemas from which the sheets developed.

Trunk and tail muscles of fishes

The musculature of the body wall and tail of fishes consists of metameric myomeres separated by zigzagging myosepta to which the muscle fibers attach (Fig. 10-4, A to C). The myomeres of jawed fishes are divided into dorsal and ventral masses by a **horizontal septum** of connective tissue that extends laterad from the transverse processes of the vertebrae to the skin (Fig. 1-2). Above the septum, lateral to the neural arches, are **epaxial** muscles; below it are **hypaxial** muscles. Middorsal and midventral raphes separate the myomeres of the left and right sides. Except in fishes with unusual vertebral columns there is a myomere for each vertebra, and a spinal nerve for each myomere (Fig. 10-6). The myosepta are seen to zigzag from dorsal to ventral when the skin has been removed, but deep within the body wall and tail they are much more elaborately folded and overlapping, so that each myomere pulls on more than one vertebra. In response to waves of motor impulses over successive spinal nerves, successive myomeres exert tensile force on the vertebral column, evoking rhythmical undulations of the trunk and tail. These propel the fish during locomotion. The myomeres of fishes contain two main functional types of

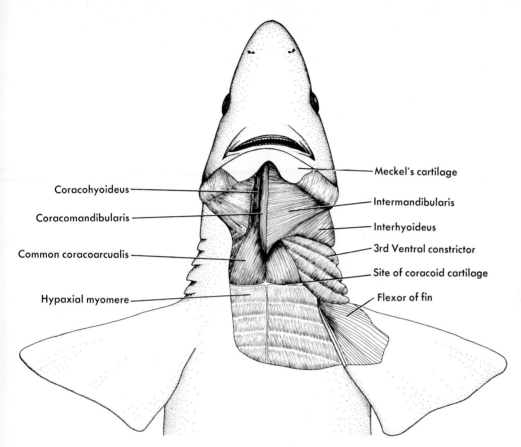

Coracohyoideus

Coracomandibularis

Common coracoarcualis

Hypaxial myomere

Meckel's cartilage

Intermandibularis

Interhyoideus

3rd Ventral constrictor

Site of coracoid cartilage

Flexor of fin

Fig. 10-8. Ventral muscles of "neck" of shark. At the left, anterior to the first hypaxial myomere, are three hypobranchial muscles. At the right are branchiomerics. The intermandibular is superficial to the coracohyoid and coracomandibular muscles and has been partly removed on the left to reveal underlying muscles.

muscle fibers: "fast" white fibers, which tire rapidly and are presumed to be important for bursts of strenuous activity, and "slow" red fibers, which are believed to be responsible for slow, sustained swimming, as in cruising. Agnathans lack a horizontal septum, perhaps because they lack centra; and the trunk muscles of the freshwater lamprey *Lampetra* are not segmented.

In many fishes a thin sheet of **oblique fibers** lies superficial to the main hypaxial mass ventrolaterally, and near the linea alba a narrow ribbon of still more superficial fibers resembling the rectus abdominis of tetrapods extends longitudinally.

The metamerism of the hypaxial muscles of fishes is interrupted where the pectoral and pelvic girdles are built into the body wall, and by the gills. Above the gills the epaxial muscles continue to the skull as **epibranchial muscles** (Fig. 10-16, *A*). Beneath the gills the hypaxials extend to the lower jaw as **hypobranchial muscles,** which lack regular myosepta (Fig. 10-8).

Trunk and tail muscles of tetrapods

Urodeles have metameric epaxial and hypaxial muscles that produce swimming movements in water by lateral undulation of the trunk and tail, as in fishes (Fig. 10-4, *D*). And because urodele limbs are not strong weight bearers, these same muscles produce squirming, swiminglike locomotion on land when a urodele runs. Amniotes, however, except limbless ones, have strong limbs and these are operated by more powerful appendicular muscles. The shift in tetrapod locomotion away from swimming movements was accompanied by loss of much of the primitive metamerism of the axial muscles. Except for the deepest slips, the *epaxials* have become long unsegmented bundles lying on the transverse processes of the vertebrae from the head to the tip of the tail (Fig. 10-9). These bundles extend (straighten) the column and support it. A similar modification

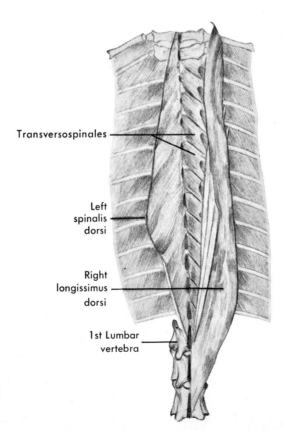

Transversospinales

Left spinalis dorsi

Right longissimus dorsi

1st Lumbar vertebra

Fig. 10-9. Two long epaxial bundles of the thorax of a hamster, dorsal view. On the right the spinalis dorsi has been removed to reveal the deeper transversospinales that connect the transverse processes with the neural spine on the second vertebra forward. The longissimus dorsi, which lies lateral to the spinalis dorsi, has been removed on the left.

occurred in the dorsalmost slips of the *hypaxials* of the trunk. They became long unsegmented **subvertebral muscles** paralleling the long epaxials and lying beneath the transverse processes. The subvertebrals flex (arch) the column. In no tetrapod is the effectiveness of this combination of extensors and flexors of the vertebral column better demonstrated than in fleet digitigrade carnivorous mammals, who usually must run to capture food, or in jackrabbits, who must run to avoid being eaten (Fig. 10-10).

In addition to forming subvertebrals the remaining hypaxial musculature also changed as vertebrates became increasingly adapted for life on land. They became reduced in volume, lost most traces of metamerism except where long ribs form, and in the trunk became disposed in superficial and deep layers whose fibers are directed more or less obliquely ventrad. Accompanying these changes, the horizontal septum became insignificant and disappeared.

EPAXIAL MUSCLES

The epaxial muscles of tetrapods extend from the base of the skull to the tip of the tail and can be divided arbitrarily into four groups: **intervertebrals, longissimus, spinales,** and **iliocostales.** The major subdivisions of these groups are listed in Table 10-2 under epaxial muscles.

Intervertebrals are the deepest epaxial muscles and the only ones to retain their primitive metamerism. They extend between the transverse processes of two successive vertebrae (intertransversarii), successive neural spines (interspinales), neural arches (interarcuales), or zygapophyses (interarticulares). Intervertebrals participate in extending and flexing the column and promote lateral flexion where possible.

The **longissimus** and **spinales** muscles are regionally subdivided and continue into the tail as extensors of the tail. The most anterior epaxials insert on the skull and participate in moving the head. In a hatching chick one of these, the **complexus,** provides the power for cracking the eggshell with the beak. The longissimus is so named because

Fig. 10-10. Rapid locomotion in a cat.

Table 10-2. Representative somatic muscles of head, trunk, and forelimbs in mammals

HEAD AND NECK	Eyeball	Tongue	Hypobranchial
	Superior oblique	Genioglossus	Geniohyoideus
	Inferior oblique	Hyoglossus	Sternohyoideus
	Medial rectus	Styloglossus	Sternothyroideus
	Lateral rectus	Lingualis	Thyrohyoideus
	Superior rectus		Omohyoideus
	Inferior rectus		

TRUNK AND TAIL	Epaxial muscles	Hypaxial muscles
	Intervertebrales	Subvertebrals
	Intertransversarii	Longus colli
	Interspinales	Quadratus lumborum*
	Interarcuales	Psoas minor*
	Interarticulares	Oblique group (parietals)
	Longissimus	Internal and external
	L. dorsi	intercostals
	L. cervicis	Internal and external
	L. capitis	obliques of abdomen
	Extensor caudae	Cremaster
	lateralis	Supracostals†
	Spinales	Scalenus
	S. dorsi	Serratus dorsalis
	S. cervicis	Levatores costarum
	S. capitis	Transversus costarum
	Transversospinales	Diaphragm
	Extensor caudae	Transverse group (parietals)
	medialis	Transversus thoracis
	Iliocostales	(subcostal)
		Transversus abdominis
		Rectus muscles
		Rectus abdominis
		Pyramidalis
		Abductors and flexors of tail

FORELIMB	Extrinsic muscles‡	Intrinsic muscles
	Levator scapulae*	See Table 10-4
	Latissimus dorsi§	
	Rhomboideus*	
	Serratus ventralis*	
	Pectoral group§	

*Secondary appendicular muscle.
†The first three may be epaxial, rather than hypaxial, by derivation.
‡The trapezius, sternomastoideus, and cleidomastoideus are probably of branchiomeric origin, hence not myotomal.
§Primary appendicular muscle.

it includes the longest epaxial bundles. Spinales include long, medium, and short bundles connecting neural spines or transverse processes with neural spines several or many segments cephalad. Transversopinales are short bundles (Fig. 10-9).

The **iliocostales** are lateral to the longissimus, arise on the ilium, and pass forward to insert on the upper ends of ribs or on uncinate processes. Extensions occur in the neck, but they are absent in the tail.

The epaxial muscles became increasingly hidden by the expanding appendicular muscles and lumbodorsal fascia, which must be removed to reveal the underlying epaxials (compare A, B, and C in Fig. 10-14). In turtles and birds the vertebral column in the trunk is rigid and epaxials are poorly represented. In limbless tetrapods, on the other hand, the epaxials along with subvertebrals and integumentary muscles attached to scutes provide most of the power for locomotion on land.

HYPAXIAL MUSCLES

The hypaxial muscles of tetrapods can be divided arbitrarily into five categories: **hypobranchials, subvertebrals** (longitudinal bundles close to the vertebral column), **parietals** (oblique and transverse sheets in the body wall), **rectus muscles** (longitudinal muscles close to the linea alba), and **abductors and flexors of the tail** (Table 10-2). The hypobranchials will be discussed shortly.

Subvertebral muscles. Bundles of subvertebral muscles lie immediately under the transverse processes of the vertebrae in the roof of the body cavity (quadratus lumborum, psoas minor, others) and in the neck (longus colli). They are not well represented in the thorax and are absent from the tail. They flex the vertebral column of the neck and trunk. These muscles are sold as tenderloin and filet mignon at meat counters in the United States.

Oblique and transverse muscles. The muscles of the lateral body wall have become stratified into superficial and deep layers, typically three: **external oblique, internal oblique,** and the **transverse muscle of the abdomen;** and **external intercostals, internal intercostals,** and the **transverse muscle (subcostal) of the thorax.** The fibers of all these pass more or less obliquely from origin to insertion. One or another of these sheets may either be split in two or lost. In aquatic urodeles, for example, the external oblique is split into superficial and deep parts. These are locomotor muscles in aquatic urodeles. In crocodilians and some lizards all three layers consist of two sheets each. In anurans the internal oblique is sometimes missing, and in birds all sheets are reduced. In turtles all layers are almost entirely absent, but a turtle couldn't care less. Because of the rigid shell, it could not use them anyway.* (If you want to make turtle soup, it will have to come from the neck, tail, or appendicular muscles!) Muscle slips from the internal oblique and transverse abdominal muscles of male mammals wrap around the spermatic cord at the inguinal ring (Fig. 14-20) to form a **cremaster** muscle. It is best developed in species with open inguinal canals into which the testes can be retracted.

External respiration in amniotes is usually accomplished with parietal muscles. When intercostals are employed, additional power is provided by **supracostal** muscles that have differentiated on the surface of the rib cage, chiefly **scalenus, serratus dorsalis, levatores costarum, transversus costarum,** and others. The first three may be epaxial derivatives. In mammals, mesenchyme from somites in the future neck region invades the embryonic septum transversum to form a **muscular diaphragm,** and this is more important in mammalian respiration than rib movements. Innervation of diaphragmatic muscle by ventral rami or cervical spinal nerves indicates its hypaxial status.

Other roles of the parietal muscles of tetrapods include supporting the abdominal viscera in a muscular sling and compression of the abdominal contents for whatever reason. Although abdominal muscles lack myosepta in amniotes, their basic metamerism is evidenced by their embryonic origin from successive somites and by their innervation by successive spinal nerves.

Rectus muscles. The rectus muscles extend between the pubic symphysis and the pectoral girdle, or even farther forward in lower tetrapods, and continue to the lower jaw as hypobranchials (Fig. 10-11, **rectus abdominis, rectus cervicis, geniohyoideus**). In mammals the unsegmented straplike rectus muscles may extend as far forward as the first ribs, as in cats, or they may stop near the caudal border of the sternum, as in humans. They aid in flexing the trunk if the vertebral column is supple, and they help support the abdominal viscera. A **pyramidal** muscle associated with the marsupial pouch is a slip of the rectus abdominis. Some higher mammals have a vestige of this muscle.

Muscles of the tail. Hypaxial muscle bundles pass caudad from the ilium and ischium to insert on the base of the tail. Farther along on the tail, bundles of hypaxial muscles lie beside the centra, below any transverse processes that are present. These two sets of muscles collectively are abductors and flexors of the tail. The extensors are epaxial muscles.

---

*See "The Lamarckian Doctrine," Chapter 18.

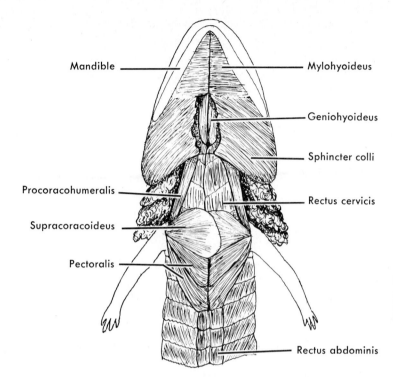

Mandible

Mylohyoideus

Geniohyoideus

Sphincter colli

Procoracohumeralis

Rectus cervicis

Supracoracoideus

Pectoralis

Rectus abdominis

Fig. 10-11. Anteroventral muscles of *Necturus*. The sphincter colli is a very thin muscular sheet on the surface of the powerful branchiohyoideus.

Hypobranchial and tongue muscles

It has already been noted that hypobranchial muscles are cephalic extensions of hypaxial blastemas beneath the pharynx (Fig. 10-6). In fishes and urodeles these extend forward from the pectoral girdle to the branchial skeleton, hyoid, and mandible (Figs. 10-8 and 10-11). In one species or another they strengthen the floor of the pharynx and pericardial cavity, aid the branchiomeric muscles in changing the shape of the pharyngeal floor, and open the mouth. With development of a long neck in amniotes they have become longer and straplike and now stabilize the hyoid and larynx or draw these forward or backward, depending on their attachments and on what other muscles are doing at the time. They bear such names as **sternohyoid, sternothyroid, thyrohyoid, omohyoid,** and **geniohyoid.**

The tongue of reptiles and mammals has become essentially a mucosal sac anchored to the hyoid skeleton and stuffed with hypobranchial muscle. This explains the fact that, in bats, muscles extend into the tongue from as far back as the sternum. The chief extrinsic tongue muscles in mammals are the hyoglossus, styloglossus, and genioglossus. Mammals and some reptiles also have an intrinsic tongue muscle, the lingualis.

Because of their derivation from the anteriormost trunk somites hypobranchial muscles are supplied by the most anterior spinal nerves or, in the case of tongue muscles, by the last cranial nerve. The motor fibers that innervate them have their cell bodies in the somatic motor column of the central nervous system. This column supplies myotomal muscles, and no other muscles, everywhere in the body (Figs. 10-6 and 15-30).

Extrinsic eyeball muscles

The muscles that move the eyeballs of elasmobranch fishes arise during embryonic development from three head somites called **preotic somites** because they form cephalad to the otocyst (Fig. 10-6). Head somite I is located where cranial nerve III emerges from the brain. This somite splits to give rise to four eyeball muscles operated by cranial nerve III (Table 10-3). Head somite II is located where cranial nerve IV emerges from the brain. This somite gives rise to the superior oblique eyeball muscle innervated by cranial nerve IV. Head somite III (with contributions from somite II) is located where cranial nerve VI emerges. This somite gives rise to the external rectus muscle supplied by cranial nerve VI and to a retractor bulbi, if one is present. In vertebrates other than elasmobranchs the head somites are evanescent, and the mesenchyme that forms eyeball muscles cannot be traced directly to them.* Nevertheless, the extrinsic eyeball muscles of all vertebrates are clearly homologous. Vertebrates with vestigial eyeballs have imperfect eyeball muscles.

Many amniotes have muscles inserting on the upper lids and nictitating membrane (pyramidalis of reptiles and birds, quadratus of

---

*The extrinsic eyeball muscles of an apodan, turtle, and several birds have been described as arising directly from preotic somites, but this has been disputed.

Table 10-3. Chief muscles derived from head somites and their innervation

Head somite	Cranial nerve supply	Extrinsic eyeball muscles	Eyelid muscles
I	III (oculomotor)	Superior rectus Inferior rectus* Medial (internal) rectus Inferior oblique	Levator palpebrae superioris
II	IV (trochlear)	Superior oblique	
III (with contributions from somite II)	VI (abducens)	External (lateral) rectus Retractor bulbi	Pyramidalis of eye Quadratus of eye

*In lampreys the inferior rectus is operated by cranial nerve VI.

birds, levator palpebrae superioris of reptiles and mammals). These, too, are myotomal muscles (Table 10-3).

The cell bodies of motor fibers innervating these eyeball muscles are in the somatic motor column of the central nervous system, so it can be said with confidence that rectus and oblique eyeball muscles are derivatives of an ancient, segmental body wall musculature. Protractors and retractors of the eyeballs of reptiles and birds, and depressors of the lower lids, when present, are evidently not myotomal since they are innervated by cranial nerve V.

APPENDICULAR MUSCLES

Appendicular muscles insert on the girdles, fins, or limbs. Anatomists divide them into two groups according to their anatomical origins. **Extrinsic appendicular muscles** have their origins on the axial skeleton or fascia of the trunk, and they insert on the girdles, fins, or limbs. **Intrinsic appendicular muscles** have their origins on the girdle or on proximal skeletal elements of the appendage, and they insert on more distal elements. All extrinsic muscles must be completely severed to permit removal of an appendage (girdle and limb) from the body. In the process, intrinsic muscles remain intact.

Appendicular muscles of fishes

Most fishes use axial, not appendicular, muscles for locomotion, and fins are employed chiefly as stabilizers or for changing direction. Consequently, the appendicular muscles of most fishes are uncomplicated and have little mass. Paired fins begin in embryos as fin folds protruding from the body wall (Fig. 10-12). Thereafter, *muscle buds from the lower edges of the myotomes invade the fin folds* and organize muscles that achieve an insertion on the developing basal and radial elements of the fin. Dorsally invading buds form **extensors (elevators)**, and ventral buds form **flexors (depressors)** (Fig. 10-13). Skates and rays, whose body shape will not permit lateral undulation of the lateral body wall, use extensors, flexors, and simple intrinsic muscles to undulate their winglike fins; otherwise, intrinsic appendicular muscle is insignificant in fishes since there are few or no distal skeletal elements to be moved. Hypaxial trunk myomeres attach to the girdles, stabilizing them.

Appendicular muscles of tetrapods

The appendicular muscles of even the lowest tetrapods make up a greater proportion of the body weight than do those of fishes, and they are far more complex because of the many levers within tetrapod limbs. The extrinsic muscles are disposed in two opposing functional groups, dorsal and ventral (extensors and flexors, as in fishes), which

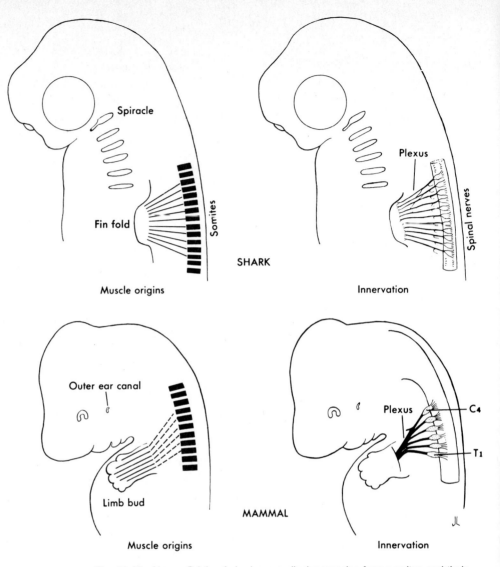

Fig. 10-12. *Above,* Origin of shark appendicular muscles from somites and their innervation by corresponding spinal nerves. *Below,* Probable phylogenetic derivation of appendicular muscles of a mammal from six somites based on their innervation. **C4** and **T1,** Dorsal root ganglia of the fourth cervical and first thoracic spinal nerves of the brachial plexus.

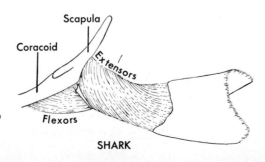

Fig. 10-13. Appendicular muscles of pectoral fin of shark. Extensors are also called levators. Flexors are adductors.

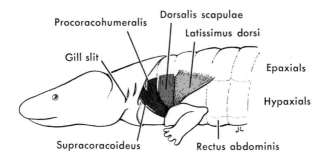

A. NECTURUS

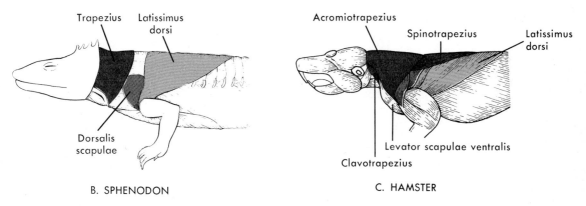

B. SPHENODON

C. HAMSTER

Fig. 10-14. Superficial shoulder muscles of an amphibian, reptile, and mammal, illustrating increased extent of shoulder muscles in successively higher tetrapods. Of the four shoulder muscles shown in the necturus, only the latissimus dorsi is extrinsic. The other three are intrinsic appendicular muscles.

have undergone extensive subdivision, multiplication, and differentiation from amphibians to mammals. These two groups converge on the girdles and skeleton of the limbs, those of the hind limbs being sparse.

Urodeles have a single **dorsal extrinsic muscle of the forelimb,** the **latissimus dorsi,** which exerts little pull on the humerus, to which it is attached (Fig. 10-14, A). It arises from a relatively weak fascia overlying the epaxial muscles of the shoulder region, and its anteroposterior extent is short. The extrinsic shoulder muscles of **reptiles** are larger, more numerous, the largest ones have achieved a tendinous attachment to neural spines directly or via aponeuroses, and their combined origins extend farther caudad on the vertebral column, providing more leverage for locomotion (Fig. 10-14, B). In **mammals** they attach to the axial skeleton all the way from the occiput to the pelvic girdle, the latissimus dorsi attaching via the tough lumbodorsal fascia (Fig. 10-14, *C*). The greater mobility of the mammalian pectoral girdle and the increased leverage that can be applied to the humerus when contrasted with reptiles is to a large degree a reflection of the complexity of these and other dorsal extrinsic appendicular muscles, including branchiomeric contributions (Table 10-2), in mammals.

The **ventral extrinsic muscles of the forelimb,** the **pectorals** and lesser ones, have a history paralleling the dorsal group, having extended their collective origin in higher tetrapods until they arise the entire length of the midventral raphe of the thorax and often continue a short distance into the neck. They are the massive extrinsic wing muscles that attach to the deeply keeled sternum of carinate birds. In contrast, the intrinsic musculature of the wings has been reduced.

As an example of the multiplication of extrinsic forelimb muscles that has taken place during evolution from generalized tetrapods, the pectoral muscles may be cited. In mammals pectoral muscles are represented by major, minor, superficial, and deep bundles, each with conventional names that differ among the species, and by muscles bearing other names, such as pectoantebrachialis and xiphihumeralis. An even greater proliferation occurred in the shoulder, which resulted in a complexity of modern shoulder muscles with many names and operating many levers. This multiplication was beyond doubt accompanied by loss of some muscles and altered attachment of others; and the combination of factors makes attempts at homologizing these muscles speculative and intuitive as well as scientific.

The **extrinsic musculature of the hind limbs** is almost negligible. This is correlated with the fact that the pelvic girdle is firmly braced against the vertebral column dorsally and united in a symphysis ventrally, which limits its mobility. The only extrinsic muscles of the hind limb of **necturus** are a deep **caudofemoralis** that passes from nearby caudal vertebrae to the femur and draws the leg backward during locomotion on land, and a weak slip or two from the tail that are probably subvertebrals. (The superficial fan-shaped muscles seen ventrally in *Necturus* between the posterior appendages, that is, the puboischiofemoralis externus and puboischiotibialis, are intrinsic muscles arising on the pelvic plate.) The caudo-femoralis is also present in **reptiles** and **birds,** being especially powerful in crocodilians. Other hind limb muscles of amphibians and reptiles are intrinsic. In **mammals** the extrinsic muscles of the hind limbs are an **iliopsoas,** which has an extensive origin on the vertebral column and ilium, and two subvertebrals, the **quadratus lumborum** and **psoas minor.** The iliopsoas is found only in generalized mammals. In higher mammals it usually splits into a **psoas major** and an **iliacus.**

Most extrinsic muscles of tetrapod limbs commence development from blastemas within the embryonic body wall, and buds from these blastemas grow toward and establish an insertion on a girdle or proximal bone of a limb. Muscles that develop in this manner are sometimes called **secondary appendicular muscles** because of their embryogenesis. The levator scapulae, serratus ventralis, and rhomboideus, all of myotomal derivation, and the trapezius, sternomastoid, and cleidomastoid of branchiomeric origin are secondary appendicular muscles of the forelimbs. The psoas minor and quadratus lumborum are secondary hind limb muscles. Secondary appendicular muscles are the most primitive appendicular muscles and the only kind in fishes. They deserve better billing!

Intrinsic muscles of tetrapod limbs organize from blastemas *within* the developing limb. These blastemas include mesenchyme cells that have invaded the limb from the lower edges of myotomes, and the intrinsic musculature is unquestionably myotomal by phylogenetic derivation. Muscles that form from blastemas within a limb are sometimes called **primary appendicular muscles.** They include the few extrinsic muscles that form when these blastemas spread trunkward to achieve an attachment on the axial skeleton. The latissimus dorsi and iliopsoas arise in this manner.

Formation of intrinsic appendicular muscles in situ is a time-saving modification that must have had selective value during phylogeny. It is one of many instances of developmental precociousness in vertebrates. No biological scientist today expects ontogeny to recapitulate phylogeny.

A recitation of the very many intrinsic muscles of the limbs will be left to laboratory studies because only there and in the field can their functional significance be appreciated. Mention should be made of the massive muscles that balance and propel birds on two hind limbs and enable them to take off in flight from ground level. These account for the voluminous musculature of the bird's thigh. Notable also are the very long postaxial tendons that pass behind a bird's heel and insert on the toes. The weight of the perching body stretches the tendons and retracts the claw-bearing toes so that a sleeping bird, muscularly relaxed and with minimal expenditure of energy, tightens its grip on the perch. The chief intrinsic muscles of the forelimbs of reptiles and mammals are listed in Table 10-4.

The pectoral girdle and limbs are joined to the trunk by extrinsic appendicular muscles and skin alone, whereas the pelvic girdle is firmly braced against the axial skeleton. This accounts partly for the fact that a cat jumps by pushing off with its hind limbs but lands on its forelimbs, where much of the shock is absorbed by the extrinsic and intrinsic muscles. Among the reasons frogs can't do this is lack of

Table 10-4. Chief intrinsic muscles of the forelimbs of reptiles and mammals*

Muscles of girdle	**Deltoideus**
Girdle to humerus,	**Subcoracoscapularis**
proximally	**Subscapularis**
	Scapulohumeralis
	Teres minor
	Supracoracoideus
	Infraspinatus
	Supraspinatus
	Coracobrachialis
	Teres major (derived from latissimus dorsi)
Muscles of upper arm	**Triceps brachii (anconeus)**
Girdle or humerus to	**Humeroantebrachialis**
proximal end of radius	**Biceps brachii**
or ulna	**Brachialis**
Muscles of forearm†	**Extensors** and **flexors** of wrist and digits
Humerus and	**Supinators** and **pronators** of hand
proximal end of radius	
and ulna to manus	
Muscles of hand‡	**Flexors, extensors, abductors,** and **adductors** of fingers

*Indentations indicate likely mammalian derivatives.
† These frequently have long tendons of insertion.
‡ Reduced in species in which digits are reduced.

a cerebellum competent to direct precision landings even if a frog had sufficient extrinsic dorsal appendicular musculature to absorb the shock, which it doesn't. The result is that frogs land awkwardly—almost abashedly—on whatever part of the body happens to touch down first. The hind limbs of ungulates are good shock absorbers because elongated metatarsals provide what amounts to an extra shock-absorbing joint in the leg.

Innervation of appendicular muscles

Branches of the ventral rami of several successive spinal nerves grow into the fin folds and limb buds to innervate the muscles within the limb. In fishes these nerves come from the same body segments that contribute muscle buds to the appendage (Fig. 10-12). Although in tetrapods the muscles within the appendage cannot be traced directly to myotomes, it seems probable that the number of spinal nerves entering a tetrapod limb is indicative of the number of somites that contributed mesenchyme to the limb phylogenetically.

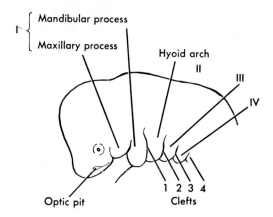

Fig. 10-15. Pharyngeal arches of a vertebrate.

BRANCHIOMERIC MUSCLES

Associated with the pharyngeal arches of vertebrates (Fig. 10-15) is a series of striated, skeletal, voluntary, visceral, branchiomeric muscles. The basic architectural pattern of these muscles is illustrated in fishes, in which they operate the jaws and successive gill arches (Fig. 10-16, *A*). In tetrapods they still operate the jaws. However, with loss of gills, the more posterior ones have acquired new functions.

That branchiomeric muscles must be classified as visceral is evident from the following facts:

1. Their position in the wall of the alimentary canal identifies them as visceral.

2. The motor nerve fibers innervating them are in a visceral motor column of the brain (Fig. 15-30, SVE) close to the column that innervates smooth muscles and glands (Fig. 15-30, GVE). They are not in the column that innervates other skeletal muscles (SE).

3. Functionally, they are associated with two visceral processes, food handling and respiration.

4. Their embryonic origin is not from myotomes.

The foregoing criteria set branchiomeric muscles apart from other striated skeletal muscles.

Muscles of the mandibular arch

In all vertebrates the muscles of the first arch are primarily jaw muscles. In *Squalus*, whose branchial muscles are relatively generalized (Figs. 10-8 and 10-16, *A*), a **levator palatoquadrati** arises on the otic capsule and inserts on the quadrate end of the upper jaw cartilage; a powerful **adductor mandibulae** arises on the quadrate process and inserts on Meckel's cartilage; and an **intermandibularis** extends between Meckel's cartilage and a strong midventral raphe in the pharyngeal floor. A slender **craniomaxillaris** inserting on the up-

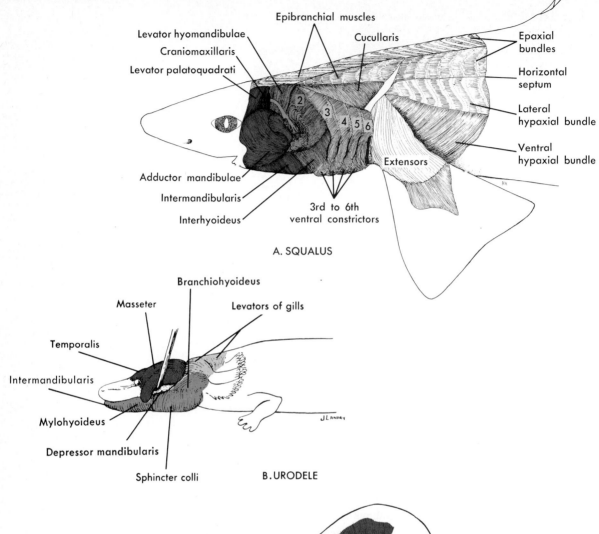

Fig. 10-16. Selected branchiomeric muscles of three vertebrates. Muscles of the first, second, and remaining pharyngeal arches are indicated by three shades of red. **2 to 6,** Dorsal constrictors of the hyoid and successive arches. Sphincter colli derivatives in mammals are shown in Fig. 10-18.

per jaw completes the first arch muscles of *Squalus*. The levator palatoquadrati raises the upper jaw, which is possible because *Squalus* has hyostylic jaw suspension (Chapter 8). The craniomaxillaris assists in this. The adductor mandibulae raises the lower jaw, thereby closing the mouth during the phase of the respiratory cycle when the spiracle is also closed and water is being forced over the gills by constriction of the walls of the orobranchial chamber. The adductor also enables the shark to hold in a viselike grip any prey unlucky enough to be caught. The intermandibularis is a ventral constrictor that elevates the anterior pharyngeal floor during respiration. The mouth is not opened by branchiomeric muscles but by the coracomandibularis, a hypobranchial muscle.

The adductor mandibulae is the most powerful muscle of the first arch from fish to man. In **tetrapods** it has become split into several muscles—many in snakes, commonly three in amniotes. These are the **masseter, temporalis,** and **pterygoideus.** They have spread in three directions on the skull and approach the mandible from these three directions, supporting the lower jaw in a muscular sling and providing most of the multidirectional tensile forces that produce the sidewise, up-and-down, forward-and-back, and rotatory chewing movements of such different mammals as herbivores, carnivores, and rodents. The masseter and temporalis muscles are illustrated in Fig. 10-16, *C*. The pterygoids are medial to the ramus of the mandible, arising in and near the pterygoid fossa of the skull (Fig. 8-27), and cannot be seen until the mandibular symphysis is separated and a dentary bone is retracted laterad. The role of temporal fossae in the evolution of chewing muscles is discussed in Chapter 8.

The intermandibular muscle is called **mylohyoid** in tetrapods (Fig. 10-11). One slip of it has probably given rise to the **digastric muscle** (**anterior belly** of the digastric when there are two bellies). One slip of the first arch muscle that was attached to the articular bone of therapsid reptiles remained attached there when the bone became a malleus in the middle ear, and that muscle, now the **tensor tympani,** puts tension on the eardrum. All mandibular arch muscles are innervated by cranial nerve V.

Muscles of the hyoid arch

The principal muscles of the hyoid arch of *Squalus* elevate the arch or constrict the pharyngeal cavity, partly as a function of respiration and feeding. A **levator hyomandibulae** and a **dorsal constrictor** arise on the neurocranium and insert on the hyomandibula and ceratohyal cartilage. An **interhyoideus** is a ventral constrictor (Figs. 10-8 and 10-16, *A*). In bony fishes the dorsal constrictor is subdivided and part of it operates the operculum. Because of the joint between the upper jaw, lower jaw, and hyomandibula, contraction of hyoid arch muscles results in movements of the jaws.

In **tetrapods,** hyoid arch muscles continue to serve some of the functions seen in fishes, but they have also acquired some quite different roles. In *Necturus* a **branchiohyoid muscle** of the hyoid arch arises on the ceratohyal cartilage and inserts on the epibranchial cartilage of the first gill. Along with levators of the gills it waves the gills back and forth in the water for respiration. A **depressor mandibulae** opens the mouth of urodeles and many reptiles (Fig. 10-16, *B*); and in mammals a **digastric muscle** (**posterior belly** when there are two) participates in chewing movements (Fig. 10-16, *C*). A slender **stylohyoid muscle** connects the styloid or jugular process of the skull with the anterior horn or body of the hyoid in mammals (Fig. 8-37). The muscle is so slim in cats that it is almost vestigial. (A posterior portion of the stylohyoid, when present, is derived from the third arch.)

A thin **sphincter colli** lies like a collar (for which it was named) under and closely adherent to the skin of the neck of lower tetrapods. It is superficial to the branchiohyoid muscle of *Necturus* (Fig. 10-16, *B*). In reptiles and birds it spreads upward around the rear of the skull to insert on the skin of the head and is called **platysma.** In mammals the platysma spreads forward onto the face to become muscles of facial expression, or **mimetic muscles.** The sphincter colli is thought to be derived from a portion of the interhyoideus of fishes.

The **stapedial muscle** of the middle ear of mammals attaches to the stapes, which is a derivative of the hyomandibula. It responds reflexly to extra loud sound.

All these hyoid arch muscles are innervated by the facial nerve (cranial nerve VII), so named because of its wide distribution to the mimetic muscles under the skin of the face of humans. The innervation of the two muscles of the middle ear by two different branchiomeric nerves, V and VII, is not surprising to those who know the phylogenetic history of the ear ossicles to which the muscles attach.

Muscles of the third and successive pharyngeal arches

The muscles of arches III through VI are **constrictors, levators, adductors,** and **interarcuals** that compress or expand the pharyngeal cavity and operate the gills for respiration. Constrictors in sharks lie just under the skin covered by tough subcutaneous fascia that is not readily removed, and they attach to strong fascia above and below the gill pouches (Fig. 10-16, *A*). The levators of these arches make up a strong muscle sheet, the **cucullaris,** which raises the pharyngeal wall assisted by the levator hyomandibulae of the second arch. The cucullaris is thought to be the precursor of the trapezius muscle of

Table 10-5. Chief branchiomeric muscles and their innervation in *Squalus* and in tetrapods

Pharyngeal arch	Pharyngeal skeleton in Squalus	Chief branchiomeric muscles		Cranial nerve innervation
		Squalus	Tetrapods*	
I Mandibular arch	Meckel's cartilage	Intermandibularis	Intermandibularis Mylohyoideus (anterior part) Digastricus (anterior part)	V
		Adductor mandibulae	Adductor mandibulae Masseter Temporalis Pterygoidei Tensor tympani	
	Pterygoquadrate cartilage	Levator palatoquadrati Craniomaxillaris		
II Hyoid arch	Hyomandibula	Levator hyomandibulae	Stapedius	VII
	Ceratohyal	Dorsal constrictor	Stylohyoideus (anterior part)	
	Basihyal	Interhyoideus	Depressor mandibulae Digastricus (posterior belly) Sphincter colli Platysma Mimetics	
III	Gill cartilages	Constrictors Levators Adductors Interarcuals	Stylopharyngeus Stylohyoideus (posterior part)	IX
IV to VI	Gill cartilages	Constrictors Levators Adductors Interarcuals	Striated pharyngeal muscles Thyroarytenoideus Cricoarytenoideus Cricothyroideus	X
		Cucullaris (derived also from dorsal constrictor 3)	Trapezius Sternomastoideus Cleidomastoideus	Occipitospinal nerves in shark; spinal roots of XI in amniotes

*Indented muscles in this column may be derivatives of the preceding muscle.

tetrapods. Adductors deep in the gill arches connect epibranchial and ceratobranchial cartilages and cause the lateral pharyngeal walls to bow outward when the muscles contract. Two sets of interarcual muscles in the roof of the pharynx just above the mucosa connect successive pharyngobranchial cartilages with epibranchials and draw these together. The interarcuals in the floor of the pharynx are not branchiomeric; they are hypobranchial muscles, the most superficial of which is the common coracoarcualis (Fig. 10-8). In bony fishes the branchiomeric muscles caudal to the hyoid arch are much reduced as a consequence of the role of the operculum in moving respiratory water across the gills.

In tetrapods, branchiomeric muscle has pretty much disappeared from what had been the gill-bearing arches. Remaining from arch III are a **stylopharyngeus** that is used in swallowing, and a **posterior belly of the stylohyoideus** in some mammals (Fig. 8-37, stylohyoideus major). Remaining from arch IV are the intrinsic muscles of the larynx: **cricothyroid, cricoarytenoid,** and **thyroarytenoid.** The chief branchiomeric muscles and their innervations are listed in Table 10-5.

INTEGUMENTARY MUSCLES

In fishes and amphibians, slips of branchiomeric or myotomal muscles insert one place or another on the dermis, attaching the skin firmly to the underlying muscle at those locations but causing little movement of the skin. **Costocutaneous muscles** of snakes are hypaxial muscles used in locomotion (Chapter 9, "Locomotion without limbs"). But it is only in mammals that integumentary muscles are well differentiated. A **panniculus carnosus (cutaneous maximus)** wraps around the entire trunk of some mammals, enabling armadillos to roll into a ball when endangered, forms a sphincter around the entrance to marsupial pouches, and vigorously shakes flies off horses (Fig. 10-17). It is poorly developed in monkeys and absent in humans. In bats, slips of the pectoral muscles insert on the skin of the wing membrane (**patagial muscles**).

The most notable integumentary muscles are **mimetics**—those that express emotion (Fig. 10-18). More than 30 different muscles in humans depress the corners of the mouth in grief, raise them for smiling, wrinkle the forehead, raise the eyebrows quizzically, tightly close the lids, pucker the lips, draw milk when suckling, dilate the nostrils, and direct the pinnas of the ears toward faint sounds. One muscle, the **caninus,** elevates the part of the upper lip that hides the spearlike canine tooth used for ripping into flesh. When man uses it he us said to be sneering.

The preceding are extrinsic integumentary muscles. Intrinsic ones

Fig. 10-17. Panniculus carnosus (cutaneous maximus) of a cat and primate. Note difference in the extent of the muscle in these two animals.

CAT   MONKEY

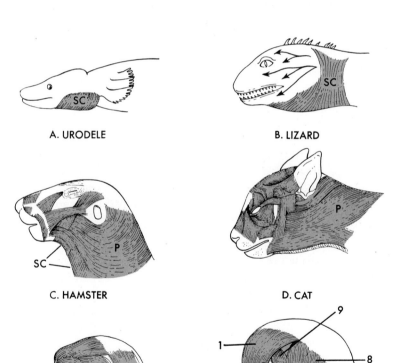

A. URODELE

B. LIZARD

C. HAMSTER

D. CAT

E. RHESUS

F. HUMAN FETUS

Fig. 10-18. Evolution of mammalian mimetic muscles from hyoid arch muscles of lower tetrapods. The sphincter colli, **SC,** spreads onto the neck in reptiles and becomes the platysma, **P,** in mammals. It then spreads forward onto the head and face, as indicated by arrows in **B,** to become muscles of facial expression. Note increasing differentiation of mimetics in the mammals shown. **1,** Frontalis; **2,** orbicularis oculi; **3,** quadratus labii superioris; **4,** risorius; **5,** triangularis; **6,** posterior auricular; **7,** occipital; **8,** superior auricular; **9,** anterior auricular. (**C** after Priddy and Brodie[14]; **E** and **F** after Huber.[12])

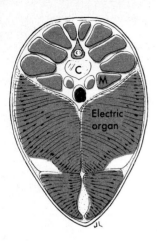

Fig. 10-19. Electric organs in tail of electric eel. Each nucleated horizontal disc (electroplax) is a modified hypaxial muscle cell. **C,** Centrum; **M,** epaxial myomere.

are found chiefly in birds and mammals. Most are smooth muscles and attach to feather or hair follicles (**arrectores plumarum** or **pilorum**). These ruffle feathers or raise hairs for insulation or in response to danger and are innervated by visceral motor fibers. Intrinsic integumentary muscles are uncommon in ectotherms.

ELECTRIC ORGANS

In many fishes certain muscle masses are modified to produce, store, and discharge electricity. In *Torpedo*, the electric ray, an electric organ lies in each pectoral fin near the gills. It is probably of branchiomeric origin, since it is supplied by cranial nerves VII and IX. In *Raia* (a skate) and *Electrophorus* (electric eel) electric organs lie in the tail and are modified hypaxial muscles (Fig. 10-19). The potential produced by these organs in eels amounts to 500 volts and is probably a protective device. Other fishes have electric organs with a lower electric potential, which serve as locating mechanisms or for signaling (communication). Certain neuromasts are receptors for these signals.

Electric organs consist of a large number of electric discs (up to 20,000 in the tail of one ray) piled in either vertical or horizontal columns. Each disc (**electroplax**) is a modified multinucleate muscle cell embedded in a vascular jellylike extracellular material and surrounded by connective tissue. Nerve endings terminating on each disc induce the discharge.

Electric organs seem to have no systematic distribution among fishes, and the various types probably result from convergent evolution. The electric organ of one teleost (a catfish native to Africa) is said to be a modified skin gland, rather than muscle.

CHAPTER SUMMARY

1. Muscle may be classified as striated, smooth, or cardiac; voluntary or involuntary; skeletal or nonskeletal; somatic (myotomal) or visceral (nonmyotomal).

2. Skeletal muscles are attached to the skeleton. They are striated and voluntary. Excepting branchiomeric muscles, they are somatic and arise from mesodermal somites directly or indirectly.

3. Nonskeletal muscle is found in the walls of hollow viscera, tubes, and vessels; in the eyeball, dermis, and miscellaneous sites. It is typically involuntary, smooth, and visceral.

4. Cardiac muscle is striated visceral muscle constituting the myocardium of the heart.

5. Classified according to their actions, muscles are flexors, extensors, abductors, adductors, protractors, retractors, levators, depressors, rotators (including pronators and supinators), constrictors, dilators, and tensors.

6. Skeletal muscles may be named on the basis of the direction of their fibers, location, number of parts, shape, attachments, action, size, and miscellaneous considerations.

7. Homologies between muscle groups are more easily discernible than homologies between muscles. Embryonic origin and nerve supply are the most reliable criteria.

8. The trunk and tail muscles of fishes and tailed amphibians are locomotor, arranged as myomeres, and divided into epaxial and hypaxial masses by a horizontal septum. Loss of myosepta tends to obscure the primitive metamerism.

9. The metamerism of axial muscles is an expression of the metamerism of embryonic somites.

10. Epaxial and hypaxial masses are innervated by dorsal and ventral spinal nerve rami, respectively.

11. In tetrapods other than urodeles epaxial muscles form long bundles, and hypaxial muscles of the trunk have lost their metamerism except where there are long ribs and are stratified into oblique, rectus, and transverse sheets.

12. Hypaxial muscles immediately ventral to transverse processes are disposed in long bundles (subvertebral muscles).

13. Hypaxial muscles extend forward under the pharynx as hypobranchial and tongue muscles.

14. The mammalian diaphragm and cremaster muscles are hypaxial muscles that have migrated accompanied by their spinal nerves.

15. Eyeball muscles arise from three preotic somites in elasmobranchs, develop in situ in higher vertebrates. They are innervated by cranial nerves III, IV, and VI and are myotomal by phylogenetic derivation.

16. Extrinsic appendicular muscles have anatomical origins on the axial skeleton and insertions on the girdles and limbs. Intrinsic appendicular muscles have no axial skeletal attachments.

17. Secondary appendicular muscles form from blastemas within the body wall and achieve an attachment to the girdle or limb. Most extrinsic appendicular muscles are of this kind.

18. Primary appendicular muscles organize from blastemas within the limb. They are the intrinsic and a few extrinsic appendicular muscles of tetrapods.

19. Branchiomeric muscles are striated, skeletal, voluntary, visceral muscles that arise from ectomesenchyme.

20. The muscles of the mandibular arch operate the jaws. In mammals a derivative operates the malleus. They are innervated by cranial nerve V.

21. The muscles of the second arch attach to the hyoid skeleton, lower jaw, and operculum. The sphincter colli spreads over the head to become platysma and mimetic muscles. Second arch muscle also attaches to the stapes. The muscles are innervated by cranial nerve VII.

22. Muscles of the third and remaining arches operate gills in fishes. In higher vertebrates they have new functions, including swallowing and vocalization. The muscles of the third arch are innervated by cranial nerve IX, those of successive arches by X.

23. The cucullaris has become subdivided into trapezius, sternomastoid, and cleidomastoid muscles in amniotes.

24. Extrinsic integumentary muscles reach peak development as the panniculus carnosus (cutaneous maximus) of mammals and mimetics of primates. Those of the trunk are myotomal. Those of the face and scalp are branchiomeric.

25. Intrinsic integumentary muscles are chiefly smooth muscles inserting on feathers and hairs.

26. Electric organs are columns of modified axial, appendicular, or branchiomeric muscle cells (electroplaxes) capable of producing, storing, and discharging electric potential. A few appear to be modified skin glands.

LITERATURE CITED AND SELECTED READINGS

1. Allen, E.R.: Development of vertebrate skeletal muscle, American Zoologist 18(1):101, 1978.
2. Alexander, R.M.: Functional design in fishes, ed. 2, London, 1970, Hutchinson University Library.
3. Auffenberg, W.: A review of the trunk musculature in the limbless land vertebrates, American Zoologist 2:183, 1962.
4. Bock, W.J.: Experimental analysis of the avian passive perching mechanism, American Zoologist 5:681, 1965.
5. Bone, Q.: Locomotor muscle. In Hoar, W.S., and Randall, D.J., editors: Fish physiology, vol. 7, New York, 1978, Academic Press, Inc.
6. Byerly, T.C.: The myology of *Sphenodon punctatum*, University of Iowa Studies in Natural History (First Series, no. 98), vol. 11, no. 6, 1925.
7. Ellsworth, A.H.F.: Reassessment of muscle homologies and nomenclature in conservative amniotes: the echidna, *Tachyglossus;* the opossum, *Didelphis;* and the tuatara, *Sphenodon,*
   Huntington, N.Y., 1975, R.E. Krieger Publishing Co., Inc.
8. Gans, C., and Parsons, T.S., editors: Biology of the reptilia, vol. 4, New York, 1973, Academic Press, Inc.
9. Grundfest, H.: Electric fishes, Scientific American 203:115, 1960.
10. Herring, S.W.: Functional design of the cranial muscles: comparative and physiological studies in pigs, American Zoologist 20(1):283, 1980.
11. Hildebrand, M.: How animals run. In Vertebrate structures and functions: readings from Scientific American with introduction by Norman K. Wessells, San Francisco, 1955-1974, W.H. Freeman and Co., Publishers.
12. Huber, E.: Evolution of facial musculature and cutaneous field of trigeminus, parts I and II, Quarterly Review of Biology 5:133, 389, 1930.
13. Keynes, R.D.: Electric organs. In Brown, M.E., editor: The physiology of fishes, New York, 1957, Academic Press, Inc.
14. Priddy, R.B., and Brodie, A.F.: Facial musculature, nerves and blood

vessels of the hamster in relation to the cheek pouch, Journal of Morphology **83**:149, 1948.

15. Raikow, R.J., Boreckt, S.R., and Berman, S.L.: The evolutionary reestablishment of a lost ancestral muscle in the bowbird assemblage, Condor **81**:203, 1979.

16. Wardle, C.S., and Videler, J.J.: Fish swimming. In Elder, H.Y., and Truman, E.R., editors: Aspects of animal movement, Cambridge, England, 1980, Cambridge University Press.

17. Zus, R.: The role of the depressor mandibulae muscle in kinesis of the avian skull, U. S. National Museum Proceedings **123**:1, 1967.

Symposium in American Zoologist

Skeletal muscle tissue, **18**:95, 1978.

CHAPTER 11

Digestive system

PROCURING FOOD

Any observant person with an interest in animal life can cite numerous means by which animals obtain energy in the form of food from their environment. Of the techniques employed, some are more obvious than others. A few will be mentioned in anticipation of better appreciating the structural adaptations associated with feeding that are described in this and other chapters.

Ancestral chordates and ostracoderms were filter feeders. This process, which can be employed only by aquatic organisms, consists of passively filtering organic matter out of the incoming respiratory stream and propelling the food particles to the rear of the pharynx for swallowing. Filter feeding in sea squirts, amphioxus, and larval cyclostomes has been described in Chapter 2. A more active version of filter feeding is employed by some fishes, such as spoonbills, tiny clupeids, and huge basking sharks. Plankton and small fishes are strained out of the respiratory water stream by long filamentous gill rakers that hang into the pharyngeal chamber from the gill arches. The largest mammals, baleen whales, strain tons of small fish, jellyfish, and other invertebrates from the sea each day through sieves of whalebone, or baleen, that hang into their oral cavity. However, whales take water into the oral cavity solely for the food it contains, since they do not breathe with gills.

With the advent in arthrodires and placoderms of jaws and muscular body walls that can be used for locomotion and pursuit, more aggressive methods of obtaining food became possible. Jaws, at first invested with bony dermal armor, ultimately were furnished with small, often sharp, single denticles that we recognize as teeth. Many organisms thereupon became predators, and their method of feeding, as in modern sharks, was a bite-tear-swallow technique that required no tongue, oral glands, or other specializations of the oral cavity.

A less energy-consuming procedure evolved as a result of further adaptations of the skull and hyoid arches. The modifications enabled

In this chapter we will examine the alimentary canal, the glands and other evaginations that arise from it, and some spectacular modifications associated with varying food habits, such as tongues that are stored under the scalp, tooth plates that crush molluscs, gizzards, ruminant stomachs, and ceca that are the home of cellulose-digesting bacteria. We will start by recalling some of the means employed by vertebrates for obtaining energy in the form of food from their environment.

some teleosts to approach close to organisms that are small enough to be swallowed, extend protrusible jaws, create suction, close the mouth, retract the jaws, and swallow. Anyone who has watched a goldfish feeding on flakes of fish food has observed this technique. Lampreys, being parasitic, have a different feeding technique. They rasp the tissues of the host with their spiny tongue and suck the debris into their pharynx.

On land, long sticky tongues are found among amphibians, squamate reptiles, and many birds and mammals. Some snakes impale prey on their upper jaw teeth. Winged tetrapods pick up grubs, seeds, and grains and perform other food-getting acts with appropriately shaped beaks, and shore birds pierce fish with them, or scoop fish from the sea, pelican fashion. Sanguinivorous bats suck whole blood, meanwhile preventing clotting by coagulants in their saliva. And baby mammals suck milk, using muscular cheeks and lips.

Herbivorous ungulates crop grasses, and carnivorous mammals use a snap-bite-tear technique that often includes the piercing effect of a saberlike tooth. Because of appropriate joints in the wrist or digits, primates can grasp food and convey it to the mouth, and rodents can hold food between their hands and nibble. Other methods of food getting will come to mind.

Food taking depends on food finding. This is accomplished by sense organs that monitor the external environment. Chemical receptors such as olfactory organs, mechanical receptors such as inner ears and lateral line organs of fishes and amphibians, thermal receptors such as the loreal pits of some snakes, capsulated touch receptors such as those on the sensitive snout of pigs, visual receptors, and electroreceptors—one or more of these alert one vertebrate or another to the presence and location of food. Once the energy-containing food is within the body the alimentary canal can process it, extract needed molecules, and return unassimilated matter to the environment.

THE DIGESTIVE TRACT: AN OVERVIEW

The digestive tract is a tube, seldom straight and often tortuously coiled, commencing at the mouth and terminating at the vent or anus (Fig. 11-1). It functions in the ingestion, digestion, and absorption of foodstuffs and in elimination of undigested wastes. In most fishes respiratory water also enters the mouth, but this water is quickly shunted through gill slits and out of the digestive tract. The role of the mouth and pharynx in respiration is discussed in Chapter 12.

Major subdivisions of the tract are oral cavity, pharynx, esophagus, stomach, and small and large intestines. Associated with the tract are accessory organs such as the tongue, teeth, oral glands, pancreas,

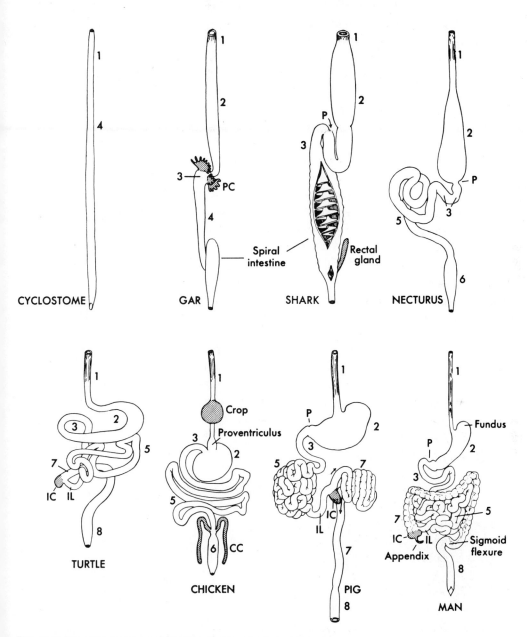

Fig. 11-1. Digestive tracts caudal to the pharynx of a few vertebrates.
1, Esophagus; **2**, stomach; **3**, duodenum; **4**, intestine; **5**, small intestine; **6**,
large intestine; **7**, colon; **8**, rectum; **CC**, paired ceca of bird; **IC**, ileocolic cecum;
IL, ileum; **P**, pyloric sphincter; **PC**, pyloric ceca. All ceca are shown in gray.

liver, and gallbladder. Blind evaginations, or ceca, of the tract are common. The digestive tract and accessory organs constitute the digestive system.

Differences in the anatomy of digestive tracts caudal to the pharynx are correlated not so much with whether an animal lives on land or in the water as with the nature and abundance of food. Is it readily absorbable when ingested, as in vampire bats, or does it require extensive enzymatic activity or mechanical maceration, as in carnivores? Is the food supply constant, so that whenever an animal is hungry the food is likely to be there, or does it have to be stalked? If the latter, the meal is probably bulky and there has to be room for it in an appropriately expandable stomach until it can be digested. And what is the shape of the animal's body? If it is long, like that of a cyclostome or snake, the tract will probably be straight. If the trunk is short, as in turtles and anurans, the intestine must be coiled in order to provide a sufficient absorptive area. Some fishes have a spiral valve, or typhlosole, that increases the absorptive area.

The entire digestive tract is ciliated in many larval vertebrates, and there are cilia in the stomach of many teleosts, in the oral cavity, pharynx, esophagus, and stomach of some adult amphibians, in the ceca of some birds, and in other locations in various species. Cilia are present for a time in the stomach of a human fetus. However, peristalsis is chiefly responsible for moving foodstuffs along the alimentary canal. The tract is lined by endoderm, as are all evaginations from it. Surrounding the endodermal lining is splanchnic mesoderm (Fig. 4-7), which provides the muscular and connective tissue coats of the

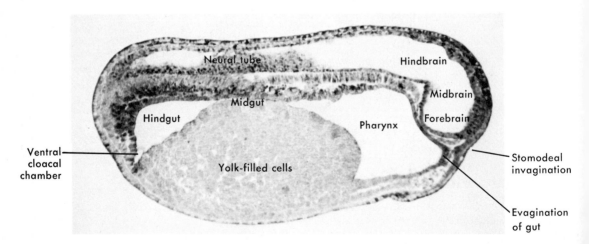

Fig. 11-2. Sagittal section of 3.5-mm frog tadpole. (From Phillips, J.B.: Development of vertebrate anatomy, St. Louis, 1975, The C.V. Mosby Co.)

tract and the visceral peritoneum and supports the visceral vessels and nerves.

The embryonic digestive tract consists of three regions. The part containing the yolk, or to which the yolk sac is attached, is the **midgut.** Anterior to the midgut is **foregut** and caudal to it is the **hindgut** (Fig. 11-2). The foregut elongates to become the posterior portion of the oral cavity, the pharynx, esophagus, stomach, and most of the small intestine. The hindgut becomes the large intestine and cloaca. Little of the midgut remains in adults. From stomach to cloaca the embryonic gut is attached to the dorsal body wall of the trunk by a continuous dorsal mesentery and to the ventral body wall by a ventral mesentery (Fig. 11-23). Much of the dorsal mesentery remains throughout life, but the ventral mesentery disappears except at two sites. It remains in all vertebrates at the liver where it is called **falciform ligament,** and it remains in tetrapods as the **ventral mesentery of the urinary bladder.**

The anterior part of the oral cavity arises from the **stomodeum,** a midventral invagination of the ectoderm of the head (Fig. 11-2). The thin membrane, or oral plate, temporarily separates the two ruptures to provide an entrance to the foregut. A similar invagination, the **proctodeum,** provides an exit from the hindgut when the cloacal plate ruptures (Fig. 1-1).

MOUTH AND ORAL CAVITY

The mouth is the entrance to the digestive tract. The oral cavity commences at the mouth and ends at the pharynx. A primitive or specialized tongue lies in its floor. In fishes the oral cavity is so short as to be almost nonexistent. For this reason the chamber commencing at the mouth and ending at the esophagus and having gill slits in its walls is often referred to as an **orobranchial cavity.**

The roof of the oral, or orobranchial, cavity is a primary palate in anamniotes, a partial or complete secondary palate in reptiles, birds, and mammals. The primary palate is pierced in lungfishes and amphibians by internal nares that open from a short nasal canal anteriorly (Fig. 11-3, *A*). In snakes, lizards, and birds it has a deep longitudinal groove, the **palatal fissure,** that channelizes the respiratory air between internal nares and pharynx (Fig. 11-4). In crocodilians and mammals the entire roof of the oral cavity is a secondary palate that separates the nasal passageways from the oral cavity all the way to the pharynx (Fig. 11-3, *B*).

A trench, the **oral vestibule,** separates the alveolar ridges (gums) from the cheeks and lips in mammals. Some rodents transport grain in cheek pouches that extend from the vestibule backward under the skin and integumentary muscles of the head, and birds use a median

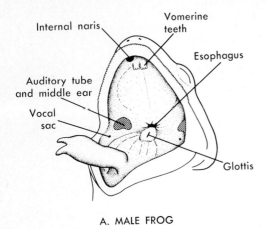

A. MALE FROG

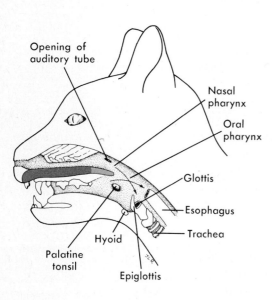

B. CAT

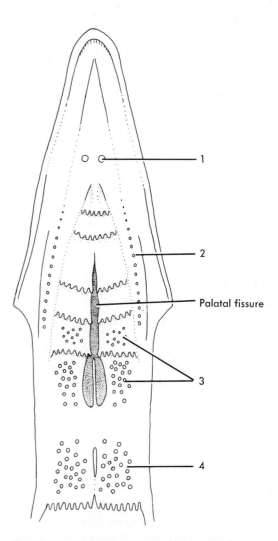

Palatal fissure

Fig. 11-3. Oral cavity of **A,** amphibian, and **B,** mammal. The roof of the oral cavity in a frog is a primary palate. In cat it is a secondary palate. The latter consists of a hard (bony) palate (darker red) and a soft palate (light red). Crossed arrows indicate pharyngeal chiasma where food and water streams cross.

Fig. 11-4. Palate of domestic hen. 1 to 4, Gland openings as follows: **1,** paired maxillaries; **2,** lateral palatines; **3,** medial palatines; **4,** sphenopterygoids. Internal nares are above palatal folds at anterior end of palatal fissure.

sublingual seed pouch in the same manner. When full, the sublingual pouch hangs beneath the rear of the oral cavity suspended in a sling formed by the mylohyoid muscle. The pouch is emptied by shaking the head. Numerous glands also empty into the oral cavity.

Tongue

The tongue of jawed fishes and perennibranchiate amphibians is a mere crescentic or angular elevation in the floor of the pharynx caused by the underlying hyoid skeleton. This lean hyoid elevation is a **primary tongue** (Fig. 11-5). The tongue of most amphibians consists of the primary tongue and an additional contribution, the **glandular field,** from the pharyngeal floor anterior to the hyoid arch (Fig. 11-5, larval frog). The tongue of reptiles and mammals has a primary tongue contribution from arch II and a pair of **lateral lingual swellings** from arch I that become stuffed with myotomal muscle. In addition, arch III contributes by growing forward over the second arch mucosa and excluding it from the surface. In birds the lateral lingual swellings are suppressed. The tongue of agnathans is not homologous with that of other vertebrates (Fig. 12-5).

The tongue is widely used for capturing or gathering food. Long sticky tongues of insectivorous tetrapods from salamanders to anteaters dart in and out at lightning speed, as do also those of nectar-feeding bats and birds. Woodpeckers have a tongue like an arrow that shoots into dark crevices in trees and stumps, impaling grubs and carrying them to the mouth (Fig. 11-6, A). The tiny tongue of hummingbirds darts rapidly back and forth between flower and mouth collecting droplets of nectar at the hollowed frayed tip (Fig. 11-6, B). A parrot's tongue is armed with two flexible, horny shields in the walls of a seed cup (Fig. 11-7). Like fingernails, they are composed of keratinized stratum corneum that grows forward from a nail-like bed halfway back on the tongue. The anterior edge is constantly being worn away and replaced. Embedded within a bird's tongue, giving flexibility to long, darting tongues and supporting them so they don't droop, is an **entoglossal** bone, an anteriorly directed process of the hyoid (Fig. 8-36, E). In many birds a long pair of **paraglossals** attach to the entoglossus near the tip of the tongue and extend caudad embedded in its edges. Lizards also have an entoglossus.

The huge immobilized muscular tongue of some baleen whales directs tons of seawater into huge reservoirs. When these are emptied by compression of their walls, organisms strained out of the water by baleen accumulate on the tongue and are then swallowed. Newborn whales have only rudiments of baleen, and there is room in the oral cavity for the quite mobile neonatal tongue to be manipulated for suckling for about 6 months before it becomes immobilized. The

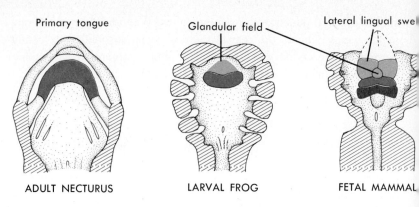

Primary tongue

Glandular field

Lateral lingual swe[ll]

Fig. 11-5. Floor of oral cavity depicting possible stages in evolution of the mammalian tongue. First arch derivatives, *light red;* second arch, *medium red;* third arch, *dark red.* Dotted outline in mammal shows final extent of lateral lingual swellings. In mammals the glandular field is also known as the tuberculum impar, and arch II endoderm is later covered by arch III endoderm.

ADULT NECTURUS

LARVAL FROG

FETAL MAMMAL

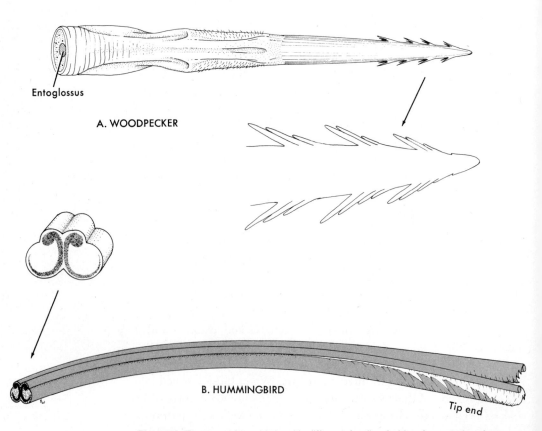

Entoglossus

A. WOODPECKER

B. HUMMINGBIRD

Tip end

Fig. 11-6. Tongues of two birds with different feeding habits. **A,** ventral surface. **B,** Lateral view.

A

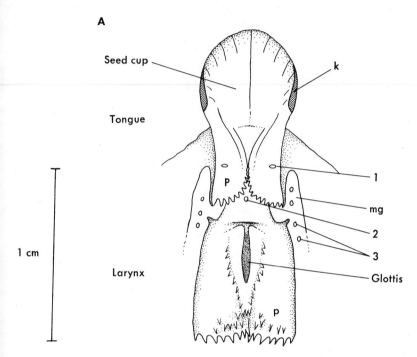

Seed cup

k

Tongue

1 cm

Larynx

P

1

mg

2

3

Glottis

p

B   P

3   p   3   1

Larynx

mg

k

sg

4

s

Fig. 11-7. Tongue and larynx of the parrot *Psittacula roseata.* **A,** Dorsal view. **B,** Right lateral view. **k,** Horny plate; **mg,** mandibular gland; **p,** papillae; **s,** site of mandibular symphysis; **sg,** sublingual gland. **1** to **4,** Openings of the following glands: **1,** paired lingual; **2,** medial lingual; **3,** mandibular; **4,** sublingual. (Courtesy D.G. Homberger, Louisiana State University, Baton Rouge.[4])

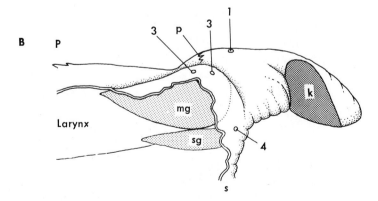

tongues of most other mammals are protrusible, although tied to the floor of the oral cavity by a ligament, the **frenulum linguae.** In human beings, if the frenulum inhibits movements of the tip of the tongue, making the individual tongue tied, it can be snipped at its anterior edge. The tongues of turtles, crocodilians, and some birds are also unprotrusible.

The mucosa of the tongue contains receptors not only for taste but for other stimuli as well, including, in amniotes, stereognosis. Encapsulated nerve endings enable insectivores to locate food by feeling, and a woodpecker knows whether it has impaled a grub or jammed into an unyielding object. Seed-eating birds use stereognostic information in manipulating a seed that is being husked in the seed cup.

When tongues are not used in procuring food or water, they manipulate fluids and solids in the oral cavity; and the tongues of all tetrapods participate in swallowing. Long tongues are used by overheated mammals as a site for cooling the blood by evaporation of saliva while panting. Lizards clean their spectacles with them. Spiny papillae are used by carnivores for rasping bones, and they are used by many mammals for grooming. The latter use accounts for hairballs that often form in the stomach of domestic cats. And, of course, human speech as we know it would not be possible without a tongue.

Oral glands

All tetrapods have multicellular oral glands that, in one species or another, secrete at least some watery or viscous fluid containing mucus, the starch-digesting enzyme ptyalin, toxins, or other substances. Saliva is a mixture of secretions and is most evident in mammals. Moisture is essential for taste buds to function, viscous secretions keep the tongue sticky, and toxins are defensive or tranquilize prey.

Oral glands are usually named according to location. Labial glands open into the oral vestibule at the base of the lips, molar glands lie near the molar tooth, infraorbital glands are in the orbit, palatal glands open onto the palate, and sublingual and submandibular glands open via papillae under the tongue. Intermaxillary (internasal) glands lie near the premaxillae. In frogs they consist of up to 25 small glands, each with its own duct that delivers a sticky secretion on the palate. The large poison gland of venomous snakes is a palatal gland. Its duct opens at the base of a maxillary tooth, and the venom exudes into a groove or tube in the fang (tooth). In *Heloderma*, the only poisonous lizard, sublingual glands secrete the toxin. The parotid gland of mammals is the largest oral gland, and ptyalin is always one of its products. Not all mammalian salivary glands secrete ptyalin, however. The parotid duct crosses the masseter muscle under the skin of the cheek and opens into the oral vestibule opposite one of

Fig. 11-8. Oral glands in a reptile and mammal. **1,** Parotid; **2,** submandibular; **3,** sublingual; **4,** molar; **5,** infraorbital; **6,** poison gland of rattlesnake; **7,** maxillary tooth with groove for transfer of toxin; **8,** tongue.

the upper molar teeth (Fig. 11-8). The poison glands of reptiles resemble the parotid gland histologically. Oral glands in birds are shown in Figs. 11-4 and 11-7.

Aquatic vertebrates have adequate moisture in their oral cavity for taste buds to function, and production of digestive enzymes would be a waste of energy since any secretion would be diluted and washed away. Male catfishes are an exception. During breeding seasons they carry fertilized eggs in temporary epithelial folds, or crypts, in the mouth, and goblet cells in the crypts produce a copious secretion. The brood pouches and goblet cells atrophy after the eggs hatch.

Dentition and the origin of teeth

Bony structures that prevented escape of live food from the orobranchial cavity or that were used for crushing shellfish, biting flesh, or rasping vegetation varied widely among early jawed fishes. Some placoderms had short jaws covered with thin plates of dermal bone that could have been used for nipping at small invertebrates or nibbling on vegetation. Some had long jaws covered with one or two long heavy bony dermal plates with sharply notched bladelike cutting edges, and the plates were braced against heavy cheek plates. In others, the bony plates bore long prongs of dentin that were affixed to the plates. Some had small plates that bore clusters of broad-based conical or star-shaped denticles, and the plates were shed at intervals. In still others the plates were apparently not shed. In placoderms all these denticle-bearing bony plates invested the underlying endoskeleton of the jaws. In acanthodians each denticle, or tooth, usually broad based, some conical, some slender and curved, some with a dozen spiny cusps arranged in whirls, was attached individually to the endoskeleton instead of being borne on plates, and the jaws often were flanked by small dermal scales. Some acanthodians were toothless or had lower teeth only. Peyer[15] has given us a comprehensive treatise on comparative odontology illustrated with over 50 pages of photographs.

Until the phylogenetic relationships between acanthodians, placoderms, and later cartilaginous and bony fishes can be ascertained, only the broadest generalizations regarding the origin of teeth can be made: *they are derivatives of dermal armor*. Evidence comes not only from paleontology but from the comparative histology of armor and teeth and from the observation that placoid scales, even today, show a gradual transition from scales to teeth as they approach the cutting edges of the jaws (Fig. 11-9).

Teeth are composed of a core of dentin surmounted by a crown of enamel (Fig. 11-10). At the base of a developing tooth and forming the core as the tooth grows is a live dermal papilla that supports

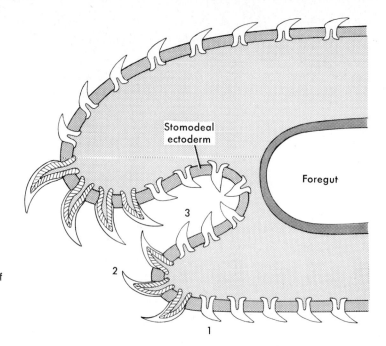

Fig. 11-9. Schematic representation of the continuity of, **1,** placoid scales, **2,** teeth, and, **3,** stomodeal denticles (not to scale).

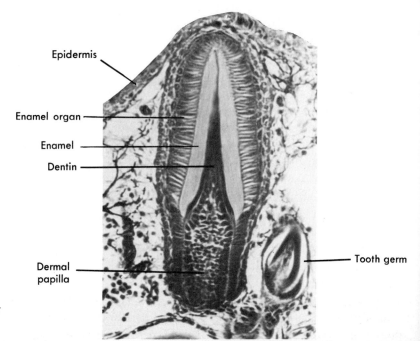

Fig. 11-10. Unerupted tooth of a garfish. The odontoblasts are seen lined up at the periphery of the dermal papilla. Tooth germ is a replacement for a tooth that will be shed. (Courtesy Paul F. Terranova, Kansas City, Kan.)

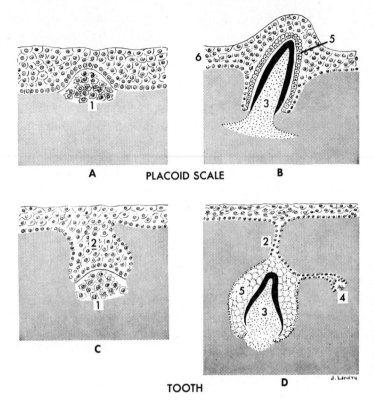

A   **PLACOID SCALE**   B

C

TOOTH   D

J. Landry

MORPHOGENESIS

Fig. 11-11. Development of placoid scale and mammalian tooth. Dermis, except dermal papilla, is gray; enamel is black. **1,** Dermal papilla; **2,** dental ridge, an ingrowth of the epidermis; **3,** dentin, produced by the dermal papilla; **4,** germ of replacement tooth; **5,** enamel organ; **6,** epidermis.

nutritive vessels and nerves and provides, at its periphery, odonto-blasts that secrete the dentin. An epidermal enamel organ composed of ameloblasts secretes enamel (Figs. 11-10 and 11-11). When the tooth is fully formed the papilla remains as pulp in the root canal. An enamel organ is present but functionless in armadillos and a few other vertebrates, so their teeth have no enamel. Around the root in bony vertebrates is a thin layer of **cementum,** a variety of bone that helps hold the tooth against the jawbone or in the socket.

Agnathans, sturgeons, some toads, sirens (urodeles), turtles, and modern birds are toothless. However, one species of terns develops an embryonic set that does not erupt, and at least one genus of turtles has enamel organs. Toothless mammals develop a set that either does not erupt or, after erupting, is soon lost.

Teeth vary among vertebrates in number, distribution within the oral cavity, degree of permanence, position with reference to the summit of the jaw, and shape. They are numerous and widely distrib-uted in the oral cavity and pharynx of living fishes. They develop on jaws, palate, and even on the pharyngeal skeleton. For example, the blue sucker has 35 to 40 teeth on the last gill arch. In early tetrapods, too, teeth were widely distributed on the palate; and even today most amphibians and many reptiles have teeth on the vomer, palatine, and pterygoid bones and occasionally on the parasphenoid. They are confined to the jaws in crocodilians, toothed birds, and mammals, and they are least numerous among mammals. Teeth, therefore, like dermal armor, have tended toward a more restricted distribution with the passage of time.

Most vertebrates through reptiles have a succession of teeth, and the number of replacements during a lifetime is indefinite but numerous (**polyphyodont dentition**). It has been estimated that an elderly crocodile may have replaced its front tooth 50 times. They and other submammalian bony vertebrates that have been studied replace teeth in waves that sweep along the jaws eliminating and replacing every other tooth. Thus in one wave, in tetrapods at least, even-numbered teeth are lost and in the next wave odd-numbered ones are lost. Meanwhile, tooth germs for the next wave of eruptions are forming. Whether the loss and replacement waves sweep from back to front or reverse is not agreed on at present. There is evidence that they sweep in different directions in different species. The waves ensure a balanced distribution of teeth along the jaws throughout life. In sharks, tooth germs form in the dermis on the oral cavity side of the jaws and while growing migrate forward into position as the tooth that is being replaced moves beyond the summit of the jaw before falling away. The cause of the migration is not known.

Only in mammals is there a definite number of teeth in a species. Most mammals develop two sets, **deciduous,** or milk, teeth and **permanent** teeth (**diphyodont dentition**). Milk teeth usually erupt and are shed after birth. A few mammals, such as the platypus, sirenians, and cetaceans, develop only a first set (**monophyodont dentition**), and, as in toothless whales, these teeth may not erupt. If they do they are usually shed. In the platypus, milk teeth are replaced by horny teeth. Every mammalian species has a definite sequence in which teeth erupt. For example, if the permanent set on one side in human beings are numbered 1 to 8 from front to rear the sequence of eruption is 6, 1, 2, 4, 5, 3, 7, 8. Eruption of tooth number 8, the last molar, is delayed in higher primates, and this "wisdom" tooth is sometimes imperfect, unerupted, or missing. A first set provides the constantly changing infant jaw with small temporary teeth adequate for an infant's diet until the jaws are more stabilized structurally and have elongated sufficiently to accommodate large teeth for macerating coarse foods.

Teeth are firmly attached by collagenous fibers anchored in the jaw

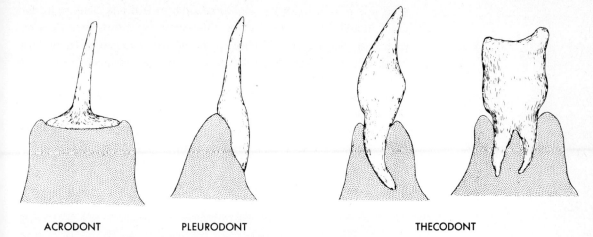

ACRODONT   PLEURODONT   THECODONT

Fig. 11-12. Variations in the relationship of teeth to jaws. Acrodont teeth are attached either at the outer surface of the jaw or, as shown, at the summit. Pleurodont teeth are attached to the inner surface of the jaw. Thecodont teeth occupy alveoli. The bone of the jaw is seen in cross section.

and in the cementum of the teeth. In nonsocketed teeth the relationship of cementum to jaw skeleton is more intimate. Jaw teeth may be attached to the outer surface or to the summit of the jawbone, as in many teleosts (**acrodont dentition**); they may be attached to the inner side of the jawbone, as in frogs, *Necturus,* and many lizards (**pleurodont dentition**); or they may occupy bony sockets, or alveoli (**thecodont dentition**) (Fig. 11-12). Socketed teeth are found in crocodilians, extinct toothed birds, mammals, and many fishes, but the sockets are deepest in mammals.

MORPHOLOGICAL VARIANTS

Most sharks are fish eaters and have numerous rows of teeth that are either flat, sharp, notched triangles that are used for cutting, or they are single or multipointed tusks that curve toward the pharynx and hold a struggling prey until it can be swallowed whole. Each tooth has a broad basal plate of dentin embedded in the dermis. A minority eat shellfish and, although the teeth at the entrance have curved caudally directed spines, the rest form batteries of rounded denticles used for crushing shells (Fig. 11-13). Tiny stomodeal denticles line the pharynx in some sharks, and these have transitional shapes between denticles and teeth as they approach the jaws.

The dental armor of holocephalans and modern lungfishes is reminiscent of that of earlier jawed fishes, consisting of a few large plates of enamel-covered dentin that bear clusters of sharp or flattened ridges or spines. *Chimaera,* a holocephalan that eats molluscs, has on each side of the upper jaw one large anterior and one small posterior denticulated tooth plate that together cover the entire upper jaw on each side. There is a single large plate on each side below. In modern lungfishes the plates are restricted to the palate and medial aspects of the lower jaw.

The teeth of actinopterygians, amphibians, and most reptiles are simple pointed cones attached to one or more membrane bones. Small teeth may be interspersed among large ones, and those in front are sometimes larger and curved slightly to the rear. Specialized shapes sometimes occur on one jaw or the other. Gars, for instance,

Fig. 11-13. Jaws of the Port Jackson shark, *Heterodontus,* showing transition of placoid scales to teeth. The rounded teeth are used for crushing molluscs. (Courtesy Ward's Natural Science Establishment, Inc., Rochester, N.Y.)

have a few fanglike teeth shaped at their ends like arrows; and the fangs of venomous snakes, borne on the maxillae, are curved or bladelike, grooved on the rear surface, or tubular, for injecting venom. When all teeth are alike the dentition is described as **homodont.**

In mammals the teeth of each individual are of different shapes—incisors, canines, premolars, molars—and this is a **heterodont dentition.** Heterodonty was first evident in synapsid reptiles, which had a pair of prominent caninelike teeth (Fig. 3-18).

Incisors, located anteriorly, are used chiefly for cropping or gnaw-

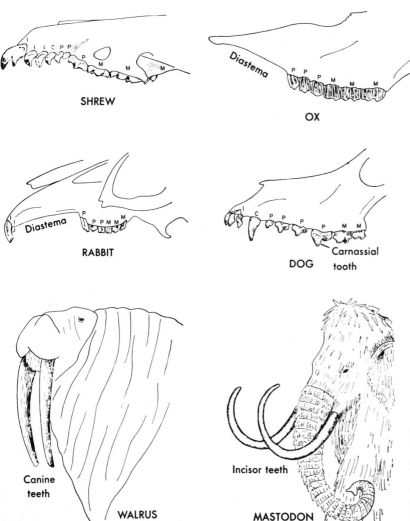

Fig. 11-14. Mammalian upper teeth, showing generalized pattern (shrew), and specializations in a herbivore (ox), in a gnawing animal (rabbit), and in a carnivore (dog). Extreme specialization of canines is seen in the walrus and of incisors in the mastodon. **I,** Incisor; **C,** canine; **P,** premolar; **M,** molar.

ing. The incisors of rodents and lagomorphs continue to grow throughout most of life, and in rodents enamel is deposited on the anterior surface only. Since enamel wears down more slowly than dentin, sharp chisel-like enamel edges result. Incisors may be totally absent, as in sloths, or lacking on the upper jaw, as in ruminants (Fig. 11-14, ox). Elephant tusks are modified incisors (Fig. 11-14, mastodon).

Canines lie immediately behind the incisors (Fig. 11-14, dog). In generalized mammals, incisors and canines scarcely differ in appearance (Fig. 11-14, shrew). In carnivores the canines are spearlike and used for piercing flesh (Fig. 11-15, *B*). They are also the tusks of the walrus (Fig. 11-14). Canine teeth are absent in rodents and lagomorphs and so there is a toothless interval, or **diastema,** between the last incisor and the first cheek tooth (Fig. 11-14, rabbit). Canine teeth attained their greatest length on the upper jaw of the now extinct saber-toothed cats, in which they extended as much as 20 cm below the lower jaw with the mouth closed.

Cheek teeth, or **premolars** and **molars,** are used for macerating food (Fig. 11-15, *A*). Molars are cheek teeth that are not replaced by a second set. They are, in reality, late arrivals of the first set. In herbivorous mammals (Fig. 11-14, ox), cheek teeth tend to be numerous, and there is little morphological differentiation between premolars and molars. In grinding vegetation, herbivores drag the lower cheek teeth across the upper ones in either back-to-front or side-to-side movements. As a result, the cusps, which in young animals are conical elevations, wear down to broad, flat, ridged, grinding surfaces. In carnivores grinding is deemphasized, the number of cheek

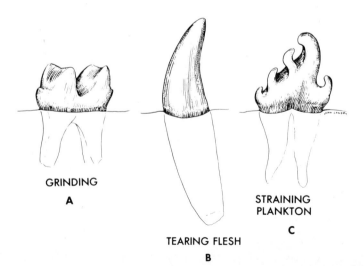

Fig. 11-15. Adaptive modifications of mammalian teeth, lateral views. **A,** Lower left molar from a young tapir, showing cusps for grinding. **B,** Lower left canine from a jaguar for tearing flesh. **C,** Lower right molar from a crabeater seal.

GRINDING
A

TEARING FLESH
B

STRAINING PLANKTON
C

teeth is reduced, and cusps, which are useful for macerating flesh, remain prominent. At least one pair of cheek teeth on each jaw of carnivores has very sharp cusps for cracking bones and shearing tendons (Fig. 11-14, dog, **carnassial tooth**). For additional discussions of adaptations for mastication see "Temporal fossae and a new jaw joint" in Chapter 8.

Generalized placental mammals have three incisors, one canine, four premolars, and three molars on each side of each jaw, a total of 44 teeth. This may be expressed by the formula $\frac{3\text{-}1\text{-}4\text{-}3}{3\text{-}1\text{-}4\text{-}3}$. The same formula applies to modern horses, although the first premolar may be missing. Dental formulae for other adult mammals are as follows:

$$\text{Cat } \frac{3\text{-}1\text{-}3\text{-}1}{3\text{-}1\text{-}2\text{-}1} \qquad \text{Man } \frac{2\text{-}1\text{-}2\text{-}3}{2\text{-}1\text{-}2\text{-}3} \qquad \text{Rabbit } \frac{2\text{-}0\text{-}3\text{-}3}{1\text{-}0\text{-}2\text{-}3}$$

Formulae for shrews, oxen, and dogs can be derived from Fig. 11-14. Teeth, along with the tongue and hyoid, constitue a functional triad that procures, manipulates, and, in mammals, masticates foodstuffs at the entrance to the digestive tract, then starts a bolus of food on its way to digestive sites.

HORNY EPIDERMAL TEETH

Horny teeth sometimes take the place of bony ones. Agnathans have horny teeth in the buccal funnel and on the tongue that are used for rasping. Anuran tadpoles have several rows of horny teeth on temporary lips perched on poorly developed jaws. They are used for rasping algae and other vegetation, which is the tadpole's diet. At metamorphosis the horny teeth are shed and replaced by bony ones that develop on membrane bones overlying the embryonic upper and lower jaw cartilages. Before hatching, turtles, crocodilians, *Sphenodon,* birds, and monotremes have a temporary egg tooth that is used for cracking the shell; and after a baby platypus has lost its first set of bony teeth horny teeth replace them throughout life. The horny beaks of turtles and birds often have serrations that perform some of the functions of teeth, although ancestral birds did not need them. They had bony teeth.

PHARYNX

The pharynx is the part of the digestive tract that had pharyngeal pouches in the embryo. The pharynx of fishes, which is a respiratory organ, is described in Chapter 12. The embryonic pharynx is described in Chapter 1.

In adult vertebrates lacking gill slits, that is, metamorphosed amphibians and amniotes, the pharynx is the part of the foregut immediately preceding the esophagus. The most constant features of the tetrapod pharynx are the **glottis** (a slit leading into the larynx), the openings of **auditory tubes,** and the opening into the esophagus (Fig. 11-3). In mammals a cartilaginous flap, the **epiglottis,** overlies the glottis. In swallowing, the larynx is drawn forward (upward in humans) against the epiglottis and prevents foreign substances from entering the pathway to the lungs. In many species below mammals a flap of mucosa performs this function.

The pharynx of adult mammals consists of a **nasal pharynx (naso-pharynx)** above the **soft palate** (the unossified caudal section of the secondary palate; Fig. 11-3, *B*) and an **oral pharynx (oropharynx)** that begins at the caudal border of the soft palate and extends to the glottis and esophageal opening. The nasal passageways, created by formation of a secondary palate, empty into the nasal pharynx anteriorly, and the two auditory tubes, derived from the first pair of embryonic pharyngeal pouches, open into its lateral walls. The nasal pharynx is completely closed off from the oral pharynx during swallowing, when extrinsic muscles draw the free caudal border of the soft palate tight against the roof of the pharynx.

The oral cavity in mammals leads to the oral pharynx. The site of continuity is a narrow passageway called the **isthmus faucium.** The isthmus is bounded dorsally by the caudal border of the soft palate and laterally by the **pillars of the fauces,** which are two muscular folds on each side of the throat that arch downward from the lateral edge of the soft palate to the side of the tongue (glossopalatine arch) and pharynx (glossopharyngeal arch). Between the two pillars on each side is a **palatine tonsil,** which develops in the wall of the embryonic second pharyngeal pouch. A remnant of the pouch often remains as a pocketlike crypt alongside the palatine tonsil. The palatine tonsils are part of a ring of lymphoidal (adenoidal) masses that encircle the isthmus. Other masses are the **pharyngeal tonsils,** often called adenoids, in the nasal pharynx and **lingual tonsils** at the root of the tongue.

A **laryngeal pharynx** is present in some mammals, including humans. It is a caudal extension of the oral pharynx dorsal to the hyoid bone and leading to the esophagus. It exists only in species in which the esophageal opening is farther caudad than the glottis. In monkeys and humans a fleshy **uvula** hangs from the caudal border of the soft palate into the oral pharynx.

In some teleosts a pair of elongated muscular tubes, or **suprabranchial organs,** evaginate from the roof of the pharynx on each side near the esophagus, extend cephalad above the membranous roof of the pharynx behind the skull, and then turn caudad to terminate as blind sacs. Elongated gill rakers from the last two gill arches form funnel-shaped baskets that extend into the entrances of the tubes, and each tube is surrounded by a cartilaginous capsule to which the striated muscle in its walls is attached. The epithelium at the blind ends has many goblet cells, and the sacs contain quantities of plankton, sometimes compressed into a bolus. It may be that one function of these in gill-breathing fishes is to trap plankton from incoming water and concentrate it into mucified masses, which are then forced out and swallowed.[10] In at least one air-breathing teleost the cavity is filled with air and the epithelial lining is highly vascular and serves as an accessory respiratory membrane.[7]

ESOPHAGUS

The esophagus is a distensible muscular tube, shortest in neckless vertebrates, connecting pharynx and stomach. Striated muscle at the cephalic end of a long esophagus is gradually replaced farther down by smooth muscle, although it may continue onto the stomach wall,

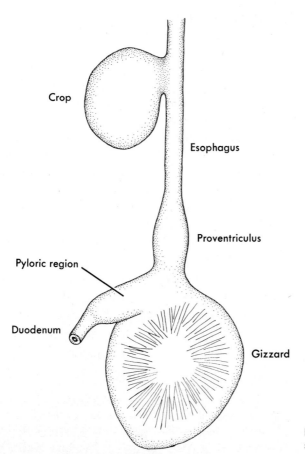

Fig. 11-16. Crop, esophagus, and stomach (gizzard) of a grain-eating bird.

especially in cud-chewing mammals that regurgitate their food for leisurely chewing.

One of the few specializations of the esophagus is the **crop** of some birds (Fig. 11-16). The crop is a paired or unpaired membranous diverticulum of the esophagus occurring primarily in grain eaters and used for initial storage of food. An enzyme for preliminary digestion may also be secreted. In male and female doves a glandular part of the lining of the crop undergoes fatty degeneration under the stimulation of prolactin. The cells are then shed and regurgitated along with partially digested food as "pigeon's milk," which is fed to nestlings. A specialization of the esophagus of sanguinivorous bats is described in Chapter 3.

STOMACH

The stomach is a muscular chamber or series of chambers at the end of the esophagus. It serves as a storage and macerating site for ingested solids and secretes digestive enzymes that partially liquefy food before injection into the small intestine. Cyclostomes scarcely have a stomach, and a boundary between esophagus and stomach is indefinite or lacking below birds. Even in birds and mammals, the mucosa of part or all of the stomach may resemble that of the esophagus (Fig. 11-17). The stomach terminates at the **pyloric sphincter**.

The stomach is straight when it first develops in the embryo (Fig. 11-23) and may remain so throughout life in lower vertebrates. More often, flexures develop producing a **J**- or **U**-shaped stomach (Figs. 11-1 and 11-18, *C* and *D*). As a result, the stomach may exhibit a concave border (**lesser curvature**) and a convex border (**greater curvature**). The stomach also undergoes torsion in higher vertebrates so

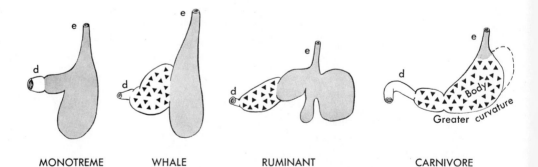

MONOTREME   WHALE   RUMINANT   CARNIVORE

Fig. 11-17. Distribution of esophageal-like epithelium (gray) and of typical gastric glands (triangles) in the stomachs of selected mammals. **d,** Duodenum; **e,** esophagus. Broken line at far right outlines region that, in *Homo,* is called the fundus.

that it lies across the long axis of the trunk. As flexion and torsion become pronounced during development of mammalian stomachs, the dorsal mesentery of the stomach (**mesogaster**) becomes twisted and finally suspended from the greater curvature, which was originally the dorsal border of the stomach. The part of the dorsal mesentery attached to the greater curvature is then called the **greater omentum.** Because the mesentery became twisted, it encloses a **lesser peritoneal cavity** continuous with the main peritoneal cavity via an **cpiploic foramen.**

The stomach of some vertebrates, especially of fishes, exhibits one or more ceca (Fig. 11-18). In birds the stomach is often divided into **proventriculus** and **gizzard** (Fig. 11-16). The proventriculus, or glandular stomach, secretes a digestive enzyme, and the gizzard converts the food into a mash. The gizzard is lined with a horny membrane and often contains pebbles. The proventriculus and gizzard are best

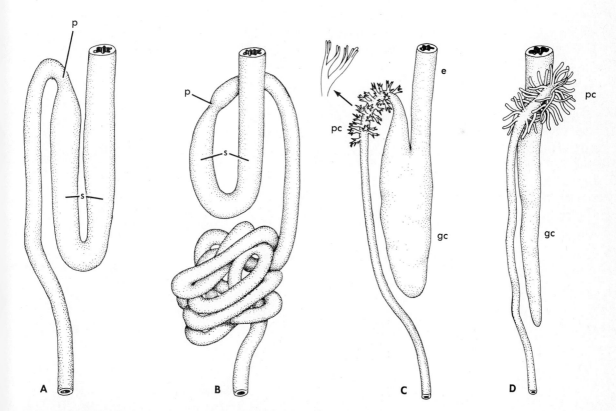

Fig. 11-18. Digestive tracts of four teleosts. **A,** *Fundulus.* **B,** *Cyprinodon.* **C,** *Elops.* **D,** *Trichiurus.* **e,** Esophagus, **gc,** cecumlike stomach; **p,** pylorus; **pc,** pyloric ceca; **s,** stomach.

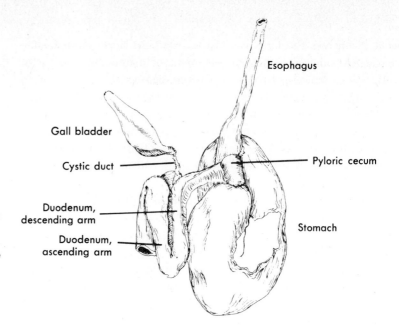

Fig. 11-19. Gizzardlike stomach and associated structures of a caiman, ventral view. The gallbladder has been displaced cephalad from its normal position between the stomach and descending arm of the duodenum. The stomach has thick muscular walls, except in the midsection (white area) where a fibrous region aids in macerating the stomach contents.

Esophagus

Gall bladder

Cystic duct

Duodenum, descending arm

Duodenum, ascending arm

Pyloric cecum

Stomach

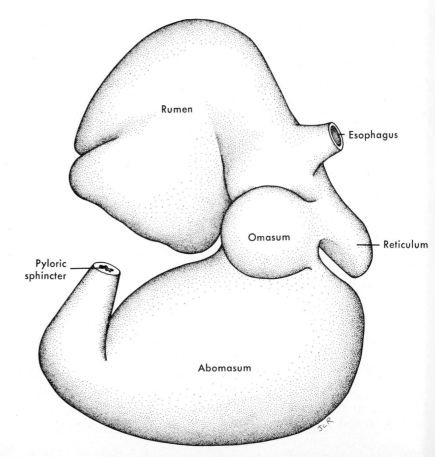

Fig. 11-20. The stomach of a calf (ruminant).

Rumen

Esophagus

Omasum

Reticulum

Pyloric sphincter

Abomasum

developed in birds that eat seeds and grain and least developed in carnivorous birds. Crocodilians also have gizzardlike stomachs (Fig. 11-19). (Birds and crocodilians had common ancestors.)

Mammalian stomachs are sometimes divided into several chambers. This is especially true in ruminants (Fig. 11-20). Grasses or grain is chewed briefly and then swallowed, after which it passes into the **rumen,** where preliminary digestion, especially by bacterial action, occurs. From the rumen, food moves into the **reticulum,** the lining of which is honeycombed (reticulated) by ridges and deep pits. In the reticulum, food is formed into a cud, which is regurgitated at will to be leisurely rechewed. After thorough chewing of the cud, the food is again swallowed. This time it passes into the **omasum,** where salivary enzymatic action continues. Finally it enters the **abomasum.** This segment exhibits the usual varieties of gastric glands, and the lining, along with that of the omasum, exhibits longitudinal ridges (**rugae**) found also in other vertebrate stomachs. The rumen, reticulum, and perhaps the omasum could equally well be considered specialized parts of the esophagus analogous to the crop of birds.

INTESTINE

The intestine extends between the stomach and cloaca or anus. It is straight in fishes and tetrapods with elongated bodies and tortuous in other tetrapods, which increases the absorptive area. A spiral valve, or typhlosole, does this for some fishes (Fig. 11-1, shark).

The **duodenum** is the first part of the small intestine; it receives ducts from the liver, gallbladder, and pancreas. Beyond the duodenum the small intestine of higher vertebrates is lined with fingerlike or leaflike **villi** containing lacteals. Villi increase the absorptive area and, by contracting and relaxing, pump chyle to larger lymphatics. In mammals the part containing villi is divisible into **jejunum** and **ileum** on the basis of the shape of the villi, nature of the mucosa, and the greater number of lymph nodules, or **Peyer's patches,** in the jejunum. The small intestine is the chief site of digestion and absorption of foodstuffs in the digestive tract. In tetrapods an **ileocolic sphincter** regulates the emptying of the small intestine (Fig. 11-21).

Fishes do not have small and large intestines. In amphibians the large intestine is straight and short. In some reptiles and birds and in mammals it is divisible into **colon** and **rectum,** the colon commencing at the ileocolic sphincter. It may have many coils, and in human beings it ends in a **sigmoid** (S-shaped) **flexure.** The rectum is the straight terminal portion of the large intestine in the pelvic cavity. Water is the chief substance absorbed in the large intestine.

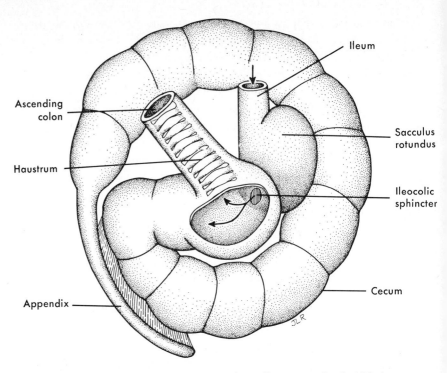

Fig. 11-21. Ileocolic junction, ceceum, and vermiform appendix of rabbit. Arrows indicate available pathways.

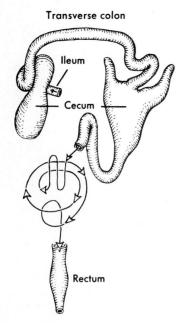

Fig. 11-22. Large intestine of a mammal *(Hyrax)* with several ceca. Arrows indicate direction taken by missing segment.

CECA

Ceca are blind diverticula that occur anywhere from esophagus to colon. A digestive cecum in its simplest form is seen in an amphioxus (Fig. 2-8, *B*). The crop sac of birds is an esophageal cecum.

In modern fishes pyloric and duodenal ceca are common, especially in species lacking spiral valves (Fig. 11-18). Up to 200 have been counted in mackerel. Beyond the duodenum ceca are rare in fishes and amphibians. Ileocolic ceca are common in amniotes; usually there are two in birds (Fig. 11-1, turtle, chicken, pig, and man). In animals that feed on cellulose they house cellulose-digesting bacteria, may be coiled, and may exceed the large intestine in capacity. In insectivorous or carnivorous mammals they are short or absent. The cecum terminates in a **vermiform appendix** in anthropoids, rodents, rabbits, and many other mammals (Fig. 11-21).

Ceca further along on the colon are not rare. *Hyrax,* for instance, has a large bicornuate cecum on the descending colon (Fig. 11-22). The liver, gallbladder, and pancreas commence ontogenetically as ceca, and the rectal gland of elasmobranchs is a cecum that secretes sodium chloride.

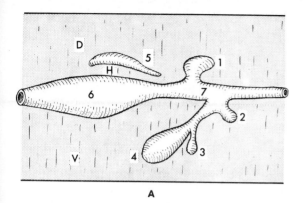

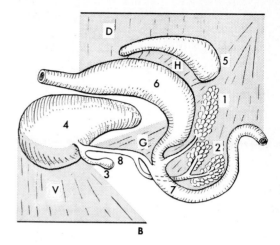

Fig. 11-23. Development of liver, pancreas, spleen, stomach, and associated mesenteries. **A,** An early stage. **B,** A later stage. **1,** Dorsal pancreatic bud from duodenum; **2,** ventral pancreatic bud from common bile duct; **3,** gallbladder; **4,** liver bud in **A** and liver in **B; 5,** spleen; **6,** stomach; **7,** duodenum; **8,** common bile duct. **D,** Dorsal mesentery; **G,** lesser omentum; **H,** gastrosplenic ligament; **V,** ventral mesentery, which remains as the falciform ligament in **B.**

LIVER

The liver arises as a hollow diverticulum (**liver bud**) from the ventral wall of the future duodenum (Fig. 11-23, *A*). The bud, occasionally multiple, invades the ventral mesentery and then grows cephalad into the ventral mesentery of the stomach. The growing tip of the bud gives rise to numerous sprouts that become the lobes of the liver and the gallbladder. The anterior pole of the liver finally becomes anchored to the septum transversum by a coronary ligament. Each lobe of the adult liver is drained by a **hepatic duct** that flows into a **common bile duct.** The terminal segment of the common bile duct is embedded in the wall of the duodenum for a short distance, where it is called the **ampulla of Vater.**

Although most of the embryonic ventral mesentery disappears during development, the mesentery ventral to the duodenum and stomach that was invaded by the liver bud remains as the **hepatoduodenal ligament** (connecting duodenum and liver) and as the **gastrohepatic ligament** (connecting pyloric stomach and liver). These two ligamentous mesenteries constitute the **lesser omentum,** which serves as a bridge transmitting the common bile duct, hepatic artery, and hepatic portal vein. The embryonic mesentery ventral to the liver remains in adults as the **falciform ligament.**

The shape of the liver conforms to the space available in the coelom. In animals with an elongated trunk the liver is elongated. In animals with short trunks it is short and broad. It manufactures bile, which aids in fat digestion and absorption. Other roles are associated with homeostasis, or maintenance of a suitable internal milieu. It helps regulate blood sugar levels by glycogenesis, glycogenolysis, and gluconeogenesis; it deaminates amino acids and hence forms ammonia, uric acid, and urea; and it manufactures several blood proteins, including certain clotting substances. The fetal liver is an important source of red blood cells, and the adult liver excretes the breakdown products of hemoglobin as bile pigments (bilirubin and biliverdin). This list of functions is not exhaustive.

GALLBLADDER

One sprout of the liver bud expands to become the **gallbladder** and **cystic duct.** A gallbladder develops in most vertebrates including hagfishes; however, no gallbladder develops in lampreys, many birds, rats, perissodactyls, or whales. The gallbladder serves primarily to store bile that emulsifies ingested fats, and animals lacking a gallbladder have little fat in their diet. Human beings live many years after surgical removal of the gallbladder, but they must avoid fats. Because of its embryonic origin from the liver bud, the cystic duct empties into the common bile duct.

EXOCRINE PANCREAS

The pancreas consists of two histologically distinct and functionally independent components—an exocrine component consisting of alveoli that secrete digestive enzymes into pancreatic ducts and an endocrine component, the pancreatic islands, that secrete hormones into the bloodstream. In cyclostomes and a few other vertebrates these components are spatially separated.

In elasmobranchs and tetrapods the pancreas is a compact organ often consisting of two lobes. In most teleosts and in hagfishes it is distributed diffusely along the blood vessels in the mesenteries of the stomach and intestine, occasionally accompanying these into the substance of the liver.

Typically, the pancreas arises as one or two ventral pancreatic buds from the liver bud and as a single dorsal bud from the foregut near the liver bud. The ventral buds invade the mesentery and form a ventral lobe, or **body of the pancreas** (Fig. 11-23, *B, 2*). The dorsal bud becomes the dorsal lobe, or **tail of the pancreas.** There are variants of this pattern. In sharks the entire pancreas develops from the dorsal bud, and in mammals it develops from one ventral and one dorsal bud. It is likely that three pancreatic buds are primitive. No pancreatic bud forms in lampreys, so the pancreatic cells remain permanently in the intestinal epithelium.

Vertebrates may have as many pancreatic ducts as there were embryonic pancreatic buds, but more often one or more of the ducts loses its connection with the bile duct or gut and the pancreas is drained by the remaining duct or ducts. For example, in sheep the duct of the dorsal lobe loses its connection with the gut and the pancreas drains into the common bile duct. In pigs and oxen, the duct of the ventral lobe loses its connection with the common bile duct and the pancreas drains into the duodenum. In still other mammals, both ducts remain. When one is larger, as in cats and human beings, the other is an **accessory pancreatic duct.**

CLOACA

The cloaca is a chamber at the end of the digestive tract that receives the intestine, and urinary and genital ducts, and opens to the exterior via the vent. It is shallow or nonexistent in adult lampreys, chimaeras, ray-finned fishes, and mammals above monotremes, having either failed to keep pace in growth with the rest of the animal or having become partitioned into two or three separate passageways, as in placental mammals (Figs. 14-40, *C* and *D*). When there is no cloaca the intestine opens directly to the exterior via an anus.

CHAPTER SUMMARY

1. Filter feeding is the oldest method of feeding. It is still employed by larval lampreys and with modifications by some teleosts, sharks, and cetaceans.

2. The embryonic digestive tract consists of foregut, midgut, and hindgut. Stomodeal and proctodeal invaginations establish an entrance and exit for the tract.

3. Major subdivisions of the adult tract are orobranchial cavity or oral cavity, pharynx, esophagus, stomach, and intestine starting with a duodenum. Chief accessory organs are tongue, teeth, oral glands, pancreas, liver, and gallbladder.

4. The mouth is an opening from the exterior to oral cavity or orobranchial chamber.

5. Nasal passageways open into the oral cavity in lobe-finned fishes and tetrapods with primary palates. Multicellular oral glands open onto the roof, walls, and floor but are scarce in fishes.

6. Fishes and perennibranchiate amphibians have a primary tongue overlying the hyoid skeleton. In higher amphibians a glandular field contributes to the tongue, and in amniotes paired lateral lingual swellings contribute. An entoglossal bone is in the tongue of lizards and birds, a pair of paraglossals in many birds.

7. Teeth are vestiges of dermal armor. They consist of dentin formed by odontoblasts in dermal papillae, enamel formed by ameloblasts of enamel organs, and cementum. In lower vertebrates they are more numerous, more widely distributed in the oral cavity, more frequently replaced, and more alike throughout the oral cavity. A few vertebrates in every class are toothless.

8. Dentition may be monophyodont, diphyodont, or polyphyodont; acrodont, pleurodont, or thecodont; and homodont or heterodont.

9. The pharynx is the part of the foregut that has pharyngeal pouches in embryos and gill slits in fishes and perennibranchiate

amphibians. In adult mammals it may be divided into nasal, oral, and, sometimes, laryngeal pharynges. Openings lead from or to the spiracle, gill pouches, suprabranchial organs, oral cavity, nasal passageways, auditory tubes, larynx, esophagus, and vocal sacs depending on the species. Lymphoid tissue encircles it in mammals.

10. The esophagus connects the pharynx with the stomach. The crop sac is a diverticulum of the esophagus in birds.

11. The stomach is a muscular enlargement at the end of the esophagus. It is compartmentalized in birds (proventriculus and gizzard) and cud-chewing ungulates (rumen, reticulum, omasum, and abomasum.) It terminates at the pyloric sphincter.

12. The intestine is digestive and absorptive. It is relatively straight in fishes, tortuous in tetrapods. Spiral valves, coils, ceca, and villi increase the absorptive area.

13. The liver, gallbladder, and pancreas arise as evaginations of the foregut. There are usually one liver bud and two or three pancreatic buds.

14. The cloaca is characteristic of most adult vertebrates. It opens to the exterior via a vent. In mammals the cloaca is divided into several passageways, one of which is the rectum, which opens to the exterior via an anus.

LITERATURE CITED AND SELECTED READINGS

1. Alexander, R.M.: Mechanics of feeding action of various teleost fishes, Journal of Zoology, London **162**:145, 1970.
2. Butler, P.M., and Joysey, K.A., editors: Development, function, and evolution of teeth, New York, 1978, Academic Press, Inc.
3. Denison, R.H.: Feeding mechanisms of Agnatha and early gnathostomes, American Zoologist **1**:177, 1961.
4. Homberger, D.G.: Functionell-morphologische Untersuchüngen zur Radiation der Ernahrungs—und Trinkmethoden der Papageien (Psittaci), Bonner Zoologische Monographien no. 13, Zoologisches Forschungsinstitut und Museum Alexander Koenig, Bonn, West Germany, 1980.
5. Kardong, K.V.: Evolutionary patterns in advanced snakes, American Zoologist **20**(1):269, 1980.
6. Lauder, G.V.: Feeding mechanics in primitive teleosts and in the halecomorph fish *Amia calva*, Journal of Zoology, London **187**:543, 1979.
7. Liem, K.F.: A morphological study of *Luciocephalus pulcher*, with notes on gular elements in other recent teleosts, Journal of Morphology **121**:103, 1967.
8. Liem, K.F.: Adaptive significance of intra- and interspecific differences in the feeding repertoires of cichlid fishes, American Zoologist **20**:295, 1980.
9. Lombard, R.E., and Wake, D.B.: Tongue evolution in the lungless sal-

amanders Plethodontidae. II. Function and evolutionary diversity, Journal of Morphology **153**:39, 1978.

10. Miller, R.: The morphology and function of the pharyngeal organs in the clupeid, *Dorosoma petenense* (Gunther), Chesapeake Science **5**: 194, 1964.

11. Moss, M.: Enamel and bone in shark teeth, with a note on fibrous enamel in fishes, Acta Anatomica **77**:161, 1970.

12. Nickel, R., and others: The viscera of the domestic mammals, New York, 1973, Springer-Verlag.

13. Oguri, M.: Rectal glands of marine and fresh-water sharks; comparative histology, Science **144**:1151,

14. Osborn, J.W.: The evolution of dentitions, American Scientist **61**:548, 1973.

15. Peyer, B.: Comparative odontology, Chicago, 1968, University of Chicago Press.

16. Pivorunas, A.: The feeding mechanisms of baleen whales, American Scientist **67**:432, 1979.

17. Zeigler, A.C.: A theory of the evolution of therian dental formulas and replacement patterns, Quarterly Review of Biology **46**:226, 1971.

CHAPTER 12

Respiratory system

The process of obtaining oxygen from the environment and eliminating carbon dioxide is external respiration. It is accomplished via respiratory membranes that are usually part of some organ. Organs that function primarily in external respiration constitute, collectively, the respiratory system.

External respiration precedes internal respiration, which is the exchange of oxygen and carbon dioxide between blood in the capillaries and the tissues. Because carbon dioxide quickly inhibits cellular activity, the continual elimination of this gas from the vicinity of the cell, and from the organism, is essential. The role of the circulatory system in the total process of respiration is therefore vital.

External respiration is carried on through respiratory membranes. Except in very early embryos, these must be highly vascular, the epithelium must be thin, the surface must be moist, and it must be in contact with the environment, or else the environment must be brought in contact with the surface.

ADAPTATIONS FOR EXTERNAL RESPIRATION

The chief organs of external respiration in adult vertebrates are external and internal gills, the buccopharyngeal mucosa, swim bladders or lungs, and skin. Less common adult respiratory devices include bushy or filamentous outgrowths of the pectoral fins (male *Lepidosiren*) or of the posterior trunk region and thigh (African hairy frog); the cloacal, rectal, or anal lining; and the lining of the esophagus, stomach, or even intestine. Embryos employ a variety of respiratory devices, including extraembryonic membranes.

Most fishes "breathe" with internal gills, and the water usually enters through the mouth. After the mouth is closed, water is forced over the gills by a **pressure pump** operated by the buccal and pharyngeal muscles, or it is drawn over the gills by suction created by muscular expansion of the gill chambers of the opercular chamber. A few fishes, such as mackerel and tuna, have few branchiomeric mus-

In this chapter we will look at some of the methods and mechanisms vertebrates have developed for obtaining oxygen and eliminating carbon dioxide in aquatic and terrestrial environments. We will see that many fishes breathe air and that lungs may be older than tetrapod limbs. Finally, we will examine respiratory pathways in successively higher air-breathing vertebrates and take a brief look at the mammalian diaphragm and its counterpart in reptiles and birds.

Adaptations for external respiration
Gills
    Cartilaginous fishes
    Bony fishes
    Agnathans
    Larval gills
    Excretory role of gills
Swim bladders and the origin of lungs
Lungs and their ducts
    Larynx
    Trachea, bronchi, and syrinx
    Amphibian lungs
    Reptilian lungs
Lungs and their ducts in birds
Mammalian lungs
Oblique septum and diaphragm
Nares and nasal canals

cles and evidently have to swim forward with the mouth open to create a flow over the gills. In sharks some water is admitted by the spiracle, which has a one-way intake valve, and in rays and skates all respiratory water enters through the spiracle, which minimizes the entrance of debris in these bottom-dwelling fishes. In a few fishes, including lampreys, water enters and also leaves by the external gill slits, and in hagfishes it enters through the naris.

Air became a source of oxygen for many fishes during the Devonian period and even before. One reason may have been that the water was warm and swampy and therefore low in dissolved oxygen. The atmosphere, on the other hand, contains 20 times the oxygen that saturated water can hold. Little wonder, then, that fishes living in such an environment, whether Devonian or recent, obtain some or all of their oxygen from above the surface of the water.

Air-breathing fishes snatch bubbles of air from just above the water surface, and it comes in contact with the buccal and pharyngeal lining. If this lining is thin and highly vascular, and the blood in it is low in oxygen, oxygen is acquired at this site. A few teleosts swallow the bubble and extract oxygen in the stomach or intestine. But saccular evaginations of the pharynx, chiefly swim bladders, provide a much larger surface for acquiring oxygen from air and lungfishes, and some ganoids use these. They, too, gulp air even though they have internal nares. A buccopharyngeal pump forces the air into the swim bladder. Expiration is a result of elasticity of the bladder, compression of the body wall by water pressure, contraction of body wall muscles, and, especially, a vacuum created by lowering the buccopharyngeal floor while mouth and nares are closed. Despite acquisition of oxygen from the air most of the carbon dioxide is eliminated by gills. Bowfins and gars use gills in cold water, but in warm water, or in water low in oxygen for other reasons, they use their swim bladders.

Aquatic amphibians that breathe with lungs do so in the same manner as lungfishes. Air enters through the mouth even though internal nares are present, and it is pumped to the lungs. Terrestrial amphibians, on the other hand, suck in air through their nostrils by closing the mouth and glottis and lowering the floor of the buccal cavity. The fresh air is then pumped to the lungs by closing the nares, opening the glottis, and raising the floor of the buccal cavity.

Respiration through the skin in water and air is employed extensively by modern amphibians. It is also used by some fishes, especially those that lack scales and therefore can have adequate capillaries close to the surface. Aquatic urodeles acquire as much as three fourths of their oxygen from the water through the skin. Tree frogs acquire only one fourth of their oxygen through the skin, and terrestrial species of *Rana* acquire only one third this way. Regardless of the proportionate role of skin and lungs in oxygen uptake, most of the carbon dioxide (up to nearly 90%) is released through the skin in amphibians. Cutaneous respiration is not important in amniotes because the thick stratum corneum insulates the capillaries from the atmosphere. Cutaneous respiration is probably more recent than branchial or pulmonary respiration; dermal scales probably had to be lost before it could be effective.

A suction (vacuum) pump is employed by reptiles, birds, and mammals for getting air into the lungs. The pump creates around and within the lung a gas pressure lower than atmospheric, and air rushes in. Suction is created in a variety of ways, but always with muscles. The ribs may be rotated outward and upward, the sternum may be moved, diaphragms in the coelom may be operated on, or the coelomic viscera may be displaced, as the liver is in crocodilians. In turtles the ribs are fused with the carapace and muscles of the pectoral girdle operate the pump. Exhalation may be passive as a result of elasticity of the lungs and relaxation of the pump muscles, or it may involve contraction of antagonistic muscles that force air out, although this is not the case in unlabored respiration in mammals. Respiration by rib movements seems to be very old. The earliest amphibians, ichthyostegals, believed to have been aquatic because they had lateral-line neuromast organs, had large ribs with overlapping uncinate processes, indicating pulmonary respiration by rib action.

GILLS
Cartilaginous fishes

In *Squalus acanthias* five exposed (naked) gill slits are visible on the surface of the pharynx. If a gill slit is probed, the instrument will enter a gill chamber. The anterior and posterior walls of the first four gill chambers exhibit a gill surface or **demibranch.** The last (fifth) gill chamber lacks a demibranch in the posterior wall. Hyoid cartilages support the demibranch in the anterior wall of the first gill chamber. The relationships of the remaining demibranchs to pharyngeal arches are diagramed in Fig. 12-1. The demibranch in the anterior wall of a gill chamber is a **pretrematic demibranch.** The one in the posterior wall of a gill chamber is a **posttrematic demibranch.** Separating the two demibranchs of a gill arch is an interbranchial septum that is strengthened by delicate cartilaginous rays. Gills rakers protrude from the gill cartilage into the pharynx and guard the entrance to the chamber. The two demibranchs of a single gill arch, together with the associated interbranchial septum, cartilages, blood vessels, branchiomeric muscles, nerves, and connective tissues, constitute a **holobranch.**

Water enters the pharynx via the mouth and spiracle and passes into the gill chambers, where it comes in contact with the demibranchs. The latter consist of many gill filaments rich in capillary beds. The capillaries are supplied by afferent branchial arterioles and drained by efferent branchial arterioles. Water is forced from the gill chambers by branchiomeric muscles.

Anterior to the first gill slit of *Squalus* is a spiracle. In the embryo the spiracle is the same size as the gill slits, but it fails to keep pace in growth with the other slits. What appears to be a rudimentary or vestigial demibranch grows in its anterior wall. It is called a **pseudobranch.**

Most elasmobranchs are pentanchid, having five gill slits, but *Hexanchus* another shark, has six and a spiracle, and *Heptanchus* has seven, the largest number of slits in any jawed vertebrate. The five

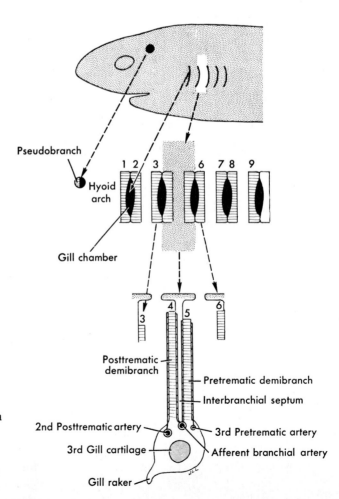

Fig. 12-1. Gills in *Squalus acanthias*, a shark with a spiracle, five naked gill slits, and nine demibranchs (**1 to 9**). The fourth pharyngeal arch has been excised and displayed in cross section.

Pseudobranch

Hyoid arch

Gill chamber

Posttrematic demibranch

Pretrematic demibranch

Interbranchial septum

2nd Posttrematic artery

3rd Pretrematic artery

3rd Gill cartilage

Afferent branchial artery

Gill raker

gill slits in adult skates and rays are on the underside of the flattened body (Fig. 12-20), but the spiracle is located dorsally, behind the eyes, and is used for water intake. In *embryonic* rays, however, the gill slits and spiracle lie in series on the side of the pharynx. In some adult elasmobranchs the spiracle is closed by a membrane.

The holocephalan *Chimaera* has only four gill pouches, the spiracle is closed, the interbranchial septa are short and do not reach the skin, and a fleshy operculum extends backward from the hyoid arch and hides the gills. In several of these traits, *Chimaera* resembles teleosts.

Bony fishes

Most bony fishes have four holobranchs and five gill slits. An **operculum,** a bony flap arising from the hyoid arch, projects backward over the gills on each side (Fig. 12-2, *A*); and extending from the ventral edge of each operculum is a folding **branchiostegal membrane** supported by bony branchiostegal rays. The two membranes are joined midventrally beneath the pharynx to form an opercular chamber that water enters after passing over the gills. This is possible because the interbranchial septa are very short or absent, rather than

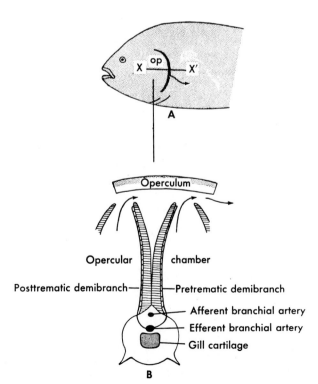

Fig. 12-2. Operculum and gill of a teleost. **A,** The operculum, **op,** extends caudad over the gills from the hyoid arch. **B,** Cross section of one holobranch in the plane **X-X′.** Arrows indicate direction of efferent water flow.

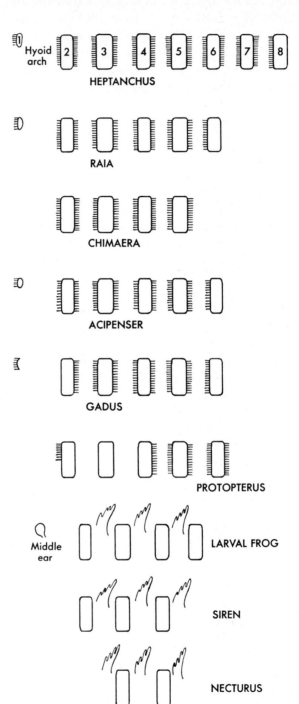

Fig. 12-3. Open pharyngeal slits in selected aquatic vertebrates and distribution of gill surfaces (horizontal lines) in fishes. *Heptanchus* is a primitive shark. *Gadus* (the cod) has a pseudobranch on the operculum, and the spiracle is closed. **1** to **8**, Pharyngeal slits. The position of external gills is indicated in the amphibians.

extending to the skin as in cartilaginous fishes (Fig. 12-2, *B*). The opercular chamber opens by crescentic clefts (small apertures in eels) just anterior to the pectoral girdle. Infrequently, it opens by a midventral aperture.

Water is drawn into the pharynx by lowering the pharyngeal floor with the mouth open and operculum closed. Simultaneous expansion of the opercular chamber by unfolding of the branchiostegal membrane draws incoming water across the gills and into the chamber; and closing the mouth, raising the pharyngeal floor, and compressing the opercular chamber by folding the branchiostegal membrane, pumps the water to the outside. Thus a suction pump and then a pressure pump, operating rhythmically, keep the gills bathed in oxygenated water. Forward motion of the fish, when sufficiently forceful, also causes water to enter the mouth and pass over the gills.

A spiracle is present in the relatively ancient chondrosteans (Fig. 12-3, *Acipenser*), but it closes during embryonic life in modern fishes and lungfishes (Fig. 12-3, *Gadus*, *Protopterus*). The demibranch on the hyoid arch is lost in most teleosts, and additional demibranchs are lost in some lungfishes.

Agnathans

Living agnathans have 6 to 15 pairs of gill pouches. *Myxine glutinosa* usually has six pairs, but occasionally there are five or seven (Fig. 12-4). The various species of *Bdellostoma* have 5 to 15 pairs. Among lampreys, *Petromyzon* has eight embryonic and seven adult pairs (Fig. 12-5).

The gill pouches in agnathans are connected to the pharynx by afferent branchial ducts and to the exterior by efferent branchial ducts. *Eptatretus stouti* has a gill slit for each efferent duct, but in *Myxine* and its relatives the efferent ducts unite to open via a common external aperture on each side (Fig. 12-4).

The pathway of flow of the respiratory water stream differs in lam-

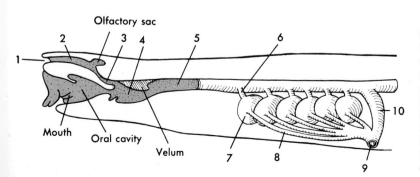

Fig. 12-4. Respiratory system in the hagfish *Myxine glutinosa*, left lateral view. **1,** Naris; **2,** nasal duct; **3,** nasopharyngeal duct; **4,** velar chamber; **5,** pharynx; **6,** afferent branchial duct; **7,** gill pouch; **8,** efferent branchial duct; **9,** common external gill aperture (present on both sides); **10,** pharyngocutaneous (pharyngeal) duct (present on left side of animal only).

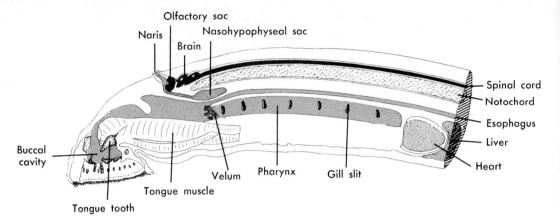

Fig. 12-5. Cephalic end of the adult lamprey *Petromyzon,* sagittal section. The duct from the naris terminates in the nasohypophyseal sac.

preys and hagfishes. In lampreys, water enters via the external gill slits and is ejected by the same route. This is essential when the lamprey is attached by its buccal funnel to a host fish, since the nasal duct does not lead to the pharynx (Fig. 12-5). In hagfishes water enters via the naris and passes via the nasopharyngeal duct to the pharynx (Fig. 12-4).

The flow of respiratory water in hagfishes is maintained by the pumping action of the **velum,** a muscular tube surrounding a **velar chamber** at the anterior end of the pharynx, into which the nasopharyngeal duct empties. The velum is composed partly of constrictor muscles and is strengthened by posterior projections of the first branchial cartilages. It pulsates 50 to 100 times per minute in alert animals and 25 to 30 times per minute in sleeping animals. The action pumps water into the pharynx and creates a vacuum, which draws in additional water through the nostril.

In hagfishes, on the left side only, a **pharyngocutaneous duct** connects the pharynx with the last efferent branchial duct or directly with the exterior (Fig. 12-4). Periodically, debris or particles too large to enter the afferent branchial ducts are forcefully ejected through the pharyngocutaneous duct. Embryonically, the duct arises like the gill pouches, and it is probable that the duct is a modified gill pouch.

The pharynx in lampreys becomes subdivided into an esophagus dorsally and pharynx ventrally at metamorphosis so that in adults it terminates blindly (Fig. 12-5).

Larval gills

Larval gills are of three kinds—**external gills** that are outgrowths from the external surface of one or more gill arches; **filamentous ex-**

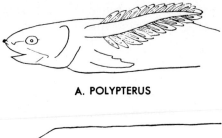

A. POLYPTERUS

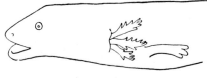

B. AMPHIUMA

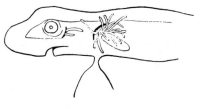

C. SCYLLIUM

Fig. 12-6. Larval gills of, **A,** a bony fish, **B,** an amphibian, and **C,** an elasmobranch. In the *Amphiuma* the gills are resorbed before the larva escapes from the egg envelope. Those of *Scyllium* are employed in histotrophic nutrition.

tensions of internal gills that project through gill slits to the exterior; and the **internal gills** of late anuran tadpoles that are hidden behind the larval operculum.

External gills usually develop before gill slits open and before any opercular fold has started to develop. They can be waved about by branchial muscles and can often be retracted. They develop in the embryonic or larval stages of most dipnoans (*Ceratodus* is an exception), in all amphibians (including apodans), and in a few ganoid fishes such as sturgeons and *Polypterus*. The latter has only one pair (Fig. 12-6, *A*). Although external gills are larval structures, there are perennibranchiate urodeles (Table 3-1) and a perennibranchiate lungfish, *Protopterus*. The latter has four pairs of larval gills and retains three pairs in a reduced state throughout life.

External gills develop in anuran tadpoles on pharyngeal arches III to V. Later, when pharyngeal pouches II to V rupture to the outside their walls become folded to form a set of internal gills. Next, from the hyoid arch a fleshy opercular fold grows backward over the gill region. The external gills then atrophy and the internal gills, hidden behind the operculum, function until metamorphosis.

Filamentous external projections of internal gills are found in the early stages of elasmobranch development (Fig. 12-6, *C*). Their presence is correlated with development in a tightly sealed egg case or in the mother's uterus. The gills project into the egg yolk or uterine fluid, where they absorb nutrients as well as having a respiratory function. Absorption of nutrients from uterine or other maternal tissue fluids is known as **histotrophic nutrition.** A few viviparous chondrosteans and some telosts develop similarly functioning filamentous gills.

Excretory role of gills

Although conventionally thought of as respiratory organs, gills also perform excretory functions. Chloride-secreting glands on the gills of lampreys and marine fishes that migrate between salt water and fresh water excrete chloride in salt water and take in chloride in fresh water, thereby assisting in homeostasis. Gills also excrete most of the nitrogenous wastes. Fishes that acquire oxygen by aerial respiration release most of the carbon dioxide through their gills.

SWIM BLADDERS AND THE ORIGIN OF LUNGS

Nearly every vertebrate from fish to man develops an unpaired evagination from the pharynx or esophagus that becomes one or a pair of sacs (swim bladders or lungs) filled with gases derived directly or indirectly from the atmosphere. The only adult vertebrates that do *not* have pneumatic sacs are cyclostomes, cartilaginous fishes, a few marine teleosts, some bottom dwellers such as flounders, and a few tailed amphibians, some of which have them as embryos. Imprints of paired sacs with ducts have even been found in one fossil placoderm. It can be said with considerable confidence that vertebrates that fail to develop pneumatic sacs have probably lost the genetic capability to do so.

After evaginating, pneumatic sacs may retain their unpaired connection with the foregut, or the duct may close. Pneumatic sacs hereafter will be called lungs in tetrapods and swim bladders in fishes, regardless of their function.

Swim bladders may be paired or unpaired, and the **pneumatic duct** when present in adults, usually connects to the esophagus dorsally or ventrally, sometimes laterally (Fig. 12-7). Infrequently, it connects to the pharynx or stomach. Swim bladders lie retroperitoneally close to the kidneys and bulge more or less into the coelom (Fig. 14-15). The walls contain elastic tissue and smooth muscle, and the lining is relatively smooth. Fishes are said to be **physostomous** when the duct is open, **physoclistous** when it is closed. Most ganoids, the more primitive teleosts, and lungfishes are physostomous. Among physostomous teleosts are catfish, carp, eels, herring, pickerel, and salmon.

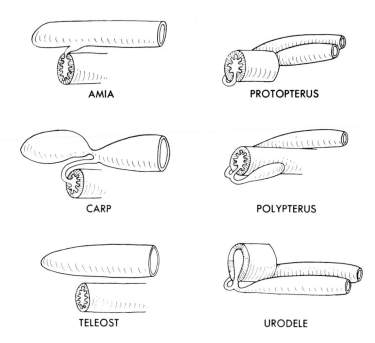

AMIA

PROTOPTERUS

CARP

POLYPTERUS

TELEOST

URODELE

Fig. 12-7. Swim bladders and lungs in aquatic vertebrates. In many teleosts the embryonic pneumatic duct later closes, and the swim bladder thereafter has no connection with the gut. *Amia* and *Polypterus* are ganoids, *Protopterus* is a lungfish, and the carp is a physostomous teleost with an anterior extension of the bladder connected with weberian ossicles.

Swim bladders in teleosts serve chiefly as hydrostatic organs. The volume of gas in the bladder can be reflexly regulated at its source, thereby altering the specific gravity of the fish and increasing or decreasing its buoyancy. The gas in the hydrostatic swim bladder usually comes from the blood. It is actively transported into the chamber of the bladder from a network of small arteries (rete mirabile) in the lining of the bladder and named the **red gland.** The gland is supplied from the celiac artery, and its associated tortuous veins empty into the hepatic portal vein. The gas is reabsorbed in an area of modified epithelium near the caudal end of the bladder. In physostomes it may be bubbled through the mouth.

The gases in swim bladders differ among fishes. Some swim bladders contain almost pure (99%) nitrogen, some up to 87% oxygen, and all contain at least traces of four atmospheric gases—nitrogen, oxygen, carbon dioxide, and argon. In deep-water fishes, nitrogen may be transported from the blood into the bladder against a nitrogen pressure of as high as 10 atmospheres.

Swim bladders perform other functions, in addition to their hydrostatic role. In teleosts with weberian ossicles they are part of the hearing mechanism; and in croakers and grunters, contractions of striated muscles attached to the bladder cause it to emit thumping sounds or force air back and forth between chambers separated by muscular sphincters.

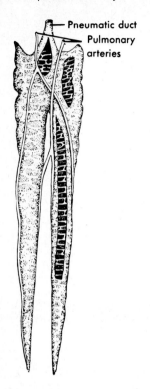

Fig. 12-8. Swim bladders (lungs) of the lungfish *Protopterus*.

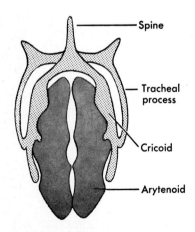

Fig. 12-9. Laryngeal skeleton of a frog. The glottis lies between the two arytenoid cartilages. The tracheal process is part of the cricoid cartilage.

Swim bladders function as lungs in living ganoids except sturgeons and spoonbills and in lungfishes, except that *Neoceratodus* uses them in this manner only when the oxygen content of the water is low. In these air-gulping fishes the swim bladder is lined with low septa and may exhibit thousands of tiny air sacs (Fig. 12-8). Like tetrapod lungs, they are supplied by arteries arising from the sixth embryonic aortic arches; and in dipnoans the venous return is to the left atrium.

The striking similarities between swim bladders and lungs suggest that these are the same organs. In the Devonian when the fresh water was warm and periodically stagnant, and therefore low in dissolved oxygen, aerial respiration may have made the difference between extinction and survival. At that time, placoderms and most crossopterygians had pneumatic ducts. We can only speculate on which came first, respiratory or hydrostatic swim bladders, but these two conclusions seem well founded: they were functioning in aerial respiration long before vertebrates ventured onto land, and closure of the pneumatic duct in physoclistous fish is probably a mutation from a more primitive, open duct condition.

LUNGS AND THEIR DUCTS

Tetrapod lungs arise as an unpaired evagination from the caudal floor of the pharynx (Fig. 1-5). The opening in the pharyngeal floor becomes a longitudinal slit, the **glottis.** The unpaired lung bud elongates only slightly before bifurcating to form bronchi and lungs (Fig. 12-19). The lung primordia push caudad underneath the foregut until they bulge into the coelom lateral to the heart. As they grow into the coelom, they carry along an investment of peritoneum, which becomes the visceral pleura. The part of the lung bud between glottis and lungs develops into larynx, trachea, and bronchi.

Larynx

In a few urodeles, including *Necturus*, the larynx consists of a single pair of lateral cartilages surrounding the glottis. Most other tetrapods below mammals have two pairs of laryngeal cartilages (Fig. 12-9), **arytenoid** and **cricoid** (in crocodilians, arytenoid and cricothyroid). Mammals have paired arytenoid cartilages in the dorsal rim of the glottis, a ringlike cricoid, and a **thyroid** that starts out paired (Fig. 12-10). Other small cartilages—cuneiforms, corniculates, procricoid, and others—develop in some species. The laryngeal cartilages of adult monotremes are all bilateral (Fig. 8-36, *F*).

Stretched across the laryngeal chamber in amphibians, some lizards, and most mammals are vocal cords, but below mammals these make few sounds discernible to humans. Hippopotami and a few other mammals lack vocal cords, and one breed of dogs, basenjis,

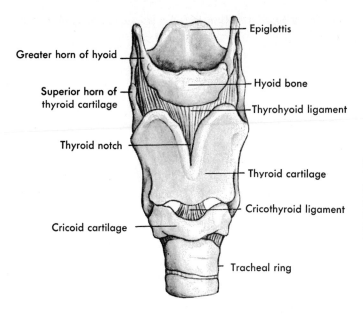

Epiglottis

Greater horn of hyoid

Superior horn of thyroid cartilage

Hyoid bone

Thyrohyoid ligament

Thyroid notch

Thyroid cartilage

Cricothyroid ligament

Cricoid cartilage

Tracheal ring

Fig. 12-10. Human larynx, frontal view. The arytenoid cartilages and glottis are located dorsally and cannot be seen from this view. (Modified from Francis, C.C., and Martin, A.H.: Introduction to human anatomy, ed. 7, St. Louis, 1975, The C.V. Mosby Co.)

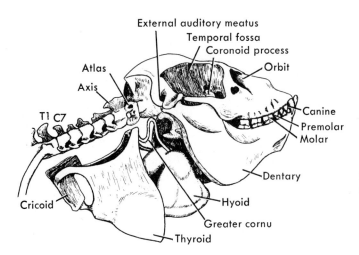

External auditory meatus

Temporal fossa

Coronoid process

Orbit

Atlas

Axis

T1 C7

Canine

Premolar

Molar

Dentary

Cricoid

Hyoid

Greater cornu

Thyroid

Fig. 12-11. Modification of hyoid bone and larynx in the howler monkey.

have poorly developed ones. By contrast, the thryoid and hyoid bones of the howler monkey are enormous plates that cause a goiter-like bulge in the neck (Fig. 12-11). Below the vocal cords on each side is a saclike recess, the laryngeal ventricle, or sinus of Morgagni. This is a resonating chamber that makes the weird howl of this monkey carry far into the jungle. Similar sinuses occur in some apes, and a vestigial recess is found in most mammals.

Several anatomical adaptations prevent food or water from entering the glottis. Crocodilians have a fleshy valve, the **palatine velum,** that

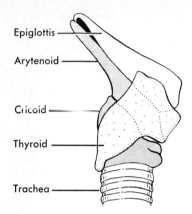

Fig. 12-12. Laryngeal skeleton of a whale. The epiglottis and arytenoid extend into the nasal pharynx.

consists of two large transverse folds suspended from the palate just anterior to the internal nares. When a matching fold at the base of the tongue is drawn upward against the velum, the glottis and pharynx are isolated from the oral cavity but have continuity with the nasal passageways. As a result, a crocodilian can be submerged with only two moundlike nostrils and the two elevated eyes protruding above the surface, thermoregulating, breathing, and meanwhile keeping an eye on the environment above the water. When they submerge totally, valves in the nostrils prevent flooding of the nasal passageways. In most terrestrial mammals a fibrocartilaginous flap, the **epiglottis,** in the floor of the oral pharynx closes off the glottis during swallowing, which draws the larynx forward against the flap (Figs. 11-3, *B,* and 12-21). In many mammals the larynx protrudes into the nasal pharynx. In whales that have surfaced to breathe this permits inhalation after water has been blown out of the nostrils, or blowholes, even though the cavernous mouth is running over with water (Fig. 12-12). In marsupials it prevents milk that is being pumped by the mother's mammary gland into the baby's esophagus from being sucked into the lungs as the baby breathes. Of course, a mammal cannot breathe through the mouth if the larynx protrudes into the nasopharynx, nor can air returning from the lungs be used for articulate speech requiring tongue and lips. The position of the human larynx helps make human speech possible.

Trachea, bronchi, and syrinx

The trachea is about as long as the neck. Therefore it is short in amphibians and long in amniotes. In birds, crocodilians, and some turtles it is longer than the neck and has to assume an S-shape. Tracheal walls are prevented from collapsing by cartilaginous or bony plates or rings. Tracheal rings are usually incomplete dorsally, and their ends are united by smooth muscle that permits changing the diameter of the tube. However, in crocodilians and birds all rings are complete. The trachea bifurcates, except in lower urodeles, to form two primary **bronchi** that are similarly stiffened.

Birds have a special voice box, or syrinx, at the bifurcation of the trachea (Fig. 12-13). A **bronchotracheal syrinx** consists of a resonating chamber with walls stiffened by the last several tracheal rings and the first bronchial half rings. Folds of the membranous lining project into the chamber and a bony pessulus bearing a similunar membrane may be present. Bird songs and birdcalls are produced when the folds and membrane are tightened by contraction of the syringeal muscles and air from the air sacs is being forced through the syrinx. Some syringes are simpler. Parts of the last several tracheal rings may be missing in a **tracheal syrinx,** which enables the membranous wall to vibrate. In

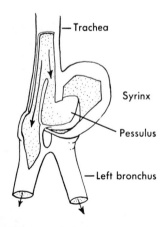

Fig. 12-13. Asymmetrical bronchotracheal syrinx of a canvasback duck. Arrows indicate path of inhaled air.

a **bronchial syrinx** the membranous wall between two bronchial cartilages folds into the chamber when the two cartilages are drawn together, and the fold vibrates.

Amphibian lungs

The lungs of amphibians are simple sacs (Fig. 12-14), long in urodeles and bulbous in anurans, conforming to the shape of the pleuroperitoneal cavity. The internal lining may be smooth throughout, there may be simple sacculations in the proximal part, or the entire lining may be pocketed. The left lung of caecilians is rudimentary, and the lungs of salamanders that inhabit swift mountain streams may be only a few millimeters long. Perhaps rudimentary lungs in the latter species made it possible for them to inhabit these streams, since buoyancy would be a disadvantage in swift currents. Plethodontids do not even form a lung bud. The lungs of aquatic urodeles function mostly as hydrostatic organs, and respiration takes place through the skin. Necturi use external gills, and only about 2% of their oxygen is obtained via lungs.

Reptilian lungs

In *Sphenodon* (Fig. 12-15, *A*) and snakes, lungs are simple sacs. The caudal third of the lining in snakes is septate and contains residual air. In lizards (Fig. 12-15, *B*), crocodilians, and turtles, septa are

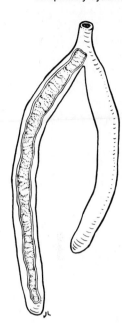

Fig. 12-14. Lungs of *Necturus.*

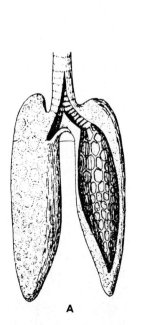
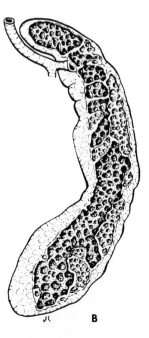

Fig. 12-15. Lungs of, **A,** *Sphenodon* and, **B,** *Heloderma,* a lizard.

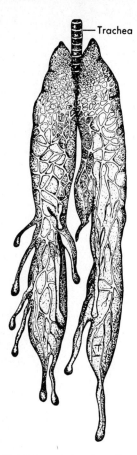

— Trachea

Fig. 12-16. Lungs of a chameleon showing saccular diverticula (air sacs).

so constructed that there are numerous large chambers, each with a multitude of individual subchambers. These lungs are spongy because of the numerous pockets of trapped air. The left lung in legless lizards and in snakes is rudimentary or absent except in a few species.

An enormous diverticulum of the left lung extends into the neck of puffing adders. Inflation of this air sac causes the neck to balloon, and superinflation of the lungs causes the entire trunk to swell. Air sacs extend among the viscera in some chameleons (Fig. 12-16); in some dinosaurs they extended into the vertebrae.

Most reptilian lungs occupy the pleuroperitoneal cavity along with other viscera. In crocodilians and a few squamates they occupy separate pleural cavities set apart by a tendinous oblique septum.

Lungs and their ducts in birds

Avian lungs are unique morphologically. Incoming air passes through the lungs nonstop and into spacious air sacs (Fig. 12-17, *A*). These extend among the viscera within the body cavity, lie among the flight muscles, and have long slender diverticula that extend into the interior of most bones including centra. Atmospheric pressure inflates the sacs when the ribs are rotated forward and upward and the sternum is actively depressed. The air sacs then act as bellows and recurrent bronchi carry air back to the lungs, where gaseous exchange takes place. Within the lungs secondary bronchi (dorsobronchi and ventrobronchi) are interconnected by innumerable parabronchi (Figs. 12-17, *B*, and 12-18) with diverticula leading to air capillaries only a few thousandths of a millimeter in diameter and containing the respiratory epithelia. The air capillaries associated with a single parabronchus are interconnected in three dimensions and air flows freely through the capillary system and returns to the parabronchus from which it began.[5] The air capillaries are suspended in a dense plexus of blood capillaries. After passing over the respiratory epithelia the air is exhaled. The details of airflow through the intrapulmonary duct system have not yet been ascertained. Air sacs and the open-ended duct system within the lungs make it possible to completely replace the air in the lungs with every inflation-compression cycle of the bellows. Consequently, unlike in other tetrapods, there is no residual air in the lungs.

Air sacs are thin walled and distensible. Most birds have five or six pairs: (1) cervical sacs at the base of the neck; (2) interclavicular sacs dorsal to the furcula and sometimes united across the midline; (3) anterior thoracic sacs lateral to the heart; (4) posterior thoracic sacs within the oblique septum; (5) abdominal sacs among the abdominal viscera; and (6) axillary sacs, less common, lying between two layers of pectoral muscle. The sacs maintain a steady flow of air over the

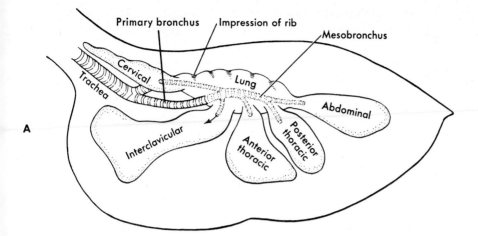

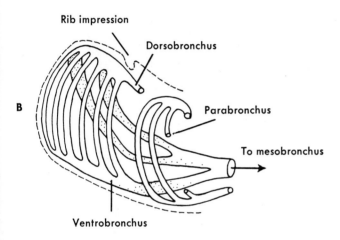

Fig. 12-17. Lower respiratory tract of a bird. **A,** Air sacs. Air leaves the sacs via recurrent bronchi (not shown). **B,** Diagramatic representation of a dorsobronchus, ventrobronchus, and several interconnecting parabronchi from which air capillaries evaginate.

respiratory epithelia. During flight the bellows is operated by rhythmical contraction and relaxation of the flight muscles and the flapping of the wings. When the bird is at rest the ribs and oblique septum operate the bellows. At this time the oxygen demand is lower, and the flow of air through the system is slower. The diverticula of the air sacs enter the bones via pneumatic foramina.

Air sacs are thermoregulatory, dissipating excess heat produced by the surrounding muscles during flight. The heat is transferred directly and not via the bloodstream, air sacs having a relatively poor vascular supply. Thermoregulation in resting doves, at least, is also accomplished partly during respiration, heat being transferred from the exceptionally vascular esophageal mucosa to the outgoing air-stream as it passes through the adjacent trachea. A bird's chief defense against overheating at rest is a reflexive increase in respiratory rate.

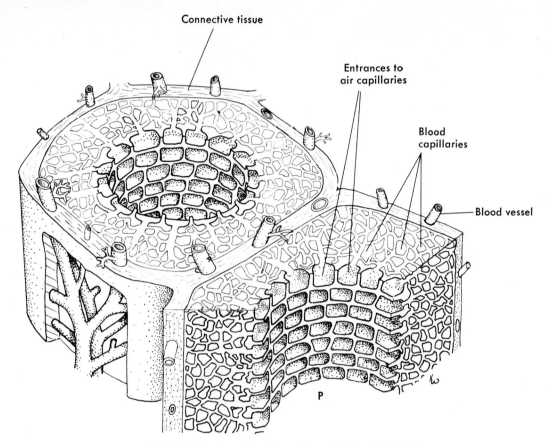

Fig. 12-18. Parabronchus, **P**, and air capillaries of a bird's lung.

Air sacs are not unique in birds. They are found in some higher lizards (Fig. 12-16) and some snakes, and they were present in dinosaurs and pterosaurs as revealed by pneumatic foramina in their bones. The extension of air sacs into bones results in energy conservation during flight by decreasing the specific gravity of the bird, making it more buoyant in air. Most ratites lack pneumatic bones and so did *Archaeopteryx*.

Mammalian lungs

The lungs of mammals are multichambered and usually divided into lobes, with more lobes on the right (Fig. 12-19, 14-mm embryo). The lungs of whales, sirenians, elephants, perissodactyls, and *Hyrax* lack lobes, and in monotremes and rats, among others, only the right lung is lobed. Left and right lungs occupy separate pleural cavities.

Each primary bronchus penetrates a lung and divides into second-

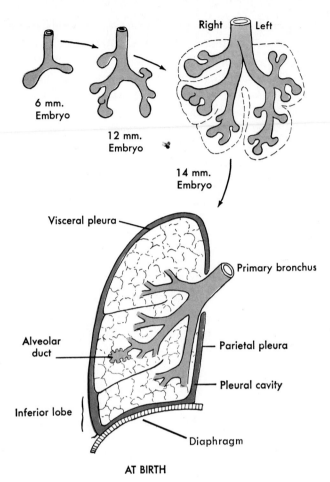

Fig. 12-19. Development of mammalian lung. Embryo lengths are applicable approximately to both the fetal pig and man. The pleural cavity (below) is in dark red.

Right Left

6 mm.
Embryo

12 mm.
Embryo

14 mm.
Embryo

Visceral pleura

Primary bronchus

Alveolar
duct

Parietal pleura

Pleural cavity

Inferior lobe

Diaphragm

AT BIRTH

ary and tertiary bronchi, which give rise to many bronchioles. These bronchioles branch into smaller and smaller tubes. The walls of the bronchi and larger bronchioles are strengthened by irregular cartilaginous plates, which finally disappear in the smaller branches. Terminal bronchioles lead into delicate, thin-walled **alveolar ducts,** the walls of which are evaginated to form clusters of **alveoli,** or respiratory pockets, estimated at 400,000,000 in humans.

OBLIQUE SEPTUM AND DIAPHRAGM

When lungs occupy separate pleural cavities, as in some reptiles and in birds and mammals, a tendinous or tendinomuscular partition separates pleural cavities from the rest of the coelom. The partition arises as membranous folds of the dorsal and lateral parietal peritoneum that grow into the embryonic coelom until they meet. The septum transversum is also incorporated into its structure. The partition is called the oblique septum in reptiles and birds, diaphragm in mammals. It is tendinous in reptiles, slightly muscular in birds, and highly muscular in mammals. The mammalian diaphragm is dome shaped and bulges into the thorax. Contraction of extrinsic or intrinsic muscles tightens the septum or flattens the diaphragm and, along with visceral or rib movements, increases the size of the pleural cavities. This lowers the gas pressure around, hence within, the lungs to below atmospheric pressure, and air enters the lungs.

In mammals the parietal peritoneum of each pleural cavity lines the inner surface of the thoracic wall as the **parietal pleura** (Fig. 12-19) and covers the cephalic surface of the diaphragm as the **diaphragmatic pleura.** At the root of the lung (where the bronchus and pulmonary vessels enter and leave) the parietal pleura is continuous with the **visceral pleura** on the surface of the lung. The space enclosed by these pleurae is the pleural cavity.

NARES AND NASAL CANALS

External nares of cartilaginous and ray-finned fishes lead to blind olfactory sacs containing olfactory epithelium. They are often divided into incurrent and excurrent openings, the former being directed forward so that forward motion of the fish when swimming causes a current of water to flow over the olfactory epithelium and then out by the more ventral excurrent opening. In lobe-finned fishes (except *Latimeria*) and amphibians paired nasal canals connect external nares with internal nares, or **choanae,** that open into the oral cavity or pharynx. With development of a secondary palate in higher tetrapods the choanae open farther caudad, and the longer the secondary palate, the farther caudad they open (Fig. 8-18). In mammals they open into the nasopharynx above the soft palate (Fig. 11-3, cat). Hagfishes have a **nasopharyngeal duct** that conveys respiratory water from the single naris to the pharynx (Fig. 12-4). In lampreys a **nasohypophyseal duct** ends blindly just beyond the medial olfactory sac (Fig. 12-5).

Nasal canals arise from paired nasal pits and oronasal grooves, the dorsolateral walls of which roll together to form tubes (Fig. 12-20). Sharks and rays lack nasal canals and oronasal grooves remain throughout life. In mammals an *olfactory* epithelium differentiates only in the upper chambers of the nasal canals, whereas the ventral part has a ciliated glandular *nasal* epithelium like that of the trachea. Hairs at the entrance to mammalian canals trap coarse particles and insects; venous plexuses under the epithelium overlying the turbinal bones (**conchae**) warm cold air; and air sinuses that open into the upper parts of the canals serve as resonating chambers for vocal sounds (Fig. 12-21).

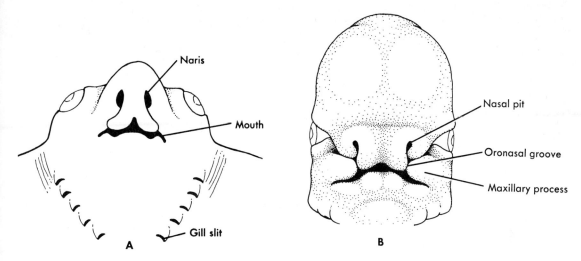

Fig. 12-20. Oronasal relationships in, **A,** an adult skate and, **B,** a 6-week (12-mm) human fetus.

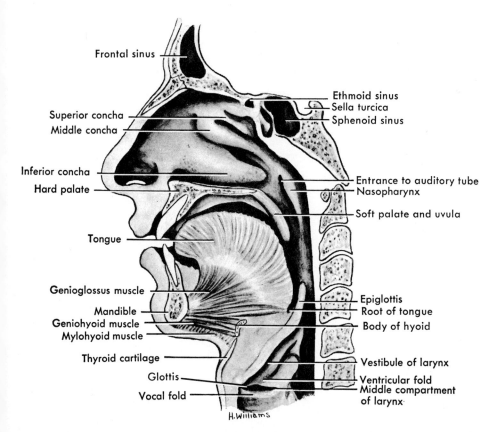

Fig. 12-21. Secondary palate and upper respiratory pathway, sagittal section, in a human being. (Modified from Francis, C.C., and Martin, A.H.: Introduction to human anatomy, ed. 7, St. Louis, 1975, The C.V. Mosby Co.)

A fleshy, partially cartilaginous proboscis (nose) develops in some mammals and carries the external nares to characteristic positions (compare the location of nostrils in cats, humans, and elephants). In whales, on the other hand, there is no proboscis, and the external nares are situated dorsally, although in fetal whales they are farther forward. In some whales the two nares become a median blowhole during later development.

CHAPTER SUMMARY

1. External respiration is the exchange of respiratory gases between organism and environment. It takes place via highly vascular membranes with thin moist epithelia.

2. Internal respiration is the exchange of gases between capillary blood and the tissues.

3. The chief adult organs of respiration are pharyngeal gills, buccopharyngeal mucosa, swim bladders or lungs, and skin.

4. Cutaneous respiration is the chief method of respiration in aquatic amphibians and some scaleless fishes.

5. Internal gills develop in the walls of gill chambers. They consist of pretrematic and posttrematic demibranchs attached to pharyngeal arches. Respiratory water usually enters the mouth, but it enters the spiracle in some elasmobranchs, the naris in hagfishes, and external gill slits in some lampreys and some fishes.

6. Elasmobranchs have naked gill slits. An operculum covers the gill chambers in chimaeras, bony fishes, and larval anurans. A branchiostegal membrane forms part of the wall of the opercular chamber in bony fishes.

7. A spiracle is present in elasmobranchs and chondrosteans. In some species it houses a pseudobranch.

8. The hyoid demibranch tends to disappear in teleosts, and the number of demibranchs is reduced still further in lungfishes.

9. Larval gills may be external or internal. They are external in lungfishes, amphibians, and a few ganoids. Anuran larvae also develop internal gills. Filamentous internal gills project to the exterior in larval elasmobranchs, viviparous chondrosteans, and some teleosts.

10. In addition to respiration, gills function in salt homeostasis and excretion of nitrogenous waste.

11. Pressure and suction pumps create a flow of respiratory water or air into and out of the vertebrate body. The chief pumps are the buccal and pharyngeal walls and floor of fishes and amphibians, the muscle-operated operculum and branchiostegal membrane of bony fishes, ribs, and fibrous or muscular diaphragms.

12. Pneumatic sacs arise from the foregut in nearly all vertebrates. They are called swim bladders in fishes, lungs in tetrapods.

13. Swim bladders and the lungs of aquatic amphibians are chiefly hydrostatic organs. Swim bladders are used for respiration in many physostomous dipnoans and ganoids.

14. Swim bladders serve also for sound transmission, sound production, and depth perception.

15. Internal nares open anteriorly into the oral cavity in dipnoans and amphibians, farther caudad when there is a secondary palate. Despite internal nares, air-breathing fishes and aquatic amphibians take air into the mouth by gulping it.

16. The glottis is the entrance to the larynx. It is protected against the entrance of water or foods by fleshy valves, by its position with respect to internal nares, and by an epiglottis in most mammals.

17. The larynx is supported by lateral cartilages in urodeles, arytenoid and cricoid (or cricothyroid) cartilages in anurans, reptiles, and birds. A thyroid cartilage is added in mammals. Other smaller cartilages may develop.

18. Vocal cords are chiefly mammalian but are also found in amphibians and some lizards.

19. Tracheal walls are supported by bony plates, rings, or half rings. The trachea bifurcates to form two bronchi. At the base of the trachea in most birds is a syrinx.

20. Tetrapod lungs arise as a midventral evagination of the pharynx. They occupy the pleuroperitoneal cavity in amphibians and lower reptiles, and pleural cavities in other amniotes. An oblique septum separates pleural from peritoneal cavities in reptiles and birds. A muscular diaphragm separates them in mammals.

21. Lungs are simple sacs in amphibians and snakes, septate in other reptiles, and spongy in birds and mammals. Saccular diverticula extend among the viscera in some reptiles and invade the bones in birds. In most limbless tetrapods one lung is rudimentary.

22. In birds inhaled air flows directly to air sacs and then via recurrent bronchi to secondary bronchi, parabronchi, and air capillaries before being exhaled. In addition to serving as bellows, air sacs are thermoregulatory and increase buoyancy.

23. External nares lead to blind olfactory sacs in jawed cartilaginous and ray-finned fishes. In lobe-finned fishes and tetrapods they are connected via nasal canals with the oral cavity or pharynx. Hagfishes have a nasopharyngeal duct that carries water. Lampreys have a blind nasohypophyseal duct.

LITERATURE CITED AND SELECTED READINGS

1. Alexander, R.M.: Physical aspects of swim bladder function, Biological Reviews **41**:141, 1966.
2. Atz, J.W.: Narial breathing in fishes and the evolution of internal nares, Quarterly Review of Biology **27**:367, 1952.
3. Ballintijn, C.M., and Hughes, G.M.: The muscular bases of the respiratory pumps in the trout, Journal of Experimental Biology **43**:349, 1965.
4. Bartmar, G.: The vertebrate nose: remarks on its structure, functional adaptation and evolution, Evolution **23**:131, 1969.
5. Duncker, H.R.: Die Anordnung des Gefäbsystems in der Vogellunge, Verhandlungen der anatomischen Gesellschaft **68**:517, 1974.
6. Gans, C.: Respiration in early tetrapods—the frog is a red herring, Evolution **24**:740, 1970.
7. Gaunt, A.S., and Gans, C.: Mechanics of respiration in the snapping turtle *Chelydra serpenta,* Journal of Morphology **128**:195, 1969.
8. Hughes, G.M., and Morgan, M.: The structure of fish gills in relation to their respiratory function, Biological Review **48**:419, 1973.
9. Johansen, K.: Comparative physiology: gas exchange and circulation in fishes, Annual Review of Physiology **33**:569, 1971.
10. McMahon, B.R.: A functional analysis of the aquatic and aerial respiratory movements of an African lungfish *Protopterus aethiopicus,* with reference to the evolution of the lung-ventilation mechanism in vertebrates, Journal of Experimental Biology **51**:407, 1069.
11. Randall, D.J., et al.: The evolution of airbreathing in vertebrates, New York, 1981, Cambridge University Press.
12. Wood, S.C., and Lenfant, C.J.M.: Respiration: mechanics, control, and gas exchange. In Gans, C.: Biology of the reptilia, vol. 5, New York, 1976, Academic Press, Inc.

CHAPTER 13

Circulatory system

The circulatory system of vertebrates consists of the heart, arteries, veins or venous sinuses, capillaries or sinusoids, and blood (**blood vascular system**) and of lymph channels and lymph (**lymphatic system**). The blood carries oxygen from respiratory organs; nutrients from extraembryonic membranes, digestive tract, and storage sites; hormones and other substances associated with homeostasis and immunity to disease; and waste products of metabolism to the excretory organs. Blood also conducts heat to and from the skin and other surfaces where heat is exchanged, thereby regulating and equalizing internal temperatures. Lymph channels collect interstitial tissue fluids not taken up by the bloodstream and emulsified fats absorbed in the small intestine. Lymph vessels terminate in venous channels.

Arteries carry blood away from the heart. They have muscular and elastic walls (Fig. 13-1) capable of distention with each intrusion of blood. (Feel your pulse!) The smallest arteries, 0.3 mm or less in diameter, are **arterioles.** They dilate and constrict reflexly and thereby assist in regulating blood pressure. They terminate in **capillaries. Veins** commence in capillaries (other than the respiratory capillaries of the gills) and carry blood toward the heart. They have proportionately less muscle and elastic tissue and more fibrous tissue than arteries and are therefore capable of less distention or constriction. The smallest veins are **venules.** They begin in capillaries. The latter consist of endothelium only, with a lumen just large enough to accommodate red blood cells in single file. In fact, the red cells must "squeeze through" and, in so doing, become deformed. The **heart** is a pump with very muscular walls. Valves in the veins and heart prevent backflow of blood.

A **portal system** is a system of veins terminating in capillaries (Fig. 13-2). In most vertebrates, blood from the capillaries of the tail passes via a **renal portal system** to capillaries of the kidney before returning to the heart. Blood from the digestive tract, pancreas, and spleen passes via a **hepatic portal system** to the capillaries of the liver before

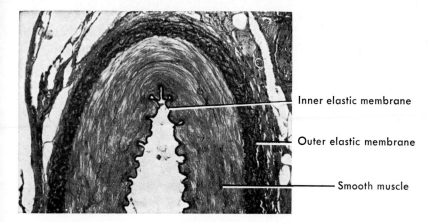

Inner elastic membrane

Outer elastic membrane

Smooth muscle

Fig. 13-1. Section of a medium-sized artery. The innermost lining is a single layer of pavementlike cells, the endothelium. (From Bevelander, G., and Ramaley, J.A.: Essentials of histology, ed. 8, St. Louis, 1979, The C.V. Mosby Co.)

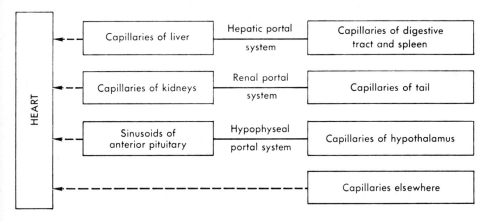

Fig. 13-2. Chief portal systems of vertebrates. The renal portal system is lacking in typical mammals, and the hypophyseal portal system has not been demonstrated in most bony fishes. Channels indicated by broken lines are not part of a portal system.

continuing to the heart. Blood containing pituitary-regulating hormones from the hypothalamus passes via a **hypophyseal portal system** to the adenohypophysis before continuing to the heart.

THE HEART AND ITS EVOLUTION

The heart is a muscular pump with an inner lining, or **endocardium,** of endothelium and elastic tissue, a muscular layer (**myocardium**) that is especially thick in the principal pumping chamber of the heart, and an outer fibrous capsule, the **epicardium.** The tissues of the heart, like tissues elsewhere, are supplied with arterial blood by coronary arteries and drained by coronary veins. Cardiac muscle contracts in response to the interaction of electrolytes in the blood that diffuses through the tissues and not because it has a nerve supply. The autonomic nervous system imposes orderliness, or rhythmicity, on these contractions. No nerve fibers supply the hearts of hagfishes. The heart occupies the pericardial cavity, an isolated portion of the coelom. The epicardium, or visceral pericardium, is equivalent to visceral peritoneum elsewhere.

In fishes, blood passes from the heart to the gills and from there directly to all parts of the body, after which it returns to the heart. Thus blood makes a single circuit during which it is pumped, oxygenated, distributed, and returned to the pump. No blood cell escapes oxygenation and none fails to enter a capillary bed where oxygen is needed. In species that breathe with lungs instead of gills a **pulmonary circuit** carries oxygen-poor blood from the heart to the lungs and brings back oxygenated blood, and a **systemic circuit** carries oxygenated blood from the heart to all parts of the body and returns oxygen-depleted blood to the heart. A two-circuit pattern requires separation of oxygenated and deoxygenated blood in the pump. Single-circuit hearts are simpler in structure.

Single-circuit hearts

The hearts of fishes other than lobe-fins are single-circuit hearts. They have four chambers in a series, a **sinus venosus, atrium, ventricle,** and **conus arteriosus,** and blood flows through these chambers in that sequence. Such a heart is seen in its simplest form in hagfishes (Fig. 13-3).

A shark has a typical fish heart (Fig. 13-4). The sinus venosus is thin walled and has little muscle and much fibrous tissue. It receives blood from all parts of the body and is filled by suction each time the ventricle contracts and relaxes. The sinus shows some contractility but is chiefly a collecting chamber. Its blood gushes through the sinoatrial aperture into the atrium as soon as the latter begins to relax after emptying. The caudal wall of the sinus venosus is anchored to the anterior face of the septum transversum. The atrium is a large, thin-walled muscular sac. Blood from the atrium pours into the ventricle through an atrioventricular aperture guarded by two valves. These prevent ventricular blood from being pumped back into the atrium when the ventricle contracts. The ventricle has very thick muscular walls. The anterior end of the ventricle is prolonged as a muscular tube of small diameter, the conus arteriosus, which passes to the cephalic end of the pericardial cavity, where it is continuous

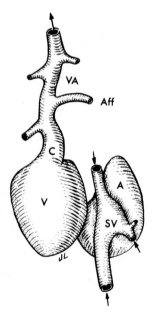

Fig. 13-3. Heart and associated vessels of the cyclostome *Myxine glutinosa,* ventral view. **A,** Atrium; **Aff,** afferent branchial artery; **C,** conus arteriosus; **SV,** sinus venosus; **V,** ventricle; **VA,** ventral aorta. Arrows indicate direction of blood flow.

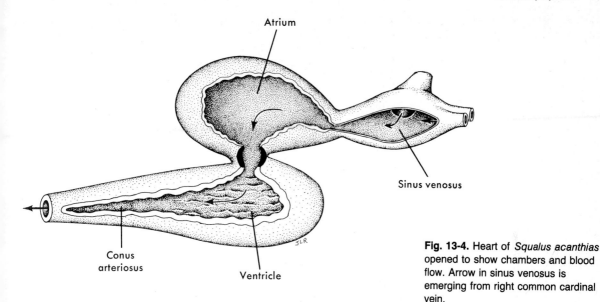

Fig. 13-4. Heart of *Squalus acanthias* opened to show chambers and blood flow. Arrow in sinus venosus is emerging from right common cardinal vein.

with the **ventral aorta.** Like the ventricle, the conus arteriosus is mostly cardiac muscle. A series of semilunar valves in the conus arteriosus prevent backflow of blood into the ventricle. Because of its contractility and elasticity, the conus maintains a steady arterial pressure into and through the gills. In teleosts the conus is short, and its function is assumed by the **bulbus arteriosus,** a muscular expansion of the ventral aorta.

The hearts of lungfishes and amphibians

Modifications in the hearts of lungfishes and amphibians are correlated with the presence of lungs and enable oxygenated blood returning from the lungs to be separated from deoxygenated blood returning from elsewhere. One modification is the establishment of a partial or complete partition within the atrium so that there is a right and left atrium (Figs. 13-5 and 13-6, Dipnoi, urodele, anuran). The partition is complete in anurans and some urodeles. The pulmonary veins empty into the left atrium so that the blood in this chamber is oxygen rich. The sinus venosus empties into the right atrium; hence, the blood in this chamber is low in oxygen. In lungless amphibians the atrium remains undivided.

A second modification is the formation of a partial interventricular septum (chiefly in lungfishes but also in *Siren,* a urodele) or of ventricular trabeculae (in amphibians). Trabeculae are shelves or ridges projecting from the ventricular wall into the chamber and running mostly cephalocaudad. Interventricular septa and ventricular trabeculae perform identical functions: they maintain separation of oxygenated and unoxygenated blood that began in the left and right atria.

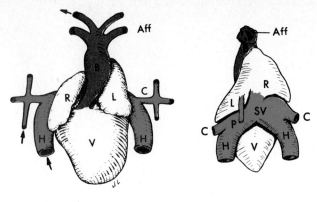

Fig. 13-5. Heart and associated vessels of necturus. Ventral view (left) and dorsal view (right). **Aff,** Common channel leading to second and third afferent branchial arteries; **B,** bulbus arteriosus; **C,** common cardinal vein; **H,** hepatic sinus; **L,** left atrium receiving pulmonary vein; **P,** pulmonary vein; **R,** right atrium; **SV,** sinus venosus; **V,** ventricle. A short conus arteriosus connects the ventricle with the bulbus. Arrows indicate direction of blood flow. Colors represent arteries (red) and veins (blue) but not necessarily oxygen content.

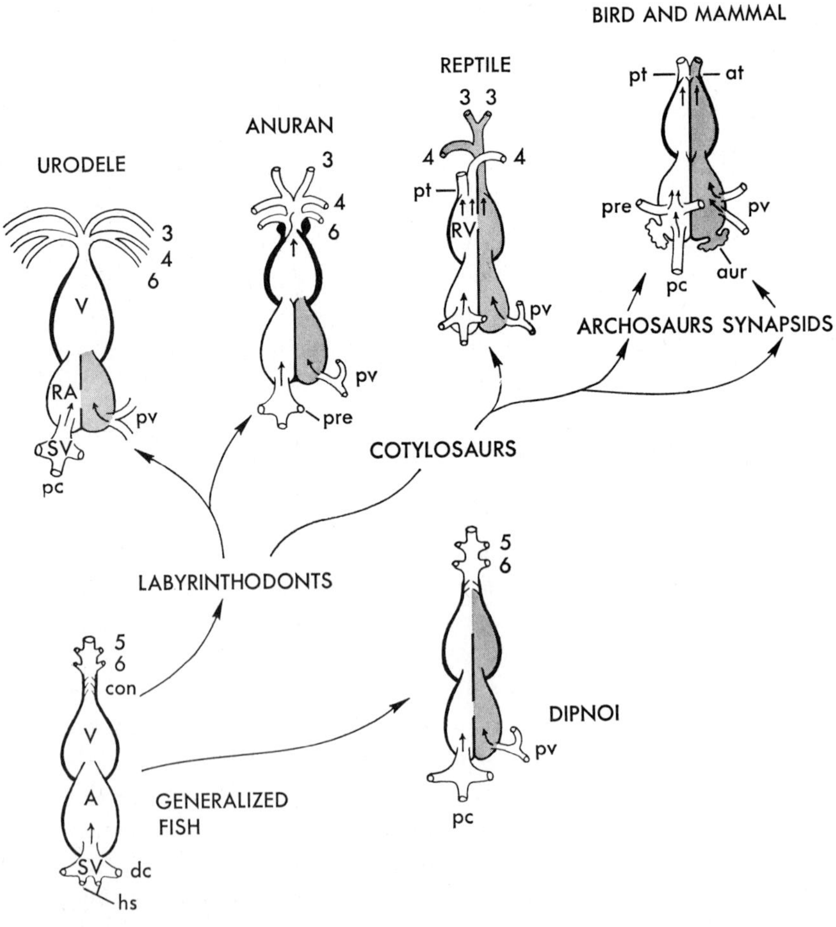

Fig. 13-6. Modifications of the atria and ventricles that result in increased separation of oxygenated and deoxygenated blood. The parts of the heart shown are, **A,** atrium; **RA,** right atrium; **V,** ventricle; **RV,** right ventricle; **SV,** sinus venosus; **con,** conus arteriosus; **aur,** auricle of mammalian heart. **3 to 6,** Third to sixth aortic arches. Other vessels are, **at,** aortic trunk; **dc,** common cardinal vein; **hs,** hepatic sinus; **pc,** postcava; **pre,** precava (common cardinal vein); **pv,** pulmonary veins; **pt,** pulmonary trunk. Gray chambers contain chiefly, or only, oxygenated blood.

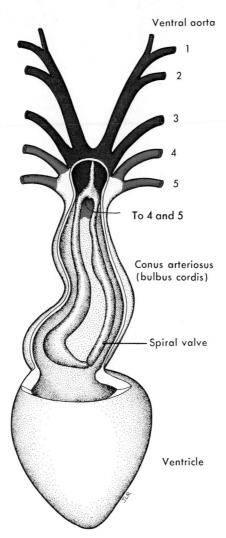

Ventral aorta

1

2

3

4

5

To 4 and 5

Conus arteriosus
(bulbus cordis)

Spiral valve

Ventricle

Fig. 13-7. Conus arteriosus and afferent branchial arteries (1 to 5) of the lungfish *Protopterus*. The spiral valve distributes oxygen-rich blood (red) to the first three afferent branchial arteries and oxygen-poor blood (blue) to the last two, which support internal gills. An interventricular septum is present but not illustrated. The fourth and fifth afferent branchial arteries in this illustration are the fifth and sixth embryonic aortic arches illustrated in Fig. 13-13, *B*.

A third modification is formation of a spiral valve in the conus arteriosus (bulbus cordis) in many dipnoans and amphibians. The valve directs oxygenated and unoxygenated blood into appropriate channels. In the lungfish *Protopterus* (Fig. 13-7) it shunts blood low in oxygen into the aortic arches that lead to internal gills. In anurans (Fig. 13-8) it blocks and unblocks the common entrance to the left and right pulmonary arches, shunting unoxygenated blood to the lungs and (via cutaneous branches) to the skin.

A fourth modification shortened the ventral aorta so that it became practically nonexistent. As a result, oxygenated and unoxygenated blood that has been kept separate in the heart by septa, trabeculae, and spiral valves, moves *directly* from the heart into appropriate ves-

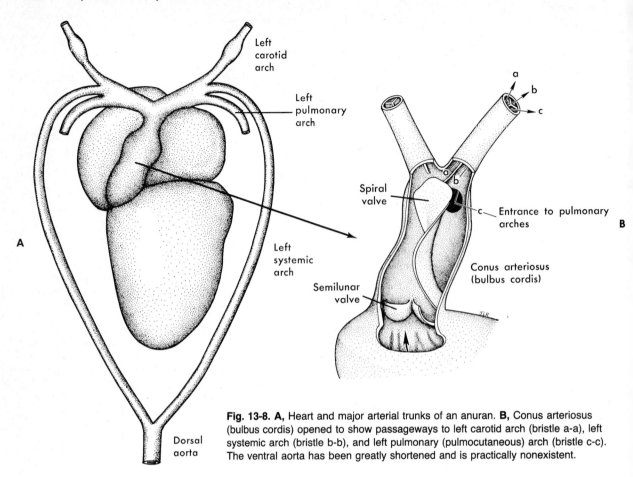

Fig. 13-8. A, Heart and major arterial trunks of an anuran. **B,** Conus arteriosus (bulbus cordis) opened to show passageways to left carotid arch (bristle a-a), left systemic arch (bristle b-b), and left pulmonary (pulmocutaneous) arch (bristle c-c). The ventral aorta has been greatly shortened and is practically nonexistent.

sels (Figs. 13-7 and 13-8). Some of the changes in dipnoans and amphibians—septa and trabeculae, for instance—presage similar changes in amniotes.

The hearts of amniotes

Amniote hearts have two atria, two ventricles, and, except in adult birds and mammals, a sinus venosus (Figs. 13-9, 13-10, and 13-16). In crocodilians the sinus venosus is partially incorporated into the wall of the right atrium. Birds and mammals have a sinus venosus during early development, but it fails to keep pace with the growth of the right atrium into which it empties and finally becomes part of the wall of that chamber. Thereafter, the vessels that emptied into the sinus venosus empty directly into the right atrium. Its embryonic location is marked in adults by the **sinoatrial node** of neuromuscular tissue, which plays a role in regulation of the heartbeat.

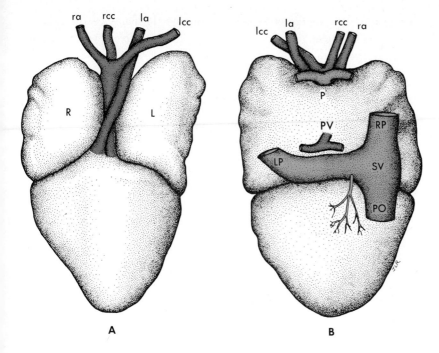

Fig. 13-9. Heart and associated vessels of *Sphenodon*. **A,** Ventral view. **B,** Dorsal view. **L,** Left atrium; **la,** left aortic trunk; **lcc,** left common carotid artery; **LP,** left precava; **P,** pulmonary trunk; **PO,** postcava; **PV,** pulmonary veins entering right atrium; **R,** right atrium; **ra,** right aortic trunk; **rcc,** right common carotid artery; **RP,** right precava; **SV,** sinus venosus. The ventricle is divided internally into two chambers. Red vessels contain oxygenated blood.

The right and left atria of adult amniotes are completely separated by an interatrial septum. Nevertheless, they are confluent during embryonic development via an **interatrial foramen (foramen ovale),** which closes about the time of hatching or at birth. The site of the obliterated foramen ovale is marked in adult hearts by a depression, the **fossa ovalis,** in the medial wall of the right atrium. The right atrium receives blood from the sinus venosus (reptiles) or blood that previously emptied into the sinus venosus (bird and mammals). It also receives blood from the coronary veins. The left atrium receives blood from the pulmonary veins.

In mammals each atrium has an earlike flap, or **auricle,** containing a blind, saclike chamber. Any functional advantage of the mammalian auricle has yet to be demonstrated.

The two ventricles are completely separated in crocodilians, birds, and mammals. In other amniotes the interventricular septum is incomplete. The internal walls of the ventricles frequently exhibit interanastomosing ridges and columns of muscle (**trabeculae carneae**).

Valves guard the passage from the atria into the ventricles. The valves are fibrous flaps (muscular on the right in crocodilians and birds) connected in mammals and some lower amniotes by tendinous cords (**chordae tendineae**) to **papillary muscles** projecting from the ventricular walls (Fig. 13-10). During relaxation of the ventricle (diastole), blood from the atria falls freely past the flaps (cusps) into the ventricles. During ventricular contraction (systole), the flaps are forced upward into the atrioventricular passageway, thereby preventing reflux of blood into the atria. Both valves have one or two flaps in reptiles and birds. In most mammals the left valve has two flaps (**bicuspid**, or **mitral, valve**) and the right has three (**tricuspid valve**).

Guarding the exits of the pulmonary and aortic trunks from the ventricles are **semilunar valves** that prevent backflow into the ventricles as the latter relax (Fig. 13-10).

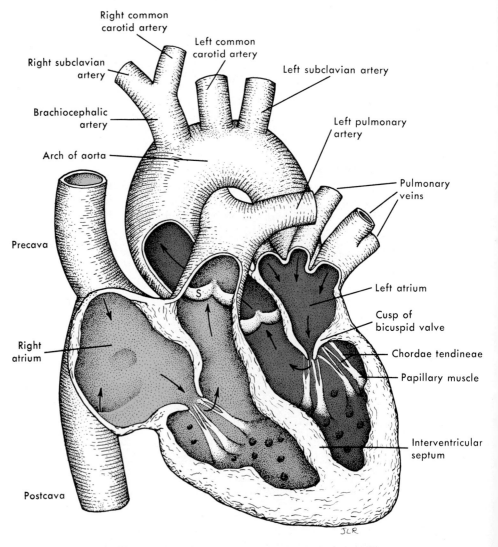

Fig. 13-10. Human heart. **S,** Semilunar valve at entrance to pulmonary trunk. The semilunar valve at entrance to ascending aorta is also shown. Blue indicates deoxygenated blood.

Morphogenesis of the heart

The heart commences as two parallel tubes that are brought together and unite in the midline under the pharynx early in development. This establishes a single, pulsating tube that receives two vitelline veins at the caudal end (Fig. 15-6) and extends forward as (temporarily) two ventral aortas. At first the tubular heart is almost straight, but as development progresses it twists into an S-shape so that the atrial region, previously at the caudal end, is carried dorsad and cephalad to lie where it is found in adult fishes (Fig. 13-4). In anurans and amniotes the twisting is carried further, so that the atria finally lie cephalad to the ventricle or ventricles (Fig. 13-9). Because of the need to propel nutrients the heart is the first organ to function, and it does so even before any nerves have reached it.

ARTERIAL CHANNELS AND THEIR MODIFICATIONS

Arterial channels supply most organs with oxygenated blood, although they carry deoxygenated blood to respiratory organs. In the basic pattern (Fig. 13-11) the major arterial channels consist of (1) a

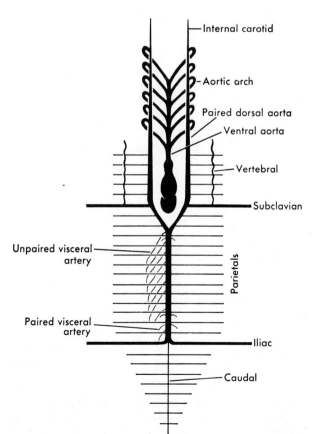

Fig. 13-11. Basic pattern of the chief arterial channels of vertebrates.

ventral aorta **(truncus arteriosus)** emerging from the heart and passing forward beneath the pharynx (paired early in embryogenesis); (2) a **dorsal aorta,** paired above the pharynx and passing caudad above the digestive tract; and (3) six pairs of **aortic arches** connecting the ventral aorta with the dorsal aorta. Branches of these major channels supply all parts of the body. Modifications affect most prominently the aortic arches, which become adapted during embryonic development for respiration by gills or lungs.

Aortic arches of fishes

Adaptive modifications of the embryonic aortic arches for respiration by gills may be illustrated in developing sharks (Fig. 13-12). The ventral aorta in *Squalus* extends forward under the pharynx and connects with the developing aortic arches. The aortic arches in the mandibular arch are the first to develop. Shortly thereafter the other five

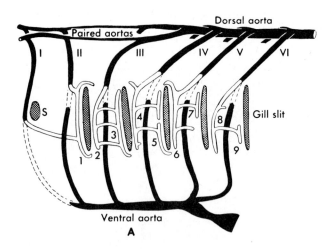

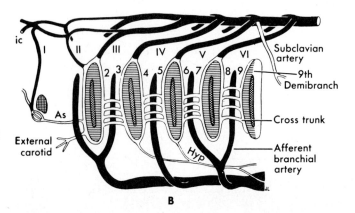

Fig. 13-12. Changes in embryonic aortic arches I to VI of *Squalus* during development, lateral view. In **A,** buds (in white) off the aortic arches are establishing pretrematic and posttrematic arteries and cross trunks. Broken lines indicate sections of the aortic arches that become occluded, forcing blood into afferent branchial arterioles (not shown). In **B, I** has become the efferent pseudobranchial artery and **II** to **VI** have become efferent branchial arteries. **1, 3, 5, 7, 9,** Pretrematic arteries; **2, 4, 6, 8,** posttrematic arteries. **As,** Afferent pseudobranchial; **Hyp,** hypobranchial; **ic,** internal carotid; **S,** spiracle.

pairs appear. Before the sixth pair is completed, the ventral segments of the first pair disappear, and the dorsal segments become the two efferent pseudobranchial arteries. The second pair sprout buds that become the first pretrematic arteries. Other buds sprout from the third, fourth, fifth, and sixth aortic arches and give rise to posttrematic arteries. The latter then sprout cross trunks, which grow caudad in the holobranch and by further budding establish the last four pretrematic arteries. Aortic arches II to VI soon become occluded at one site (broken lines in Fig. 13-12, *A*). The segments ventral to the occlusions become afferent branchial arteries. The dorsal segments become efferent branchial arteries. In the meantime, capillary beds are developing within the nine demibranchs. Afferent branchial arterioles (not shown in Fig. 13-12) connect the afferent branchial arteries with the capillaries. Efferent branchial arterioles return oxygenated blood from the capillaries to the pretrematic and posttrematic arteries.

As a result of these modifications of the embryonic aortic arches, blood entering an aortic arch from the ventral aorta of fishes must pass through gill capillaries before proceeding to the dorsal aorta. The aortic arches have thus been modified to serve the gills.

The same developmental changes convert the six pairs of embryonic aortic arches of bony fishes into afferent and efferent branchial arteries. The specific number converted determines the number of functional gills. In most teleosts the first and second aortic arches tend to disappear (Fig. 13-13, *A*). In *Protopterus* (Fig. 13-13, *B*) the third and fourth embryonic aortic arches do not become interrupted by gill capillaries.

In lungfishes a pulmonary artery sprouts off the left and right sixth aortic arch and vascularizes the swim bladders. This happens also in two ganoid fishes, *Amia* and *Polypterus*.* This is precisely how tetrapod lungs are vascularized!

Aortic arches of tetrapods

Embryonic tetrapods, like fishes, construct six pairs of embryonic aortic arches (Fig. 1-5). The first and second arches are transitory and not found in adults (Fig. 13-13, *C* to *H*). After arches I and II disappear, the third aortic arches and the paired dorsal aortae anterior to arch III are named internal carotid arteries. With the exception of a few tailed amphibians, tetrapods lose also the fifth aortic arches during embryonic life (Fig. 13-13, *E* to *H*). Pulmonary arteries sprout off the sixth arches to vascularize the lung buds (Figs. 1-5; 13-13, *C* to

---

*In most other actinopterygians the swim bladders (lungs) are supplied from the dorsal aorta.

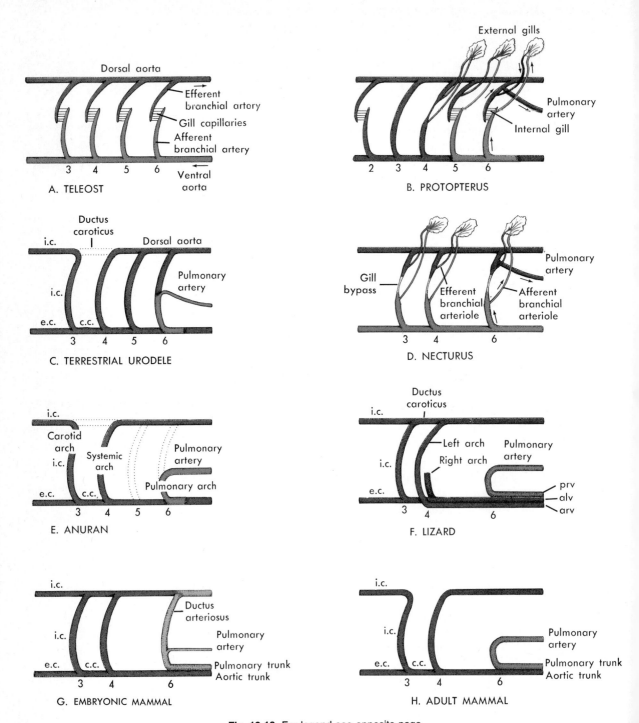

Fig. 13-13. For legend see opposite page.

Fig. 13-13. Persistent left aortic arches in representative vertebrates. **2** to **6,** Second through sixth embryonic aortic arches. Dotted lines in **C** indicate vessel present in some species; in **E,** vessels that are functional in larvae. Arrows indicate direction of blood flow. **alv,** Aortic trunk from left ventricle; **arv,** aortic trunk from right ventricle; **cc,** common carotid artery, which is the paired segment of the embryonic ventral aorta; **ec,** external carotid; **ic,** internal carotid; **prv,** pulmonary trunk from right ventricle. In **B, C,** and **E** the ventral aorta carries venous blood (blue) during one phase of a single ventricular contraction and arterial blood (red) during the next phase. In **B** the oxygen content of each vessel depends on the extent to which oxygen is being acquired via the gills as compared to the swim bladder. In **C** the sixth arch carries only oxygenated blood after the pulmonary artery is filled with unoxygenated blood. In **G** all blood in arches is mixed and colors designate predominant condition.

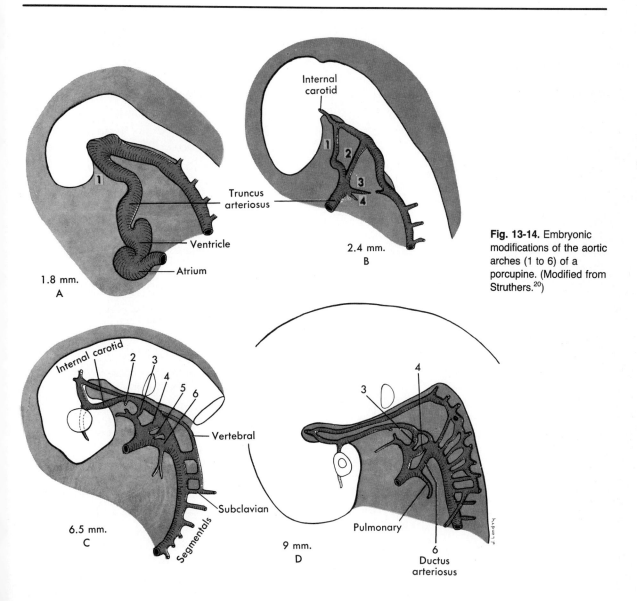

Fig. 13-14. Embryonic modifications of the aortic arches (1 to 6) of a porcupine. (Modified from Struthers.[20])

H, and 13-14, *D*). Further modifications of the aortic arches and associated vessels will be discussed under amphibians, reptiles, birds, and mammals.

AMPHIBIANS

Most terrestrial urodeles retain four pairs of aortic arches (Fig. 13-13, *C*). Aquatic urodeles typically retain three because the fifth arches either drop out or unite with the fourth. In aquatic urodeles that retain gills throughout life, afferent branchial arterioles pass to the gills, efferent branchial arterioles return oxygenated blood to the arch, and a short section of each arch becomes a gill bypass (Fig. 13-13, *D*). Bypasses carry little blood as long as the animal is using its gills; however, when the water is low enough in dissolved oxygen to cause the animal to gulp air, the gills shrink, and the bypasses carry more blood. Similarly, when resorption of the gills of *Siren* is brought about by thyroid hormone injections, the animal gulps air, and the bypasses carry all the blood entering the arches. On the ventral aorta of perennibranchiates a bulbus arteriosus (Fig. 13-5) maintains a steady nonpulsating arterial pressure in the gills.

Larval anurans (tadpoles) retain four aortic arches (III through VI) for a while. Arch VI sprouts a pulmonary artery that vascularizes the lung bud. Arches III, IV, and V supply larval gills on the third, fourth, and fifth pharyngeal arches. Gill bypasses are prominent at first, then become temporarily occluded while the external gills are functioning.

With loss of gills at metamorphosis, three changes affect the aortic arches and associated vessels of anurans (Fig. 13-13, *E*): (1) Aortic arch V disappears. (2) The dorsal aorta between aortic arches III and IV (**ductus caroticus**) disappears. As a result, blood entering aortic arch III (**carotid arch**) can pass only to the head. (3) The segment (**ductus arteriosus**) of aortic arch VI dorsal to the pulmonary artery disappears. (This also occurs in a few urodeles.) Blood entering arch VI (**pulmonary arch**) can now pass only to the lungs and skin. Aortic arch IV (**systemic arch**) on each side continues to the dorsal aorta to distribute blood to the rest of the body (Fig. 13-8, *A*).

Oxygenated blood from the left atrium and deoxygenated blood from the right are kept remarkably well separated as they pass through the ventricle in amphibians. In frogs this is accomplished by ventricular trabeculae, by the movement out of the ventricle of right atrial blood first and by action of a spiral valve in the conus arteriosus (Fig. 13-8, *B*). At the start of ventricular systole the valve is flipped into a position that closes off the entrance to the systemic and carotid arches, thereby directing deoxygenated blood into the aperture leading to the pulmonary arteries. Then, as back pressure builds up within the pulmonary arteries because of filling of the lung capillaries, the spiral valve flips into an alternate position, which directs oxygenated blood into the systemic and carotid arches. Late in ventricular systole some of the left atrial blood enters the pulmonary arches. In a marine toad studied by angiocardiography, the mixing was only slightly greater.[1,13]

Adult apodans retain three complete aortic arches (III, IV, VI), although the ductus arteriosus and ductus caroticus are reduced and carry little blood.

REPTILES

Modern reptiles exhibit three adult aortic arches—III, IV, and the base of VI (Fig. 13-13, *F*). Although the ductus arteriosus and ductus caroticus usually close before birth, both remain in primitive lizards; and in a few other reptiles one or the other may persist.

An innovation has been introduced in the ventral aorta of reptiles. Instead of developing a spiral valve to shunt fresh and deoxygenated blood into the proper arches, reptiles underwent a series of mutations that split the truncus arteriosus (unpaired segment of the ventral aorta) into three separate passages—two **aortic trunks** and a **pulmonary trunk** (Fig. 13-3, *F*).* The effects of these changes were as follows (Fig. 13-15, *B*): (1) The pulmonary trunk emerges from the right ventricle and leads to the left and right sixth aortic arches. Deoxygenated blood from the right atrium is therefore sent to the lungs. (2) One aortic trunk emerges from the left ventricle and carries oxygenated blood to the *right fourth* aortic arch and to the carotid arches. (3) The other aortic trunk leads out of what appears from external view to be the right ventricle and leads to the *left fourth* aortic arch. Studies of the oxygen content of this arch show that it, too, carries oxygenated blood.

Since the left systemic arch receives blood from the right side of the heart, how can it carry oxygenated blood? A series of studies using cinefluoroscopy have provided the answer. In turtles, lizards, and snakes, the interventricular septum is incomplete in the vicinity where the two aortic trunks leave the ventricle and that region is converted into a separate pocket (**cavum venosum**) by trabeculae (Fig. 13-16). Oxygenated blood from the left ventricle is directed into

---

*It is an attractive hypothesis that in early reptiles the truncus arteriosus was divided into two trunks that corresponded to the two ventricles. A pulmonary trunk from the right ventricle would have led to the sixth aortic arches, and an aortic trunk from the left ventricle would have led to the fourth and third aortic arches. This simple condition would then have been altered in three directions: toward the three trunks of modern reptiles, toward the condition in modern birds, and toward the condition in modern mammals.

this pocket, which leads to the two systemic arches. Therefore both left and right systemic arches receive oxygenated blood. Unoxygenated blood from the right atrium is directed by trabeculae toward the entrance to the pulmonary trunk, which is also located in a pocket, the **cavum pulmonale.** The arteries emerging from a turtle's heart are illustrated in Fig. 13-17.

A shunting of blood from right to left ventricle, and therefore away from the lungs, occurs in aquatic turtles and snakes that remain sub-

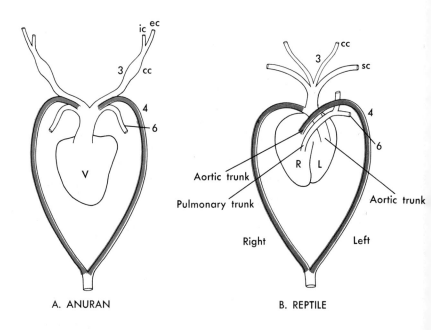

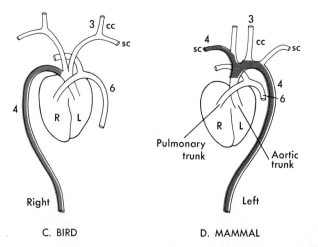

Fig. 13-15. Fate of the fourth aortic arches (red) in selected tetrapods, ventral view. **3,** Third arch (carotid); **4,** fourth arch (systemic); **6,** sixth arch (pulmonary). The relationships of the vessels have been adjusted to emphasize homologies. **cc,** Common carotid; **ec,** external carotid; **ic,** internal carotid; **sc,** subclavian artery; **L,** left ventricle; **R,** right ventricle; **V,** ventricle. Distribution of oxygenated blood in turtle heart is shown in Fig. 13-17.

merged without breathing for long periods. (When insufficient oxygen is available for metabolism while submerged, aquatic turtles and snakes derive energy from glycolysis, an anaerobic process.) Shunting from right to left is also observed when radiant heat is applied to the body. This may be thermoregulatory, enabling blood warmed by basking in sunlight to avoid the lungs, where heat loss would occur during exhalation. This would be valuable in cold weather. Reverse shunting, left to right, takes place when resistance to blood flow in

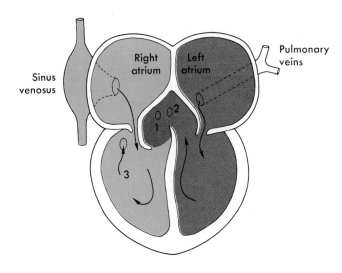

Fig. 13-16. Circulation in a turtle's heart. Red indicates oxygenated blood. **1** and **2,** Entrances to left and right aortic trunks, respectively, in the cavum venosum; **3,** entrance to pulmonary trunk in cavum pulmonale of right ventricle.

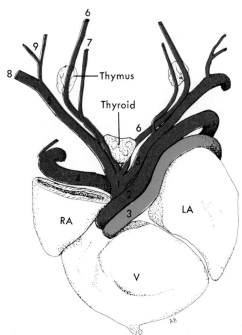

Fig. 13-17. Heart and aortic arches of turtle, ventral view. **LA,** Left atrium; **RA,** right atrium, partially removed to reveal the right aorta; **V,** ventricle. **1,** Brachiocephalic artery, a branch of the right aorta (see Fig. 13-16, *B*); **2,** left aorta (left systemic arch) emerging from cavum venosum; **3,** pulmonary trunk from cavum pulmonale; **4,** right aorta (right systemic arch) from cavum venosum; **5,** subclavian artery; **6,** common carotid artery; **7,** ventral cervical artery; **8,** axillary artery; **9,** arteries to pectoral and shoulder muscles. Red, oxygenated blood; blue, unoxygenated blood.

pulmonary vessels is lowered by dilation. This causes some blood from the lungs to return to the lungs. The survival value of shunting is mostly conjectural. (Fetal mammals and unhatched birds also have a right-left shunt away from the lungs, the function of which is obvious, as described later.)

Crocodilians have no way to shunt blood between ventricles because the interventricular septum is complete. However, an opening, the **foramen of Panizza,** connects right and left systemic trunks at their base, and blood can be shunted between these vessels at that location. During normal respiration some of the well-oxygenated blood in the right arch can be shunted to the left.

Most snakes and limbless lizards lose their left sixth aortic arch, which is correlated with absence of the left lung; and in snakes the left third arch also disappears. The right third arch (right carotid artery) has a bilateral distribution. All that adult snakes have left of the original six pairs of aortic arches are the right third, left and right fourth, and the ventral part of the right sixth.

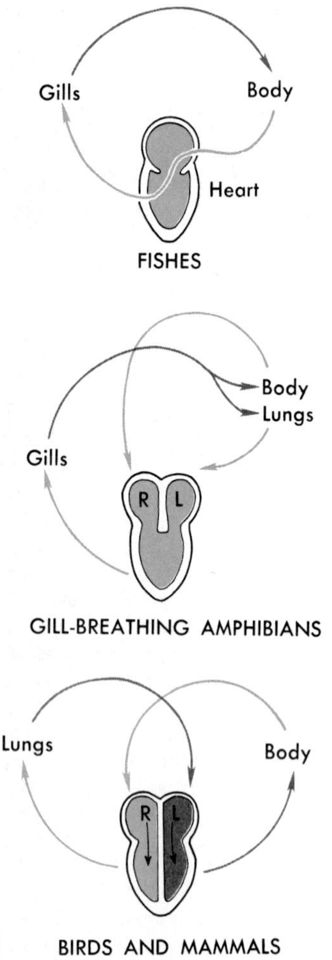

BIRDS AND MAMMALS

In birds and mammals, for the first time since the introduction of pulmonary respiration, circulatory routes have evolved in which there is no opportunity for mixing of oxygenated and unoxygenated blood. This has been achieved by closing the interventricular foramen and dividing the ventral aorta into two trunks. The pulmonary trunk (Fig. 13-15, *C* and *D*) emerges from the right ventricle and leads only to the sixth aortic arches and lungs. The aortic trunk emerges from the left ventricle and leads to the third and fourth aortic arches. *The left fourth aortic arch disappears in birds, and most of the right fourth disappears in mammals.* The part of the right fourth that remains in mammals becomes the proximal part of the right subclavian artery (Fig. 13-15, *D*).

In birds and mammals, therefore, six aortic arches develop in the embryo, and the first, second, fifth, and left fourth (in birds) or most of the right fourth (in mammals) disappear. The ductus caroticus also disappears. The ductus arteriosus functions until hatching or birth to shunt unoxygenated blood away from the lungs and into the dorsal aorta, which has branches leading to the allantois (the embryonic respiratory organ). Circulation in fetal mammals will be described later.

As a result of these modifications, all blood returning to the right side of the heart passes to the lungs. From there it returns to the left side of the heart to be recirculated (Fig. 13-18).

The left fourth aortic arch (systemic arch) of mammals is referred to simply as "the" aortic arch by mammalian anatomists. The common

Fig. 13-18. Normal circulatory routes in fishes, gill-breathing amphibians, including necturus, and birds and mammals.

carotid and external carotid arteries were part of the paired embryonic ventral aortae, and the internal carotids form from the third aortic arches and paired dorsal aortae (Fig. 13-13, *H*). A few individual and species differences in the vessels arising from "the" aortic arch in mammals are illustrated in Fig. 13-19.

The development of six aortic arches in all vertebrate embryos and the systematic modification or elimination of first one vessel and then another in successively higher vertebrates are in accordance with the biogenetic law.

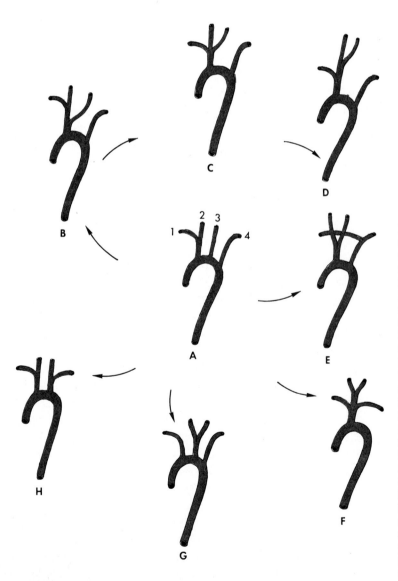

Fig. 13-19. Selected individual and species differences in the relationships of the common carotid and subclavian arteries in selected mammals. **A,** Basic pattern, seen also in man,* porcupine,* rabbit,* pig; **B,** cat,* dog,* pig,* man, and rabbit; **C** and **D,** rabbit, domestic cat, with **D** occurring with lower frequency; **E,** anomalous right subclavian artery in cat, man, and rat; **F,** many perissodactyls; **G,** walrus; **H,** man, porcupine, and rabbit. An asterisk indicates this to be a predominant condition in the populations examined. If there is no asterisk, the condition is common but not predominant. **1,** Right subclavian; **2,** right common carotid; **3,** left common carotid; **4,** left subclavian. The anomalous condition shown in **E** has been induced experimentally in rats by irradiation of the fetus.[5] Because all conditions illustrated are developmental modifications of a single embryonic pattern, any of the variants could, and probably do, occur in every mammalian species.

Dorsal aortae

The dorsal aorta is paired in the head and pharyngeal region in early embryos. In adults it is represented by the internal carotid in which blood flows cephalad. The dorsal aorta of the trunk is unpaired and gives off a series of somatic and visceral branches. It continues into the tail as the caudal artery.

Paired somatic branches arise segmentally from the aorta in the trunk and tail. These give off vertebromuscular branches to the epaxial muscle, skin, and vertebral column and long parietal branches that encircle the body wall to the midventral line. Where there are long ribs, the parietals are called intercostal arteries. Lumbar and sacral arteries are segmentals.

The subclavian and iliac arteries are enlarged segmentals (Fig. 13-11). Subclavians arise in embryos as sprouts off the paired or unpaired dorsal aorta, or from the third (some birds) or fourth (some mammals) aortic arches close to the aorta. However, these relationships often become reoriented during later development (Fig. 13-19). Branches of the subclavian and iliac arteries pass longitudinally in the body wall to anastomose (meet and unite end-to-end). Anastomoses ensure that if one of the anastomosing vessels supplying a region becomes occluded, the vessel approaching from the opposite direction will fill the affected arterial tree beyond the occlusion. Anastomoses also occur elsewhere in the body.

A series of **unpaired visceral branches** (splanchnic vessels) pass via dorsal mesenteries to the unpaired viscera, chiefly digestive organs, suspended in the coelom. The number of such vessels is largest in generalized species such as *Necturus*. As few as three unpaired trunks—frequently celiac, superior mesenteric, and inferior mesenteric—may occur in higher vertebrates. Anastomoses between two successive visceral branches occur along the entire length of the gut. Among anastomosing visceral branches in mammals are a superior pancreaticoduodenal branch of the celiac, which anastomoses with an inferior pancreaticoduodenal branch of the superior mesenteric; a middle colic branch of the superior mesenteric, which anastomoses with a left colic branch of the inferior mesenteric; and a superior rectal branch of the inferior mesenteric, which anastomoses with a middle rectal branch of the internal iliac. Anastomoses are also common on the greater and lesser curvatures of the stomach.

Paired visceral branches of the aorta include arteries to the urinary bladder, reproductive tract, gonads, kidneys, and adrenals. A series of gonadal and renal arteries occur in lower vertebrates, several pairs in reptiles and birds, and usually a single pair in mammals.

The early embryonic dorsal aorta of amniotes ends at the level of the hind limbs by bifurcating into right and left **allantoic (umbili-**

cal) **arteries** that carry blood to the allantois (Fig. 13-30). Internal iliacs sprout off the umbilical arteries as development progresses, and the umbilicals finally become branches of the iliacs.

Coronary arteries

The walls of all arteries and veins except the smallest are supplied with blood vessels called **vasa vasorum** ("vessels of the vessels"). The heart is no exception, and here the vessels are called coronary arteries and veins. In elasmobranchs the coronary arteries arise from hypobranchials that receive aerated blood from several arterial loops around the gill chambers (Fig. 13-12). In frogs they arise from the carotid arch. In reptiles and birds they arise from the aortic trunk leading to the right fourth arch, or from the brachiocephalic. In mammals they arise from sinuslike dilations at the base of the ascending aorta just beyond the semilunar valves. In a few vertebrates, including urodeles, the coronary supply consists of many small arteries.

Retia mirabilia

Certain arteries along their course become highly tortuous and then straighten out again. Such structures are retia mirabilia (singular, rete mirabile), or "wonderful networks." Retia are found in the head on the carotid arteries of a variety of vertebrates. They may affect the blood pressure within the brain or other organs of the head. The pseudobranch of *Squalus acanthias* is a rete. It probably regulates the blood pressure in the eyeball. Whales have extensive retia consisting of generous-sized arteries in the thorax in a protected position beneath the transverse processes of vertebrae and within the bony vertebral canal beside the spinal cord. These retia are all confluent and are supplied by segmental arteries and drained by vertebral arteries that are en route to the brain (Fig. 13-20). When the whale dives, the thoracic and abdominal viscera are compressed and blood is forced out of the visceral organs into the retia, which are protected from compression by their bony surroundings. These retia constitute a reservoir of blood that was oxygenated just before the whale dived. The oxygen is used by the brain during the dive, which may last for 2 hours.

Often, the tortuous artery is associated with an equally tortuous vein in such manner that artery and vein lie side by side with the blood flowing in opposite directions, or **countercurrents.** In birds that wade in icy waters, countercurrents in retia above the thigh result in transfer of heat from the artery entering the leg to the vein emerging. This conserves body energy in the form of heat and at the same time warms returning blood to body temperature. Polar bears and arctic seals have retia that serve the same function. On the other hand,

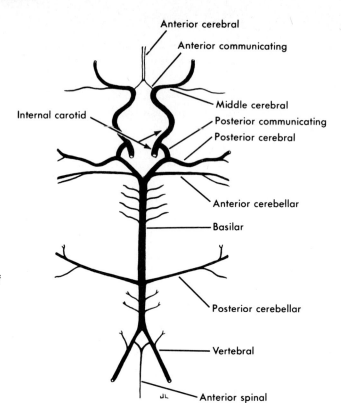

Fig. 13-20. Blood supply to the circle of Willis and brain of a mammal.

retia do not occur in arctic animals in which it would be a disadvantage—for instance, in those that are so well insulated by feathers or hair that the metabolic heat generated by exercise needs to be eliminated rather than retained. Mammals with testes in scrotal sacs have a rete, the **pampiniform plexus,** in each inguinal canal. Heat is transferred from spermatic artery to spermatic vein, assuring that the temperature within the scrotal sac will be lower than body temperature, a necessity for the viability of sperm in those species.

In the lining of the swim bladder of some fishes, conspicuous retia, the **red glands,** maintain high gas pressures within the bladder. The pressure forces some of the gas in the bladder to enter the veins of the bladder, into which lactic acid is also being secreted by the bladder cells. Lactic acid alters the pH of the venous blood, releasing oxygen from hemoglobin and carbon dioxide from bicarbonates, and these gases are returned to the bladder by arteries that receive them by countercurrent exchange in the rete. Thus the bladder builds up pressure and volume as needed.

VENOUS CHANNELS AND THEIR MODIFICATIONS

A generalized venous system consists of the following major streams (Fig. 13-21, *A*): cardinals, renal portal, lateral abdominal, hepatic portal, hepatic sinuses, and coronaries. The hepatic portal system is derived from the embryonic subintestinal and the distal portion of embryonic vitellines, and the hepatic sinuses are derived from the vitellines between liver and heart. Two additional streams develop in lungfishes and tetrapods, a pulmonary stream from the lungs and a postcava from the kidneys. These channels and their tributaries drain the entire body—head, trunk, tail, appendages. As development progresses they are slowly modified by deletion of some vessels and addition of others. Modifications are few in lower vertebrates, numerous in higher ones.

The basic pattern: sharks

An adult shark is an ideal living swimming blueprint of the basic venous channels of vertebrates. A knowledge of the venous channels of sharks and how they are derived during development is therefore a good introduction to the venous channels of other vertebrates.

Cardinal streams. The sinus venosus receives all blood returning to the heart of sharks. Most of this blood, except that from the digestive organs, enters the sinus by a pair of **common cardinal veins** (Fig. 13-21, *B*). These use the transverse septum as a bridge from the lateral body walls to the heart. They appear early in development and remain essentially unchanged thereafter.

Blood from the head other than the lower jaw is collected by a pair of **anterior cardinal** (precardinal) **veins** lying dorsal to the gills. The anterior cardinals pass caudad and empty into the common cardinals. The embryonic anterior cardinals, like common cardinals, remain essentially unchanged throughout life.

The earliest embryonic **posterior cardinal** (postcardinal) **veins** are continuous with the caudal vein (Fig. 13-21, *A*). These embryonic postcardinals pass cephalad lateral to the developing kidneys from which they receive a series of renal veins. They then empty into the common cardinals. Their anterior ends in adult sharks expand to become posterior cardinal sinuses.

While these embryonic postcardinals are functioning, a new pair of postcardinal veins is forming *between* the kidneys from a subcardinal plexus. (A similar plexus in turtles is illustrated in Fig. 13-27.) These new veins become confluent with the old postcardinals at the anterior end of the kidneys and they, too, drain the kidneys. As more and more blood from the kidneys flows into the new veins the older postcardinals are lost anterior to the kidneys (Fig. 13-21, *B*). Thereafter,

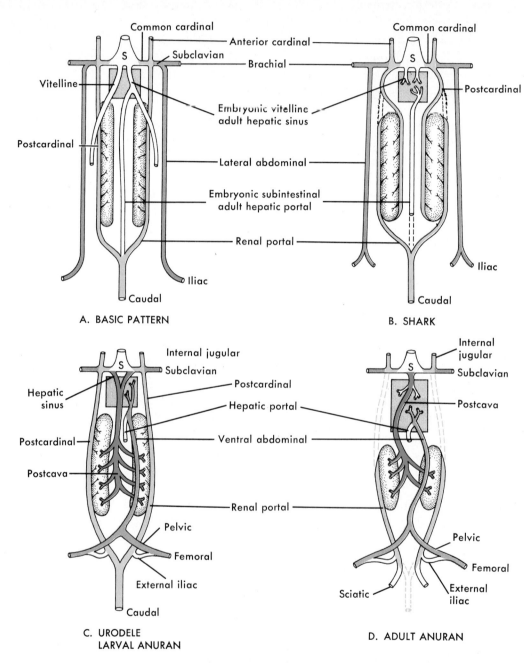

Common cardinal

Anterior cardinal

S

Subclavian

Brachial

Vitelline

Embryonic vitelline
adult hepatic sinus

Postcardinal

Postcardinal

Lateral abdominal

Embryonic subintestinal
adult hepatic portal

Renal portal

Iliac

Caudal

A. BASIC PATTERN

Common cardinal

S

Postcardinal

Iliac

Caudal

B. SHARK

Internal jugular

S

Subclavian

Postcardinal

Hepatic
sinus

Hepatic portal

Postcardinal

Ventral abdominal

Postcava

Renal portal

Pelvic

Femoral

External iliac

Caudal

**C. URODELE
LARVAL ANURAN**

Internal
jugular

S

Subclavian

Postcava

Pelvic

Femoral

Sciatic

External
iliac

D. ADULT ANURAN

Fig. 13-21. Modifications of the basic venous channels in sharks and amphibians. Broken lines indicate lost segments. Light blue, cardinal and caudal streams; dark blue, postcava, receiving renal veins; red, abdominal stream. **S,** Sinus venosus. The kidneys are stippled and the liver is gray. The venous channels medial to the kidneys in **B, C,** and **D** develop from an embryonic subcardinal plexus.

the name "posterior cardinal" is applied to the newer vessels. In adults they drain chiefly the kidneys, body wall, and gonads.

Renal portal stream. At an early stage in development some of the blood from the caudal vein continues forward beneath the gut as a subintestinal vein that drains the digestive tract (Fig. 13-21, *A*). Later, the connection of the caudal vein with the subintestinal is lost (Fig. 13-21, *B*). When the old posterior cardinals are lost anterior to the kidneys, all blood from the tail thereafter enters the capillaries surrounding the kidney tubules (peritubular capillaries). The result is a portal system.

Lateral abdominal stream. Commencing at the pelvic fin from which it receives an **iliac vein** and passing forward in the lateral body wall on each side is a **lateral abdominal vein** (Fig. 13-21, *B*). At the level of the pectoral fin it receives a **brachial vein,** after which the vessel turns abruptly toward the heart to enter the common cardinal vein. The part of the abdominal stream between brachial and common cardinal is the **subclavian vein.** In addition to collecting blood from the paired fins, the abdominal stream also receives a **cloacal vein,** a metameric series of **parietal veins** from the lateral body wall, and minor tributaries. This basic channel remains unmodified during subsequent development.

Hepatic portal stream and hepatic sinuses. Among the first vessels to appear in embryos are paired **vitelline,** or **omphalomesenteric, veins** from the yolk sack to the heart (Figs. 4-8 and 13-21, *A*). One of the vitelline veins is soon joined by the embryonic **subintestinal vein** that drains the digestive tract. As the developing liver enlarges, it encompasses the vitelline veins, causing them to be broken into many sinusoidal channels. Caudal to the liver one vitelline vein disappears and the other, with the subintestinal vein, becomes the hepatic portal system that drains the digestive organs of the coelom, and the spleen. Between liver and sinus venosus the two vitelline veins become **hepatic sinuses** (Fig. 13-21, *B*).

Other fishes

The venous channels of other fishes are much like those of sharks. Cyclostomes have no renal portals and no left common cardinals, although two common cardinals develop in embryos.[3] Abdominals are lacking in most ray-finned fishes, and the pelvic fins are drained by the postcardinals. In dipnoans they are drained by an unpaired ventral abdominal vein that ends in the sinus venosus, and the right postcardinal is missing. Blood from the swim bladders of all ray fins empties into the hepatic or common cardinal veins; in dipnoans it empties into the left atrium. Coronary veins in all fishes empty into the sinus venosus.

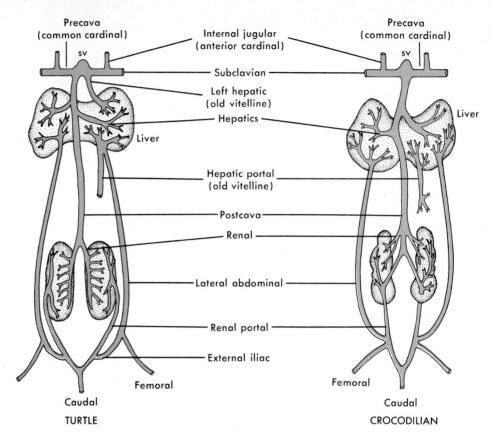

Fig. 13-22. Systemic veins of two reptiles. Only vessels of the basic pattern illustrated in Fig. 13-21, *A,* are shown. A strong branch of the renal portal vein of crocodilians continues directly to the postcava without ending in the kidney capillaries. **sv,** Sinus venosus.

Tetrapods

The early embryonic venous channels of tetrapods are basically the same as those of embryonic sharks. We have just seen how, by adding a vessel here and dropping one there during development, the basic pattern of a shark embryo is converted into the veins of an adult shark. We will now see how the same embryonic pattern is converted into the veins of adult tetrapods.

CARDINAL VEINS AND THE PRECAVAE

Embryonic tetrapods have postcardinals, precardinals, and common cardinals. In urodeles the postcardinals persist between the caudal vein and common cardinals throughout life (Fig. 13-21, *C*). In this respect, a necturus is less modified than a shark. In anurans, most reptiles, and birds the postcardinals disappear anterior to the

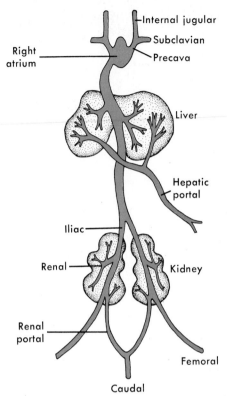

Fig. 13-23. Major systemic veins of a bird.

kidneys (Figs. 13-21, *D*, 13-22, and 13-23). In mammals the right postcardinal persists under the name **azygos,** and part of the left persists as the **hemiazygos** (Figs. 13-24 to 13-26).

Common cardinal veins in tetrapods are better known as **precavae,** and anterior cardinals are called **internal jugular veins.** Although most mammals retain both the left and right precavae, some, including cats and humans, lose the left precava during embryonic life (Fig. 13-24). In this case a transverse vessel, the **left brachiocephalic,** carries blood from the left side of the head and left arm to the right precava. A remnant of the left precava remains as a **coronary sinus.** The persisting right precava in humans is better known as the **superior vena cava.**

THE POSTCAVA

The postcava arises during embryonic life in a subcardinal venous plexus that receives renal veins from the kidneys (Fig. 13-27). One subcardinal channel predominates (usually the right), grows into the mesentery in which the liver is developing, and becomes confluent with the hepatic sinuses. This vessel is the postcava. The enlarging liver envelops it but does not break it into capillaries. Thus the post-

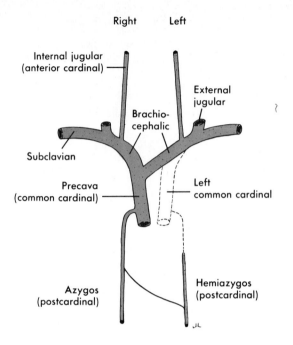

Fig. 13-24. Basic anterior venous channels of cat and man, ventral view. Broken lines indicate vessels obliterated during ontogeny. These sometimes remain as anomalies in adult mammals, including cats, pigs, and humans. Internal and external jugulars are sometimes confluent. Compare channels with those of a rabbit illustrated in Fig. 13-26.

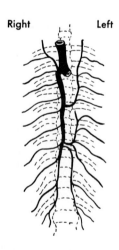

Fig. 13-25. The azygos (on the animal's right) and the hemiazygos (on the animal's left) in a rhesus monkey, ventral view. This condition is one of many variants in this species. Similar variants are seen in humans. The azygos is shown flowing into the precava. (Redrawn from Seib.[18])

cava becomes an expressway from kidneys to heart via the hepatic sinuses (Fig. 13-21, *C*). In most tetrapods the two hepatic sinuses ultimately fuse to form a median vessel that becomes part of the postcava (Fig. 13-21, *D*). In humans the postcava is also called the **inferior vena cava.**

In crocodilians, birds, and mammals, veins from the hind limbs establish direct connections with the postcava (Figs. 13-22, crocodilian, and 13-23), and the latter becomes the chief or sole drainage channel of the hind limbs.

With establishment of a postcava, blood that previously passed from kidneys to the heart via postcardinal veins now uses the postcava, and the postcardinals are reduced in size or disappear.

ABDOMINAL STREAM

In the early embryos of tetrapods, paired veins similar to the lateral abdominals of sharks commence in the body wall at the level of the future hind limbs, pass cephalad in the lateral body wall, receive veins from the developing forelimbs, and terminate in the common cardinal veins or sinus venosus. As development progresses in tetrapods this stream alters its course, becoming dissociated from the forelimb drainage and finally terminating in the liver, using the falciform ligament as a bridge across the coelom. The abandoned channels anterior to the liver disappear.

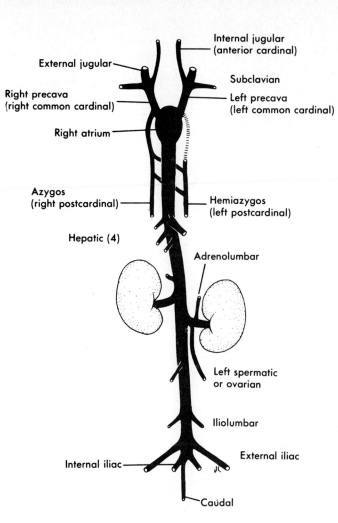

External jugular

Right precava
(right common cardinal)

Right atrium

Azygos
(right postcardinal)

Hepatic (4)

Internal jugular
(anterior cardinal)

Subclavian

Left precava
(left common cardinal)

Hemiazygos
(left postcardinal)

Adrenolumbar

Left spermatic
or ovarian

Iliolumbar

Internal iliac

External iliac

Caudal

Fig. 13-26. Major systemic venous channels of a rabbit, ventral view. Broken line indicates obliterated segment of left posterior cardinal vein. Entrance of one spermatic or ovarian vein into a renal vein is uncommon in rabbits, common in cats.

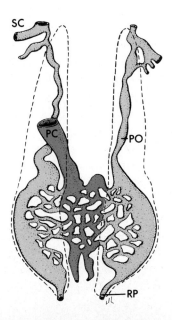

SC

PC

PO

RP

Fig. 13-27. Embryonic subcardinal venous plexus and origin of the postcava in the turtle *Chrysemys,* ventral view. The mesonephros is indicated by broken lines. **PC,** Postcava; **PO,** left postcardinal; **RP,** renal portal vein; **SC,** subclavian vein. (Modified from De Ryke.[4])

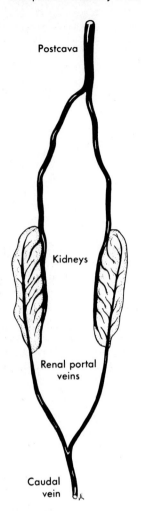

Fig. 13-28. Renal portal system and venous drainage of the kidneys in a snake. The postcava commences at the confluence of right and left efferent renal veins.

In amphibians the two embryonic lateral abdominals unite in the midventral line to form a median **ventral abdominal vein** (Fig. 13-21, *C* and *D*). In reptiles the two lateral abdominals do not unite (Fig. 13-22). However, they acquire a temporary embryonic tributary, the **allantoic vein,** which is lost along with the allantois at hatching. In birds none of the embryonic abdominal stream remains in adults (Fig. 13-23).

In mammals, the **umbilical veins** are all that is left of the ancient abdominal stream, and they are confined to the fetus. The part of the umbilical veins within the umbilical cord is the allantoic vein with a new name. The part in the ventral body wall beginning at the navel and continuing in the falciform ligament to the liver is the embryonic abdominal vein. No connection develops with veins from the hind limbs. The abdominal (umbilical) stream in mammals has no function other than to drain the placenta; and when the umbilical cord is severed at birth, blood no longer flows through the intraembryonic portion and this becomes converted into the **round ligament of the liver,** extending between navel and liver. The embryonic umbilical vein carries a heavy load of blood and it erodes a broad channel, the **ductus venosus,** directly through the liver and into the postcava (Fig. 13-30). After birth the channel becomes a ligament (**ligamentum venosum**).

RENAL PORTAL SYSTEM

The renal portal system in amphibians acquires a tributary, the **external iliac vein** (not homologous with a vessel of the same name in mammals), which carries some blood from the hind limbs to the renal portal vein (Fig. 13-21, *C* and *D*). This channel provides an alternate route from the hind limbs to the heart. The connection persists in reptiles (Fig. 13-22, turtle). (This route may be one factor that made it possible to dispense with the abdominal stream in mammals.)

Snakes have no hind limbs, so the renal portal system is seen in its primitive relationships (Fig. 13-28); but in crocodilians, some blood passing from the hind limbs to the renal portal is able to bypass the kidney capillaries, going straight through the kidneys into the postcava (Fig. 13-22, crocodilian). By the time birds evolved, this had become a common pathway (Fig. 13-23). In mammals above monotremes the renal portal system disappears as an adult structure; however, it appears transitorily in mammalian embryos.

From the foregoing it can be seen that the posterior appendages during phylogeny (fins first, limbs later) have been drained by a series of vessels (Fig. 13-29): first, the abdominal stream; then, the renal portal system; and, finally, the postcava directly. The venous realign-

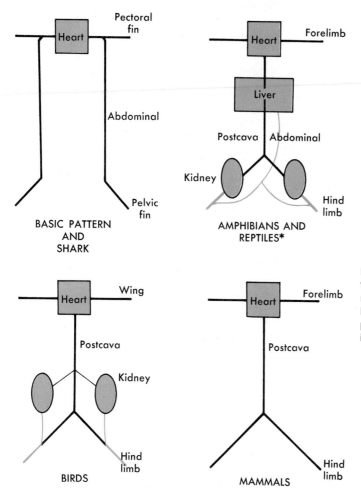

Fig. 13-29. Venous routes from paired fins and limbs, diagramatic. Vessels represented by thin lines carry relatively less blood. Blue in a vessel indicates a portal stream. (*The abdominal stream in reptiles is paired.)

ment necessitated by the displacement of the caudal end of the mammalian nephrogenic mesoderm to form the mammalian kidney may have struck the final evolutionary blow to the renal portal system.

HEPATIC PORTAL SYSTEM

The hepatic portal system is similar in all vertebrates. It drains chiefly the stomach, pancreas, intestine, and spleen and terminates in the capillaries of the liver. Its origin from the embryonic vitelline and subintestinal veins has been described earlier. The abdominal stream (allantoic in birds, umbilical in mammals) becomes a tributary of the hepatic portal system, commencing with amphibians. Veins from the swim bladders are usually tributaries of the hepatic portal system in bony fishes.

CORONARY VEINS

Many amphibians seem to lack a definitive coronary system. In frogs, one coronary vessel (vena bulbi anterior) enters the left precava, and another (vena bulbi posterior) empties into the ventral abdominal vein near the liver. In reptiles, birds, and mammals coronary veins empty into the right atrium directly or via a coronary sinus that is a remnant of the embryonic right precava when the latter disappears.

CIRCULATION IN THE MAMMALIAN FETUS AND CHANGES AT BIRTH

In the mammalian fetus, blood passes from the caudal end of the dorsal aorta into the umbilical arteries (Fig. 13-30). These extend out the umbilical cord to the placenta. From the placenta oxygenated blood returns to the fetus via an umbilical vein that traverses the falciform ligament to enter the liver. Some of this blood enters liver capillaries, but most of it continues nonstop via the ductus venosus, into the postcava, and finally into the right atrium. From the right atrium most of it passes via an **interatrial foramen** (**foramen ovale** of

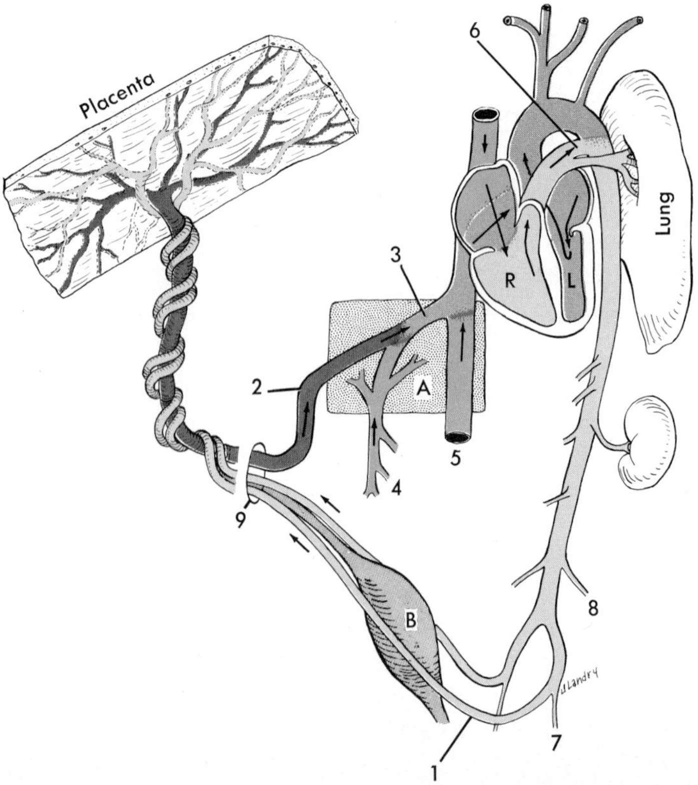

Fig. 13-30. Circulation in the mammalian fetus. **1,** Umbilical artery; **2,** umbilical vein; **3,** ductus venosus; **4,** hepatic portal vein; **5,** inferior vena cava; **6,** ductus arteriosus; **7,** internal iliac; **8,** external iliac growing into hind limb bud; **9,** umbilicus; **A,** liver; **B,** base of the allantois, which is developing into a urinary bladder; **L,** left ventricle; **R,** right ventricle. Much of the blood returning to the right atrium from the placenta passes through a foramen ovale (not illustrated) into the left atrium to be distributed via the left ventricle to the head and anterior limbs. *Darker red* indicates blood rich in oxygen; *darker blue,* low in oxygen; *light red,* mixed, considerable oxygen; *light blue,* mixed.

the heart) into the left atrium. The foramen is guarded by a one-way flaplike valve. The rest of the aerated blood, along with blood returning to the right atrium from the head, enters the right ventricle and is pumped into the pulmonary trunk. Because the ductus arteriosus is open and functional (Fig. 13-30), most of the blood in the pulmonary trunk is shunted into the dorsal aorta. This is an advantage, since blood in the ductus arteriosus is mostly unaerated and some of it will pass down the dorsal aorta to enter the umbilical arteries leading to the fetal respiratory membranes.

Blood coming from the lungs, which is unaerated and in small quantities, enters the left atrium and, along with the blood coming into the left atrium via the interatrial foramen, passes into the left ventricle. This blood is then pumped into the ascending aorta. From this account it can be seen that the blood in the fetus is either venous (that is, lacking oxygen) or mixed except in the umbilical vein. An essentially identical allantoic circulation occurs in unhatched chicks. The embryonic bird, however, depends on the vitelline (yolk sac) circulation for nourishment.

At birth, major circulatory changes adapt the organism for pulmonary respiration:

1. The ductus arteriosus closes as a result of nerve impulses passing to its muscular wall. These impulses are initiated reflexly when the lungs are filled with air with the first gasp after delivery. In birds this is usually the day before hatching, when the imprisoned chick pecks a hole in its extraembryonic membranes and starts breathing the air entrapped between these membranes and the shell. When the chick inside the shell starts to peep, it already has air in its lungs! Shortly thereafter, all blood entering the pulmonary trunk goes to the lungs, and the ductus arteriosus becomes converted into an **arterial ligament (ligamentum arteriosum).**

2. The flaplike interatrial valve is pressed against the interatrial foramen by the sudden increase in pressure in the left atrium that results from the greatly increased volume of blood entering from the lungs. This valve prevents the unoxygenated blood in the right atrium from entering the left atrium, which now contains only oxygenated blood from the lungs. Within a few days the foramen ovale is permanently sealed and only a scar, the **fossa ovalis,** remains.

3. At birth, the umbilical arteries and vein are severed at the umbilicus. Thereafter, no blood passes through the umbilical arteries beyond the distal tip of the urinary bladder. From bladder to navel the umbilical arteries become converted into **lateral umbilical ligaments** in the free border of the ventral mesentery of the bladder.

4. Blood no longer flows through the umbilical vein, and this vessel becomes converted into the round ligament of the liver. At the same

time, the ductus venosus is converted into the ligamentum venosum. (This occurs halfway through gestation in whales.) As a result of these changes, the fetal mammal (and bird, too) is changed from an allantoic-respiring organism to one capable of breathing air.

Failure of the interatrial foramen to close or of the ductus arteriosus to fully constrict results in cyanosis (blueness) of the skin of the newborn, since blood continues to be shunted away from the lungs and hence has the bluish color of venous blood.

LYMPHATIC SYSTEM

A lymphatic system is found in all vertebrates. It consists of thin-walled lymph vessels (lymphatics), fluids in transit, lymph nodes, and, in some species, lymph hearts (Fig. 13-31). In contrast to blood, lymph flows in only one direction—toward the heart.

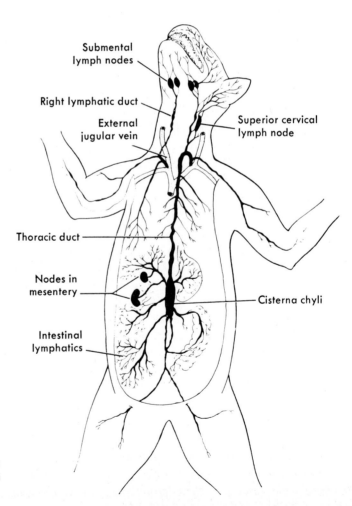

Submental lymph nodes

Right lymphatic duct

External jugular vein

Superior cervical lymph node

Thoracic duct

Nodes in mesentery

Cisterna chyli

Intestinal lymphatics

Fig. 13-31. A few of the superficial and deep lymphatics of a mammal. The large veins of the neck approaching the heart are stippled. Mammals lack lymph hearts.

Lymphatics penetrate nearly all the soft tissue of the body and commence as blind-end **lymph capillaries** that collect interstitial fluids. Once inside the lymph capillaries, the fluid is colorless or pale yellow and is called **lymph.** Lymph from different areas passes into larger vessels, which finally empty into a vein. The walls of the larger lymphatics are strengthened by smooth muscle.

Lymphatics in intestinal villi collect fat absorbed from the intestine after a meal. If the meal has been particularly fatty, the lymph in these vessels is milky. For this reason, lymphatics of intestinal villi are called **lacteals,** and the lymph therein is **chyle.** Some lymphatics in cyclostomes, cartilaginous fishes, and even humans contain red blood cells. The fluid in such vessels is called **hemolymph.**

Lymph nodes are masses of hemopoietic tissue interposed along the course of lymph channels in birds and mammals only. They may be no larger than a pinhead, or they may measure several centimeters in diameter. These are the "swollen glands" that can be palpated in the neck, axilla, and groin of humans when there is inflammation in the areas drained. They consist of a connective tissue reticulum enmeshing large numbers of lymphocytes. Their sinusoidal passageways are lined by phagocytic cells that ingest bacteria and other foreign particles. Lymph enters a node via several afferent lymphatics, filters through the sinusoidal spaces, and leaves via a single large efferent lymphatic.

Lymph channels in birds and mammals are provided with valves that assist in preventing backflow. Valves may also guard the exits from the major lymph ducts into veins.

The flow of lymph results from numerous factors. In many fishes and in amphibians and reptiles muscular pulsating **lymph hearts** are situated at strategic locations along the lymphatics. Frogs have four pairs, two near the thigh and two under the scapula. Urodeles have as many as 16 pairs and caecilians as many as 100 pairs. Amphibians have more active seepage from their vascular channels than other vertebrates, and so their lymph hearts move a large volume of fluid hourly. They also have large lymph reservoirs beneath the skin and tongue (subcutaneous and sublingual **lymph sinuses**). In the absence of lymph hearts, lymph flow is maintained by activity of skeletal muscles, movements of the viscera, and rhythmical changes in intrathoracic pressure as a result of respiratory movements.

Lymphatics that drain the body wall, limbs, and tail of lower vertebrates empty into nearby veins such as the caudal, iliac, postcardinals, or subclavian. Those draining viscera are usually paired in lower vertebrates; but in most mammals a single **thoracic duct** commences in a large abdominal lymph sinus, the **cisterna chyli,** and empties into the brachiocephalic, the left subclavian, or a jugular vein at the base of the neck (Fig. 13-31). The thoracic duct also receives lymphatics from the left side of the head and neck and from the left forelimb. One or more additional major lymphatics drain the right side of the body anteriorly.

Miscellaneous lymphoid masses in addition to lymph nodes are scattered throughout the body. These include the spleen (absent in cyclostomes), thymus, Peyer's patches in the small intestine of amniotes, the bursa of Fabricius of young birds, and mammalian tonsils.

CHAPTER SUMMARY

1. The circulatory system includes the blood vascular and lymphatic systems.

2. The blood vascular system consists of the heart, arteries, capillaries, and veins.

3. The lymphatic system consists of lymphatics (including lacteals), lymph capillaries, sinuses, nodes in higher forms, and lymph hearts (absent in birds and mammals). Lymph is transported from tissue spaces, and chyle from intestinal villi to major venous channels.

4. A sinus venosus occurs in fishes, amphibians, and reptiles. It is absent in adult birds and mammals, having been incorporated into the right atrial wall.

5. A single atrium receives blood from the sinus venosus in most fishes. In lung-breathing vertebrates the atrium is partitioned into two chambers by a septum, which is incomplete in lungfishes and some urodeles, complete in other tetrapods. The right atrium receives the sinus venosus or the largest systemic veins and, in amniotes, coronary veins. The left atrium receives pulmonary veins.

6. A single ventricle occurs in fishes and amphibians. Lungfishes have an incomplete ventricular septum partially dividing the ventricle in two. Amniotes have two ventricles separated by an incomplete septum in most reptiles, a complete septum in crocodilians, birds, and mammals.

7. A conus arteriosus is part of the heart in fishes. In dipnoans and amphibians it is short and is also called bulbus cordis. It is absent in adult amniotes.

8. A ventral aorta leads cephalad from the heart to the aortic arches. The unpaired segment emerging from the heart is sometimes called truncus arteriosus. In teleosts and perennibranchiate urodeles the ventral aorta exhibits a swelling, the bulbus arteriosus.

9. Oxygenated blood and unoxygenated blood are kept separate in the hearts of dipnoans and tetrapods by partial or complete interatrial and interventricular septa, trabeculae, and spiral valves.

10. In reptiles the truncus arteriosus is split longitudinally into an aortic trunk leading from the left ventricle to the third and right fourth arches, a second aortic trunk from the right ventricle leading to the left fourth arch, and a pulmonary trunk from the right ventricle leading to arch VI.

11. In birds and mammals two trunks emerge from the heart: an aortic trunk (ascending aorta) leads to the carotid and systemic arches, and a pulmonary trunk leads to the pulmonary arteries.

12. An aortic arch is a blood vessel connecting ventral and dorsal aortae and located in a visceral arch. Typically, six pairs of aortic arches develop in each vertebrate embryo. During ontogeny the aortic arches are reduced in number, the highest vertebrates retaining the fewest. In fishes the aortic arches become interrupted by gill capillaries. In fishes and amphibians with external gills, detours from the aortic arches carry blood to the external gills. In lungfishes, two ganoids, and tetrapods the sixth aortic arch sprouts pulmonary arteries.

13. Aortic arch I usually disappears, in part at least. Elasmobranchs retain parts of aortic arches II to VI. Modern fishes and many terrestrial urodeles retain arches III to VI. Aquatic urodeles and amniotes retain parts or all of arches III, IV, and VI.

14. The dorsal aorta between aortic arches III and IV (ductus caroticus) disappears in some amphibians, most reptiles, and all birds and mammals. The dorsal segment of aortic arch VI (ductus arteriosus) disappears in anurans, most reptiles, and birds and mammals. Birds also lose the left fourth aortic arch, and mammals lose much of the right fourth. As a result of loss of the ductus caroticus, blood entering arch III (carotid) must continue to the head. As a result of loss of the ductus arteriosus, blood entering arch VI must pass to the lungs.

15. Birds and mammals lose arches I, II, V, the left or most of the right side of IV, the dorsal segment of VI on both sides, and the ductus caroticus.

16. As a result of modifications in the heart and ventral aorta and deletions in the aortic arches, a system of vessels appropriate for respiration via gills is translated phylogenetically and ontogenetically into one suitable for lung respiration.

17. There is little mixing of oxygenated and unoxygenated blood in any adult vertebrate. Mixing occurs in fetal birds and mammals.

18. Dorsal aortae in the trunk have segmental somatic branches, unpaired visceral branches to digestive organs in the coelom, and paired visceral branches to the urinogenital system and adrenals.

19. Major venous channels in the basic pattern are anterior cardinals, postcardinals, common cardinals, abdominals, renal portals, hepatic portals, hepatic sinuses, coronaries, and pulmonaries. Dipnoans and tetrapods add postcavae. Subintestinals and vitellines are embryonic precursors of hepatic portals.

20. Anterior cardinals (internal jugulars) drain the head and empty into the common cardinals.

21. Postcardinals are absent in anurans, reptiles, and birds. They persist in mammals under new names (azygos, hemiazygos).

22. Abdominal veins drain pectoral and pelvic fins except in ray-finned fishes. They lose their connection with the forelimbs in tetrapods and with the hind limbs in birds and mammals. In mammals they remain as umbilical veins.

23. The renal portal system drains only the tail in fishes. It acquires a connection from the hind limbs in amphibians. In crocodilians and birds this connection partly bypasses the kidneys and goes directly to the postcava. There is no renal portal system in cyclostomes or adult mammals above monotremes.

24. The postcava becomes increasingly prominent in higher vertebrates. Commencing in dipnoans and amphibians as an alternate route to the heart from the kidneys, it finally drains hind limbs, most of the trunk, and tail.

25. Remnants of embryonic vascular channels in adult mammals include the round ligament of the liver (remnant of left umbilical vein), ligamentum venosum (remnant of ductus venosus), ligamentum arteriosum (remnant of left ductus arteriosus), lateral umbilical ligaments (remnants of paired umbilical arteries from urinary bladder to umbilicus), and fossa ovalis (occluded interatrial foramen ovale between the atria of the fetus).

26. Gill-breathing fishes have a single circulation as follows: heart, gills, body, heart. Birds and mammals have a double circulation: left side of heart, body (except lungs), right side of heart, lungs, left side of heart. Dipnoans, amphibians, and reptiles have a functionally double circulation with essentially no mixing of blood when environmental oxygen is adequate.

LITERATURE CITED AND SELECTED READINGS

1. Angell, C.S., and Hipona, F.A.: Angiographic studies of the anuran double circulation, American Zoologist **5**:668, 1965.
2. Berg, T., and Steen, J.B.: The mechanism of oxygen concentration in the swim bladder of the eel, Journal of Physiology **195**:631, 1968.
3. Brodal, A., and Fänge, R., editors: The biology of *Myxine,* Oslo, 1963, Norway Universitetsforlaget.
4. De Ryke, W.: The development of the renal portal system in *Chrysemys marginata Belli* (Gray), University of Iowa Studies in Natural History (New Series, no. 88), vol. 11, no. 3, 1925.
5. Fox, M.H., and Goss, C.M.: Experimentally produced malformations of the heart and great vessels in rat fetuses: transposition complexes and aortic arch anomalies, American Journal of Anatomy **102**:65, 1958.
6. Glenny, F.H.: A systematic study of the main arteries in the region of the heart. Aves: Piciformes, Proceedings of the Zoological Society of London, Series B, **113**:179, Part IV, 1943.
7. Heatwole, H.: Adaptations of marine snakes, American Scientist **66**(5):594, 1978.
8. Johansen, K., and Hanson, D.: Functional anatomy of the hearts of lungfishes and amphibians, American Zoologist **8**:191, 1968.
9. Kampmeier, O.F.: Evolution and comparative morphology of the lymphatic system, Springfield, Ill., 1969, Charles C Thomas, Publisher.
10. Lawson, R.: The anatomy of the heart of *Hypogeophis restratus* (Amphibia, Apoda) and its possible mode of action, Journal of Zoology **149**:320, 1966.
11. Millen, J.E., et al.: Circulatory adaptation to diving in the freshwater turtle, Science **145**:591, 1964.
12. Nandy, K., and Blair, C.B.: Double superior venae cavae with completely paired azygos veins, Anatomical Record **151**:1, 1965.
13. Ogren, H., and Mitchen, J.: Tracing oxygenated and unoxygenated blood through the organs of a frog by means of radioisotopes, Turtox News **45**(5):130, 1967.
14 Ottaviani, G., and Tazzi, A.: The lymphatic system. In Gans, C., and Parsons, T.S., editors: Biology of the reptilia, vol. 6, New York, 1977, Academic Press, Inc.
15. Ruszynák, I., Földi, M., and Szabó, G.: Lymphatics and lymph circulation: physiology and pathology, ed. 2, New York, 1967, Pergamon Press, Inc.
16. Satchell, G.H.: Circulation in fishes, Cambridge, England, 1971, Cambridge University Press.
17. Scholander, P.F.: The wonderful net. In Vertebrate structures and functions: readings from Scientific American with Introduction by N.K. Wessells, San Francisco, 1955-1974, W.H. Freeman and Co., Publishers.
18. Seib, G.A.: On the azygos vein in *Pithecus (Macacus) rhesus,* Anatomical Record **51**:285, 1932.

19. Simons, J.R.: The heart of the Tuatara, *Sphenodon punctatus,* Journal of Zoology **146:**451, 1965.
20. Struthers, P.H.: The aortic arches and their derivatives in the embryo porcupine *(Erethizon dorsatus),* Journal of Morphology and Physiology **50:**361, 1930.
21. White, F.N.: Circulation. In Gans, C., and Dawson, W.R., editors: Biology of the reptilia, vol. 5, New York, 1976, Academic Press, Inc.
22. Wood, J.E.: The venous system, Scientific American **218:**86, 1968.
23. Zweifach, B.W.: The microcirculation of the blood. In Vertebrate structures and functions: readings from Scientific American with Introduction by N.K. Wessells, San Francisco, 1955-1974, W.H. Freeman and Co., Publishers.

Symposium in American Zoologist

Functional morphology of the heart of vertebrates, **8:**177, 1968.

CHAPTER 14

Urinogenital system

In this chapter we will see that the urinary and reproductive organs of all vertebrates, male and female, develop in accordance with a basic architectural pattern, and how the pattern is modified phylogenetically and ontogenetically. We will look at how saltwater and desert animals conserve water and how freshwater vertebrates get rid of it. And we will briefly examine extrarenal routes for elimination of excess salts. At the end we will see how a simple chamber, the cloaca, is partitioned in male and most female mammals to produce one passageway for urine and reproductive products and a second for the digestive tract; and how, in female rodents and primates, a third passageway forms solely for the reproductive tract.

Although the function of kidneys is different from that of gonads, their ducts are so intimately related developmentally and functionally that neither the urinary nor the genital system can be discussed without reference to the other. For this reason, urinary and genital organs are discussed in a single chapter. Discussions of vertebrate eggs, external and internal fertilization, oviparity, viviparity, and extraembryonic membranes will be found in Chapter 4.

KIDNEYS AND THEIR DUCTS

Vertebrate life began in the water, and the early stages of the evolution of kidneys took place in that medium. Their function was osmoregulatory. They maintained the appropriate osmotic concentration of the blood by eliminating excess water (if any), by preventing the escape of water when necessary, and by regulating the excretion of certain salts. In the latter role they evidently had the assistance of the gills. These roles are still performed in environments that are much more diversified as a result of invasion of the land.

Basic plan and the archinephros

Vertebrate kidneys, or nephroi, are all built in accordance with a basic structural pattern consisting of (1) **glomeruli,** usually incorpo-

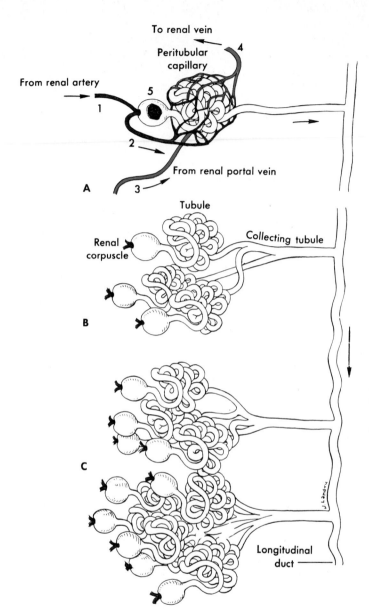

To renal vein

Peritubular
capillary

From renal artery

Tubule

Renal
corpuscle

Collecting tubule

From renal portal vein

A

B

C

Longitudinal
duct

Fig. 14-1. Basic structure of vertebrate kidney. **A,** Functional renal unit, or nephron. **1,** Afferent glomerular arteriole; **2,** efferent glomerular arteriole; **3,** vessel from renal portal system; **4,** tributary of renal vein; **5,** encapsulated glomerulus (red). **B,** Primary, secondary, and tertiary tubules in a single body segment. **C,** The increased number of tubules per segment disrupts the metamerism of the kidney.

rated in renal corpuscles; (2) **tubules,** surrounded by peritubular capillaries; and (3) a **pair of longitudinal ducts** (Fig. 14-1). Variations in the details from fish to man are primarily in the number and arrangement of glomeruli and in the relative length of the tubules.

Glomeruli are tufts of arterial capillaries where water, ions, and certain other substances are filtered out of the bloodstream as a result of blood pressure. They are the chief site for removal of water. In some species glomeruli are large enough to be seen with a naked eye

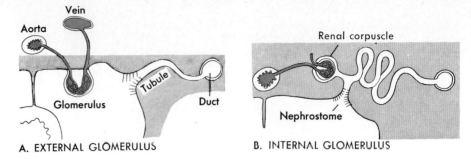

Fig. 14-2. A, External glomerulus suspended in coelom. **B,** Internal glomerulus surrounded by Bowman's capsule to form a renal corpuscle.

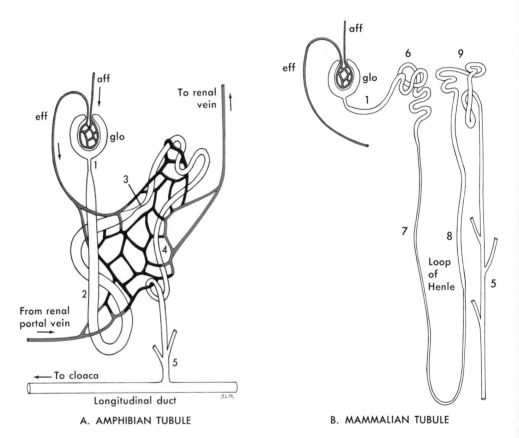

A. AMPHIBIAN TUBULE

B. MAMMALIAN TUBULE

Fig. 14-3. Kidney tubules. **A,** Mesonephric tubule of an aquatic urodele showing associated vessels. **B,** Mammalian tubule. The segments in **A** are, **1,** neck; **2,** proximal segment; **3,** intermediate segment; **4,** distal segment; **5,** collecting tubule; **6,** proximal convolution; **7,** descending arm of loop of Henle; **8,** ascending arm; **9,** distal convolution. The mammalian tubule is characterized by the loop of Henle. **aff,** Afferent glomerular arteriole; **eff,** efferent glomerular arteriole; **glo,** renal corpuscle consisting of a glomerulus (red) and Bowman's capsule. Purple in **A** indicates mixing of arterial and venous blood in peritubular capillaries. Tubules of placental mammals receive no portal supply.

or a hand lens. In others they are microscopic. The most primitive glomeruli are suspended in the coelom and hence are called **external glomeruli,** as opposed to **internal glomeruli,** which are encapsulated by part of a kidney tubule to form a renal corpuscle (Fig. 14-2). External glomeruli are confined to embryos and larvae. Supplying a glomerulus is an **afferent glomerular arteriole,** and emerging from it is an **efferent glomerular arteriole.** The latter leads to a **peritubular capillary bed** (Fig. 14-1, *A*). Venules drain the peritubular capillaries and lead to renal veins. Only cyclostomes lack peritubular capillaries, but, as compensation, the kidney duct has an unusually rich capillary bed.

Kidney tubules are microscopic passageways that collect glomerular filtrate and conduct it to the longitudinal ducts. They consist of several segments (Fig. 14-3), each of which may add to, or subtract from, the glomerular filtrate that trickles through them. Reclaimed substances are returned to the blood in the peritubular capillaries. The tubules thereby regulate the amount of water, salts, and other substances that finally reach the longitudinal ducts.* Kidney tubules other than those associated with an external glomerulus commence as **Bowman's capsule** that surrounds a glomerulus. The capsule and glomerulus together constitute a **renal corpuscle.** A corpuscle, tubule, and the associated peritubular capillaries constitute a **nephron,** the functional unit of the kidney.

The more anterior kidney tubules in a few fishes and in many embryos and larvae have a ciliated funnel, or **nephrostome,** that opens into the coelom (Fig. 14-2). Nephrostomes may be vestiges of a hypothetical early vertebrate kidney, or **archinephros,** in which all glomeruli may have been external and all tubules segmental and which extended the length of the coelom (Fig. 14-4). It would have drained coelomic fluid just as do nephridia of some annelids and the protonephridia of the amphioxus.

Kidney tubules differentiate from a ribbon of embryonic nephrogenic (intermediate) mesoderm that lies beside the mesodermal somites and extends the length of the embryonic trunk from immediately behind the head to the cloaca (Figs. 1-11 and 15-6). The earliest tubules appear at the anterior end of the ribbon, and additional tubules are added as the embryonic trunk elongates. The paired longitudinal ducts commence development as caudally directed extensions of the first tubules, and each duct grows caudad until it opens into the cloaca (Fig. 14-5). The ducts participate in the induction of additional tubules as the body elongates.

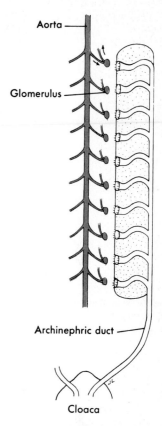

ARCHINEPHROS

Fig. 14-4. Hypothetical primitive kidney, also called holonephros, with external glomeruli and nephrostomes.

---

*Tubules in most fishes excrete largely Mg^{++}, Ca^{++}, $SO_4^=$, and phosphate. Most of the Na^+ and Cl^- is excreted extrarenally.

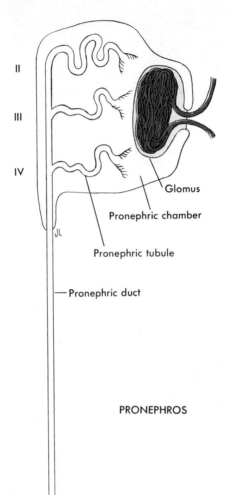

Fig. 14-5. Pronephric kidney of a 15-mm larval frog. **II, III,** and **IV,** Location of the second, third, and fourth somites. The glomus is three fused external glomeruli. The next tubule to form will be a mesonephric tubule at the level of somite VII.

Kidneys and the environment

Vertebrates that are submerged in fresh water inevitably acquire water by absorbing it through the gills, oropharyngeal membranes, or skin and by unavoidably swallowing it with their food. Salts, on the other hand, are scarce in fresh water, the chief source being food. Therefore one osmoregulatory necessity for freshwater organisms is to *excrete water and conserve salt*. Animals that are submerged in salt water face a different osmotic problem. Instead of accumulating too much water, they are in danger of accumulating too much salt. Survival in salt water depends on *conserving water and excreting salt*. Whether kidneys evolved in fresh water or salt water is not settled.[16] But the structure of the archinephros, whatever it may have been, was such that, with adaptive modifications, it was able to maintain later vertebrates in salt water, in fresh water, on land, and even in a desert. By varying the size and number of glomeruli in species in different habitats, water can be excreted abundantly or sparingly; and by varying the length of specific segments of kidney tubules, either salt or water, as necessary, can be recovered from the filtrate, or salt can be excreted abundantly. In general, glomeruli are larger in freshwater fishes and aquatic amphibians, smaller in marine fishes and tetrapods, especially tetrapods living in arid environments. (Elasmobranchs are an exception. Freshwater and marine sharks have very large renal corpuscles.)

Some marine teleosts have renal corpuscles that are poorly vascularized, cystic, or vestigial. In some others the distal segments of their tubules are abbreviated or lost. Loss of glomeruli results in increased water retention, and shortening of the distal segment of the tubules eliminates a major site for resorption of salts and, therefore, increased salt excretion, both of which have survival value in salt water. There are, however, freshwater teleosts with the same mutations. In these, water excretion is principally tubular, and they seem to compensate for any excessive salt loss in urine by active uptake of salt via their gills. There is reason to believe that these are former saltwater species that became adapted to a freshwater habitat. In fishes that migrate between salt and fresh water, and in terrestrial vertebrates, pituitary and other hormones "turn on" and "turn off" various segments of the kidney tubules as well as extrarenal sites of absorption and excretion of water and salts. In tetrapods, dehydration is the principal stimulus for release of hormones that reclaim water from glomerular filtrate.

Thus far nothing has been said about excretion of nitrogenous wastes because in no fish is the kidney of primary importance in excretion of nitrogenous compounds. These are eliminated through gills and sometimes skin in fishes. In tetrapods the kidneys dispose of nitrogenous wastes. Nitrogen is excreted chiefly as ammonia, which is highly soluble in water when water is plentiful, as in freshwater teleosts and aquatic amphibians (ammonotelic animals). It is also excreted as ammonia by most marine fishes other than elasmobranchs. The solvent is provided by drinking sea water and rapidly eliminating the salt. Nitrogen is excreted as urea by elasmobranchs and mammals (ureotelic animals) and as uric acid in a semisolid urine when water is scarce, as in terrestrial reptiles and birds (uricotelic animals).

Pronephros

The earliest embryonic tubules arise from the anterior end of the nephrogenic mesoderm. Because they are the first to appear and are anteriorly located they are called **pronephric tubules.** They are segmentally arranged, one opposite each of the more anterior somites (Fig. 14-5).

Each pronephric tubule arises as a solid bud of cells that later organizes a lumen and, except in birds and mammals, a nephrostome. Associated with each pronephric tubule may be a glomerulus. The number of pronephric tubules is never large—3 in larval frogs, 7 in human embryos opposite somites VII to XIII, and about 12 in chicks commencing at somite V. The tubules lengthen and become coiled. The region of the nephrogenic mesoderm having these metameric tubules is the pronephros, and its duct is the **pronephric duct.** It has also been called **archinephric duct** because it is the most primitive kidney duct of vertebrates.

Pronephric tubules are temporary. They function only until the ones farther back are able to work. This is at the end of the larval stage in amphibians and at an equivalent stage in fishes. At that time the glomeruli lose their connection with the dorsal aorta and commence to regress. The tubules regress more slowly, and traces of them may remain in adult fishes. However, the pronephric duct does not regress. It continues to drain the tubules farther back. Although a pronephros always develops in amniotes, it is doubtful that it ever functions as an excretory organ in these vertebrates.

Mesonephros

Under the partial stimulus of the pronephric duct acting as an inductor, additional tubules develop sequentially in the nephrogenic mesoderm behind the pronephric region. The new tubules establish connections with the existing pronephric duct. For at least several segments these tubules, too, may be segmentally disposed, exhibit the same convolutions as the ones anterior to them, and often have open nephrostomes. In fact, there is seldom justification for drawing at any specific point a boundary between the embryonic pronephros and the rest of the embryonic kidney. There is usually a gradual transition from tubules characteristic of the pronephric region to those found farther back.

In the transitional area secondary and tertiary tubules develop as buds from the initial (primary) tubule in each segment (Fig. 14-1, *B*). As these additional tubules enlarge and encroach on one another, the metamerism of the developing kidney is at first obscured and then lost altogether. Another feature of the transitional region is the development of internal glomeruli and of tubules that are longer and more convoluted and lack nephrostomes. However, many embryonic fishes and amphibians develop nephrostomes for a long distance back, and some fishes retain a few throughout life.

With the disappearance of pronephric tubules the pronephric duct

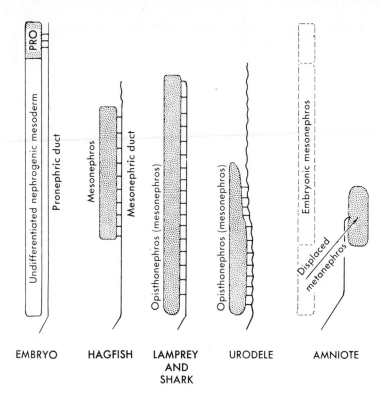

EMBRYO   HAGFISH   LAMPREY AND SHARK   URODELE   AMNIOTE

Fig. 14-6. Fate of the nephrogenic mesoderm in representative vertebrates. The pronephric duct of the embryo persists in adult anamniotes to drain the mesonephric (opisthonephric) kidney.

is thereafter called the **mesonephric duct** and the new kidney region it drains is the mesonephros (Fig. 14-6). It is the adult kidney of cyclostomes, jawed fishes, and amphibians, and the functional embryonic kidney of amniotes (Fig. 14-9). When the mesonephros serves as an adult kidney it is sometimes called an **opisthonephros.**

The mesonephros of the adult hagfish *Myxine* is almost like an archinephros. The glomerular part occupies a 10-cm segment of the nephrogenic mesoderm commencing some distance behind the regressed pronephros and terminating some distance anterior to the cloaca. This segment consists of 30 to 35 large renal corpuscles up to 1.5 mm in diameter, strictly segmental, and connected to the mesonephric duct by very short tubules. There are no peritubular capillaries and no detectable renal portal system. Between the glomerular region and the regressed pronephros are a variable number of corpuscles that lack glomeruli or have lost their connection with the longitudinal duct. Caudal to the functional region there are additional aglomerular corpuscles. The total number of corpuscles, typical and atypical, is about 70 and they are rigidly segmental.

The adult kidneys of fishes and amphibians commence varying distances behind the pronephric region, depending on how many anterior embryonic tubules disappear. In lampreys, sharks, and caecilians

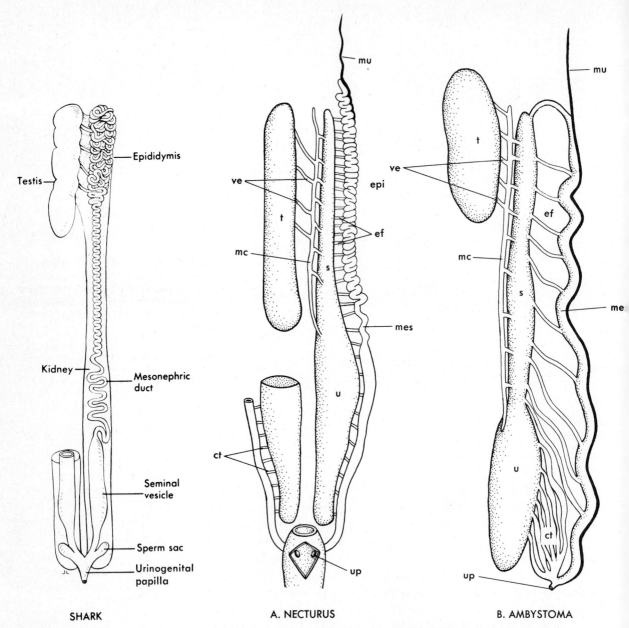

SHARK

A. NECTURUS

B. AMBYSTOMA

Fig. 14-7. Urinogenital system of a male shark. An accessory urinary duct, not shown, drains the more posterior kidney tubules.

Fig. 14-8. Left mesonephroi (opisthonephroi) and associated reproductive structures of two male urodeles, ventral view. The testes have been displaced mediad and the mesonephric ducts laterad. The sexual portion of the mesonephros serves solely for sperm transport. **ct,** Collecting tubules; **ef,** efferent epididymal ducts; **epi,** epididymis; **mc,** marginal canal; **mes,** mesonephric duct; **mu,** rudimentary muellerian duct; **s,** sexual kidney; **t,** testis; **u,** uriniferous kidney; **up,** urinogenital papilla opening into cloaca; **ve,** vasa efferentia. (**B** after Baker and Taylor.[2])

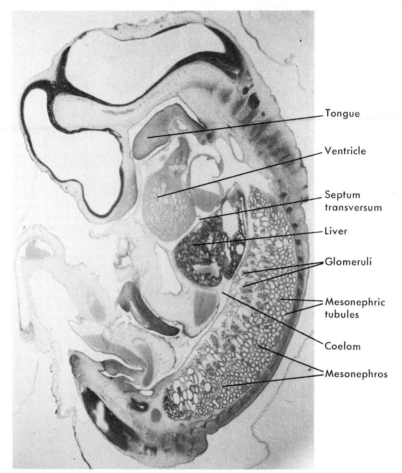

Tongue

Ventricle

Septum
transversum

Liver

Glomeruli

Mesonephric
tubules

Coelom

Mesonephros

Fig. 14-9. Sagittal section of a 20-mm pig embryo. The mesonephros extends about half the length of the body. (From Phillips, J.B.: Development of vertebrate anatomy, St. Louis, 1975, The C.V. Mosby Co.)

the kidneys begin far forward and extend the length of the coelom (Figs. 14-6, lamprey and shark). In other fishes and amphibians a longer series of transitional tubules usually disappears (Fig. 14-6, urodele). In male fishes and amphibians the anteriormost tubules of the mesonephros usually have no connection with glomeruli and, instead, conduct sperm from the testis to the mesonephric duct. This part of the male mesonephros is the **sexual,** or **epididymal, kidney,** and the coiled part of the mesonephric duct that drains it is the epididymis (Figs. 14-7 and 14-8). The corresponding part of the mesonephroi of females is often nonfunctional.

The mesonephric ducts in some species of male sharks and some male salamanders are preempted for sperm transport and carry very little urine. In sharks an accessory urinary duct carries more or less of the urine depending on the species (Fig. 14-22, *B*). Kidney drainage in two contrasting families of urodeles is illustrated in Fig. 14-8.

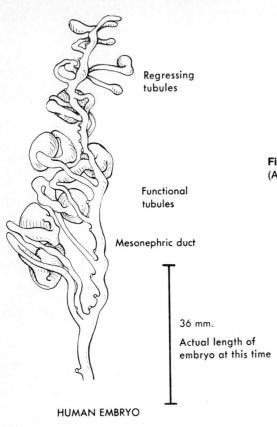

Regressing
tubules

Functional
tubules

Mesonephric duct

36 mm.

Actual length of
embryo at this time

HUMAN EMBRYO

Fig. 14-10. Right functional mesonephros of a 36-mm human embryo. (After Altschule.[1])

Fig. 14-11. Developmental changes in the urinogenital system of a female amniote. In the early stage (left) the mesonephric kidney and duct are present (red), and the metanephric bud has formed. An undifferentiated muellerian duct is present. In the later stage (right) the mesonephric kidney and duct have regressed, except for remnants (red), and the muellerian duct has differentiated to form a female reproductive tract.

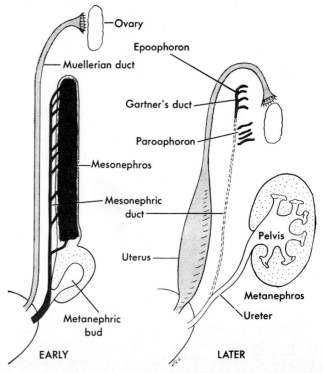

Ovary

Epoophoron

Muellerian duct

Gartner's duct

Paroophoron

Mesonephros

Mesonephric
duct

Pelvis

Uterus

Metanephros

Ureter

Metanephric
bud

EARLY

LATER

The mesonephros is the functional kidney of amniotes during part of embryonic or fetal life (Fig. 14-9). In embryonic chicks it reaches its peak on the eleventh day of incubation—halfway through embryonic life. In mammals it peaks earlier—at 9 weeks of gestation in humans. The first mesonephric tubules of human beings appear after 4 weeks of embryonic life. A wave of differentiation sweeps along the nephrogenic mesoderm, but before the last mesonephric tubules have formed the earliest ones have already regressed (Fig. 14-10). As a result the human mesonephros at its peak consists of about 30 functioning renal corpuscles, although as many as 80 have formed.[1] During the time time the mesonephros is functioning in amniotes a new kidney, the metanephros, is organizing. When the metanephros is able to function, the mesonephros disappears except for remnants. However, it functions as late as the first hibernation in some lizards and the first molt in some snakes; and it is still functioning in monotremes and marsupials at hatching or birth.

MESONEPHRIC REMNANTS IN ADULT AMNIOTES

Vestiges of the mesonephros remain in adult mammals as two groups of blind tubules, the **epoophoron** and **paroophoron** near the ovary (Fig. 14-11), and the **paradidymis** and **appendix of the epididymis,** both near the epididymis (Fig. 14-23). The mesonephric ducts remain as sperm ducts in all male amniotes. In females, mesonephric duct remnants include a short, blind **Gartner's duct (ductus deferens femininus)** in the mesentery of each mammalian oviduct (Fig. 14-11) and vestiges near the ovaries of some lower amniotes. **Vasa efferentia ovarii,** homologous with male vasa efferentia, are found in the ovaries of most female mammals.

Metanephros

The metanephros organizes from the caudal end of the nephrogenic mesoderm, which has been displaced cephalad and laterad during development (Figs. 14-6, amniote; and 14-11). This is the same mesoderm that gives rise to the caudal part of the mesonephros of fishes and amphibians. The number of tubules that form from this caudal section in amniotes is extremely large—up to an estimated 4.5 million. Differentiation of the metanephric kidney begins when a metanephric bud sprouts from the caudal end of the mesonephric duct (Fig. 14-11). Surrounding the bud is nephrogenic mesoderm. The bud grows cephalad carrying the metanephric blastema along with it. Eventually it gives rise to the metanephric duct, or **ureter,** and the **pelvis of the kidney** (Fig. 14-11, later). From the pelvis many finger-like outgrowths invade the surrounding kidney blastema and become collecting tubules (Fig. 14-3, *B,* 5). Meanwhile, S-shaped tubules are

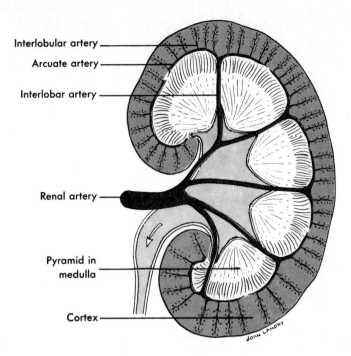

Interlobular artery

Arcuate artery

Interlobar artery

Renal artery

Pyramid in medulla

Cortex

JOAN LANDRY

Fig. 14-12. Mammalian kidney, frontal section. The renal vein and its tributaries have been removed. Gray area is pelvis and ureter. Glomeruli are confined to the cortex (light red). Loops of Henle and common collecting tubules make up the medulla. Some mammalian kidneys have only one pyramid.

organizing within the blastema. One end of each tubule grows toward and encapsulates a glomerulus to form a renal corpuscle; the other end grows toward, and finally empties into, a collecting tubule.

The tubules of mammalian kidneys have a long, thin, U-shaped **loop of Henle** (Fig. 14-3, *B*) interposed between proximal and distal convolutions. As the loops of Henle elongate, they grow away from the surface of the kidney where the glomeruli are located and toward the renal pelvis. The kidney therefore has a **cortex,** containing renal corpuscles, and a **medulla,** consisting of hundreds of thousands of loops of Henle and common collecting tubules (Figs. 14-12 and 14-13). The loops secrete or absorb water, ions, and other substances and are especially active in water resorption when dehydration threatens. Birds have much shorter segments homologous to the loops of Henle.

The loops and collecting tubules give the renal medulla a striated appearance in frontal section. They are aggregated into one or several **conical pyramids** (Fig. 14-12). The pyramids taper to a blunt tip (**renal papilla**) that projects into the pelvis. Each collecting tubule drains a smaller number of metanephric tubules (7 to 10 in humans) and empties into the pelvis at the tip of a renal papilla.

Most metanephric kidneys are lobulated, each lobe consisting of clusters of many tubules (Fig. 14-14). The kidneys of snakes and legless lizards are elongated, conforming to the slender body. In birds

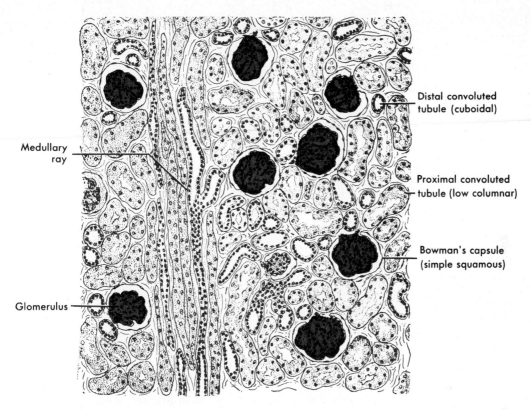

Medullary ray

Glomerulus

Distal convoluted tubule (cuboidal)

Proximal convoluted tubule (low columnar)

Bowman's capsule (simple squamous)

Fig. 14-13. Frontal section of a small area of the cortex of a mammalian kidney. Medullary rays consist of collecting tubules and loops of Henle. (From Bevelander, G., and Ramaley, J.A.: Essentials of histology, ed. 8, St. Louis, 1979, The C.V. Mosby Co.)

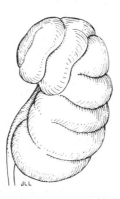

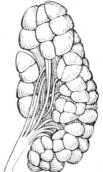

LIZARD

NEWBORN HUMAN

ADULT OTTER

Fig. 14-14. Several lobulated metanephric kidneys.

they lie snugly against the contours of the sacrum and ilium. In most mammals they are smooth and bean shaped, and the arteries, veins, nerves, and ureter enter and leave at a median notch, the **hilum.**

Because of their embryonic origin as buds off the mesonephric ducts the ureters at first terminate in the latter, and they do so throughout life in the primitive *Sphenodon* and in lizards (Fig. 14-24). In other reptiles and in birds and monotremes they ultimately open into the cloaca; and in placental mammals they open into the urinary bladder (Fig. 14-28).

Extrarenal salt excretion in vertebrates

Vertebrates that live in an environment laden with salt, or that inhabit arid environments and cannot afford much body water to carry off accumulated salts, have extrarenal structures for salt excretion. Marine fishes have chloride-secreting glands on the gills, and elasmobranchs have rectal glands that perform this function. (The rectal glands of bullsharks caught in fresh water are smaller than those caught in salt water and show regressive changes.) Marine reptiles and birds that scoop fish out of salt water have nasal glands that excrete salt. So do terrestrial lizards and snakes that live in an arid habitat. These same lizards and snakes have atrophied glomeruli, which also conserves water.

The salt-secreting nasal glands of lizards are located outside the olfactory capsule and empty into the nasal canals via small ducts. Whitish incrustations of sodium chloride and potassium can be seen in the nasal canal or at the nostrils.

The nasal gland of marine birds is a large paired gland located above the orbit. It is drained by a long duct that opens close to a nostril. A groove extends from the opening to the tip of the beak. Within 15 minutes after these birds have drunk water containing sodium chloride and potassium, minute drops of fluid containing these salts trickle down the groove and drip or are shaken off the beak.

Sweat glands eliminate some salt in mammals, but salt loss by this route is merely incidental to secretion of water for its evaporative cooling effect. It is not a regulated route for salt excretion and, in fact, salt lost by this route usually must be replaced.

The excretion of electrolytes is regulated chiefly by hormones, especially of the pituitary and adrenal glands. Physiological adaptations of vertebrates to environments of various salinities and water content are discussed in textbooks of comparative physiology.

URINARY BLADDERS

Most vertebrates have a urinary bladder. Exceptions include chiefly the cyclostomes and elasmobranchs among fishes; snakes, crocodilians, and some lizards; and birds other than ostriches. The bladders of most fishes are terminal enlargements or evaginations of the mesonephric ducts known as **tubal bladders** (Fig. 14-15). The bladders of amphibians through mammals arise as evaginations of the ventral wall of the embryonic cloaca (Fig. 14-16).

In amniote embryos the evagination that gives rise to the bladder is prolonged beyond the ventral body wall as an extraembryonic

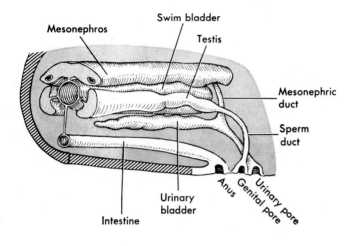

TELEOST

Fig. 14-15. Caudal end of urinogenital system of a male teleost (pike), left lateral view. The unpaired urinary bladder arises as a bud off the united bases of the two mesonephric ducts. Note absence of cloaca.

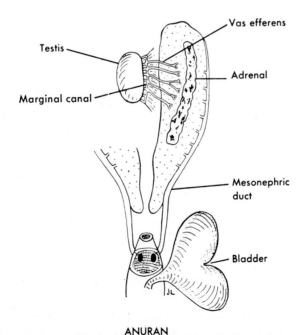

ANURAN

Fig. 14-16. Urinogenital system and adrenal of a male frog, ventral view.

membrane, the allantois (Fig. 4-9, *B*). Only the base of the allantois—the part proximal to the cloaca—contributes to the adult bladder (Fig. 13-30). After birth the distal part of the allantois within the body remains in mammals as a **urachus** connecting the tip of the bladder with the umbilicus. The urachus lies in the anterior border of the ventral mesentery of the bladder, along with the obliterated umbilical arteries.

Turtles and some lizards have large bladders, and some freshwater turtles have **accessory bladders** (Fig. 14-25). The latter are used by females to carry water for moistening the soil when building a nest for the eggs. If they have other functions, these have not been demonstrated. In amphibians and reptiles the urine backs up into the bladder from the cloaca. In mammals the kidney ducts empty directly into the bladder, and the bladder is drained by a urethra.

The adaptive value of the tetrapod urinary bladder seems to be that it stores water that may be needed later. Antidiuretic hormone release evoked by dehydration causes active water resorption from the bladder.

GONADS

The embryonic gonads arise as a pair of elevated **gonadal (genital) ridges.** These are thickenings in the coelomic epithelium just medial to the mesonephroi (Fig. 14-17). The ridges are longer than the resulting mature gonad, which suggests that at one time gonads may have extended the length of the pleuroperitoneal cavity, a condition still present in cyclostomes. Although the gonadal ridges are paired, a few adult vertebrates have a single testis or ovary because of fusion of the two ridges across the midline (lampreys, a few teleosts), or because one of the juvenile gonads fails to differentiate (hagfishes, some viviparous elasmobranchs, some female crocodilians, some lizards, most female birds). A few mammals, among which are the platypus and some bats, have only one ovary. As the gonads approach sexual maturity, they enlarge and usually acquire a dorsal mesentery, the **mesorchium** in males and **mesovarium** in females.

The ovary in some teleost fishes is a permanently hollow sac (Fig. 14-32). The condition results from entrapment of a small part of the coelomic cavity within the developing ovary (Fig. 14-18). Consequently the ovarian *cavity* is lined by germinal epithelium, which is the source of eggs. In some other teleosts the cavity within the ovary results from a secondary hollowing out of the interior of the ovary at each ovulation. In either case, the eggs, or, in viviparous teleosts, the young, are discharged into the ovarian cavity, which is continuous with the lumen of the oviduct (Fig. 14-32). The ovaries of most other fishes are compact. The amphibian ovary is also a hollow sac, but the germinal epithelium is on the surface and eggs are shed into the coelom. At the end of each reproductive season the ovaries of fishes and amphibians regress to a state resembling juvenile ovaries.

The ovaries of reptiles, birds, and monotremes develop numerous irregular, fluid-filled cavities (**lacunae**) by rearrangement of the internal tissues. Such ovaries are said to be "lacunate." The mammalian ovary is compact, with no large chambers or lacunae.

In many mammals a membranous fold of peritoneum, the **ovarian bursa**, entraps part of the coelom in a small chamber along with the

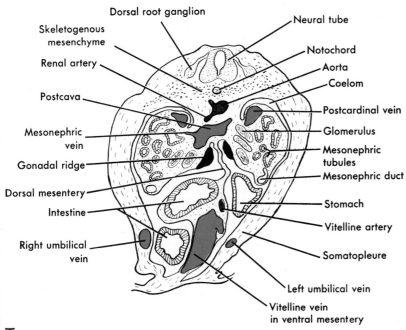

Fig. 14-17. Opossum embryo *(Didelphis)* 6½ days after cleavage, cross section. The gonadal primordia are shown in black. The umbilical veins carry oxygenated blood.

Actual length of above embryo (8 mm.)

Actual length of opossum at birth (10 mm.)

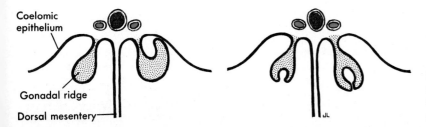

Fig. 14-18. Two methods of entrapment of coelom to form a permanently hollow ovary in teleosts. The gonadal ridges are shown in cross section.

ovary and ostium of the oviduct. The bursa may be broadly open to the main coelom, as in cats and rabbits; it may communicate by only a slitlike passage, as in most carnivores and rats; or it may be closed completely, as in hamsters. The bursa increases the probability that all ovulated eggs will enter the oviduct.

Mature testes are usually smaller than ovaries because sperm, although more numerous, are very much smaller than eggs, especially eggs with yolk. The testes of mammals, on the contrary, are larger than ovaries because mammalian eggs (other than monotremes') lack yolk, and ova ripen a few at a time.

The embryonic testis of anurans is subdivided into an anterior portion, **Bidder's organ,** which usually disappears before sexual maturity, and a more caudal portion, which becomes the adult testis. Bidder's organ persists in adult male toads (Fig. 14-19) and contains large undifferentiated cells resembling immature ova. If the testes are removed experimentally, Bidder's organs develop into functional ovaries, and the rudimentary female duct system enlarges under the influence of female hormones from the new ovaries.

Instances of sex reversal occur in nature in many submammalian vertebrate groups. Hens have been known to cease laying eggs, crow, and develop other roosterlike characteristics. This comes about when the left ovary atrophies and the right one, which is rudimentary, enlarges and produces male hormones. (They apparently cannot produce sperm.)

During early development the gonads are indistinguishable as to sex, and male and female ducts appear in every embryo. Under the influence of sex chromosomes and hormones the indifferent early gonads develop into either testes or ovaries, and the appropriate ducts, male or female, enlarge, whereas the other set remains rudimentary or disappears. True hermaphroditism* (production of eggs and sperm by the same individual) is common in cyclostomes and occasional in bony fishes, but it is rare among other lower vertebrates and absent among higher ones.

Translocation of ovaries and testes in mammals

The caudal pole of each embryonic ovary and testis is connected by a ligament to a shallow evagination of the coelom (**genital swelling,** Fig. 14-41), which becomes the **scrotal sac** in males, **labium majus** in females (Fig. 14-20). In females the cephalic part of the ligament is named the **ovarian ligament,** and the caudal part is **round ligament**

---

*Hermaphroditos was the son of Hermes and Aphrodite. While bathing in the mythical fountain of Salmacis, he became united in one body with the nymph living in the fountain.

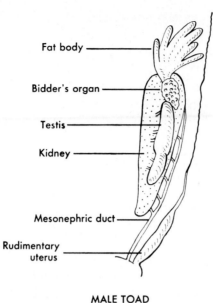

Fat body

Bidder's organ

Testis

Kidney

Mesonephric duct

Rudimentary
uterus

Fig. 14-19. Bidder's organ and the
rudimentary female reproductive tract in
a young male *Bufo,* ventral view. Only
the left organs are illustrated.

MALE TOAD

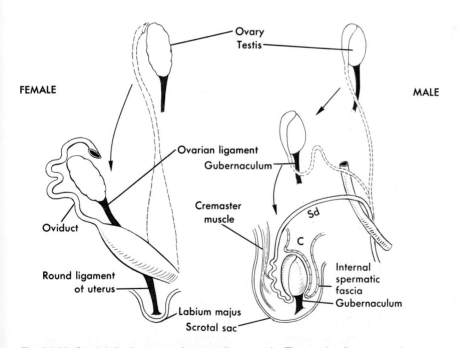

Ovary
Testis

FEMALE

MALE

Ovarian ligament
Gubernaculum

Cremaster
muscle

Sd

C

Oviduct

Internal
spermatic
fascia

Round ligament
of uterus

Gubernaculum

Labium majus

Scrotal sac

Fig. 14-20. Caudal displacement of mammalian gonads. The ovarian ligament and
round ligament of the uterus collectively are homologous with the male
gubernaculum. Arrows indicate the route of translocation of the right gonads,
ventral view. **C,** Scrotal recess of coelom; **Sd,** spermatic duct arching over the
ureter.

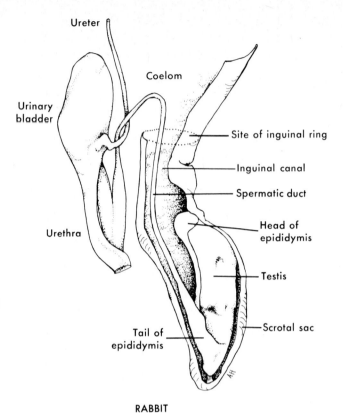

Ureter

Coelom

Urinary
bladder

—— Site of inguinal ring

—— Inguinal canal

—— Spermatic duct

Urethra

Head of
epididymis

—— Testis

—— Scrotal sac

Tail of
epididymis

RABBIT

Fig. 14-21. Rabbit testis in scrotal cavity. The inguinal canals are broadly open to the main coelom at the inguinal ring; therefore the testes are retractable.

of the uterus (Fig. 14-20, female). In males the ligament is the **gubernaculum.** Partly as a result of shortening of the ligaments, partly because elongation of the ligaments does not keep pace with elongation of the trunk, and partly for unknown reasons,* the ovaries and testes are displaced caudad toward the labia or scrotal sacs. The ovaries are not displaced as far caudad as the testes.

The testes remain retroperitoneal and descend permanently into scrotal sacs in many mammals including most marsupials, ungulates, carnivores, and higher primates. In others they are lowered into the sacs and retracted at will (rabbits, bats, a few rodents, some primitive primates, for example). The passage between the abdominal cavity and the scrotal cavity is the **inguinal canal** (Fig. 14-21). The opening of the canal into the abdominal cavity is surrounded by a fibrous **inguinal ring** (often the site of inguinal hernia). In species that retract their testes, the canal remains broadly open. In species in which the testes are permanently confined to the scrotum, the inguinal canal is only wide enough to accommodate the spermatic cord.

*Removal of the gubernaculum does not always prevent descent of the testes.

The **spermatic cord** contains the spermatic duct, arteries, veins, lymphatics, and nerves. These are all wrapped in a single sheath, the internal spermatic fascia, and all are dragged into the scrotum along with the testis. Scrotal sacs do not develop in monotremes, some insectivores, elephants, whales, and certain other mammals. In these the testes remain permanently in the abdomen.

In mammals whose testes are permanently in scrotal sacs the spermatic artery and vein lie side by side in tight coils within the inguinal canal. This rete of vessels is the **pampiniform plexus.** The arterial blood is at body temperature; the venous blood has been cooled in the scrotal sac. Heat is transferred in the plexus from arterial to venous blood so that blood reaching the testis is cool and blood returning to the internal circulation has been prewarmed. This adaptation protects the sperm of these species from temperatures that would kill them, while conserving body heat. Avian sperm can withstand high temperatures.

MALE GENITAL DUCTS

The mesonephric duct of male vertebrates transmits sperm except in those few species in which the generalized pattern has undergone mutations (Fig. 14-22, *A* to *D*). Connections between the mesonephroi and testes are established early in embryonic life (Fig. 14-23). Some of the anterior mesonephric tubules—a few to 24 or more, depending on the species—grow across the mesorchium to connect with the **rete testis,** a network of sperm passageways within the testis. These modified mesonephric tubules become the **vasa efferentia.** Consequently the mesonephric duct transmits sperm.

A modification of the pattern is seen in *Polypterus* and teleosts, in which the mesonephric ducts carry only urine and a new sperm duct has developed (Fig. 14-22, *E* and *F*). A duct that carries only sperm is a **vas deferens** (ductus deferens) whether it is a mesonephric duct or a substitute. Cyclostomes present a problem. Sperm (and eggs) are shed into the ciliated coelom, are propelled caudad by body undulations and ciliary action, and exit via genital pores. Whether this is a primitive route for shedding gametes in vertebrates is conjectural; living agnathans are a mosaic of primitive and specialized traits.

The spermatic ducts (male mesonephric ducts) empty into the cloaca in reptiles and birds (Figs. 14-24 to 14-27) and into a derivative of the cloaca in mammals (Fig. 14-28). The anatomical relationships of the spermatic ducts in mammals are affected by (1) complete separation of the embryonic cloaca into a urinogenital sinus and rectum (Fig. 14-40, *E*) and (2) caudal migration of the testes. As a result of subdivision of the cloaca, the spermatic ducts finally empty into the urinogenital sinus, which is the male urethra (Fig. 14-28). As a result

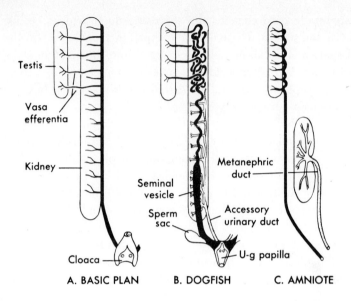

A. BASIC PLAN **B. DOGFISH** **C. AMNIOTE**

Fig. 14-22. The mesonephric duct (black) as a carrier of sperm and urine. **A,** Basic plan, carrying both sperm and urine. **B,** Carrying urine from the anterior end of the kidney only; chiefly a spermatic duct. **C,** Carrying sperm only. **D to F,** Increasing tendency toward a separate sperm duct, the mesonephric duct carrying urine. **U-g papilla,** Urinogenital papilla. For a variation in the termination of the teleost mesonephric duct see Fig. 14-15.

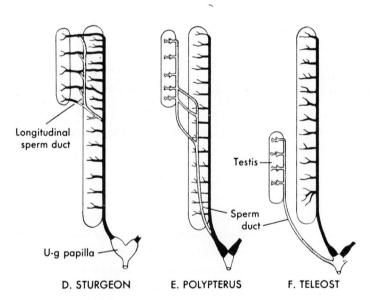

D. STURGEON **E. POLYPTERUS** **F. TELEOST**

of caudal migration of the testes, the spermatic ducts become "caught" or "hung up" on the ureters in such a way that they must loop over the ureters en route to the urethra (Figs. 14-20 and 14-28). Near the junction of spermatic ducts and urethra in mammals are one or more accessory sex glands that produce some of the constituents of semen (Fig. 14-29).

The urethra in male mammals is frequently called **prostatic urethra** where the prostate glands empty, **membranous urethra** from prostate to penis, and **spongy urethra** within the penis.

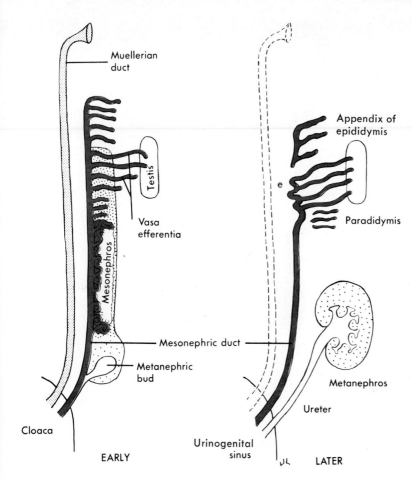

Fig. 14-23. Urinogenital system of developing male amniote. In the earlier stage (left) some of the mesonephric tubules have invaded the testis to become vasa efferentia. In the later stage (right) the mesonephros has regressed except for remnants (appendix of epididymis, paradidymis), and the muellerian duct has regressed (broken lines at right). The mesonephric duct remains to carry sperm. Mesonephric duct and tubules are red. **e,** Epididymal portion of mesonephric duct.

GENITAL PORES

Cyclostomes lack genital ducts, and sperm and eggs are shed into the coelom and exit via a pair of funnel-shaped **genital pores** in the caudal abdominal wall. These lead into a median papilla (genital in hagfishes, urinogenital in lampreys) that opens to the exterior just behind the anus.

Similar pores lead from the coelom directly to the exterior in some elasmobranchs and a number of bony fishes. They have also been described in turtles and crocodilians. In none of these, however, do the pores convey gametes, since genital ducts are present. Whether they are homologous with the genital pores of agnathans is not known, and it seems unlikely. For this reason it is preferable to call them **abdominal pores** in gnathostomes. What role abdominal pores may perform in vertebrates having genital ducts is obscure. In some marine teleosts the pores are present only in females and open only

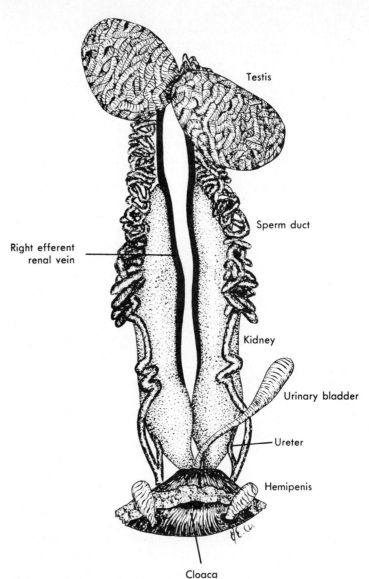

Fig. 14-24. Urinogenital organs of male lizard *Anolis carolinensis,* ventral view. The kidneys are metanephric. The sperm duct is the persistent mesonephric duct. The hemipenes are seen in an everted (erect) position.

Testis

Sperm duct

Right efferent renal vein

Kidney

Urinary bladder

Ureter

Hemipenis

Cloaca

during breeding seasons. They may play a role in reproduction, or they may be functionless vestiges that retain a hereditary responsiveness to reproductive hormones.

INTROMITTENT ORGANS

When fertilization is internal, the male, with few exceptions, develops intromittent, or copulatory, organs for introducing sperm into the female reproductive tract. These are present in reptiles and mammals. They are also present in fishes with internal fertilization, the

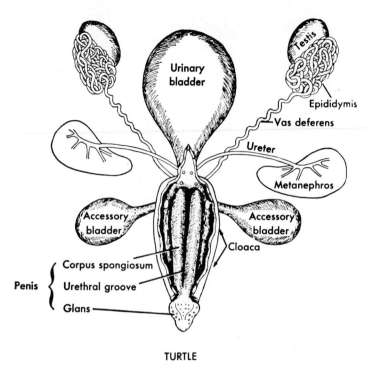

Penis {
Corpus spongiosum
Urethral groove
Glans

TURTLE

Fig. 14-25. Urinogenital system and cloaca of a male turtle. The dorsal wall of the cloaca has been removed, and the penis is in an extended position. The rectum, which enters the cloaca dorsal to the urinary bladder, has been removed.

anuran family Ascaphidae, and a few birds. In most birds the cloaca of both sexes is eversible.

The intromittent organs of elasmobranchs are grooved, fingerlike appendages of the pelvic fins known as **claspers** (Fig. 9-8). In basking sharks they transfer a sperm-filled spermatophore up to 3 cm in diameter. Embedded in the fin at the base of the clasper in some sharks is a muscular **siphon sac** that contributes copious quantities of an energy-rich mucopolysaccharide to the seminal fluid. In many teleosts the anal fin is modified for sperm transfer and is called a **gonopodium.** In *Ascaphus* the intromittent organ is a permanent tubular tail-like extension of the cloaca.

Intromittent organs of amniotes are of two types—hemipenes and penis. Male snakes and lizards have a pair of **hemipenes,** which are pocketlike diverticula of the caudal wall of the cloaca that extend under the skin at the base of the tail (Fig. 14-24). Each is held in place by a retractor muscle. During copulation the muscle relaxes and the pocket turns inside out and protrudes through the vent in an erect position. Sperm passes along spiral grooves on its surface. Hemipenes are present, but much smaller, in females.

Male turtles, crocodilians, a few birds (swans, ducks, ostriches, a few others), and male mammals exhibit an unpaired erectile **penis.** In its simplest form (Figs. 14-25 and 14-26), the penis is a thickening of

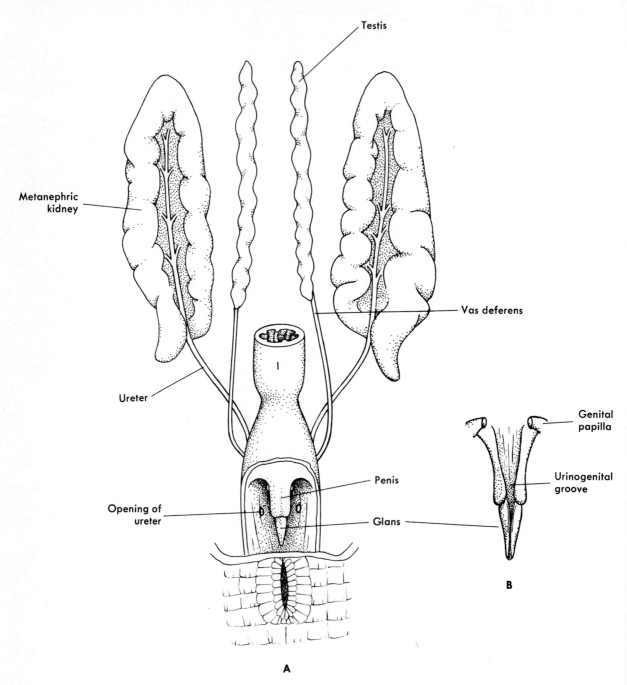

Fig. 14-26. Urinogenital system of a male alligator. **A,** Ventral view. **I,** Large intestine. The ureters open in the dorsal wall of the cloaca. **B,** Dorsal view of penis. The vasa deferentia open onto the floor of the cloaca via genital papillae.

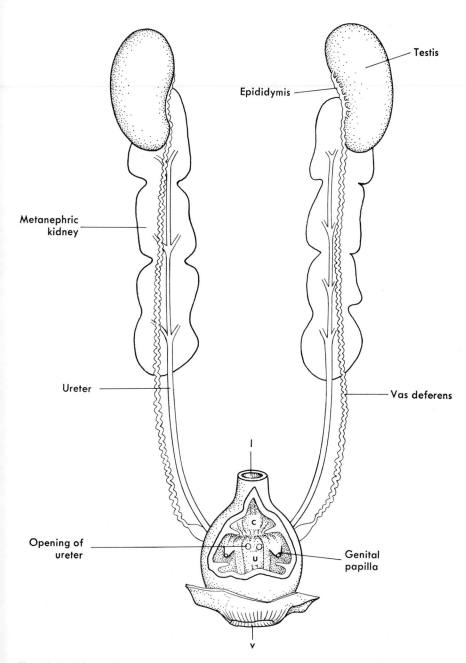

Fig. 14-27. Urinogenital system of a rooster. **c,** Coprodeum; **l,** large intestine; **u,** urodeum; **v,** vent.

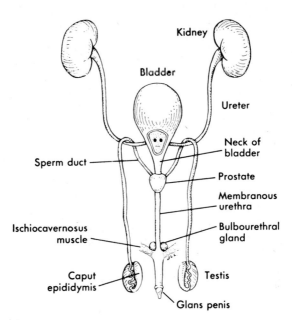

Fig. 14-28. Urinogenital system of a male cat, ventral view.

CAT

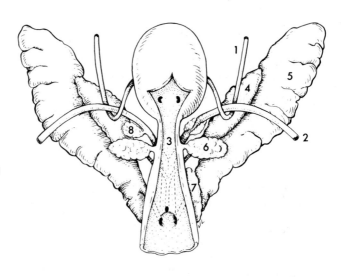

Fig. 14-29. Accessory sex organs of a male hamster, ventral view. The bladder and urethra have been opened to show entrances of ducts. **1,** Ureter; **2,** spermatic duct; **3,** urethra; **4,** coagulating gland; **5,** seminal vesicle; **6,** cranial prostate; **7,** caudal prostate; **8,** ampullary gland. A bulbourethral gland enters the urethra farther caudad.

the floor of the cloaca that consists chiefly of a mass of spongy erectile tissue, the **corpus spongiosum,** containing blood sinuses, bearing a groove that channels sperm and urine, and ending in a **glans penis.** When the sinuses are distended with blood, the penis is swollen and firm. The glans is richly supplied with sensory endings that reflexly stimulate ejaculation, and in mammals it is sheathed by a fold of skin, the **prepuce,** except during erection. The penis of monotremes is reptilian in structure and in its location in the cloacal floor. In placental mammals the grooved embryonic corpus spongiosum becomes a tube with the groove, now the **spongy urethra,** folded inside. It extends beyond the body at the pelvic symphysis accompanied by two additional erectile masses, the **corpora cavernosa.**

The mammalian penis develops from a **genital tubercle** found both in male and female embryos (Fig. 14-41). It lies at the anterior end of two **genital swellings** that later become scrotal sacs or labia majora. In genetic males the tubercle becomes grooved and then tubular and elongates to form a penis. In females no tube develops and the tubercle becomes the **clitoris.** The clitoris usually remains embedded in the floor of the urinogenital sinus or vagina and is erectile. In female rodents, however, it becomes a penislike urinary papilla (Fig. 14-42). In female hyenas the urinogenital sinus becomes enclosed within the clitoris and the latter looks exactly like a penis. It carries urine, copulation takes place through it, and young are delivered through it.

FEMALE GENITAL DUCTS

The typical female reproductive tract consists of a pair of muscular tubes that begin at coelomic funnels, or **ostia,** and empty into the cloaca (Fig. 14-30). The tubes differentiate from a pair of **muellerian ducts** present in the embryos of both sexes. In mature females the ducts transport eggs, and certain segments are modified for specific functions including, in one species or another, coating the eggs with protective or nutrient substances, holding eggs or living young and maintaining them in a viable state until the eggs are shed or young are delivered, expelling eggs or young, receiving the male intromittent organ, and storing and maintaining sperm in those numerous species in which the eggs are not mature at the time of mating.

Ostia appear to be phylogenetic derivatives of one or a few pronephric nephrostomes. That is how they arise in living elasmobranchs and amphibians; and in these same vertebrates muellerian ducts arise by longitudinal splitting of the pronephric ducts. This illustrates again the intimate phylogenetic and embryological relationship between genital and urinary organs. In most other vertebrates except ganoids and teleosts each muellerian duct arises as a longitudinal groove in

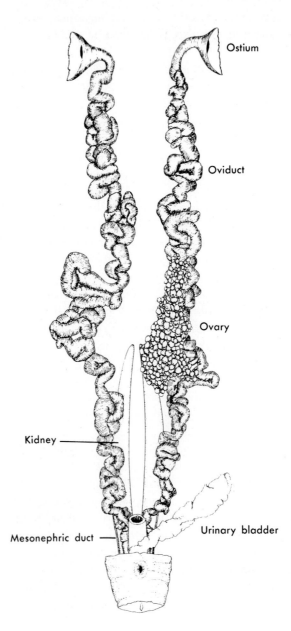

Fig. 14-30. Urinogenital system of female necturus, ventral view.

the coelomic mesothelium paralleling the pronephric duct.* The groove subsequently becomes a tube, except at the ostium, and acquires an opening into the cloaca.

When fertilization is internal, sperm usually penetrate the eggs in the upper reaches of the oviduct, and eggs are propelled along the tract by cilia or peristaltic action of smooth muscles. Teleost eggs are often fertilized while still in an ovarian follicle. Female urodeles, however, have sperm storage pockets, **spermathecae,** in the dorsal wall of the cloaca, that receive and store spermatophore sperm and expel them onto mature eggs as they pass by later. Some lizards and snakes have spermathecae that are crypts of the oviducal lining located, of necessity, just above the shell gland. These reptiles lay a succession of eggs during the season, and spermathecae ensure the availability of viable sperm at the time of each ovulation. Sperm are sometimes stored in spermathecae for many months.

Fishes and amphibians

In female elasmobranchs the muellerian ducts give rise to oviducts with shell (nidimental) glands and to paired uteri that open to the cloaca (Fig. 14-31). The cephalic half of the shell gland secretes albumen, and the caudal half secretes the shell. The two embryonic ostia unite to form a single adult ostium in the falciform ligament, a condition not typical of vertebrates.

The oviducts of ray-finned fishes are peculiar. Usually, they are either short funnels at the end of the coelom or they are directly continuous with the ovarian cavity. In either case they lead to a genital pore located between the urinary aperture and the vent (Fig. 14-32). The genital pore is sometimes at the end of a genital papilla, and in teleosts the papilla is sometimes elongated to form a tubelike **ovipositor.** Their development is such as to make it doubtful that they are muellerian duct derivatives. Cyclostomes have no oviducts; eggs exit the coelom via a pair of genital pores that open into a urinogenital papilla.

The female tracts of lungfishes, urodeles, and caecilians are long and somewhat convoluted (Fig. 14-30). In anurans they are much more tortuous as an accommodation to the short wide trunk. The caudal end of amphibian ducts may become voluminous **ovisacs** where eggs accumulate before being shed. When filled in anurans, ovisacs occupy the entire coelom and distend the abdomen. In ovoviviparous urodeles they serve as uteri. The two tracts open independently into the cloaca in lungfishes and most amphibians, but in toads

---

*For this reason embryonic muellerian ducts are sometimes called paramesonephric ducts.

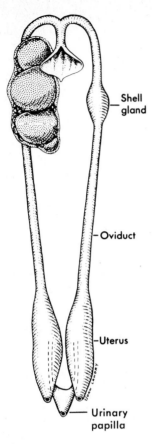

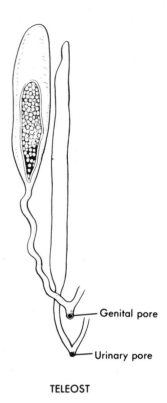

Fig. 14-31. Reproductive system of female *Squalus,* ventral view. The left ovary has been removed.

TELEOST

Fig. 14-32. Female reproductive system of a teleost. Ova are shed into the ovarian cavity. In some teleosts the ovary reaches almost to the genital pore.

they unite just anterior to the vent and exit through a common genital pore. The oviducal lining in amphibians is richly supplied with glands that secrete several jelly envelopes around each egg as it moves down the tube. Between reproductive seasons the female tract regresses to a juvenile state as a result of lack of ovarian hormone stimulation.

Reptiles, birds, and monotremes

The female tracts of reptiles, birds, and monotremes conform to the basic vertebrate pattern (Figs. 14-33 to 14-36). However, only one muellerian duct differentiates in crocodilians, some lizards, and most female birds (Fig. 14-35). In oviparous amniotes other than snakes and lizards, albumen glands line a segment of the oviduct, and all have a shell gland just anterior to the cloaca (Figs. 14-35 and 14-

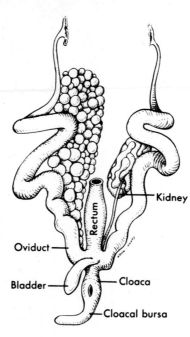

Fig. 14-33. Urinogenital system of female aquatic turtle, *Trionyx euphraticus,* ventral view. The left ovary has been removed. (Courtesy Mohamad S. Salih, University of Baghdad.)

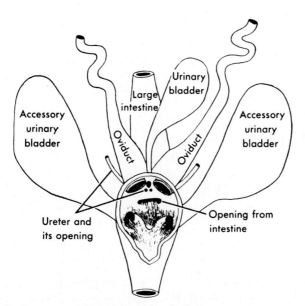

Fig. 14-34. Cloaca of a female terrestrial turtle, ventral view. Clitoris has been removed.

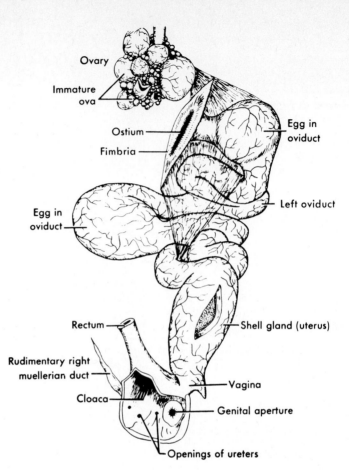

Fig. 14-35. Reproductive tract of a hen. The presence of two eggs in the oviduct is unusual.

Ovary

Immature ova

Ostium

Fimbria

Egg in oviduct

Egg in oviduct

Left oviduct

Rectum

Shell gland (uterus)

Rudimentary right muellerian duct

Cloaca

Vagina

Genital aperture

Openings of ureters

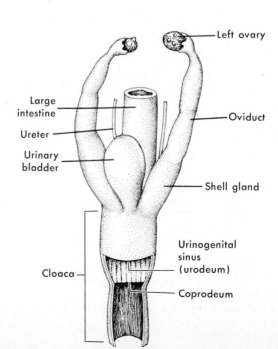

Fig. 14-36. Genital tract and cloaca of female monotreme, ventral view. The right ovary is usually smaller than the left. The cephalic half of the cloaca is divided by a partition into urinogenital sinus (receiving oviducts and ureters) and coprodeum.

Left ovary

Large intestine

Ureter

Urinary bladder

Oviduct

Shell gland

Urinogenital sinus (urodeum)

Coprodeum

Cloaca

36). The shell remains leathery or becomes brittle in air, depending on the constituents of the secretion.

In birds the albumen-secreting region is the **magnum** and the thick-walled shell gland is called, inappropriately, the **uterus** (Fig. 14-35). The short muscular terminal segment, the **vagina,** secretes mucus that seals the pores of the shell to water vapor but not to oxygen, thus retarding moisture loss from the egg after it has been laid. The vagina then expels the egg.

Placental mammals

The muellerian ducts of placental mammals give rise to **oviducts, uteri,** and **vaginae.** Except in marsupials muellerian ducts unite at their caudal ends. As a result, the adult female tract above marsupials is paired anteriorly and unpaired posteriorly, terminating as an unpaired vagina. The oviducts, or fallopian tubes, are relatively short, small in diameter, convoluted, and lined with cilia. They commence at an oviducal funnel containing the **ostium** and bordered by a delicate membranous fringe, the **fimbria of the oviduct.**

UTERI

In most marsupials there is no fusion of the embryonic muellerian ducts. Therefore the entire female tract is paired. They have a **duplex uterus** and paired vaginae (Fig. 14-37).

In other placental mammals there are varying degrees of fusion of the caudal ends of the muellerian ducts, which results most often in two **uterine horns,** a **uterine body,** and a single **vagina** (Fig. 14-38, rabbit). When there are two complete lumens with the body of the uterus, it is said to be **bipartite** (Fig. 14-39, hamster). When there is a single lumen within the body and there are two horns, the uterus is said to be **bicornuate** (Fig. 14-39, ungulates). There are species with uteri intermediate between the bipartite and bicornuate condition. When there are uterine horns, the blastocysts implant in the horns. In some mammals one horn is much larger, and the blastocysts implant in that horn—the right in impalas—even though both ovaries produce eggs.

In apes, monkeys, humans, some bats, and armadillos there are no uterine horns, and the oviducts open directly into the body of the **simplex** uterus (Fig. 14-38, monkey). Except in ectopic pregnancies—pregnancies in which blastocysts implant in abnormal locations, such as the oviduct (tubal pregnancies) or coelom (abdominal pregnancies)—the usually single fetus or the twins, triplets, quadruplets, or quintuplets all implant in the body of the simplex uterus.

The body of all uteri narrows to form a **cervix** (neck), the lower end of which projects into the vagina as the **lips** of the cervix. The lips

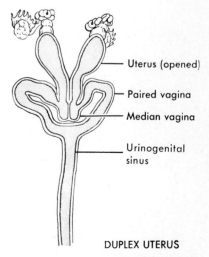

Uterus (opened)

Paired vagina

Median vagina

Urinogenital sinus

DUPLEX UTERUS

Fig. 14-37. Internal passageways of the reproductive tract of a female opossum. Compare with the external view in Fig. 14-38, marsupial.

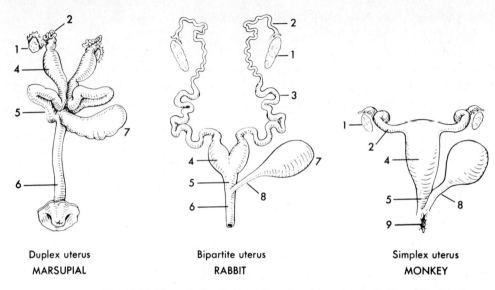

Duplex uterus
MARSUPIAL

Bipartite uterus
RABBIT

Simplex uterus
MONKEY

Fig. 14-38. Reproductive tracts of three female mammals. **1,** Ovary; **2,** oviduct; **3,** horn of uterus; **4,** body of uterus; **5,** vagina; **6,** urinogenital sinus; **7,** urinary bladder; **8,** urethra; **9,** vestibule of primate. In the primate (rhesus monkey) the urethra opens into the shallow vestibule just anterior to the opening of the vagina. The marsupial (redrawn from McCrady[9]) is an opossum, shown also in Fig. 14-37.

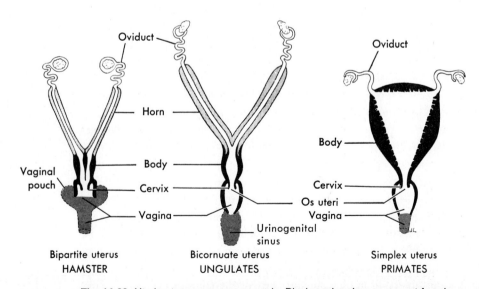

Bipartite uterus
HAMSTER

Bicornuate uterus
UNGULATES

Simplex uterus
PRIMATES

Fig. 14-39. Uterine types among mammals. Blackened regions represent fused caudal ends of the muellerian ducts; red represents the cloaca or a derivative thereof. Note the two lumens in the body of the bipartite uterus.

surround the opening (**os uteri**) leading from uterus into vagina. The cervix must dilate under the influence of hormones for the young to be delivered.

Sperm deposited in the vagina pass through the os uteri en route to the upper part of the oviducts where one sperm penetrates an egg. The uterine lining (**endometrium**) becomes highly vascular under the stimulus of hormones before implantation of a blastocyst. The thick, muscular layer of the uterine wall (**myometrium**) assists in ejection of the young at birth, provided it, too, has been hormonally prepared for this action.

VAGINAE

Above marsupials the vagina is the fused terminal portion of the muellerian ducts, and it opens into the urinogenital sinus (Fig. 14-39, ungulates). In many rodents and primates, however, the vagina extends almost to the exterior and the vaginal lining is cornified for reception of the penis (Fig. 14-38, monkey).

The vagina of marsupials is unusual (Fig. 14-37). Just beyond the uteri the two muellerian ducts meet to form a **median vagina,** which may or may not be paired internally. Beyond the median vagina the two ducts continue as **paired (lateral) vaginae.** The pouchlike median vagina projects caudad and lies against the urinogenital sinus, separated by a septum. At birth the fetus is usually forced through the septum directly into the urinogenital sinus. The new passageway thus established may remain throughout life, which results in a **pseudo-vagina,** although it closes in opossums. As an adaptation to dual vaginae, the penis of male marsupials is forked at the tip.

Muellerian duct remnants in adult males

Although muellerian ducts do not fully mature in males, they often develop into prominent structures. In male elasmobranchs a pair of **rudimentary oviducts** encircle the anterior end of the liver and end in a rudimentary ostium in the falciform ligament. The **sperm sac** is a caudal product of the muellerian duct. A complete, although rudimentary, female tract is common in male amphibians (Figs. 14-8 and 14-19) and reptiles. In anurans, after removal of testicular hormones by orchidectomy the rudimentary muellerian ducts develop into functional oviducts and uteri. Remnants in male mammals include an **appendix testis** and a **prostatic sinus,** or **vagina masculina,** an unpaired sac near the prostate gland homologous with the female vagina.

Entrance of ova into oviduct

After seeing the very large size of a shark's egg, laboratory students often inquire how such a large egg can get into the ostium and down the relatively small oviduct. We know the answer with reference to the equally large egg of the chick or monotreme. Under the influence of hormones at the time of ovulation, the fringe (**fimbria**) of the oviducal funnel waves gently in an undulating movement. When it comes in contact with an egg, whether still in the ovary or separated from it, the fimbria clasps the egg, delicately at first and then more firmly, until the egg is engulfed by the funnel. At this time, the egg is a shapeless mass of flowing yolk (like the yolk in a fresh chicken egg) contained in a nonrigid membrane. Muscular contraction of the funnel squirts the shapeless mass into the oviduct. Thereupon, peristalsis of the wall of the oviduct moves the egg caudad. Cilia play a relatively unimportant role. In the case of the tiny eggs of mammals, however, the cilia are more important, although the fimbria also plays a role. In mammals the ovary is partially surrounded by the fimbria at all times, and this increases the probability that the egg will enter the oviduct. In mammals with an ovarian bursa the egg can go nowhere else.

THE CLOACA

The cloaca is the terminal segment of the hindgut that receives the large intestine and the urinary and genital ducts. It has become shallow or nonexistent in adult lampreys, chimaeras, and ray-finned fishes; and in placental mammals the embryonic cloaca is partitioned into several separate passageways and no longer exists as an adult structure. With these exceptions, a cloaca is present in all vertebrates. It acquires an opening to the exterior when the cloacal membrane, which separates hindgut from proctodeum, ruptures (Fig. 1-1). The contribution of proctodeum to adult cloaca is minor, except in amphibians.

The cloaca of fishes and amphibians receives the large intestine and the mesonephric ducts and, in females, the oviducts. In amphibians a urinary bladder opens from the ventral wall. The cloaca of reptiles, birds, and monotremes receives the same structures—large intestine, mesonephric ducts (but in males only, carrying sperm), oviducts in females, and urinary bladder unless absent. In addition, the ureters of reptiles, birds, and monotremes open into the cloaca except in those few male reptiles in which the ureters retain their embryonic connection with the mesonephric duct (Fig. 14-24). The penis or clitoris, when present, is embedded in the cloacal floor, and a lymphoid pouch, the bursa of Fabricius, opens into the cloaca of young birds.

In reptiles, birds, and monotremes a horizontal partition, the **urorectal fold,** separates the cephalic portion of the cloaca into two chambers, a **coprodeum** that receives the large intestine, and a **urodeum** that receives the oviducts and ureters (Figs. 14-27 and 14-36). The terminal portion of the cloaca in birds is called the **proctodeum,** but it is not entirely homologous with the ectodermal structure of the same name in vertebrate embryos.

Fate of the cloaca in placental mammals

We have seen how, in monotremes, a urorectal fold divides the cephalic end of the cloaca into a urodeum and coprodeum (Fig. 14-36). In placental mammals the urorectal fold grows caudad until it reaches the cloacal membrane separating the cloaca from the exterior. By this process the cloaca becomes completely divided into a **rectum** dorsally and a **urinogenital sinus** ventrally (Fig. 14-40, C and E). Rupture of the cloacal membrane at two points provides an **anus** and a **urinogenital aperture** (Fig. 14-41). The early embryonic urinogenital sinus (Fig. 14-40, B) receives the mesonephric ducts, muellerian ducts (which are initially present in both sexes), and the future urinary bladder (allantois), like the urodeum of monotremes.

As development progresses in males, the muellerian ducts disappear and the urinogenital sinus elongates (compare Fig. 14-40, B and E). The urinogenital sinus becomes continuous with the spongy urethra that has developed independently in the penis (compare Fig. 14-40, E and F). The urinogenital sinus now consists of the prostatic and membranous urethra (Fig. 14-28). The ureters become reoriented to open into the bladder, whereas the mesonephric ducts (now spermatic ducts) continue to empty into the urinogenital sinus (Figs. 14-28 and 14-40, F).

As development progresses in females, the mesonephric ducts disappear, and the muellerian ducts unite at their caudal ends to form the body of the uterus and the vagina (Fig. 14-40, C). The part of the urinogenital sinus between bladder and entrance of the vagina is the urethra (Fig. 14-40, C). As a result of these changes, most adult female mammals have two caudal openings to the exterior, a urinogenital aperture and an anus.

In most female primates (including humans) and in some rodents, an additional partition forms in the cloaca—this one in the urinogenital sinus. It separates the urinogenital sinus into a urethra and a vagina (Fig. 14-40, D). As a result, the embryonic cloaca in these species becomes subdivided into three passages: urethra, vagina, and rectum. Each passageway leads to the exterior via its own aperture (Fig. 14-42). In this regard the females of these species have evolved farther than the males. The vagina in these females has a dual origin.

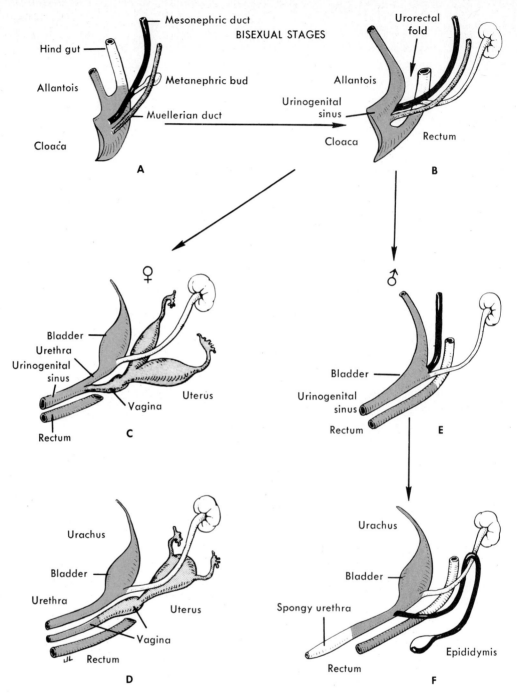

Fig. 14-40. Fate of the mammalian cloaca and allantois (red), muellerian ducts (gray), and mesonephric duct (black). **A** and **B,** Bisexual stages. Only the left muellerian and mesonephric ducts are shown. In **B** the cloaca is becoming subdivided by the urorectal fold into a urinogenital sinus ventrally and a rectum dorsally. **C,** Typical adult female mammal. **D,** Female primate, a modification of the condition shown in **C.** In **C** and **D,** the contributions of both the left and right muellerian ducts are shown. **E,** Developing male, showing intermediate stage in reorientation of mesonephric and metanephric ducts. **F,** Adult male.

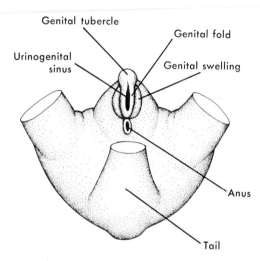

Fig. 14-41. External genitalia of sexually indifferent stage of a 29-mm human embryo (about 12 weeks of age). The cloaca has already been divided into urinogenital sinus and rectum. The genital tubercle becomes penis or clitoris, the genital swellings become scrotal sacs or labia majora, and the urinogenital sinus becomes the urethra in a male and is partitioned in a female to form the vagina and urethra.

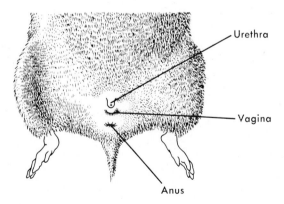

Fig. 14-42. Perineal region of a female hamster. The urethra opens at the tip of a penislike urinary papilla.

Table 14-1. Some homologous urinogenital structures in male and female mammals

Indifferent structure	Mature male	Mature female
Mesonephric duct	Ductus deferens (vas deferens)	Ductus deferens femininus* (Gartner's duct)
	Epididymis	
Mesonephric tubules	Vasa efferentia	Vasa efferentia ovarii*
	Appendix of epididymis*	Epoophoron*
	Paradidymis*	Paroophoron*
Muellerian duct	Appendix testis*	Oviduct
		Uterus
	Vagina masculina* (prostatic sinus)	Vagina, *cephalic to urinogenital sinus*
Genital ridge	Testis	Ovary
	Rete testis	Rete ovarii*
Gubernaculum	Gubernaculum	Ovarian ligament
		Round ligament of uterus
Genital swellings	Scrotal sacs	Labia majora
Genital tubercle	Penis	Clitoris
Genital folds	Contribute to penis	Labia minora
Urinogenital sinus	Urethra, *prostatic and membranous portions*	Urethra
		Urinogenital sinus
		Lower vagina in rodents and primates

*Vestigial.

The cephalic part is derived from the fused muellerian ducts, and the terminal part is cloacal.*

Table 14-1 summarizes the fate in adult males and females of the chief sexually indifferent urinogenital structures found in all mammalian embryos.

---

*In higher primates the urethra and vagina actually open into a shallow vestibule (Fig. 14-38) derived from the very distal end of the urinogenital sinus.

CHAPTER SUMMARY

1. Kidneys arise from a ribbon of nephrogenic mesoderm that extends the length of the trunk. A wave of differentiation sweeps along the ribbon, giving rise to convoluted tubules. The tubules are associated with glomeruli and open into a longitudinal duct that terminates in the cloaca when the latter is present.

2. Glomeruli are capillaries that filter water and other substances from the blood. The most primitive ones (external glomeruli) dangle into the coelom. The remaining ones (internal glomeruli) are encapsulated by Bowman's capsule. Glomerulus and capsule constitute a renal corpuscle.

3. Kidney tubules are tiny convoluted ductules that collect glomerular filtrate, selectively reabsorb some substances, add others, and conduct the final filtrate to the longitudinal duct.

4. A renal corpuscle with its associated tubule is a nephron, the functional renal unit.

5. An archinephros is a hypothetical primitive kidney with external glomeruli, nephrostomes, and simple tubules arranged metamerically the length of the trunk.

6. The first embryonic tubules are segmental and often have nephrostomes in lower vertebrates. These tubules are temporary and constitute a pronephros.

7. A mesonephros organizes behind the pronephros. It is the functional kidney of adult fishes and amphibians and of embryonic amniotes. It consists of closely packed nephrons. It is also called opisthonephros in anamniotes.

8. The pronephric duct persists to drain the adult kidney of fishes and amphibians except in a few males in which it is preempted for sperm transport.

9. Some of the anteriormost mesonephric tubules in all male vertebrate embryos invade the testes and become vasa efferentia. As a

result, the cephalic end of the adult kidney of male fishes and amphibians may be preempted for sperm transport and is then called a sexual (epididymal) kidney.

10. The metanephros is the adult amniote kidney. It organizes from the caudal end of the nephrogenic mesoderm, which is displaced craniad and laterad. Its duct (ureter) arises as a bud from the mesonephric duct and empties into the cloaca of reptiles and birds, urinary bladder of mammals.

11. The mammalian kidney tubule has a loop of Henle between proximal and distal convolutions and lacks an afferent supply from the renal portal system except in monotremes. All renal corpuscles are in a cortex.

12. Vertebrates excrete some salts extrarenally via gills, rectal glands in elasmobranchs, and nasal glands in marine reptiles, shore birds, and lizards and snakes in arid habitats.

13. Most vertebrates have urinary bladders. In fishes they are usually enlargements or evaginations of the mesonephric ducts (tubal bladders). In tetrapods they are evaginations of the floor of the cloaca, at least in the embryo.

14. Gonads arise from paired gonadal ridges located close to the mesonephroi. Unpaired gonads result when the paired ridges fuse or one fails to differentiate. Gonads tend to be displaced caudad in mammals.

15. The ovaries of teleosts and amphibians are saccular. Those of reptiles, birds, and monotremes are lacunate. Some mammalian ovaries are enclosed within an ovarian bursa.

16. Cyclostomes lack reproductive ducts, and the eggs and sperm exit from the coelom via genital pores. In other vertebrates the mesonephric ducts carry sperm, and, except in teleosts and ganoids, muellerian ducts convey eggs and the products of conception. The caudal ends of the muellerian ducts unite in female mammals above marsupials to form an unpaired uterine body and vagina.

17. Mammalian uteri are duplex, bipartite, bicornuate, or simplex, depending on the extent of fusion of the caudal ends of the muellerian ducts.

18. Male intromittent organs of fishes are modifications of pelvic or anal fins. Snakes and lizards have hemipenes. Turtles, crocodilians, some birds, and monotremes have an unpaired penis in the cloacal floor containing a corpus spongiosum. Mammals above monotremes have an external penis with a corpus spongiosum and two corpora cavernosa.

19. Female turtles, crocodilians, and mammals develop a clitoris.

20. Most adult vertebrates below marsupials have a cloaca. In lampreys, chimaeras, and most ray-finned fishes the cloaca becomes shallow or nonexistent in adults.

21. In reptiles, birds, and monotremes the cephalic end of the cloaca is partitioned by a urorectal fold into a urodeum that receives the urinary and genital tracts and a coprodeum that receives the large intestine. The caudal end of the cloaca is unpartitioned.

22. Above monotremes the cloaca is completely partitioned into urinogenital sinus and rectum, and the two empty separately to the exterior.

23. In some rodents and most female mammals the urinogenital sinus is also subdivided into two passageways, so that there are three passageways to the exterior—urethra, vagina, and rectum.

24. Early gonads are indistinguishable as to sex, and duct systems for both sexes are present in embryos. Table 14-1 lists the chief sexually indifferent structures of the urinogenital system of mammalian embryos and their fate in adult males and females.

LITERATURE CITED AND SELECTED READINGS

1. Altschule, M.D.: The change(s) in the mesonephric tubules of human embryos ten to twelve weeks old, Anatomical Record **46:**81, 1930.
2. Baker, C.J., and Taylor, W.W.: The urogenital system of the male *Ambystoma*, Journal of the Tennessee Academy of Sciences **39:**1, 1964.
3. Breeder, C.M., and Rosen, D.E.: Modes of reproduction in fishes, Garden City, N.Y., 1966, Natural History Press.
4. Brodal, A., and Fänge, R., editors: The biology of *Myxine*, Oslo, 1963, Norway Universitetsforlaget.
5. Dunson, W.A.: Salt glands in reptiles. In Gans, C., and Dawson, W.R., editors: Biology of the reptilia, vol. 5, New York, 1976, Academic Press, Inc.
6. Fox, H.: The amphibian pronephros, Quarterly Review of Biology **38:**1, 1963.
7. Fox, H.: The urinogenital system of reptiles. In Gans, C., and Parsons, T.S., editors: Biology of the reptilia, vol. 6, New York, 1977, Academic Press, Inc.
8. Kent, G.C., Jr.: Reproductive systems of vertebrates. In Encyclopae-

dia Britannica, ed. 15, vol. 15, Chicago, 1974, Encyclopaedia Britannica, Inc., p. 707.

9. McCrady, E., Jr.: The development and fate of the urinogenital sinus in the opossum, *Didelphys virginiana*, Journal of Morphology **66**:131, 1940.

10. Moffat, D.B.: The mammalian kidney, New York, 1975, Cambridge University Press.

11. Mossman, H. W., and Duke, K.L.: Comparative morphology of the mammalian ovary, Madison Wis., 1973, University of Wisconsin Press.

12. Pang, P.K.T., Griffith, R.W., and Atz, J.W.: Osmoregulation in elasmobranchs, American Zoologist **17**: 365, 1977.

13. Peaker, M., and Linzell, J.L.: Salt glands in birds and reptiles, Monographs of the Physiological Society, New York, 1975, Cambridge University Press.

14. Prosser, C.L., editor: Comparative animal physiology, ed. 3, vol. 2, Philadelphia, 1973, W. B. Saunders Co.

15. Sharman, G.B.: Evolution of viviparity in mammals. In Austin, C.R., and Short, R.V., editors: Reproduction in mammals. Book 6, Cambridge, England, 1976, Cambridge University Press, p. 32.

16. Stahl, B.J.: Vertebrate history: problems in evolution, New York, 1974, McGraw-Hill Book Co.

17. Taylor, D.H., and Guttman, S.I., editors: The reproductive biology of amphibians, New York, 1977, Plenum Press.

Nervous system

The vertebrate nervous system plays three basic roles. It acquaints the organism with its external environment and stimulates the organism to orient itself favorably in that environment; it participates in regulation of the internal environment; and it serves as a storage site for information. These functions are accomplished by the nerves, spinal cord, and brain in association with **receptors** (sense organs) and **effectors** (chiefly muscles and glands).

The organism exists in an external environment that is sometimes friendly, sometimes inimical, and seldom neutral. An environment is friendly if it contains food for nourishment, a mate for the propagation of the species, and shelter from enemies. An environment is unfriendly if it leads to the weakening of the organism or of the species.

The organism must constantly monitor the external environment in order that it may go deeper into a friendly area or withdraw from an unfriendly one. The information is supplied by afferent (sensory) nerves commencing in sense organs. The response (body movement) is initiated by nerve impulses over efferent (motor) nerves that stimulate the skeletal muscles of the body and thus cause the fish to swim or the tetrapod to crawl, run, or fly deeper into, or out of, an area. Information from the external environment is also employed in the regulation of internal secretions, such as seasonal release of reproductive hormones (Fig. 17-5).

The organism also has an internal environment that must be continually monitored and controlled. Afferent nerves from visceral receptors carry information in the form of nerve impulses to the central nervous system; efferent nerves carry impulses from the center to visceral effectors, chiefly smooth and cardiac muscles and glands.

Memory (information storage and recall) is a function of the nervous system. Without information storage no animal could modify its behavior in accordance with experience, and every situation would be faced as if it were the first time. In other words, there could be no *conditioned* responses. As experiences multiply, information accumulates and the penalty of past errors and the rewards of successes modify behavior accordingly. The brain seems to be the chief site of information storage.

The nervous system is subdivided for convenience into central and peripheral nervous systems. The **central nervous system** consists of the brain and spinal cord. The **peripheral nervous system** consists of cranial, spinal, and autonomic nerves, their branches, and certain autonomic ganglia and plexuses. The autonomic components innervate visceral effectors.

THE NEURON

To understand the anatomy of the nervous system, one must be acquainted with the neuron—the living nerve cell. The neuron is to the nervous system what a muscle cell is to the muscle system: it performs the specific function of the system. The neuron, rather than the nerve, transmits the nerve impulse. Neurons exhibit many shapes, but all have a **cell body** and one or more **processes** (Fig. 15-1). The longest process, distinguished cytologically by the absence of Nissl material, is the **axon**, or **nerve fiber** (Fig. 15-2). It transmits nerve impulses to a synapse or effector. Some nerve fibers extend short or long distances up or down the brain and spinal cord aggregated into functional groups called **fiber tracts** (Figs. 15-4, *A*, and 15-9, low cervical). Nerve fibers are also in nerves. In fact, a **nerve** is one or more bundles of nerve fibers outside the central nervous system wrapped in a connective sheath (**epineurium**) and supplied by blood vessels, the **vasa nervorum** (Fig. 15-3). The other processes of neurons are **dendrites.** They are short extensions of the cell body that provide an increased surface for receipt of incoming impulses from axons. Like cell bodies, they display prominent Nissl material, which

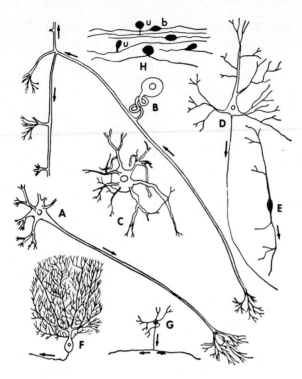

Fig. 15-1. Several morphological varieties of neurons. **A,** Motor cell body in the spinal cord; the fiber extends into the ventral root of a spinal nerve; **B,** dorsal root ganglion cell (sensory); the fiber terminates at the left in the spinal cord; **C,** sympathetic ganglion cell; **D** and **E,** pyramidal and horizontal cells from the cerebral cortex; **F** and **G,** Purkinje and granular cells from the cerebellum; **H,** a group of embryonic dorsal root ganglion cells in transition from bipolar, **b,** to unipolar, **u. A, C, D, F,** and **G,** Multipolar neurons; **E,** bipolar; **B,** unipolar. Arrows indicate direction of impulse.

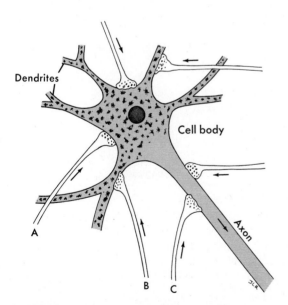

Fig. 15-2. Synaptic endings on a motor neuron. **A,** Synapse between an axon terminal (synaptic knob, terminal button) and a cell body; **B,** between axon terminal and a dendrite; **C,** between axon terminal and another axon. Dark splotches in dendrites and cell body are Nissl material.

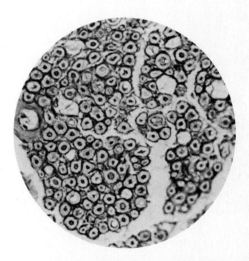

Fig. 15-3. Cross section of a small part of a nerve. The nerve fibers (black dots) are surrounded by fatty myelin sheaths of varying thicknesses.

constitutes sites of high protein synthesis. To observe how the neuron fits into the peripheral nervous system we will examine a sensory nerve, a motor nerve, and two mixed nerves.

A typical sensory nerve is diagramed in Fig. 15-4, *A*. It commences in a sense organ (in this instance, the membranous labyrinth) and terminates in the brain. Like all nerves, it is made of nerve fibers. The cell bodies of sensory nerve fibers, with few exceptions, are found in a sensory ganglion on the pathway of the nerve. A **ganglion**

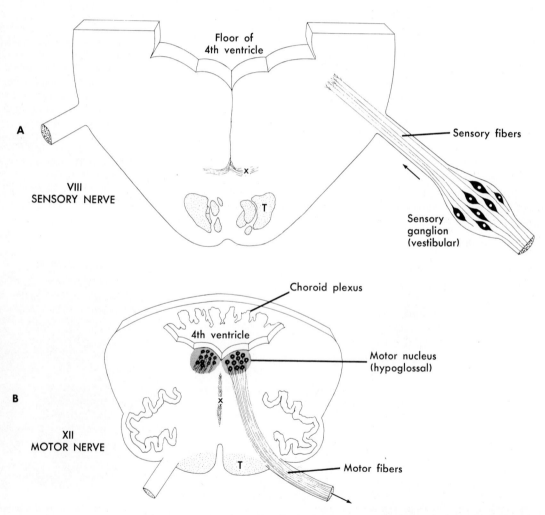

Fig. 15-4. Typical locations of cell bodies (black) of sensory and motor fibers. **A,** Sensory nerve with sensory cell bodies in a sensory ganglion. **B,** Motor nerve (hypoglossal) with motor cell bodies in a motor nucleus in the brain. **T,** Descending fiber tract (corticospinal); **x,** decussating fibers. Arrows indicate direction of nerve impulses.

is a group of cell bodies outside the central nervous system. A *sensory ganglion* contains sensory cell bodies. In lower vertebrates some sensory cell bodies are scattered along the nerve.

A typical motor nerve is diagramed in Fig. 15-4, *B*. The cell bodies of most motor neurons are inside the central nervous system in a **motor nucleus.** Neurologically speaking, a **nucleus** is a group of cell bodies within the brain or cord. Motor nuclei contain the cell bodies of motor nerve fibers. The motor fibers of cranial nerve XII terminate

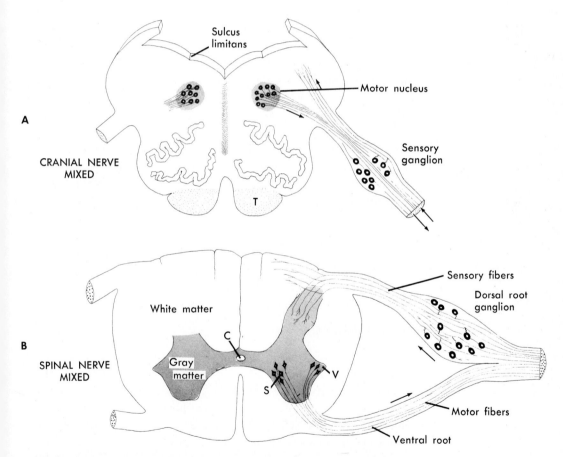

Fig. 15-5. Locations of cell bodies of mixed nerves. **A,** Mixed cranial nerve with sensory cell bodies in a sensory ganglion and motor cell bodies in a motor nucleus in the brain. Not all fiber components of this nerve are shown. **B,** Spinal nerve with sensory cell bodies in dorsal root ganglion and motor cell bodies in gray matter of cord. **C,** Central canal of cord; **S,** somatic motor nucleus in ventral (anterior) horn of gray matter; **T,** descending fiber tract (corticospinal); **V,** visceral motor nucleus in lateral (visceral) horn of gray matter. Arrows indicate direction of nerve impulses.

in striated muscle. There are almost no purely motor nerves in vertebrates, since most nerves supplying striated muscles have sensory fibers for proprioception from the muscle (Fig. 16-20).

Mixed nerves contain both sensory and motor fibers and are illustrated in Fig. 15-5. Their sensory cell bodies are in sensory ganglia, and their motor cell bodies are in motor nuclei. Most vertebrate nerves are mixed.

The site where a nerve impulse is transferred from one neuron to the next is a **synapse.** As an axon approaches a synapse it branches into a multitude of very tiny **telodendria,** usually a thousand or more, each of which ends as a tiny **synaptic knob** in contact with the cell body, a dendrite, or the axon of another neuron (Fig. 15-2), of which there are usually a large number. Nerve impulses are transmitted across the synapse by short-lived secretions, chiefly amines (norepinephrine, acetylcholine, serotonin, and others) that are released from the synaptic knobs when a nerve impulse arrives. These amines are **neurotransmitters.** Neurotransmitters are also released from axon terminals in contact with effectors, causing the effector (muscle, gland, pigment cell) to respond.

Some neurons (**neurosecretory neurons**) with cell bodies in the central nervous system secrete small polypeptides from their axon terminals. These polypeptides, called **neurosecretions,** are hormones. Instead of terminating in synapses or at effectors, most neurosecretory fibers terminate at sinusoidal vascular channels into which they release their neurosecretions (Fig. 17-1).

GROWTH AND DIFFERENTIATION OF THE NERVOUS SYSTEM

To achieve insight into the architecture of the adult nervous system, it is necessary to know how the nervous system develops.

Neural tube

An early embryonic neural tube is illustrated in Fig. 15-6. The cephalic end of the tube is the embryonic brain. The rest is future spinal cord. A cross section of the neural tube at this time exhibits three zones (Fig. 15-7, *B*): a **germinal layer** of actively mitotic cells, a **mantle layer** of cells proliferated from the germinal layer, and a **marginal layer.** Some of the mantle layer cells are **neuroblasts,** which sprout axons and dendrites to become neurons. The rest are **spongioblasts** that give rise to neuroglia. As the neuroblasts differentiate, their axons grow into and add to the marginal layer, which therefore consists partly of nerve fibers. Because many axons become surrounded by a fatty myelin sheath, the marginal layer looks white when fresh and is called **white matter.** The protoplasm of the cell

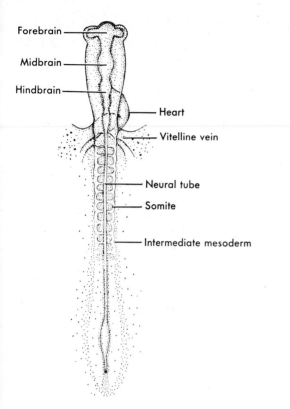

Forebrain
Midbrain
Hindbrain
Heart
Vitelline vein
Neural tube
Somite
Intermediate mesoderm

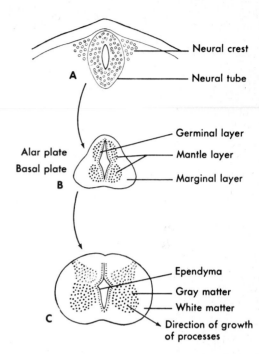

Neural crest
Neural tube
A

Alar plate
Basal plate
B
Germinal layer
Mantle layer
Marginal layer

C
Ependyma
Gray matter
White matter
Direction of growth
of processes

Fig. 15-7. Embryogenesis of the spinal cord. The alar plate contains association neuroblasts with which incoming (sensory) nerve fibers will synapse. The basal plate contains motor neuroblasts, some of the axons of which are growing in the direction of the arrow in **C** to become part of a nerve.

Fig. 15-6. Chick embryo of 33 hours' incubation. The optic vesicles are beginning to evaginate from the forebrain.

bodies of the mantle layer causes this zone to look gray; hence the name **gray matter.**

Some of the nerve fibers that grow into the marginal layer turn upward or downward in the cord or brain to synapse with neurons elsewhere in the central nervous system. The earliest of these fibers extend only one segment, a primitive condition. The later and longer ones become aggregated in long ascending and descending fiber tracts, each composed of functionally related fibers.

The embryonic cord, hindbrain, and midbrain consist of an **alar** and **basal plate** located, respectively, above and below a sulcus limitans (Fig. 15-7, B, and 15-30). The alar plate receives incoming (sensory) impulses, whereas the basal plate becomes motor in function.

When all the nerve cells have been formed that will ever be formed in the cord or brain, the cells of the germinal layer cease to divide. The undifferentiated cells that remain adjacent to the central canal, or **neurocoel,** become ependymal cells. The **ependyma** is the connective tissue–like lining of the central canal (Fig. 15-7, C).

Development of motor components of nerves

Many of the axons that sprout from neuroblasts in the basal plate grow out of, and away from, the neural tube (Fig. 15-7, *C*) to make contact with striated muscles. These become motor fibers of the cranial and spinal nerves. Because these fibers sprout from neuroblasts within the central nervous system, their cell bodies are within the adult brain or cord. Notice the location of motor cell bodies in Figs. 15-4, *B*, and 15-5.

Some of the fibers that sprout from neuroblasts in the basal plate grow out of the neural tube to make contact with neuroblasts in autonomic ganglia. These are **preganglionic fibers** of the autonomic nervous system (Fig. 15-10, PRE). The neuroblasts in autonomic ganglia sprout **postganglionic fibers** that grow toward, and innervate, smooth muscles and glands. Thus all motor neurons have their cell bodies in the cord or brain with one exception—postganglionic neurons of the autonomic system have their cell bodies in autonomic ganglia.

Most neuroblasts of autonomic ganglia are migrants from neural crests (Fig. 15-7, *A*). A few, in amphibians at least, migrate outward from the basal plate of the neural tube.

Development of sensory components of nerves

At the time the neural groove is closing to form a tube, a longitudinal ribbon of neurectoderm (ectoderm that forms nervous tissue) separates from the developing tube dorsolaterally on each side and soon segments to form a metameric series of **neural crests,** one pair in each body segment (Figs. 4-7 and 15-7, *A*). Some neural crest cells become neuroblasts that give rise to sensory neurons of spinal and cranial nerves. In doing so they pass through a bipolar stage (Fig. 15-1, *H*) in which one process grows into the alar plate of the cord or brain and the other grows into a sense organ. Thus there is established a neuronal connection between sense organ and central nervous system. Since each neural crest gives rise to a large number of sensory neurons, the result is a sensory ganglion on the nerve close to the central nervous system. Neurons whose cell bodies are in sensory ganglia are **first-order sensory neurons.** They conduct an impulse from a sense organ to the central nervous system. Inside the cord or brain they synapse with **second-order sensory neurons** (Fig. 15-10, *2*) that conduct the impulse elsewhere. Because most cell bodies of first-order sensory neurons arise from neural crests, we can make the following generalization: the cell bodies of sensory neurons of cranial and spinal nerves are usually in sensory ganglia on the pathway of nerves.

There are three major exceptions to the rule that the cell bodies of first-order sensory neurons are in ganglia on the pathway of nerves. (1) Olfactory nerve fibers sprout from neuroblasts in the embryonic olfactory epithelium. Their long processes grow into the nearest part of the brain, which is the olfactory bulb. Therefore the cell bodies of the olfactory nerves are in the olfactory epithelia (Figs. 15-23 and 16-16). (2) Neuroblasts that give rise to sensory fibers of the optic nerves are in the embryonic retinas (Fig. 16-4, *B*, optic cup), and their long processes grow brainward along the optic stalk. Therefore the cell bodies of optic nerve fibers are in the retina. Actually, the retina is part of the brain, since it arises as an evangination from the diencephalon and never separates from it. The term "optic nerve" is a misnomer. (3) The cell bodies of proprioceptive fibers in most, if not all, cranial nerves are not in ganglia. Neuroblasts within the alar plate of the embryonic midbrain sprout long processes that grow out to the muscles. Therefore the cell bodies of proprioceptive fibers in cranial nerves are in the midbrain in the **mesencephalic nucleus of the trigeminal nerve.**

Olfactory neurons and rods and cones (which are modified first-order sensory neurons) are the only neurons with cell bodies in sensory epithelia in vertebrates, and they are sometimes called **neurosensory cells.** These are the only sensory neurons in some diploblastic metazoans and appear to be phylogenetically older than sensory neurons with cell bodies in ganglia. In coelenterates the axons of some neurosensory cells end in direct contact with effector cells, providing a simple two-neuron reflex arc. Such arcs are rare in vertebrates. The phylogeny of neurons and their gradual organization into complex nervous systems have been discussed by Bullock and Horridge.[2]

Several of the sensory ganglia in the head do not arise from neural crests but from a row of ectodermal thickenings, or placodes, on the side of the embryonic head above the pharynx (**epibranchial placodes** in fishes). The precise contribution of these placodes to specific sensory ganglia of the head varies with the species. In effect, placodes are an alternate method of producing neural crests.

NEUROGLIA AND NEURILEMMA

Not all undifferentiated cells of the embryonic neural tube become neurons. Nearly half the bulk of the brain and cord consists of interstitial cells, or neuroglia, that arise from spongioblasts in the mantle layer. Glial cells, smaller than many neurons and with nonneural dendritic processes, fill all the "space" in the brain and cord not occupied by neurons or blood vessels, performing roles that are only partly understood at present. Ependymal cells are the phylogenetic precursors of neuroglia and the only glial cells of an amphioxus and

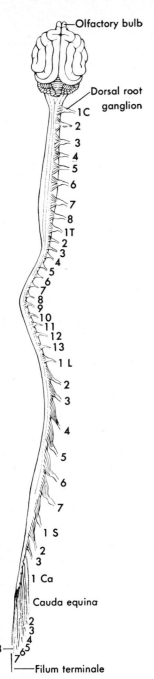

Olfactory bulb

Dorsal root ganglion

1C
2
3
4
5
6
7
8
1T
2
3
4
5
6
7
8
9
10
11
12
13
1 L
2
3
4
5
6
7
1 S
2
3
1 Ca
Cauda equina
2
3
4
5
8 6
7
Filum terminale

Fig. 15-8. Brain and spinal cord of a cat. The dura mater has been removed. **C,** Cervical spinal nerve; **T,** thoracic; **L,** lumbar; **S,** sacral; **Ca,** caudal spinal nerves. Note origin of spinal nerves by multiple rootlets, and enlargements of the cord in the cervical and lumbar regions.

cyclostome. Their ciliated cell bodies line the neurocoel, and at least some of their processes in vertebrates as well as in an amphioxus extend radially all the way to the margin of the spinal cord. In an amphioxus, blood vessels do not penetrate the cord, and the processes evidently have a nutritive function for the neurons. A progressive differentiation of glial cells is seen from cyclostomes to teleosts and from amphibians to amniotes, in which some ependymal cells lose their connection with the margins of the neural tube, become isolated among cell bodies and processes, and become functionally specialized. A few simple varieties of neuroglia are also found among higher invertebrates.

Oligodendroglia wrap their processes around axons in the central nervous system and elaborate myelin, a fatty electrical insulation that speeds conduction of the nerve impulse. **Microglia** are phagocytes that remove debris, including disintegration products of neurons after trauma or cell death. **Astroglia,** named because their processes radiate like a star in all directions, have been implicated in the bioelectrical activity associated with the nerve impulse. They also provide communication between neurons and blood vessels. In addition to serving in a number of metabolic roles, glial cells may play a yet-to-be-clarified role in information storage. Mechanical support seems only incidental to the other roles.

Glial cells are not found in nerves, but glialike **Schwann cells** migrate from the neural tube and neural crests into the nerves to form a living tube, the **neurilemma,** around each axon outside the central nervous system. Schwann cells elaborate myelin of varying thicknesses (Fig. 15-3). In general, heavily myelinated fibers conduct nerve impulses faster than lightly myelinated ones. The thickest sheaths are on fibers from encapsulated endings for touch, on proprioceptive fibers, and on motor fibers supplying striated muscle, which combination provides a very fast reflex motor response to danger signals arising on the body surface.

SPINAL CORD

The spinal cord occupies the vertebral canal and is packed in fat. Along with the brain it is surrounded in most fishes by a connective tissue membrane, the **meninx primitiva.** In some teleosts and in amphibians, reptiles, and most birds, this primitive meninx later forms an outer fibrous **dura mater** and an inner vascular **leptomeninx.** In mammals and a few birds the leptomeninx differentiates into a web-like **arachnoid** membrane and a **pia mater,** the latter intimately applied to the cord. Thus mammalian cords and brains are surrounded by three meninges.

The spinal cord commences at the foramen magnum, but there is no abrupt landmark on the brain or cord delimiting the two. Instead, there is a gradual internal and external rearrangement of fiber tracts and nuclei that is completed in about one body segment.

The adult cord extends to the caudal end of the vertebral column in vertebrates with abundant tail musculature. In other vertebrates the embryonic vertebral column elongates more rapidly than the spinal cord, with the result that at birth the cord is shorter than the column. In humans the spinal cord terminates at the third lumbar vertebra. In frogs it ends anterior to the urostyle. In a few bony fishes the cord is actually shorter than the brain. It is only an inch or so in length in one fish that is several feet long.

When the cord is as long as the vertebral column, each spinal nerve passes directly laterad to an intervertebral foramen through which it emerges from the vertebral canal. If, however, the column subsequently elongates more than the cord, the spinal nerves must then pass caudad within the vertebral canal to reach their foramina. As a result, the more caudal spinal nerves form a bundle of parallel nerves, the **cauda equina,** within the vertebral canal (Fig. 15-8). Nonnervous elements (ependyma and meninges) of the cord continue farther caudad as a delicate strand, the **filum terminale.**

The spinal cord exhibits cervical and lumbar enlargements at the level of the anterior and posterior appendages. The enlargements result from the large number of cell bodies and fibers innervating the appendage. When one pair of appendages is particularly muscular, such as the hind limbs of massive dinosaurs, the corresponding enlargement of the cord is especially pronounced. Conversely, the spinal cord of turtles is very slender in the trunk because the thoracic and abdominal musculature is greatly reduced. In many fishes the cord exhibits a swelling, the urophysis, at its caudal end (Fig. 17-4).

The cord is flattened in cyclostomes but tends to be cylindrical or quadrilateral in higher vertebrates. In general, the neurocoel, or cavity within the cord, is relatively large in lower forms and constricted in higher ones.

A cross section of a typical cord reveals the nuclei arranged in a definite pattern surrounding the central canal, where they make up the gray matter (Fig. 15-9, high sacral). The nerve fibers occupy the periphery of the cord and, with neuroglia, constitute the white matter. The ascending and descending fibers are aggregated into fiber tracts that interconnect one level of the cord with another or with the brain. Fibers for touch constitute one tract, those for voluntary motor control another, and so forth. The fiber tracts of the cord are relatively few and simple in cyclostomes. They increase in number and complexity in amphibians because of the additional innervation of tetrapod limbs.

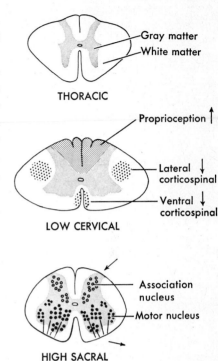

Fig. 15-9. Human spinal cord in cross section at three levels, showing a few fiber tracts (arrows) at the cervical level and a few nuclei at the sacral level. The cervical level is largest because it contains many cell bodies supplying the anterior limb, all fibers ascending to the brain from lower levels, and all fibers descending from the brain to lower levels. The corticospinal tracts carry voluntary motor impulses from the cerebral cortex. The motor horn in the thoracic region is small because there are no limb muscles to be supplied at this level. Association nuclei contain the cell bodies of second-order sensory neurons.

SPINAL NERVES
Roots and ganglia

Except in lampreys, spinal nerves arise from the cord by dorsal and ventral roots (Fig. 15-10, *B*). Each root is composed of a series of very short rootlets that unite close to the dorsal root ganglion. The dorsal root exhibits a ganglion and is predominantly sensory. The ventral root is entirely motor. There is considerable evidence that in the earliest vertebrates (1) the dorsal and ventral roots did not unite but continued independently to their destinations; (2) the dorsal roots were mixed; (3) there were no dorsal root ganglia; and (4) when sensory cell bodies first aggregated in ganglia, they were bipolar. These

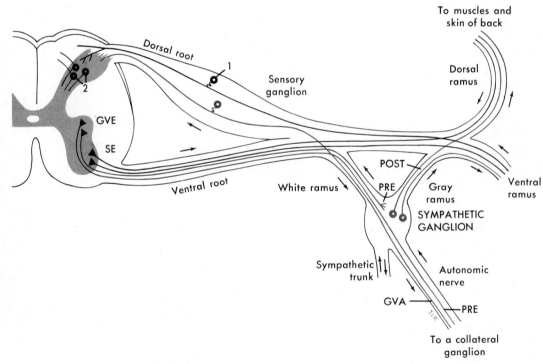

Fig. 15-10. Diagram of thoracic spinal nerve to show gray and white rami communicantes and visceral fibers (dark red). The preganglionic fiber shown in the autonomic nerve distal to the sympathetic ganglion did not synapse in the ganglion but will do so in a collateral ganglion such as the celiac (see splanchnic nerve, Fig. 15-32). **1**, Cell body of first-order sensory neuron in dorsal root ganglion; **2**, second-order sensory cell bodies in a sensory nucleus; **GVA**, general visceral afferent fiber; **GVE**, general visceral efferent nucleus, source of preganglionic fibers, in lateral horn of gray matter; **SE**, somatic efferent nucleus in ventral horn; **POST**, postganglionic fiber; **PRE**, preganglionic fiber. The dorsal ramus contains somatic sensory fibers that are not shown. Somatic fibers are black.

conclusions are based partly on study of spinal nerves of lower chordates.

In an amphioxus only the dorsal root contains nerve fibers. These roots arise from the cord at the level of a myoseptum and pass into the myoseptum to be distributed to the skin (sensory) and viscera (visceral motor). The cell bodies for the visceral motor fibers are in the cord, and those for the sensory fibers are either in the cord or within the nerves scattered along much of their length. Therefore there is no aggregation of sensory cell bodies at one location on a nerve, which means there are no sensory ganglia. Also, the sensory cell bodies remain bipolar throughout life.

The ventral roots of amphioxus emerge from the cord between two myosepta, do not unite with dorsal roots, and enter myomeres. Electron microscopy indicates that they do not contain axons but bundles of very delicate long extensions of striated muscle fibers from the myomeres.[3] These muscular filaments enter the cord through the ventral root. Inside the cord they are stimulated by nerve fibers that synapse with them. Thus the somatic muscles actually "come to the cord" for their stimuli. An analogous condition exists in echinoderms.

Dorsal and ventral roots alternate and remain independent in lampreys but unite in hagfishes except in the tail. Some of the cell bodies of sensory fibers are for the first time aggregated in ganglia on the dorsal root, and most of these remain bipolar. Other first-order sensory cell bodies are within the cord. Visceral motor fibers are in both roots, and the ventral root is entirely motor.

Above cyclostomes dorsal and ventral roots always unite. The dorsal root still contains numerous visceral motor fibers in many bony fishes, but in cartilaginous fishes and tetrapods most of these have been lost from that root. The cell bodies of first-order sensory neurons are in dorsal root ganglia. They are bipolar in cartilaginous fishes; bipolar, intermediate, and unipolar in bony fishes; chiefly unipolar in amphibians; and almost entirely unipolar in amniotes (Fig. 15-1, *B*). The ventral root is motor (somatic and visceral), with cell bodies inside the cord.

Metamerism

In gnathostomes a spinal nerve arises from each segment of the cord except near the end of the tail. These nerves are metamerically distributed to the body wall and tail. At the level where a fin or limb bud forms, they supply the appendage (Figs. 10-12 and 15-11). The segmental distribution of spinal nerves is best illustrated in fishes, since the metamerism of their body wall muscles is relatively undisturbed. Tadpoles have as many as 40 pairs of spinal nerves and lose all but 10 pairs when the tail is resorbed at metamorphosis.

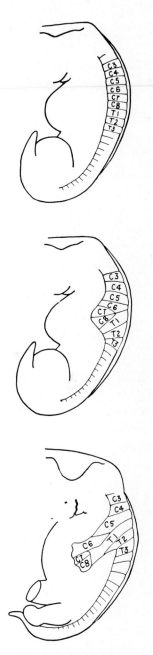

Fig. 15-11. Innervation of the skin of the mammalian forelimb by successive spinal nerves. **C,** Cervical, and **T,** thoracic somites and area of cutaneous distribution of their associated nerves.

Rami and plexuses

Shortly after emerging from the vertebral canal, each typical spinal nerve divides into at least two branches (see *3* and *4* in Fig. 1-2). A **dorsal ramus** supplies the epaxial muscles and skin of the dorsum. A larger **ventral ramus** passes into the lateral body wall and supplies the hypaxial muscles and skin to the midventral raphe. In the thoracic and lumbar regions, additional branches, **rami communicantes,** pass to ganglia of the sympathetic trunk (Fig. 15-10, white ramus, gray ramus). They carry visceral fibers.

The ventral rami of successive spinal nerves often unite to form a plexus from which large nerve trunks arise (Fig. 10-12, mammal). The chief plexuses are the brachial and pelvic (lumbosacral in amniotes), which supply nerves to the anterior and posterior appendages. These plexuses are relatively simple in anamniotes but become increasingly complicated in tetrapods (compare shark and mammal, Fig. 10-12). Autonomic plexuses occur on visceral pathways.

Occipitospinal nerves

In many fishes and amphibians one or more pairs of **occipitospinal nerves** arise between the vagal nerve and the first pair of spinal nerves (Fig. 15-26). They supply the hypobranchial musculature, including the tongue when present, and usually lack sensory roots. Embryonic frogs have an occipitospinal nerve immediately cephalad to the spinal nerve that supplies the tongue, but it becomes suppressed during later development. Cranial nerves XI and XII of amniotes lack

Table 15-1. Fiber components of typical spinal nerves

Components	Innervation
Sensory	
General somatic afferent fibers (GSA)	General cutaneous receptors (touch, pain, temperature, and pressure)
	Receptors on striated muscle, tendons, and bursae (proprioceptive)
General visceral afferent fibers (GVA)	Viscera, including general receptors in endoderm
Motor	
Somatic efferent fibers (SE)*	Myotomal muscle
General visceral efferent fibers (GVE)†	Smooth and cardiac muscle, and glands

*The fibers to myotomal muscle are designated simply as SE, rather than as GSE (general somatic efferent), because there are no special somatic efferent fibers.
†Autonomic fibers. Visceral fibers to skin are vasomotor (to arterioles), plumomotor or pilomotor (to erector muscles of feathers and hairs), or secretory (to skin glands), and also supply melanophores in lower vertebrates.

sensory roots and appear to be derived in part from occipitospinal nerves.

Fiber components of spinal nerves

The nerve fibers in a typical spinal nerve are of four functional varieties (Table 15-1). Three of the varieties are referred to as **general** fibers (GSA, GVA, and GVE) to differentiate them from **special** types found only in cranial nerves.

BRAIN

The cephalic end of the embryonic neural tube in every vertebrate exhibits three primary brain vesicles—the future forebrain, midbrain, and hindbrain (Fig. 15-6). The embryonic forebrain differs from the rest of the neural tube in that it is not divided into alar and basal plates. In adults it consists of two regions, **telencephalon** and **diencephalon.** The midbrain, or **mesencephalon,** develops without further subdivision. The hindbrain differentiates into **metencephalon** and **myelencephalon.** Differentiation involves thickening of the lateral walls and floor in some places, and dorsal, lateral, or ventral evagination in others until the adult brain has taken shape. Homologous parts in adults are readily demonstrable throughout the vertebrate series (Fig. 15-12). However, to display them from dorsal view in mammals requires removal of the overgrown cerebral hemispheres and cerebellum (Fig. 15-22). When these are removed, what remains is the **brain stem.** The brain, like the cord, is surrounded by meninges. The major subdivisions of the brain are listed in Table 15-2.

Metencephalon and myelencephalon: the hindbrain

The myelencephalon of the hindbrain is represented chiefly by the **medulla oblongata,** which merges imperceptibly with the spinal cord. The area of transition is characterized internally by gradual relocation of the fiber tracts, which constitute the white matter. As a result, whereas in the cord the gray matter is compact and centrally located, in the medulla it becomes dispersed into isolated masses (gray columns or nuclei) separated from one another by fiber tracts.

The most conspicuous dorsal feature of the hindbrain is the **cerebellum,** a dorsal evagination of the metencephalon. It functions in the coordination of the skeletal muscles in response to input from the membranous labyrinth, lateral-line canals, and proprioceptors in muscles, joints, and tendons, and from reflex and voluntary motor centers in the forebrain. Its size is correlated with the complexity of the activities of the striated musculature. It is smaller—that is, it has fewer cell bodies and fibers—in fishes and amphibians than in higher tetrapods whose bodies are supported well above the ground against

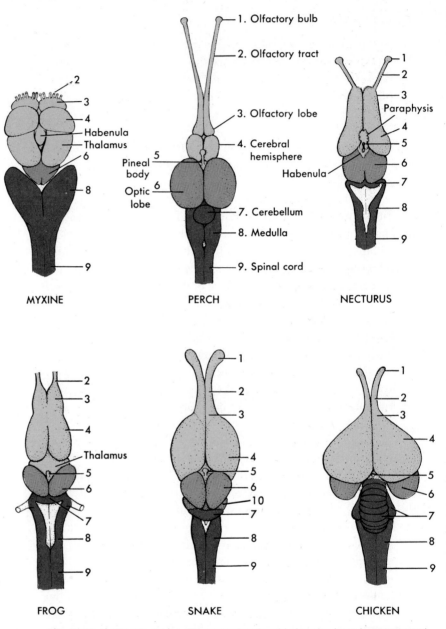

1. Olfactory bulb

2. Olfactory tract

3. Olfactory lobe

4. Cerebral hemisphere

5. Pineal body

6. Optic lobe

7. Cerebellum

8. Medulla

9. Spinal cord

MYXINE

PERCH

NECTURUS

FROG

SNAKE

CHICKEN

Fig. 15-12. Vertebrate brains. The posterior choroid plexuses have been removed to expose the fourth ventricle in necturus, frog, and snake. The prosencephalon, mesencephalon, and rhombencephalon are differentially colored. **1** to **9,** See perch for key; **10,** auditory lobe.

Table 15-2. Major subdivisions and components of the brain*

Component	Subdivision		
Prosencephalon (forebrain)	Telencephalon		Rhinencephalon Cerebral hemispheres *Lateral ventricles*
	Diencephalon		Epithalamus Thalamus Hypothalamus *Third ventricle*
Mesencephalon (midbrain)			Tectum Tegmentum *Cerebral aqueduct*
Rhombencephalon (hindbrain)	Metencephalon		Cerebellum Tegmentum *Fourth ventricle*
	Myelencephalon		Medulla oblongata *Fourth ventricle*

*For a listing of all parts discussed in this chapter, see p. 496.

gravity by muscular levers. It is larger in fishes than in amphibians since swimming, which involves schooling, vertical movements, adjusting to water currents, and keeping the dorsal part of the body from tipping over, requires more synergistic muscle activity than dragging the belly along the ground or squatting on a lily pad. Lacking a large cerebellum, aquatic urodeles rely to a large extent on spinal cord reflexes and primitive nuclei in the hindbrain for muscle coordination when swimming. The cerebellum is largest in birds and mammals, which require a large computer-like neural center to coordinate the muscles of the head, neck, trunk, and appendages in such diverse activities as flying, running, climbing, balancing, or, in the case of human beings, playing a piano. The cell bodies of the cerebellum are in a cortex on the surface, a condition found elsewhere only in the cerebral hemispheres of higher amniotes. In cyclostomes the cerebellum is not well developed and does not cause a bulge on the brain.

Other topographical features of the hindbrain are various swellings that indicate underlying nuclei and elevated ridges or transverse bands that contain fiber tracts. These topographical markings are most prominent in mammals. However, one nucleus (nucleus solitarius) in the alar plate becomes enormous in fishes that have taste buds over the entire surface of the body. The resulting swelling, or **vagal lobe** (Fig. 15-13), is the termination of the many incoming sensory

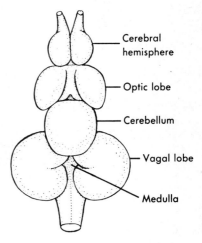

MODIFICATION FOR BOTTOM-FEEDING

Fig. 15-13. Brain of the buffalo fish *Carpiodes velifer.* Note unusual bulge (vagal lobe) on the alar plate of the medulla. Here terminate the many incoming taste fibers characteristic of bottom feeders.

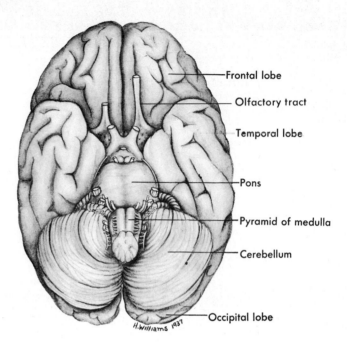

Frontal lobe

Olfactory tract

Temporal lobe

Pons

Pyramid of medulla

Cerebellum

Occipital lobe

H.Williams 1937

Fig. 15-14. Brain of man, ventral view. The olfactory bulbs and pituitary have been cut away. (Adapted from Francis, C.C., and Martin, A.H.: Introduction to human anatomy, ed. 7, St. Louis, 1975, The C.V. Mosby Co.)

fibers for taste and contains the second-order sensory neurons whose fibers are projected to reflex and relay centers elsewhere in the brain. Among ventral ridges on the mammalian hindbrain are the **pyramids,** which contain the **corticospinal (pyramidal) tracts** that carry voluntary motor impulses from the cerebral cortex; and the **pons,** which consists of fibers crossing (decussating) from one side of the brain to the other (Fig. 15-14).

The cavity of the hindbrain is the fourth ventricle (Figs. 15-4, *B,* and 15-18). The cerebellum is part of its roof. The rest of the roof is a membranous **tela choroidea,** part of which hangs into the ventricle as the **choroid plexus of the fourth ventricle** (Fig. 15-17).

Mesencephalon: the midbrain

The roof of the mesencephalon, or **tectum,** displays a pair of prominent **optic lobes** in all vertebrates. These bulging gray masses serve partly as optic reflex centers that receive fibers from the retina. They are especially large in birds, which have large eyes and rely on visual stimuli for much information about the environment. A pair of **auditory lobes** lies caudal to the optic lobes in the tectum commencing with reptiles, and the four bodies (optic lobes and auditory lobes) constitute the **corpora quadrigemina.** Fishes have auditory nuclei in this location but they are not large enough to bulge from the surface. The auditory lobes receive input from the part of the membranous labyrinth that is sensitive to vibratory stimuli and from other sources. Phylogenetically, they enlarge along with the cochlea. A prominent nucleus in the alar plate (not in the tectum) of the midbrain is the **mesencephalic nucleus of the trigeminal nerve.** It contains the cell bodies of the proprioceptive fibers of most, if not all, cranial nerves that have them.

The part of the mesencephalon that lies in the floor of the neurocoel and includes the basal plate is greatly thickened by numerous motor nuclei and ascending and descending fiber tracts. This is the **tegmentum,** and it is continuous with the tegmentum of the hindbrain. In mammals some of these tracts become massive; one pair, the **cerebral peduncles,** is visible on the ventral surface of the midbrain just caudal to the pituitary gland.

The ventricle of the midbrain is quite large in fishes and amphibians and extends dorsally into the optic lobes as the optocoel. In higher vertebrates the optic lobes are not hollow, and the midbrain ventricle is constricted to a narrow **cerebral aqueduct** (Fig. 15-20), also called the **aqueduct of Sylvius.**

Diencephalon

A ventral view of the diencephalon shows three important structures, the **optic chiasma, hypothalamus,** and **pituitary** (Fig. 15-15). Fishes also have a **saccus vasculosus.** Within the diencephalon is the **third ventricle.** The optic chiasma is the cephalic boundary of the diencephalon ventrally. It is where the optic nerves reach the brain and where some or all of the fibers cross before entering the brain to become optic tracts (Fig. 15-16). The pituitary is caudal to the optic chiasma and connected to the diencephalic floor by a stalk of brain tissue, the **infundibulum.** The hypothalamus is the floor and ventrolateral walls of the third ventricle above the pituitary stalk (Figs. 15-17 and 17-7).

The hypothalamus is the most important center in the body for homeostasis, or maintenance of a constant internal environment. It consists of nuclei that exert major reflex control over the autonomic nervous system and that produce neurosecretions that regulate the pituitary, and it has receptors that monitor the sodium chloride and glucose levels of the blood and its temperature. In general, the anterior nuclei are associated with parasympathetic functions, the caudal nuclei with sympathetic ones. Among the nuclei are fiber tracts, and entering and leaving the nuclei are nerve fibers.

The saccus vasculosus, or infundibular organ, of fishes is a thinwalled ventral evagination of the third ventricle, just behind the infundibulum (Fig. 15-15). It is lined with sensory hair cells like those of the neuromast organs and inner ear and probably monitors the

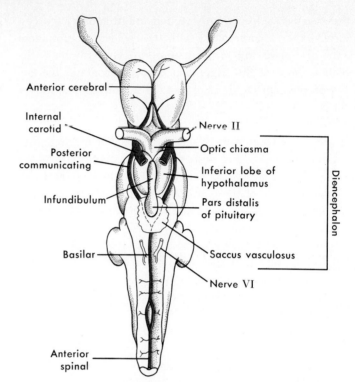

Fig. 15-15. Brain of *Squalus,* ventral view, showing arterial supply. The arteries encircling the diencephalon ventrally make up the circle of Willis.

Anterior cerebral

Internal carotid

Posterior communicating

Infundibulum

Basilar

Anterior spinal

Nerve II

Optic chiasma

Inferior lobe of hypothalamus

Pars distalis of pituitary

Saccus vasculosus

Nerve VI

Diencephalon

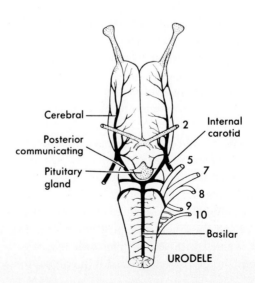

Fig. 15-16. Brain of a urodele, ventral view. Numerals identify cranial nerve roots.

Cerebral

Posterior communicating

Pituitary gland

Internal carotid

2

5

7

8

9

10

Basilar

URODELE

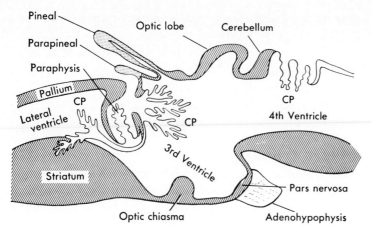

Fig. 15-17. Diencephalon and adjacent areas of a vertebrate brain, sagittal section, anterior end to the left. **CP,** Choroid plexus of lateral, third, and fourth ventricles. Based on the brain of a larval frog.

pressure of the cerebrospinal fluid as a function of depth analysis. It is largest in deep-sea fishes, rudimentary in cyclostomes, and absent in lungfishes and tetrapods.

The roof of the diencephalon is the **epithalamus.** It consists of a **pineal** or **parapineal** organ or both (Figs. 15-17 and 16-15); and a pair of knoblike thickenings, the **habenulae** (median in hagfishes; Fig. 15-12, *Myxine*). When a pineal and parapineal are both present, they are referred to collectively as the **epiphyseal complex.**

The pineal is a club-shaped or knoblike organ, sometimes thread-like or saccular, projecting above the diencephalon and, in amniotes, wedged between the caudal poles of the enlarged cerebral hemispheres (Figs. 15-12, 15-20, and 15-22). It is connected to the diencephalon by a stalk that sometimes contains an extension of the third ventricle. In lampreys, at least, the pineal is a photoreceptor. Otherwise, it functions as an endocrine organ that is stimulated in part by light entering the lateral eyes, the impulses being relayed through cranial nuclei and cranial, spinal, and autonomic nerves. The pineal is vestigial or absent in hagfishes, one genus of electric rays, crocodilians, and some adult mammals (sirenians, porpoise, and others). It is relatively large in humans and sheep (Figs. 15-20 and 15-22). Its role as an endocrine organ is discussed in Chapter 17.

The parapineal was a constant feature of bony fishes of the Devonian and of ancestral amphibians and reptiles, serving as a third (parietal) eye. It is now found only in a few bony fishes, larval anurans, *Sphenodon,* and some lizards in which it occupies a foramen of the skull just under a patch of translucent skin. The pineal and parapineal at one time may have constituted a *pair* of dorsal photoreceptors. This is suggested by their embryogenesis and the relationships and morphology of the two organs in lampreys (Fig. 16-15, *A*). Both organs are present, the parapineal being connected by nerve tracts with the left side of the brain and the parapineal with the right, and both contain photosensory cells. The pineal and parapineal as sense organs are discussed in Chapter 16.

The habenulae are ancient nuclei that preceded the amniote cerebral cortex and recieve and correlate input from olfactory and other centers of the brain. They are largest in species that rely heavily on smell for locating food; they are inconspicuous in birds, which have a poorly developed olfactory sense.

The **thalamus** is the largest subdivision of the diencephalon. It is a mass of many nuclei in the lateral walls of the third ventricle and comes to the surface dorsally just behind the cerebral hemispheres (Fig. 15-12, *Myxine*, frog). In amniotes it is hidden by the caudal poles of the hemispheres, which must be removed to reveal it (Fig. 15-22). All sensory pathways ascending to the telencephalon from the cord, hindbrain, or midbrain synapse in a thalamic nucleus before continuing to the telencephalon. The thalamus becomes increasingly prominent in higher vertebrates, relaying an increased number of sensory impulses to the hemispheres. In mammals the thalamus is so enlarged that the left and right masses bulge into the third ventricle and meet to form a gray (middle) commissure (Fig. 15-20).

The third ventricle is continuous with the ventricle of the midbrain (a narrow cerebral aqueduct in mammals) and with the ventricle in each hemisphere (via a small interventricular foramen in mammals;

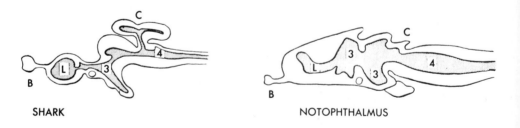

SHARK   NOTOPHTHALMUS

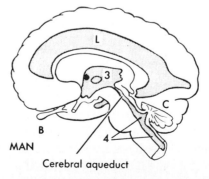

Fig. 15-18. Sagittal brain sections showing the ventricles. **B,** Olfactory bulb; **C,** cerebellum; **L, 3,** and **4,** lateral, third, and fourth ventricles. The black foramen in the third ventricle in humans is the interventricular foramen connecting the third and right lateral ventricles.

MAN

Cerebral aqueduct

Fig. 15-18). It is laterally compressed by the thalamus in its lateral walls. An optic recess of the ventricle extends toward the optic chiasma and an infundibular recess extends into the pituitary stalk. The nonnervous roof of the ventricle remains thin, becomes highly vascularized, and hangs into the ventricle as the **choroid plexus of the third ventricle.**

Telencephalon

The telencephalon consists of **cerebral hemispheres** and **rhinencephalon.** In fishes, the olfactory lobe of the rhinencephalon is as prominent as the cerebral hemispheres, which emphasizes the importance of olfaction in their survival (Fig. 15-26). In reptiles and birds the hemispheres increased in size, and in mammals they have grown forward over the rhinencephalon, relegating it to an inconspicuous anteroventral location (Figs. 15-19 and 15-20). The increased size of the hemispheres mirrors their dominant role in mammalian behavior.

At the boundary between diencephalon and telencephalon immediately anterior to the epiphyseal complex, the thin roof of the ventricle evaginates upward in some members of every vertebrate class to form a wrinkled, thin-walled sac, the **paraphysis** (Fig. 15-17). It is present in lampreys, sharks, and urodeles but is seldom seen in the classroom because it is easily torn. It is confined to embryos in most amniotes other than *Sphenodon*. Little is known of its function. It resembles a choroid plexus, but its role seems to be different. The

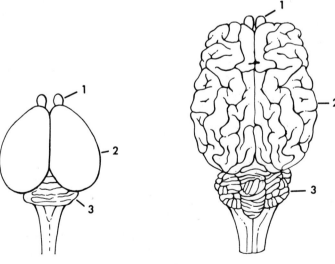

PLATYPUS　　　　　**SHEEP**

Fig. 15-19. Brain of a primitive mammal (platypus) lacking cortical gyri, and brain of sheep. **1,** Olfactory bulb; **2,** cerebral hemisphere; **3,** cerebellum.

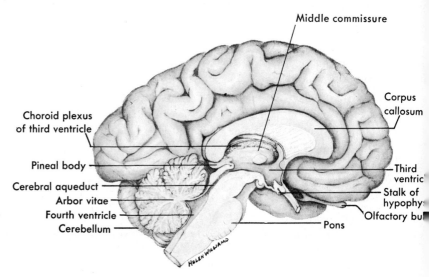

Fig. 15-20. Human brain, left half, sagittal section. (Adapted from Francis, C.C., and Martin, A.H.: Introduction to human anatomy, ed. 7, St. Louis, 1975, The C.V. Mosby Co.)

paraphysis is assigned arbitrarily to either the telencephalon or diencephalon since in some embryos its specific relationship is not evident.

RHINENCEPHALON

The rhinencephalon consists of olfactory bulbs, tracts, and lobes (Fig. 15-12). In mammals it is dwarfed by the huge cerebral hemispheres and often hidden by them when the brain is viewed from above (Figs. 15-19 and 15-20). The olfactory bulbs lie close to the olfactory epithelium separated by the olfactory capsule. Fiber tracts connect the rhinencephalon with other parts of the brain.

CEREBRAL HEMISPHERES AND THEIR EVOLUTION

When one thinks of cerebral hemispheres, what usually comes to mind are the huge cerebral hemispheres of mammals with their thick cortex of gray matter. However, the cerebral cortex is a relatively recent acquisition. Primitive hemispheres are seen in fishes.

In fishes each hemisphere consists chiefly of a **paleostriatum,** so named because it has a striated internal appearance. It is a mass of motor nuclei whose cell bodies receive input chiefly from the rhinencephalon and whose efferent fibers enter ancient descending tracts that end in motor nuclei of cranial and spinal nerves. Thus

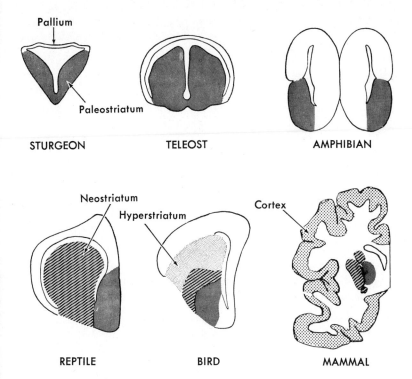

Fig. 15-21. Evolution of the cerebral hemispheres as seen in cross sections. Only the left hemisphere is shown in the lower figures. Reptiles have added a neostriatum to the old paleostriatum. Birds added a hyperstriatum. Note the striatal complex (now called basal ganglia) still present in mammals, and the addition of a cortex on the surface of the mammalian hemisphere.

olfactory stimuli result in reflex, survival-oriented activity of the muscles of the head, trunk, and tail. The paleostriatum (striatum as it is called throughout the vertebrate classes), the lateral ventricle, and the thin roof of the ventricle, or **pallium,** consitute the entire cerebral hemisphere (Fig. 15-21, sturgeon, teleost). Only a few sensory fibers from other sense organs are projected *forward* into the paleostriata by the thalami.

The hemispheres of amphibians are primarily paleostriatum. Amphibian thalami project a few more sensory fibers into the hemispheres than do those of fishes, giving amphibian hemispheres an increased role in reflex responses to external stimuli other than smell; but the role is small compared with amniotes, and amphibian hemispheres are still preempted by olfactory stimuli.

In reptiles additional nuclei are added to the hemispheres and these constitute a **neostriatum.** These nuclei receive many more sensory fibers from the thalamus, and a trace of cortex appears on the surface of the pallium. Because of the added cell bodies, synapses, and neuroglia, the hemispheres of reptiles are larger than those of amphibians. They bulge laterally, dorsally, and backward over the diencephalon. Because of increased input of sensory information into the hemispheres they have more control over motor activity.

Bird hemispheres are essentially reptilian, but additional strata of nuclei, the **hyperstriatum,** are superimposed (Fig. 15-21). To the hyperstriatum come many sensory impulses, which, after being relayed to the older striata, result in stereotyped behavior such as nest building, incubation of eggs, and care of young. The cortex is better developed than in reptiles, but almost complete experimental ablation of the cortex has little observable effect. The olfactory lobes are very small, and smell has less influence on behavior.

In mammals the striata, now part of what are called **basal ganglia,** continue to play a motor role, not thoroughly understood, although pathologic conditions result in certain types of muscular tremors in humans. The **cerebral cortex** on the greatly expanded pallium has become the most conspicuous part of the brain. As a result of the enormous balloonlike expansion of the pallium in all available directions the striata, diencephalon, and midbrain become hidden from dorsal view (Fig. 15-20). Removal of the overgrown pallium and of the cerebellum reveals the primitive telencephalic location of the striata, represented in dorsal view by the **caudate nucleus,** one of the basal ganglia (Fig. 15-22).

The mammalian cortex has at least four roles. (1) It is the highest center to which sensory impulses can be projected. These impulses give rise in the cortex to sensations of a discriminative (epicritic) nature, such as recognizing minor differences in the temperature, texture, or weight of two small objects held in the hand. This ability contributes to the esthetic enjoyment of sensory stimuli. (2) It ap-

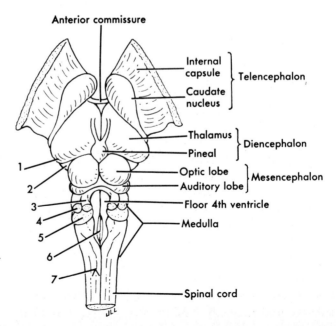

Fig. 15-22. Brain stem of a sheep. The cerebral hemispheres and cerebellum have been cut away to reveal the primitive vertebrate structures.
1, Location of lateral geniculate body of thalamus; **2,** medial geniculate body; **3** to **5,** anterior, middle, and posterior cerebellar peduncles, which carry fibers to and from the cerebellum (the peduncles had to be cut when the cerebellum was removed);
6, hypoglossal trigone in the floor of the fourth ventricle marking the location of the hypoglossal nuclei; **7,** posterior funiculus containing ascending fibers for proprioception. The caudate nucleus is part of the striatum of the cerebral hemisphere. Optic and auditory lobes make up the corpora quadrigemina.

Anterior commissure

Internal capsule ⎱ Telencephalon
Caudate nucleus ⎰

Thalamus ⎱ Diencephalon
Pineal ⎰

Optic lobe ⎱ Mesencephalon
Auditory lobe ⎰

Floor 4th ventricle

Medulla

Spinal cord

pears to be one of the locations where past experiences are stored as memory. (3) It is a center where data, incoming or recalled, may be correlated, analyzed, and employed in making choices. (4) It is the center from which voluntary motor activity is initiated. The cortex is therefore the "thinking" part of the brain. The manner in which the cerebral cortex is employed in the solution of human problems will determine the future fate of civilization insofar as it is under the control of man.

In many mammals, but not all, the cerebral cortex becomes so voluminous that it is folded into numerous ridges (**gyri**) and grooves (**sulci**) (Fig 15-20). Under the cortex in the roof of the ventricles except in monotremes and marsupials lies a broad transverse sheet of commissural nerve fibers, the **corpus callosum.** It connects the cortices of the two hemispheres (Fig. 15-20). Separating the two lateral ventricles is a thin, double-walled vertical partition, the **septum pellucidum.**

Choroid plexuses and cerebrospinal fluid

The cavities of the brain and cord are filled with lymphlike cerebrospinal fluid secreted partly by choroid plexuses. A typical choroid plexus consists of the thin ependymal roof of the ventricle and of the pia mater or leptomeninx invaded by a rich vascular plexus. A choroid plexus hangs into the third and fourth ventricles. From the third ventricle it extends forward into the lateral ventricles (Fig. 15-17).

Cerebrospinal fluid secreted into the ventricles moves sluggishly caudad into the central canal of the spinal cord partly by ciliary action. From the fourth ventricle the fluid passes into submeningeal spaces via apertures in the walls of the fourth ventricle under cover of the cerebellum. From the submeningeal spaces the cerebrospinal fluid passes outward along the roots of the cranial and spinal nerves for short distances, it passes centrally along the nerve rootlets into the cord and brain and bathes each motor neuron, and it seeps to the inner ear, where it contributes to the perilymph.

Cerebrospinal fluid is removed by lymph channels, especially along the roots of the spinal nerves. In higher vertebrates it is also removed by clusters of macroscopic **arachnoid villi** that penetrate the dura mater and hang into the large venous sinuses of the brain. The fluid assists in protecting the central nervous system from concussion. It also exchanges metabolites with the tissues it bathes.

CRANIAL NERVES

The first 10 cranial nerves of all vertebrates are distributed in accordance with a basic pattern. For convenience, these nerves may be grouped as follows: predominantly sensory nerves (I, II, and VIII), eyeball muscle nerves (III, IV, and VI), and branchiomeric nerves (V, VII, IX, and X). Amniotes have two additional cranial nerves (XI and XII) that are purely or predominantly motor. The generalized distribution of cranial nerves is seen in fishes.

The site where a cranial nerve emerges from the surface of the brain, or enters it, is its **superficial origin** as distinguished from the origins of its fibers, which usually come from a number of internal nuclei scattered throughout the brain stem. Unlike spinal nerves, cranial nerves do not have dorsal and ventral roots. Nerves supplying myotomal (somatic) muscles, except nerve IV, have ventral roots only, and branchiomeric nerves and nerve XI have lateral roots. The three purely sensory nerves have still other superficial origins.

Predominantly sensory cranial nerves*
NERVE I (OLFACTORY)

In all vertebrates the cell bodies of the olfactory nerve fibers are located in the olfactory epithelium. The fibers terminate in the olfactory bulb (Fig. 15-23). In *Squalus* the olfactory epithelium lies so close to the bulb that an olfactory nerve cannot be distinguished as an anatomical entity. In *Scoliodon* (Fig. 15-24, A), another shark, and in some teleosts, the sac containing the olfactory epithelium is sufficiently removed from the olfactory bulb that an olfactory nerve is demonstrable. In most vertebrates, one or more short bundles of olfactory fibers (**filia olfactoria**) extend between the olfactory epithelium and the bulb and constitute collectively the olfactory nerve.

In mammals the olfactory epithelium is in the upper part of the nasal passage, separated from the olfactory bulb by the cribriform plate of the ethmoid bone (derived from olfactory capsule). The foramina in the ethmoid bone (Fig. 8-4) transmit the filia olfactoria. When the brain of a vertebrate is lifted from the cranial cavity, the olfactory nerve bundles are torn, and only stumps remain attached to the brain.

The olfactory nerve frequently has a separate division that supplies the vomeronasal organ. When present, it is called the **vomeronasal nerve.**

A terminal nerve lies close to the olfactory bulb and tract in all vertebrates including man. It arises from the ventral surface of the forebrain and supplies general sensory and vasomotor fibers to a rather small area of the nasal epithelium and mucosa, but it has no olfactory function. The terminal nerve appears to be a vestige of a branchiomeric nerve that was present at one time anterior to the trigeminal.[12]

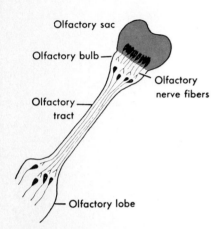

Fig. 15-23. Olfactory sac (red, containing olfactory epithelium) and rhinencephalon (olfactory bulb, tract, lobe) of dogfish shark. Olfactory nerve fibers synapse in olfactory bulb with second-order neurons. Olfactory sac is not part of the brain.

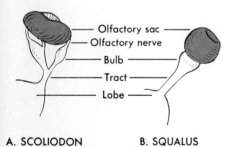

A. SCOLIODON   B. SQUALUS

Fig. 15-24. Olfactory sacs (red) and rhinencephalon of two sharks. Olfactory nerve fibers between sac and bulb form a discrete nerve in *Scoliodon* but not in *Squalus.*

---

*Nerves II and VIII, although functionally sensory, contain a number of efferent fibers from the brain to the deep layer of the retina or to the vestibular hair cells. These fibers apparently influence the discharge of sensory impulses from the receptor.

NERVE II (OPTIC)

The cell bodies of the optic nerve fibers are in the retina. The nerve emerges from the rear of the eyeball and extends to the optic chiasma where the optic tracts begin. Except in mammals, all or nearly all the optic nerve fibers decussate in the chiasma to enter the opposite side of the brain. A few fibers do not decussate in anurans, lizards, snakes, and some birds. In primates whose eyes are directed forward only the fibers from the nasal side of the retina cross (Fig. 15-25). Other mammals are intermediate between the two conditions. Overlap of the visual field results in depth perception, or binocular vision.

NERVE VIII (VESTIBULOACOUSTIC)

The eighth nerve* in all vertebrates has an anterior and a posterior root that comes off the medulla very close to nerves V and VII. The branches of the anterior root in fishes innervate the utriculus and ampullae on the anterior vertical and the two horizontal semicircular

---

*Conventionally called auditory or acoustic in tetrapods, although it has more than an auditory function.

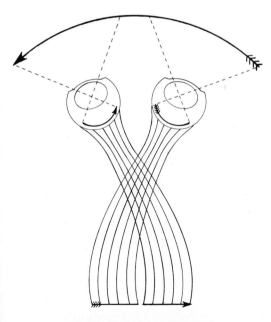 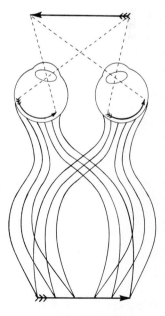

SUBMAMMALIAN VERTEBRATE   HIGHER PRIMATE

Fig. 15-25. Decussation of optic nerve fibers in optic chiasma in vertebrates below mammals contrasted with higher primates.

ducts. The posterior root innervates the ampulla on the posterior vertical duct, the sacculus, and the lagena.

Commencing with amphibians the lagena enlarges and becomes the cochlea for hearing. As a result, the posterior root enlarges and, with its branches, becomes the **cochlear nerve.** The anterior root is then called the **vestibular nerve.** The nerves have a **cochlear** or **vestibular ganglion** on their pathway. Since the cochlear ganglion spirals within the cochlea of mammals it is also called the **spiral ganglion.**

In some mammals (rat and mouse but not cat or bat) large sensory cell bodies are distributed within the eighth nerves along their entire length. These are cell bodies of second-order sensory neurons. They are stimulated by collateral (side) branches of incoming fibers; and because their axons end on other second-order neurons in the medulla they reinforce stimuli coming from the receptor.

Eyeball muscle nerves

NERVES III, IV, AND VI (OCULOMOTOR, TROCHLEAR, AND ABDUCENS)

The third, fourth, and sixth nerves supply the superior oblique (IV), external rectus (VI), the four remaining extrinsic eyeball muscles (III), and certain other myotomal muscles of the eyes (Table 10-3). These eyeball muscle nerves resemble spinal nerves that have lost their dorsal roots. In addition to somatic motor fibers the nerves contain sensory fibers for proprioception from the muscles innervated.

Nerve III arises ventrally from the mesencephalon. Nerve IV is the only nerve arising dorsally from the brain (anterior roof of the fourth ventricle) and one of the few nerves with motor fibers that decussate before emerging. Nerve VI emerges ventrally at the anterior end of the hindbrain. Nerves IV and VI are the smallest of the cranial nerves, having fewest fibers. The cell bodies of all fibers in these nerves, both motor and proprioceptive, are in nuclei within the central nervous system. Therefore the nerves have no sensory ganglia.

Nerve III contains visceral motor fibers that end in the ciliary ganglion of the autonomic nervous system (Fig. 15-32). From the ganglion, postganglionic fibers pass to the sphincter muscles of the iris diaphragm and constrict the pupil, and to the ciliary body of the eye, which governs the position or thickness of the lens for visual accommodation.

Branchiomeric nerves

One characteristic of vertebrates is the development of a series of embryonic pharyngeal arches. The fate of the skeleton and muscles of these arches has already been discussed. Whether the animal is to become fish or tetrapod, the muscles derived from the first arch are supplied by cranial nerve V; those from the second arch, by nerve VII; from the third arch, by nerve IX; and from succeeding arches, by nerve X. Since V, VII, IX, and X innervate branchiomeric muscles, they are branchiomeric nerves.

Branchiomeric nerves are mixed nerves. In addition to innervating branchiomeric muscles, they have other important motor and sensory functions. Some of their motor fibers are components of the autonomic nervous system, their sensory fibers supply several varieties of sense organs, and each nerve includes proprioceptive fibers. The distribution of branchiomeric nerves in *Squalus* illustrates the generalized pattern (Fig. 15-26). Alterations in tetrapods are chiefly the result of elimination of gills and other adaptations to terrestrial life.

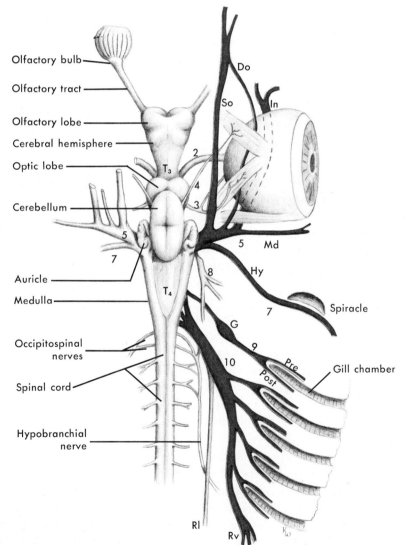

Fig. 15-26. Brain and cranial nerves II to X of *Squalus acanthias,* dorsal view. Branchiomeric nerves are shown in red. **Do,** Deep ophthalmic; **G,** petrosal ganglion; **Hy,** hyomandibular; **In,** infraorbital; **Md,** mandibular; **Pre,** pretrematic; **Post,** posttrematic; **So,** superficial ophthalmic; **Rl,** ramus lateralis (lateral-line nerve) of vagus; **Rv,** ramus visceralis of vagus; **T$_3$** and **T$_4$,** tela choroidea of third and fourth ventricles. The pineal body has been removed. The three eyeball muscles shown are, commencing anteriorly, superior oblique, superior rectus, and lateral rectus.

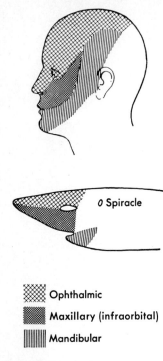

0 Spiracle

▨ Ophthalmic

▨ Maxillary (infraorbital)

▥ Mandibular

Fig. 15-27. Cutaneous distribution of the trigeminal nerve of vertebrates.

NERVE V (TRIGEMINAL)

The fifth nerve arises from the anterior end of the hindbrain and typically exhibits three divisions: **ophthalmic, maxillary,** and **mandibular.** In fishes the ophthalmic may be subdivided into superficial and deep ophthalmic nerves and the maxillary is also called infraorbital. All branches contain sensory fibers. Only the mandibular branch contains motor fibers.

Via its three divisions cranial nerve V is sensory to the ectoderm of the head, including the teeth, anterior part of the tongue, and nasal epithelium, for general cutaneous sensation (Fig. 15-27). The mandibular branch also contains proprioceptive fibers. The cell bodies of all sensory fibers except proprioceptive are found in the **trigeminal ganglion** unless, as in some lower vertebrates, the ophthalmic division has its own ganglion.

The mandibular nerve is motor to all muscles derived from the first pharyngeal arch. The predominant distribution is therefore to muscles of the jaws. It also operates the **tensor tympani** muscle attached to the malleus in mammals. This is not surprising since the malleus has been shown to be the displaced posterior tip of the lower jaw of synapsid reptiles. Table 10-5 gives the motor distribution of cranial nerve V.

NERVE VII (FACIAL)

The seventh nerve arises from the anterior end of the hindbrain in close association with the fifth. In sharks the fifth and seventh nerves have common (trigeminofacial) roots.

Nerve VII is sensory to the neuromast organs on the head of fishes and aquatic amphibians. With adaptation to land, these sensory fibers were lost. Branches also supply taste buds in the pharynx at the level of the first and second arches, any taste buds on the external surface of fishes, and taste buds on the anterior part of the tongue in tetrapods. Nerve VII also contains general sensory fibers from the endoderm of the second arch and proprioceptive fibers from the muscles of the arch. The cell bodies of all sensory fibers, except proprioceptive, are in the **facial ganglion.**

The facial nerve is motor to muscles of the second arch (Table 10-5). These include the mimetic muscles of mammals. Since the stapes is a derivative of the hyoid arch, the stapedial muscle of mammals is also innervated by the seventh nerve. The seventh nerve in mammals also contains visceral motor fibers to the submandibular and sphenopalatine ganglia (Figs. 15-29 and 15-32). The submandibular ganglion innervates the submandibular and sublingual salivary glands. The sphenopalatine innervates the lacrimal gland and mucous membranes of the nose.

NERVE IX (GLOSSOPHARYNGEAL)

The ninth nerve arises from the medulla. In sharks it has three major branches and typifies the distribution of branchiomeric nerves. These branches are **pretrematic** (sensory), **pharyngeal** (sensory), and **posttrematic** (mixed).* The pretrematic branch supplies the anterior demibranch of the first gill chamber for general sensation (Fig. 15-26). The pharyngeal branch supplies taste buds and general visceral receptors in the pharyngeal mucosa at the level of the third visceral arch. The posttrematic branch is sensory to the demibranch in the posterior wall of the first gill chamber, motor to the muscles of the third visceral arch, and proprioceptive from those muscles. A small **lateral-line branch** of IX supplies a short segment of the lateral-line canal at the junction of head and trunk.

Preganglionic fibers of the autonomic nervous system are present in IX. They have not been fully explored in all vertebrates, but in mammals they innervate the otic ganglion, from which postganglionic fibers pass to the parotid salivary glands.

With loss of gills and neuromast organs during adaptation to life on land, the ninth nerve lost many fibers. It continues to supply surviving taste buds on the third arch mucosa (on the posterior part of the tongue of mammals) and general receptors on the posterior part of the tongue and in the upper pharynx. Of the branchiomeric muscles of the third arch, only a stylopharyngeus remains in mammals.

The sensory cell bodies of nerve IX, except those for proprioception, are found in the **petrosal ganglion** of lower vertebrates, and in the **superior** and **inferior glossopharyngeal ganglia** of mammals. The superior ganglion is derived from a neural crest. The inferior ganglion is derived chiefly from an ectodermal placode. In fishes the lateral-line branch has its own ganglion.

NERVE X (VAGUS)

The vagus arises from a series of rootlets along the lateral aspect of the medulla. The branchiomeric components of the vagus in *Squalus* consist of a series of four trunks (more in elasmobranchs with more gill chambers), each exhibiting a pretrematic, posttrematic, and pharyngeal branch distributed as in nerve IX (Fig. 15-26). The pretrematic branches supply the anterior walls of the last four gill chambers. Posttrematic branches supply the posterior walls of these chambers and are motor to arches IV to VII. The vagus is therefore the

---

*The maxillary and mandibular branches of nerve V in fishes are functionally equivalent to pretrematic and posttrematic nerves farther caudad. The pretrematic branch of VII in fishes has joined the maxillary of V to form an infraorbital trunk, and the posttrematic branch of VII (behind the spiracle) is the hyomandibular nerve. The pharyngeal branch of VII in sharks is better known as the palatine.

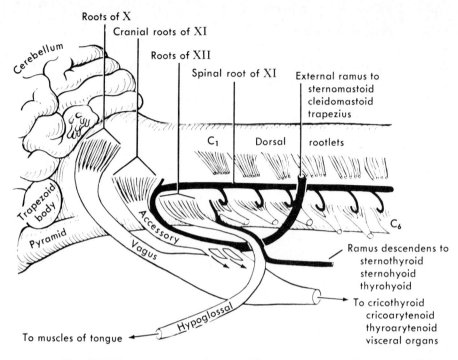

Fig. 15-28. Vagus, spinal accessory, and hypoglossal nerves of a mammal. The hypoglossal rootlets are in series with the ventral roots of the spinal nerves. Components in black are spinal nerve contributions. C_1, Dorsal rootlets of the first cervical spinal nerve; C_6, ventral rootlets of the sixth cervical spinal nerve. Nerve XI contributes an internal ramus (arrows) to the vagus.

chief respiratory nerve of fishes. The pharyngeal branches supply the pharyngeal epithelium for taste and general sensation.

In addition to branchiomeric components, the vagus in *Squalus* has two other major trunks. The **ramus lateralis** is sensory to the lateral-line canal all the way to the tip of the tail, and the **ramus visceralis** supplies afferent and efferent visceral fibers to the coelomic viscera.

During the process of adapting to land the vagus lost those functions associated solely with life in the water but retained the others. The prominent lateral-line branch disappeared. The sensory branches to gill chambers were lost. However, general receptors in the pharyngeal epithelium and taste buds in the vicinity of the glottis continue to be supplied by the vagus. Surviving also are the motor branches to any remaining branchiomeric muscles of the fourth and successive arches. These are chiefly the cricothyroid, cricoarytenoid, and thyroarytenoid muscles. Since much of the distribution of the vagus has been lost in tetrapods, the ramus visceralis has become the major component of the nerve. It continues to supply afferent and efferent fibers to the heart and other coelomic viscera.

In fishes as well as in tetrapods the vagus supplies preganglionic fibers to certain terminal ganglia of the autonomic system in the trunk (Fig. 15-32). Included in amniotes are autonomic fibers contributed by the internal ramus of the accessory nerve (Fig. 15-28). The vagal nerve also contains proprioceptive fibers.

The cell bodies of all sensory fibers of the vagal nerve, except those for proprioception, are found in one or more ganglia. In some elasmobranchs each of the four or more branches to the gills has its own **epibranchial ganglion,** and it is likely that these branches were at one time four separate cranial nerves. In birds and mammals nerves IX and X have two sensory ganglia, a **superior,** chiefly somatic, and an **inferior,** chiefly visceral. The superior ganglia are derived from neural crests, the inferior ganglia from epibranchial placodes.

The innervation of the mucosa of the oral cavity and pharynx by nerves V, VII, IX, and X, *in that sequence,* in all vertebrates from fish to man, demonstrates the negligible effects of life on land on the sensory innervation of the moist pharyngeal endoderm.

Accessory and hypoglossal nerves

NERVE XI (ACCESSORY)

The spinal accessory nerve constitutes an eleventh cranial nerve in amniotes. It is purely motor. In mammals it has a series of **cranial roots,** which arise from the medulla, and a **spinal root** from the cord (Fig. 15-28). It appears to be derived from a primitive posteriormost branchial nerve and one or more occipitospinal nerves, which are otherwise missing in amniotes.

The nucleus of origin of the motor fibers in the spinal root of the accessory nerve occupies several segments of the cord—five or six in humans, seven in horses, fewer in many mammals. The spinal root-lets unite to form a common trunk that passes cephalad close to the cord and enters the cranial cavity via the foramen magnum. Within the cranial cavity the spinal root joins the cranial roots to form the eleventh nerve (Fig. 15-28). Near the jugular foramen the cranial root fibers join the vagus to be distributed with the latter as the **internal ramus of the accessory nerve.** The internal ramus is composed of motor fibers to striated muscles of the pharynx and larynx and of preganglionic fibers to the coelomic viscera. The fibers of spinal origin form the **external ramus** supplying the trapezius, sternomastoid, and cleidomastoid muscles. The motor cell bodies for the fibers of spinal origin are not in the somatic efferent column of the cord, which consists of cell bodies whose fibers supply myotomal muscles. This is one basis for thinking that part of the accessory nerve is a vestigial branchiomeric nerve.

NERVE XII (HYPOGLOSSAL)

The twelfth nerve of amniotes is motor except for proprioceptive fibers. It arises from the hypoglossal nucleus in the medulla by a series of ventral rootlets and innervates the muscles of the tongue (Figs. 10-6, 15-4, *B*, and 15-28). On emerging from the hypoglossal foramen in mammals the nerve may receive fibers from one or more anterior cervical spinal nerves. Some of these spinal nerve fibers are distributed via the hypoglossal nerve to the geniohyoid muscle. The rest emerge from nerve XII as a **ramus descendens,** which joins a loose plexus of cervical spinal nerves supplying the sternohyoid, sternothyroid, and thyrohyoid muscles of the neck.

That the hypoglossal is a cranial rather than a spinal nerve is dictated solely by the location of the foramen magnum. *Actually,* it is a spinal nerve that became "locked up" in the braincase. Like spinal nerves, the hypoglossal develops an embryonic dorsal root and ganglion (**Froriep's ganglion**). The root and ganglion later disappear.

The twelfth nerve is a derivative of the occipitospinal series of fishes and amphibians, as may be deduced from the following facts: (1) Occipitospinal nerves have been reduced in number above fishes, whereas the number of cranial nerves has increased. (2) The twelfth nerve, like many occipitospinal nerves, lacks a dorsal root. (3) The occipitospinal nerves of lower vertebrates supply hypobranchial muscles, and the tongue is hypobranchial muscle. (4) Whereas the tongue muscle is supplied by the last cranial nerve in amniotes, it is supplied by the first spinal nerve in amphibians.

Innervation of the mammalian tongue: an anatomical legacy

The innervation of the mammalian tongue illustrates how a single organ may be served by numerous nerves, depending on the ontogenetic and phylogenetic history of its parts (Fig. 15-29). The mucosa of the anterior part of the tongue is first arch endoderm and is therefore innervated by nerve V for general sensations. The taste buds on this part of the tongue are innervated by nerve VII, which supplies taste buds on the first and second arches in fishes. The mucosa on the posterior part of the tongue is innervated by nerve IX for both general sensation and taste because of the origin of this mucosa from the third visceral arch. The muscles of the tongue are myotomal and are innervated by nerve XII.

Although four cranial nerves innervate the tongue, only three nerves may be traced into it, since the taste fibers from nerve VII (in the chorda tympani branch) unite with the lingual branch of nerve V just before the latter reaches the tongue.

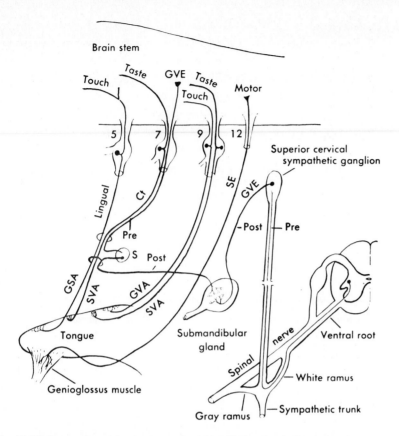

Fig. 15-29. Innervation of the tongue and submandibular gland of a mammal (based on cat and man). **5, 7, 9,** and **12,** Cranial nerves; **Ct,** chorda tympani; **Pre** and **Post,** preganglionic and postganglionic fibers of the autonomic nervous system; **S,** submandibular ganglion of the autonomic system. A key to the fiber components (**GSA, SE,** and so forth) is given in Tables 15-1 and 15-3.

Fiber components of cranial nerves

As mentioned earlier, fibers in spinal nerves may be classified in four functional categories (GSA, GVA, SE, and GVE), each supplying specific types of general receptors or effectors (Table 15-1). One or more of these components may be found also in most cranial nerves: SE in III, IV, VI, and XII; GVE (autonomic fibers) in III, VII, IX, X, and XI; GSA chiefly in V; and GVA in VII, IX, and X. In addition to the foregoing *general* fiber components, certain cranial nerves contain *special* components of which there are three types—SSA, SVA, and SVE (Table 15-3). Each of the foregoing varieties of nerve fibers commences or terminates in the brain or cord in a column of nuclei preempted by that specific component (Fig. 15-30).

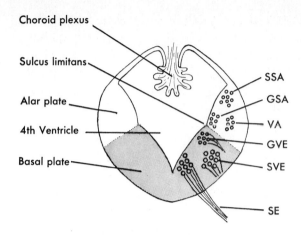

Fig. 15-30. Cross section of medulla showing location of certain nuclei. Sensory nuclei are in the alar plate; motor nuclei, in the basal plate. The two plates are delimited by the sulcus limitans. **Se,** Somatic motor fibers from cell bodies in somatic motor column. **VA,** Sensory nucleus for visceral input, except smell. The remaining nuclei are identified in Tables 15-1 and 15-3.

Table 15-3. Special fiber components of cranial nerves*

Components	Innervation and nerve

Special somatic afferent fibers (SSA)	Special somatic receptors
	  Retina (II)
	  Membranous labyrinth (VIII)
	  Neuromast organs (VII, IX, and X)

Special visceral afferent fibers (SVA)	Special visceral receptors
	  Olfactory epithelium (I)
	  Taste buds (VII, IX, and X)

Special visceral efferent fibers (SVE)	Branchiomeric muscle (V, VII, IX, X, and XI)

*In addition to these special components, cranial nerves other than I, II, and VIII have one or more of the general components listed in Table 15-1.

AUTONOMIC NERVOUS SYSTEM

The autonomic nervous system is that part of the nervous system that innervates glands and smooth and cardiac muscle. It consists chiefly of autonomic nerves, plexuses, and ganglia (Figs. 15-31 and 15-32). It does not, however, constitute an anatomical entity; that is, it cannot be completely dissected away from the rest of the nervous system, since its components commence inside the central nervous system and emerge via cranial or spinal nerves. It is entirely a visceral motor system. However, sensory fibers from the viscera use autonomic pathways to reach cranial and spinal nerves.

Two motor neurons in series conduct the impulse from the brain or cord to a typical visceral effector. The cell body of the first neuron (**preganglionic neuron**) is in a visceral efferent nucleus in the central nervous system, and the preganglionic fiber terminates in an autonomic ganglion. The cell body of the second neuron (**postganglionic neuron**) is in an autonomic ganglion. Its fiber extends to the effector (see Fig. 15-10 and nerve III in Fig. 15-32). Autonomic fibers have a very thin myelin sheath or none.

The autonomic nervous system is composed of (1) a **sympathetic system** that emerges from the cord via most of the spinal nerves of the trunk (thoracicolumbar nerves in the higher vertebrates) and (2) a **parasympathetic system** that emerges from the brain via cranial nerves III (except cyclostomes), VII, IX, X, and XI and, in tetrapods, from the cord via sacral spinal nerves (Fig. 15-32). Most visceral effectors except those in the skin are supplied by postganglionic fibers from both systems (Fig. 15-32, iris diaphragm, stomach, urinary bladder). The stimulatory effects of one system modulate the inhibitory effects of the other to bring about an appropriate response. The heart of cyclostomes has no innervation; in other fishes it is innervated by the vagus only, and in tetrapods it has a double innervation, the vagus being inhibitory, the sympathetic system excitatory. All major components of the sympathetic system of reptiles, birds, and mammals are already present in amphibians. Differences in higher tetrapods are more quantitative than qualitative.

Autonomic ganglia may be classified in three categories: **paravertebral, collateral,** and **terminal.** Paravertebral ganglia lie close to the vertebral column. In teleosts and all tetrapods they are interconnected by longitudinal strands of autonomic fibers to form a ganglionated chain, the **sympathetic trunk** (Fig. 15-32, gray). There is usually one paravertebral ganglion for each spinal nerve of the trunk. There are fewer in the neck and none in the sacral region. Paravertebral ganglia of the trunk are connected to the nearest spinal nerve by a **white ramus communicans,** which conducts preganglionic fibers from the spinal nerve to the ganglion (Fig. 15-10).* Postganglionic fibers with cell bodies in paravertebral ganglia supply viscera of the head, neck, coelom, and visceral effectors in the skin (vasomotor, plumomotor or pilomotor, secretory, chromatophores). Postganglionic fibers going to the skin are returned to the spinal cord by a **gray ramus communicans** (Figs. 15-10 and 15-32). The skin of cyclostomes and elasmobranchs, however, appears to lack autonomic innervation, and there are no gray rami. White rami also conduct visceral afferent fibers *to* spinal nerves (Fig. 15-10, GVA).

Collateral ganglia are in the head (ciliary, submandibular, sphenopalatine, otic, in mammals) and in the abdomen at the base of a major

---

*There are no white rami in the neck or sacral region.

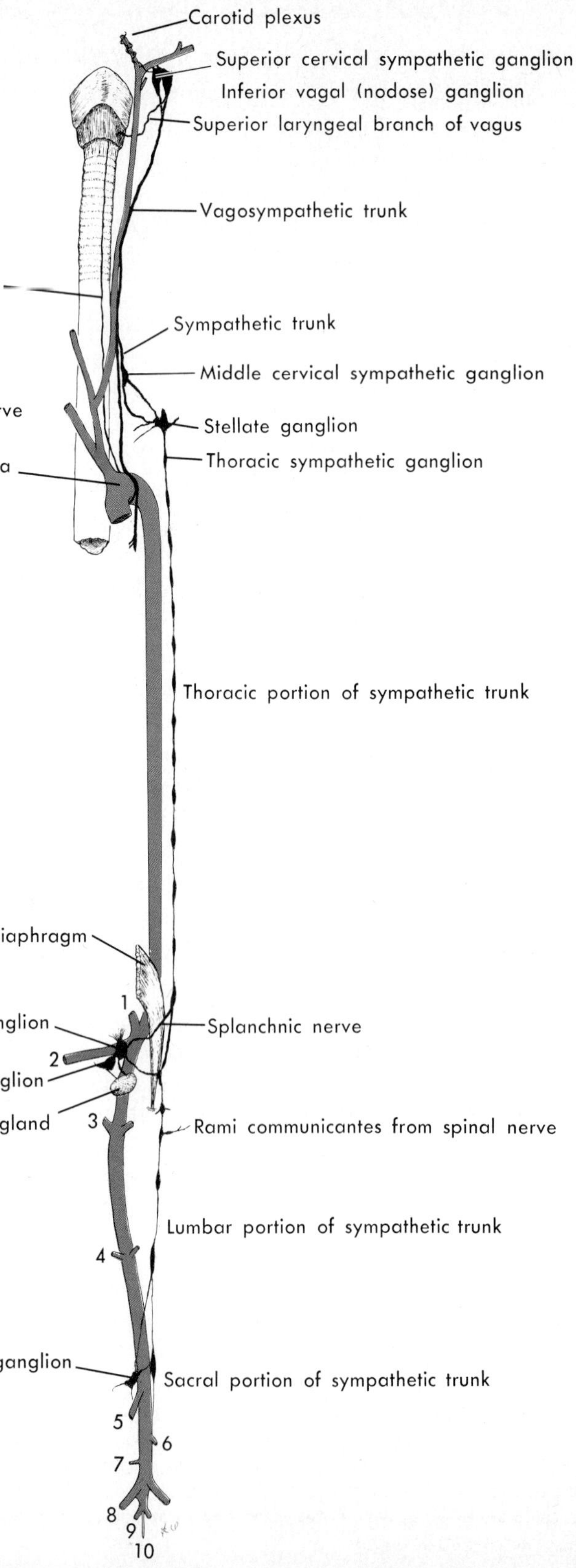

Carotid plexus

Superior cervical sympathetic ganglion

Inferior vagal (nodose) ganglion

Superior laryngeal branch of vagus

Vagosympathetic trunk

Left recurrent laryngeal nerve

Sympathetic trunk

Middle cervical sympathetic ganglion

Vagal nerve

Stellate ganglion

Arch of aorta

Thoracic sympathetic ganglion

Fig. 15-31. Left sympathetic trunk and associated structures of a cat. **1** to **10**, Major branches of abdominal aorta: **1**, celiac; **2**, superior mesenteric; **3**, renal; **4**, spermatic or ovarian; **5**, inferior mesenteric; **6** and **7**, left and right iliolumbars; **8**, external iliac; **9**, internal iliac; **10**, median sacral. The recurrent laryngeal nerve is not part of the autonomic system. In cats, as in some other mammals, the vagus nerve and sympathetic trunk in the neck are wrapped in a common sheath to form a vagosympathetic trunk.

Thoracic portion of sympathetic trunk

Crus of diaphragm

Celiac ganglion

Splanchnic nerve

Superior mesenteric ganglion

Adrenal gland

Rami communicantes from spinal nerve

Lumbar portion of sympathetic trunk

Inferior mesenteric ganglion

Sacral portion of sympathetic trunk

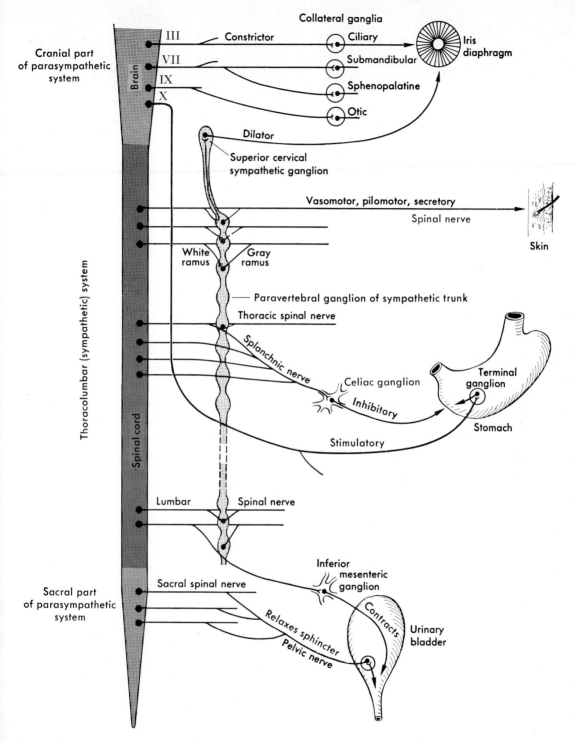

Fig. 15-32. Representative components of the autonomic nervous system of a mammal. Innervation of iris diaphragm, skin, stomach, and urinary bladder. Arrows emphasize dual control exerted elsewhere than in the skin by craniosacral and thoracolumbar systems. Preganglionic fibers are those with a cell body (black dot) in the central nervous system. Postganglionic fibers are those with a cell body in a ganglion. Other spinal nerves in addition to those shown contain autonomic fibers. Sympathetic trunk is gray.

Table 15-4. Innervation and peripheral distribution of autonomic ganglia of the head of mammals

Ganglion	Receives fibers from:	Projects fibers to:
Ciliary	Oculomotor nerve	Ciliary body of eye Sphincter muscles of iris
Submandibular	Facial nerve	Submandibular gland Sublingual gland
Sphenopalatine	Facial nerve	Lacrimal gland Glands of nose and pharyngeal mucosa
Otic	Glossopharyngeal nerve	Parotid gland

branch of the aorta (coeliac, superior mesenteric, inferior mesenteric, and others). They are not part of a chain. Collateral ganglia in the trunk receive preganglionic sympathetic fibers from spinal nerves via autonomic nerves such as the splanchnic (Fig. 15-32) and supply postganglionic fibers to abdominal and pelvic viscera. The neural connections of collateral ganglia of the head of mammals are given in Table 15-4.

Terminal ganglia are embedded in the walls of the organ innervated. They occur only in the trunk at the endings of preganglionic fibers of the parasympathetic system. Cell bodies in these ganglia send very short postganglionic fibers to the innervated tissue.

On emerging from autonomic ganglia, postganglionic fibers (other than those returning to spinal nerves via a gray ramus) form plexuses on the surface of nearby blood vessels and accompany these vessels to the organs. For example, the carotid and celiac plexuses consist of fibers emerging from the superior cervical and celiac ganglia, respectively.

In all vertebrates the autonomic nervous system is primarily involuntary; that is, motor impulses are initiated reflexly by visceral afferent inpulses. We are seldom aware of the stimulus or the response. Some voluntary control is possible by the use of biofeedback.

CHAPTER SUMMARY

1. The neuron is the functional unit of the nervous system. It consists of a cell body and one or more processes. The long process is an axon, or nerve fiber.

2. A nerve is a bundle of nerve fibers outside the central nervous system. A tract is a bundle of nerve fibers within the central nervous system.

3. A nucleus is a group of similarly functioning cell bodies inside the central nervous system. Nuclei constitute the gray matter of the brain and cord.

4. A ganglion is a group of cell bodies outside the central nervous system. Ganglia are sensory or autonomic (motor).

5. Neurotransmitters are amines that transmit nerve impulses across synapses. Neurosecretions are polypeptide hormones secreted by neurosecretory neurons.

6. The embryonic neural tube caudal to the forebrain consists of alar and basal plates that are sensory and motor, respectively. The alar plate gives rise to second-order sensory neurons. The basal plate gives rise to motor neurons other than postganglionic. Neural crests and ectodermal placodes give rise to most first-order sensory neurons and, by migration of neuroblasts, to postganglionic motor neurons.

7. The cell bodies of motor neurons are inside the brain or cord with one exception: the cell bodies of postganglionic fibers of the autonomic nervous system are in autonomic ganglia.

8. Cell bodies of first-order sensory neurons in higher vertebrates are found in sensory ganglia on the nerves with three major exceptions: the cell bodies of olfactory nerve fibers are in the olfactory epithelium, the cell bodies of optic nerve fibers are in the retina, and those of proprioceptive fibers of cranial nerves are in the mesencephalon. Olfactory neurons and rods and cones are neurosensory cells.

9. Most spinal nerves exhibit sensory ganglia on their dorsal roots. The following cranial nerves have sensory ganglia: V (trigeminal), VII (facial), VIII (cochlear and vestibular), IX (petrosal; in mammals, inferior and superior glossopharyngeal), and X (in mammals, inferior and superior vagal).

10. Spinal nerves are metameric in origin and distribution. Most spinal nerves exhibit dorsal and ventral roots and dorsal, ventral, and communicating rami. Ventral rami often unite to form simple or complicated plexuses.

11. There is evidence that in the earliest vertebrates dorsal and ventral roots did not unite, dorsal roots were mixed and ventral roots were motor, and the cell bodies of the sensory fibers were not aggregated in ganglia. These conditions are found in lampreys, except that some sensory cell bodies aggregate on the dorsal root. Above cyclostomes, dorsal and ventral roots unite, ventral roots are motor, and dorsal roots are chiefly or wholly sensory.

12. Spinal nerves contain the following fiber components: GSA, SE, GVA, and GVE. Cranial nerves may contain one or more of the preceding and also one or more of the following: SSA, SVA, and SVE.

13. Occipitospinal nerves lacking sensory roots and supplying hypobranchial musculature arise between the vagus and first typical spinal nerves. They are more numerous in lower vertebrates and are represented in amniotes by part of nerve XI and by nerve XII.

14. Anamniotes have 10 pairs of cranial nerves, amniotes have 12. Nerves I, II, and VIII are purely sensory. Nerves III, IV, and VI supply the myotomal muscles of the eyeball. Nerves V, VII, IX, and X are branchiomeric.

15. Cranial nerve V is the chief nerve for cutaneous sensation on the surface of the head and the ectodermal part of the oral cavity. Nerves VII, IX, and X supply neuromast organs and tast buds.

16. Nerve XI has cranial and spinal roots and is derived from the caudal end of the branchiomeric series and from occipitospinal nerves. The internal ramus contains GVE fibers that are distributed with the vagus. The external ramus supplies the trapezius and sternocleidomastoid muscles.

17. Nerve XII represents one or more occipitospinal nerves and supplies the muscles of the tongue.

18. The terminal nerve is a vestige of an anterior branchiomeric nerve. It supplies a restricted region of the nasal mucosa with general sensory and vasomotor fibers.

19. The autonomic nervous system innervates smooth and cardiac muscles and glands. Preganglionic fibers of the craniosacral (parasympathetic) division emerge from the brain via cranial nerves III, VII, IX, X, and XI and from the sacral region of the cord via sacral spinal nerves. Preganglionic fibers of the thoracolumbar (sympathetic) division emerge from the cord via thoracic and lumbar spinal nerves.

20. The autonomic ganglia of the head and their associated nerves are ciliary (III), sphenopalatine (VII), submandibular (VII), and otic (IX). These are parasympathetic ganglia.

21. Autonomic ganglia are paravertebral (sympathetic chain), collateral (in head or near abdominal aorta), and terminal (in trunk close to or within the organ innervated). They contain cell bodies of postganglionic neurons.

22. Most viscera are supplied by sympathetic and parasympathetic fibers, but skin receives only sympathetic fibers.

23. A meninx primitiva surrounds the brain and cord in some fishes. A dura mater and leptomeninx develop in most vertebrates. In a few birds and in mammals the leptomeninx differentiates into pia mater and arachnoid membranes.

24. The spinal cord often exhibits cervical and lumbar enlargements and, in fishes, a urophysis. When the cord is shorter than the vertebral column, the cord terminates in a filum terminale surrounded by a cauda equina.

25. Cerebrospinal fluid is secreted by choroid plexuses in the lateral, third, and fourth ventricles. The fluid fills the brain ventricles and central canal of the spinal cord and escapes to the meningeal spaces via foramina in the roof of the fourth ventricle.

26. Neuroglia consists of oligodendroglia, microglia, and astroglia. Schwann cells make up a neurilemma in the periphery and produce myelin in nerves.

27. The brain has three major subdivisions: prosencephalon (forebrain), mesencephalon (midbrain), and rhombencephalon (hindbrain). The more prominent brain stuctures are outlined in the following chart.

PROSENCEPHALON (FOREBRAIN)
Telencephalon
  Rhinencephalon
    Olfactory bulbs
    Olfactory tracts
    Olfactory lobes
  Cerebral hemispheres
    Corpora striata (basal ganglia)
    Corpus callosum
    Neocortex on pallium
    Paraphysis
  Lateral ventricles
Diencephalon
  Epithalamus
    Habenulae
    Pineal
    Parapineal
  Thalamus
  Hypothalamus
  Optic chiasma
  Infundibular stalk and pituitary
  Saccus vasculosus
  Third ventricle
  Circle of Willis

MESENCEPHALON (MIDBRAIN)
Optic lobes ⎫
Auditory lobes ⎬ Tectum (roof)
Cerebral peduncles (tegmental)
Mesencephalic nucleus
Cerebral aqueduct

RHOMBENCEPHALON (HINDBRAIN)
Metencephalon
  Cerebellum
  Pons
  Fourth ventricle
Myelencephalon
  Medulla oblongata
  Vagal lobes
  Pyramids
  Fourth ventricle

LITERATURE CITED AND SELECTED READINGS

1. Ariëns Kappers, C.U., Huber, G.C., and Crosby, E.C.: The comparative anatomy of the nervous system of vertebrates, including man, New York, 1936, The Macmillan Co. (Republished by Hafner Publishing Co., Inc., 1960.)

2. Bullock, T.H., and Horridge, G.A.: Structure and function in the nervous systems of invertebrates, 2 vols., San Francisco, 1965, W.H. Freeman and Co., Publishers.

3. Flood, P.R.: A peculiar mode of muscular innervation in amphioxus. Light and electron microscopic studies of the so-called ventral roots, Journal of Comparative Neurology **126**:181, 1966.

4. Gans, C., Northcutt, R.G., and Ulinski, P., editors: Biology of the reptilia, vols. 9 and 10, New York, 1979, Academic Press, Inc.

5. Kier, E.L.: The cerebral ventricles: a phylogenetic and ontogenetic study, St. Louis, 1977, The C.V. Mosby Co.

6. Morell, P., and Norton, W.T.: Myelin, Scientific American **242**(5):88, 1980.

7. Nicol, J.A.C.: Autonomic nervous system in lower chordates, Biological Reviews **27**:1, 1952.

8. Noback, C.R.: The human nervous system, ed. 2, New York, 1975, McGraw-Hill Book Co.

9. Norris, H.W., and Hughes, S.P.: The cranial, occipital, and anterior spinal nerves of the dogfish, *Squalus acanthias*, Journal of Comparative Neurology **31**:293, 1920.

10. Pearson, R., and Pearson, L.: The vertebrate brain, New York, 1976, Academic Press, Inc.

11. Pick, J.: The autonomic nervous system: morphological, comparative, clinical, and surgical aspects, Philadelphia, 1970, J.B. Lippincott Co.
12. Sarnat, H.B., and Netsky, M.G.: Evolution of the nervous system, New York, 1974, Oxford University Press.
13. Shuangshoti, S., and Netsky, M.G.: Choroid plexus and paraphysis in lower vertebrates, Journal of Morphology **120:**157, 1966.
14. Stevens, C.F.: The neuron, Scientific American **241**(3):54, 1979.

Symposium in American Zoologist

Revent advances in the biology of sharks. Section III. Central nervous system and sense organs, **17:**411, 1977.

CHAPTER 16

Sense organs

Natural selection has resulted in the evolution of a large variety of simple and complex sense organs, or receptors, for monitoring the external and internal environments. Sense organs are transducers of energy. They change mechanical, electrical, thermal, chemical, or radiant energy into nerve impulses in sensory fibers.

Somatic receptors provide information about the external environment and the individual's orientation in it. The category does not include chemoreceptors. Their sensory fibers terminate in somatic sensory nuclei in the cord or brain (Fig. 15-30, SSA, GSA). As a result of this information an animal makes appropriate striated muscle responses that tend to ensure survival. For example, stimuli from an approaching potential enemy will initiate locomotion or a change in posture, and input from surrounding fishes in a school reflexly maintains the individual's orientation in the dynamic mass.

Visceral receptors provide information about the environment within the animal, and olfactory and gustatory (taste) information. Their sensory fibers end in the cord or brain in visceral sensory nuclei (Fig. 15-30, VA), or in the olfactory bulb. As one result, the internal environment is reflexly maintained or adjusted as necessary. Since most chemical stimulants for smell and taste originate in the environment, they evoke reorientation of the organism in space as well as affecting the internal environment.

Although the endings of most sensory fibers are stimulated directly, some require an intermediary nonnervous **receptor cell** to serve as a transducer of the energy. **Hair cells** are one variety. They are elongated or bulblike epithelial cells with a variable number of short stereocilia and usually a single kinocilium projecting into the fluid that bathes the sensory epithelium. The cilia are usually embedded in a gelatinous mass (Fig. 16-1). In contact with the base of a hair cell is the sensory ending. Mechanical displacement of the cilia initiates impulses in the sensory fiber. Epithelial cells with microvilli instead of cilia serve as intermediary transducers of stimuli that invoke taste, but not smell.

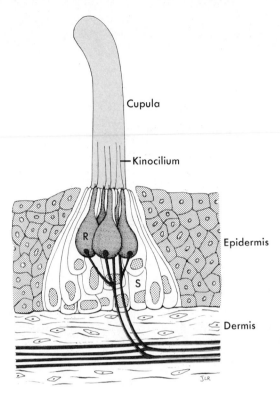

Cupula

Kinocilium

Epidermis

Dermis

Fig. 16-1. A neuromast organ in the epidermis of a necturus. **R,** Hair cell (receptor cell) innervated by a heavily myelinated sensory nerve fiber (dark red) and having a single kinocilium and three or four short delicate stereocilia extending into the cupula; **S,** supporting cell.

Sense organs can be classified as either general or special. **General receptors** are widely distributed on or in the body. **Special receptors** have a limited distribution, being confined to the head except in fishes and aquatic amphibians.

SPECIAL SOMATIC RECEPTORS
Neuromast organs

Neuromasts are receptors in the skin of fishes and aquatic amphibians that consist of hair cells embedded in a gelatinous **cupula, supporting (sustentacular) cells,** and **sensory nerve endings** (Fig. 16-1). They monitor mechanical, electrical, and thermal components of the surrounding water. They are on the head and in a longitudinal line on the side of the trunk and tail. Primitive neuromasts lie in shallow pits or grooves in the epidermis, where the cupula can project directly into the external aqueous environment. These **external neuromasts** are characteristic of cyclostomes, larval amphibians, and aquatic urodeles.

In jawed fishes some neuromasts lie in fluid-filled pits beneath the epidermis and opening to the exterior (**pit organs**), or at the bottom of **ampullae** that secrete their own fluid and retain a long slender

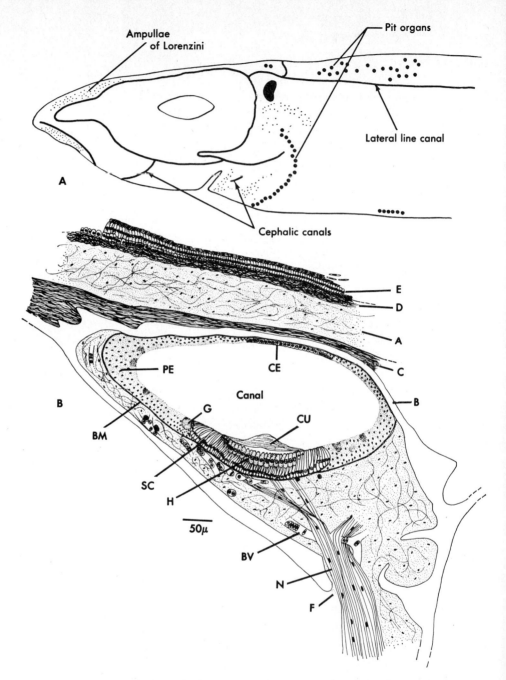

Fig. 16-2. A, Distribution of neuromast organs in skin of a shark. The precise distribution of the several types varies among species. **B,** Lateral-line canal of bony fish in cross section at the level of a neuromast organ. The canal runs longitudinally under the skin embedded in dermal bone *(B)*. *E,* Epidermis; *A, C,* and *D,* dermis. The epithelial lining of the canal rests on a basement membrane *(BM)* and exhibits a cuboidal epithelium *(CE)*, a pseudostratified epithelium *(PE)*, goblet cells *(G)*, and the neuromast organ. The latter is composed of sustentacular cells *(SC)*, sensory cells *(H)*, and a cupula *(CU)*. The sensory nerve *(N)* innervating the neuromast organ penetrates the bone via a foramen *(F)*. A blood vessel *(BV)* is shown approaching the receptor. (From Branson and Moore.[4])

duct to the surface. Ampullae of Lorenzini are abundant on the heads of sharks (Fig. 16-2, *A*), and *Amia* has as many as 3700 on the head alone. Some neuromasts of electric rays are in closed **vesicles of Savi.**

In modern fishes neuromasts have become increasingly isolated from the aqueous environment and lie under the skin in sunken **cephalic** and **lateral-line canals** that are usually embedded in dermal bone (Fig. 16-2, *B*). The canals have pores to the surface at intervals. In sharks the canals are closed on the head but they are open grooves on the tail. In chimaeras the canals form elevated ridges on the surface. Grooves on the dermal armor of acanthodians and placoderms indicate that in early jawed fishes the system was a network of superficial canals covering the entire body. The network has been reduced in modern fishes by loss of many branches and by interruption of the canals at one or more locations. In some recent fishes the canals are restricted to the head.

When larvae of the salamander *Notophthalmus* metamorphose into red efts and migrate to land, the neuromast organs become buried under the proliferating stratum corneum. Later—several years later in some localities— when the eft returns to the water as a sexually mature newt the stratum corneum is shed and the system is again exposed. A well-developed lateral-line canal of anuran tadpoles disappears permanently at metamorphosis. No traces of neuromasts are found in reptiles.

There is considerable agreement that at least part of the neuromast system responds to water currents, to compression waves of low frequencies in the water, to hydrostatic pressure, and to weak electric potentials. Water currents include flow past the organism and currents caused by passing prey, by swimming movements, or by reflection of waves from nearby objects. The information would enable an organism to orient itself appropriately in flowing water (rheotaxis), to avoid enemies, and to participate in schooling. Blind carnivorous fishes inhabiting dark caves may locate food with this system.

With reference to electroreception, most animals produce enough electric potential when their muscles are contracting to make their presence detectable by electroreceptive neuromasts at short range. Electroreception has been demonstrated in the ampullae of Lorenzini. Environmental salinity changes might also be a source of electric potential stimuli. Investigators are hesitant to ascribe sound detection to the system because of the semantic problem of a definition of "sound." Also, there is a possibility that waves of a length usually associated with sound may not activate the system.

The function of the system is probably broad, and its predominant biological role probably varies with habitat—swiftly flowing streams as opposed to the depths of the ocean, for example. Although the precise role of the system remains to be demonstrated, there is no doubt that the neuromast system, along with chemoreceptors and visual organs, consitutes a very important site of information about the external environment in aquatic species.

Neuromast organs arise from embryonic ectodermal placodes that sink into the skin. The membranous labyrinths of fishes arise from identical placodes in linear series with those of the lateral-line canal system and are, therefore, highly complex neuromast systems. Membranous labyrinths and the other neuromasts of fishes collectively make up the **acousticolateralis system** of sense organs, innervated by cranial nerves VII, VIII, IX, and X.

Membranous labyrinth

All vertebrates from fish to man have a pair of fluid-filled membranous labyrinths, or inner ears, embedded in the otic capsule of the skull. The fluid within is **endolymph.** In fishes other than cyclostomes each labyrinth consists of three **semicircular ducts** and two membranous sacs, the **utriculus** and **sacculus** (Fig. 16-3). The lumina of the semicircular ducts are continuous with the cavity within the utriculus, and each duct has a dilation, or **ampulla,** near the junction. The anterior and posterior semicircular ducts are in vertical planes that are perpendicular to each other; the third, or lateral, duct is in a horizontal plane. In the floor of each sacculus in fishes there is a hollow pocket, the **lagena.** In higher tetrapods the lagena has elongated to become a cochlear duct housing the receptor for sound. Emerging dorsally from the site of confluence of the sacculus and utriculus is an **endolymphatic duct** that terminates in a blind endolymphatic sac, except in elasmobranchs, in which they open to the exterior through two small endolymphatic pores on the top of the head. Lampreys have only the vertical semicircular ducts and hagfishes have only the posterior vertical ones. One can only speculate whether the presence

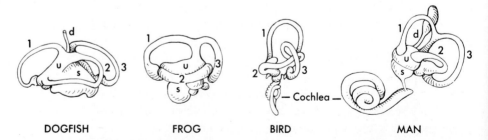

DOGFISH   FROG   BIRD   MAN

Fig. 16-3. Left inner ears of representative vertebrates. **1,** Anterior semicircular duct; **2,** lateral semicircular duct; **3,** posterior semicircular duct; **d,** endolymphatic duct and, in man, sac; **s,** sacculus; **u,** utriculus.

of fewer ducts in cyclostomes is primitive or the result of phylogenetic loss of the missing parts.

In the epithelial lining of the sacculus, utriculus, lagena, and each of the ampullae there are one or more neuromast sites consisting of hair cells, supportive cells, a gelatinous cupula surrounded by endolymph, and sensory endings of the eighth cranial nerve. The sites in the ampullae are **cristae;** those elsewhere are **maculae.** Both are neuromast organs differing only in details. Cristae are perched on an epithelial papilla and have a tall blunt cupula that extends far into the lumen of an ampulla; maculae are broad, flat epithelial mounds having sandlike or stony calcareous **otoliths** embedded in the uppermost layer of a flattened cupula where they form an **otolithic membrane** above the hair cells. (A modified mammalian macula is seen in Fig. 16-7.) The labyrinth is lined by simple squamous epithelial cells except where there are papillae or mounds. Cristae and maculae respond to different components of the stresses created in the endolymph by movements of the head, and the maculae of the utriculus and sacculus lie in different planes.

Otoliths are crystals of calcium carbonate combined with a protein. They grow by accretion. In some species a single otolith nearly fills the sacculus. In others, otoliths are microscopic and abundant. Species differences have made it possible for some fossil sharks to be identified to species level from otoliths alone when only fragments of a skeleton were available. The grains of microscopic otoliths of common laboratory sharks spill out of the sacculus when the latter is ruptured. They can be readily observed with a low-power lens.

Membranous labyrinths arise during embryonic life from surface ectoderm as a pair of auditory placodes, which, in fishes and aquatic amphibians, are in line with the placodes of the lateral-line neuromasts. Each placode sinks into the body to become a fluid-filled vesicle, or **otocyst** (Fig. 16-4). When differentiated, each membranous labyrinth occupies a similarly shaped fluid-filled space, the **cartilaginous or bony labyrinth.** The fluid surrounding the membranous labyrinth is **perilymph,** through which auditory waves must pass to reach the receptors for sound. Fine strands of connective tissue extend across the perilymphatic spaces stabilizing the membranous labyrinth and anchoring it in place.

EQUILIBRATORY FUNCTION OF THE LABYRINTH

The maculae are stimulated in part by acceleration of the head when the animal is traveling in a straight line. For example, linear acceleration tends to carry along the hairs of the macula of the utriculus, but the otolithic membrane, being weighted down by otoliths, resists acceleration. As a result, the hairs are bent in a direction opposite to that of the direction of acceleration and this stimulates the sensory nerve endings. The cristae, on the other hand, projecting pillarlike far into the ampullae, are stimulated as the endolymph in one semicircular duct or another is disturbed by rotation of the head. The sensory impulses generated in the ducts, sacculus, and utriculus by changes in position of the head, or of the head and body, are transmitted to the brain stem and cerebellum, where, as one result, reflex movements of the eyeballs are initiated so the eyes are always looking in a direction compatible with the position of the head. *Voluntary* effort is required to turn your head swiftly to the left while continuing to gaze straight ahead. (Try it!) That the labyrinth controls eyeball movements can be demonstrated by spinning someone in a revolving chair rapidly a number of times and then stopping the chair abruptly. The individual will feel dizzy, and an observer will note that the eyeballs continue to exhibit rapid, jerky, side-to-front-to-side

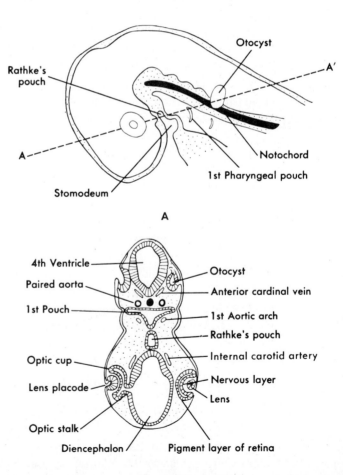

Fig. 16-4. Origin of inner ear (from otocyst), retina (from optic cup), and lens (from lens placode). **A,** Head region of embryo. **B,** Cross section of head at level of A—A'. Left side of **B** is slightly earlier than right side.

movements (nystagmus), which cease as the inert endolymph ceases to apply a shearing force on the cristae of the semicircular ducts.

Input from the labyrinth that is projected to the cerbellum results in reflex changes in position of the head (via neck muscles), trunk, and appendages, which restore the body to proper orientation, as when a cat is turned upside down, dropped from a height, and lands on its paws. The labyrinth therefore plays a role along with proprioceptors in reflexly maintaining appropriate body posture and therefore balance, or equilibrium.

AUDITORY FUNCTION OF THE LABYRINTH AND EVOLUTION OF THE COCHLEA

The labyrinth has an auditory function as far down the phylogenetic scale as some teleost fishes in which maculae respond to longitudinal sinusoidal waves of the amplitude and frequency of sound (low amplitude, high frequency). In Ostariophysi, a very large superorder of mostly freshwater teleosts that includes catfish, goldfish, and carp, sound waves in water evoke waves of similar frequency in the gas in the turgid swim bladder, and these are transmitted to the labyrinth by **weberian ossicles** (Fig. 16-5). These are a series of modified transverse processes of the first three (occasionally four or five) trunk vertebrae that extend between the swim bladder and the **sinus impar,** an extension of the perilymphatic space. These fish can hear, although the mechanism provides no information as to the direction

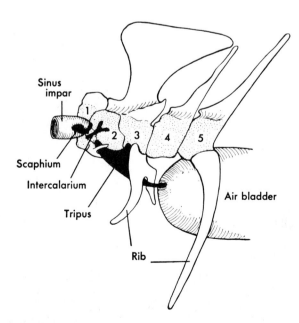

Fig. 16-5. Weberian ossicles (black) of a teleost. **1** to **5,** Centra of first five vertebrae. The sinus impar is an extension of the perilymphatic space. The ossicles are connected by modified intervertebral ligaments.

from which sounds are coming. The specific maculae that detect these sounds are not known. It is known, however, that the maculae that respond to sound in lower tetrapods are in the sacculus near the lagena. In Clupeiformes, an order of herringlike teleosts, an anterior extension of the swim bladder comes in direct contact with the labyrinth, but whether this is a route for transmitting sound waves is not known. Without doubt, there are also other teleosts that have maculae with low enough threshold to detect sound waves.

An account of the evolution of the mammalian cochlea begins with amphibians. In addition to the usual maculae associated with the sacculus and lagena of fishes, amphibians have two receptor sites that resemble maculae except that they have a **tectorial membrane** instead of a cupula. (A mammalian tectorial membrane is illustrated in Fig. 16-7.) These receptor sites are called papillae. One of them is the **amphibian papilla** of the sacculus, so named because it is not found in any other vertebrate (Fig. 16-6, A). The other is the **basilar papilla** in the basilar recess of the sacculus. These two papillae are receptors for sound.

The basilar papilla and the lagena were destined to become the chief components of the mammalian cochlea. In lizards the lagena has become a prominent sac suspended from the sacculus. It still houses

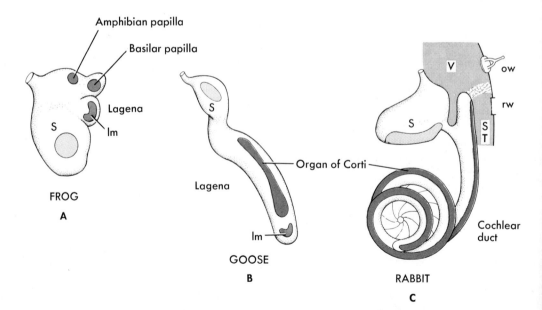

Fig. 16-6. Receptor sites for sound (red) and evolution of cochlear duct in selected tetrapods. **lm,** Lagenar macula; **ow,** stapes at oval window; **rw,** round window; **S,** sacculus and its macula; **ST,** base of scala tympani; **V,** vestibule of cochlea. (Not to scale; **A** and **B** modified from Retzius.)

the lagenar macula, whose function is unknown, and the basilar papilla is now at its entrance. In crocodilians, birds, and monotremes the lagena has become a long tube and the basilar papilla has become an elongated **organ of Corti** within the tube (Fig. 16-6, *B*).* Elongation of the lagena is accompanied by a corresponding extension of the perilymphatic space.

In placental mammals the duct housing the organ of Corti has elongated still more and now spirals *upward* around a bony pillar (the **modiolus**) of the petrosal bone, accompanied by the perilymphatic spaces, to become a **cochlea,** or "snail shell" (Fig. 16-6, *C*). The spiral provides a compact organ occupying little space. The duct containing the organ of Corti has become the **cochlear duct,** or **scala media** of the cochlea, and the associated perilymphatic spaces are the **scala vestibuli** and **scala tympani** (Fig. 16-7). The scala vestibuli begins at the **vestibule,** a portion of the perilymphatic space at the **oval window** where sound waves enter the labyrinth (Fig. 16-6, *C*). It spirals upward with the cochlear duct, bends around the blind upper end of the latter, and spirals back down as the scala tympani. The scala tym-

---

*The term "cochlear duct" is often applied to this tube, but only in placental mammals is it part of a spiral (cochlear) hearing organ.

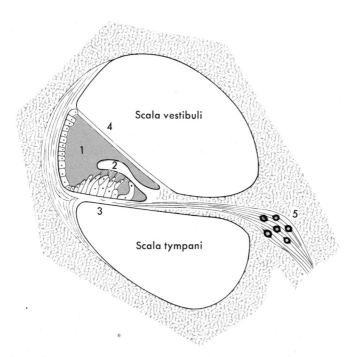

Fig. 16-7. Cross section of one turn of a mammalian cochlea. **1,** Cochlear duct (scala media) containing endolymph (red); **2,** tectorial membrane; **3,** basilar membrane supporting organ of Corti; **4,** Reissner's membrane; **5,** spiral ganglion and cochlear nerve fibers. The scala vestibuli and scala tympani are perilymphatic spaces. The diameter of a similar section of the human cochlea would be less than 1 mm.

Scala vestibuli

Scala tympani

pani ends at the **round window,** which faces the middle ear cavity. Sound waves induced by the stapes in the perilymph of the vestibule are transmitted throughout the perilymph. They pass through Reissner's membrane and the basilar membrane of the cochlea and displace the endolymph that lies between the hair cells and the tectorial membrane. This bends the hair cells and initiates impulses in the cochlear nerve. Vibrations in the perilymph are dissipated instantaneously at the round window, which is closed by a flexible **secondary tympanic membrane.** Lower tetrapods as well as mammals have oval and round windows in their otic capsules.

With expansion of the basilar papilla to become an organ of Corti the nuclei in the brain on pathways for sound became increasingly larger. In reptiles for the first time the auditory nuclei in the tectum of the mesencephalon bulge to form auditory lobes; and differentiation of an auditory cortex in the cerebral hemispheres of mammals was accompanied by an increase in size and number of secondary sensory nuclei and relay centers.

THE MIDDLE EAR

The most common route of conduction of sound waves from air to the inner ear of tetrapods is across a middle ear cavity, or **cavum tympanum,** to the oval window (**fenestra ovalis**) in the otic capsule via one or more ear ossicles (Fig. 16-8). All tetrapods have a **stapes**— also called columella in lower tetrapods because of its shape—unless the middle ear is rudimentary. The stapes, or columella, is derived from the hyomandibula of fishes. An intermediate condition in the evolution of a sound-conducting hyomandibula is seen in primitive urodeles (Fig. 8-12, *B*). In reptiles and birds the stapes is composed of two segments, one of which, the **extrastapes,** also of hyomandibu-

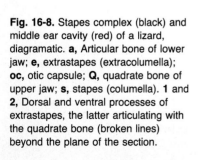

Fig. 16-8. Stapes complex (black) and middle ear cavity (red) of a lizard, diagramatic. **a,** Articular bone of lower jaw; **e,** extrastapes (extracolumella); **oc,** otic capsule; **Q,** quadrate bone of upper jaw; **s,** stapes (columella). **1** and **2,** Dorsal and ventral processes of extrastapes, the latter articulating with the quadrate bone (broken lines) beyond the plane of the section.

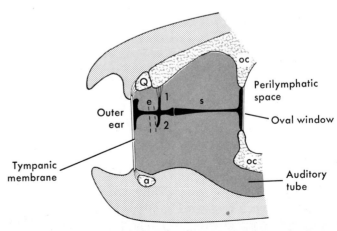

lar origin, remains cartilaginous. Mammals have two additional ossicles, a **malleus** and **incus** (Fig. 16-9), derived from the articular and quadrate bones of reptiles (Chapter 8). Because the eardrum is much larger than the oval window the pressure applied to the drum is multiplied many times when delivered via the ossicles to the perilymph.

The middle ear cavity arises as an evagination of the first pharyngeal pouch that grows toward the developing ear ossicle or ossicles and partially surrounds them, isolating them from other tissues (Figs. 8-34 and 17-16). The cavitation process is completed by erosion of any remaining mesenchyme. The adult middle ear cavity remains in communication with the pharynx via an **auditory tube,** which ensures that the pressure of the air on both sides of the eardrum will be the same as long as the auditory tube is not blocked. Blockage is less likely in frogs, which have a wide, short, permanently open tube, than in mammals, whose tube is long and of small diameter, leads to the nasopharynx, and is open only during swallowing (Fig. 11-3).

Although conduction of sound via an eardrum and ear ossicles is the predominant route in tetrapods, a drum is not always present. Urodeles, apodans, a few anurans (*Ascaphus,* for example), *Sphenodon,* and most limbless reptiles have no eardrum, and the middle ear cavity and auditory tube are vestigial. In urodeles even the stapes is vestigial and probably functionless; but in aquatic urodeles the lateral-line system compensates in part for lack of auditory stimulation.

Absence of an eardrum does not mean that the tetrapod has no auditory input. Sound travels through soil, mud, rocks, and tree trunks just as it does through air, and these sounds are detected through the skeleton of the lower jaw or forelimbs in contact with the substrate. The mandible articulates with the quadrate bone, and the latter is in contact with either the squamosal or supratemporal with

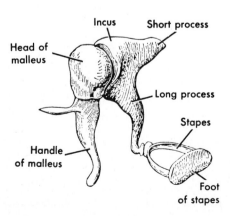

Fig. 16-9. Middle ear ossicles of a mammal. (From Schottelius, B.A., and Schottelius, D.D.: Textbook of physiology, ed. 17, St. Louis, 1973, The C.V. Mosby Co.)

which a process of the extrastapes is also in contact. In some squamates a process of the extrastapes is in direct contact with the quadrate (Fig. 16-8). In the burrowing amphisbaenians a long process of the extrastapes extends forward under the skin covering the mandible and ends in a broad subcutaneous plate that detects sound waves in the substrate directly. When a horn of the hyoid contacts the extrastapes, sound can be detected through the floor of the buccopharynx. A connection between the scapula and extrastapes in a few species provides one route for sound from the anterior limbs. In anurans a muscle connects the pectoral girdle with a small ossification, the operculum (not homologous with a fish's operculum), in the membrane of the oval window, but the role of this operculum is not known.

In mammals, as in fishes with hyostylic jaw suspension, the articular bone (**malleus**) articulates with the quadrate (**incus**), and the latter articulates with the hyomandibula (**stapes**), which ends at the otic capsule containing the membranous labyrinth. There are two tiny muscles in the middle ear cavity of mammals. A **tensor tympani** inserts on the malleus and regulates the tension of the eardrum, and a **stapedius** inserts on and restrains the movements of the stapes. Very loud sounds cause the muscles to contract, which damps the sound and protects the hair cells of the organ of Corti. Relaxation of the muscles results in amplification of weak sounds, as when one "strains one's ears" to hear.

THE OUTER EAR

The outer ear or, more appropriately, the outer ear canal (**external auditory meatus**), is a shallow pit or a short or long passageway for airborne sound waves that extends from the surface of the head to the eardrum (Fig. 16-8). It is present only in some lizards (Fig. 5-14, A) and in crocodilians, birds, and mammals. In other lizards and in anurans and turtles the eardrum is flush with the surface of the head, or nearly so, and these animals have no appreciable outer ear canal (Fig. 16-10). Neither do animals that lack eardrums. In most mammals a fibrocartilaginous appendage, the **pinna**, or **auricle**, collects sound waves and directs them into the canal, but aquatic mammals—cetaceans, Pinnipedia, Sirenia—and some moles have a very small pinna or none. The outer ear canal of whales is minute, but whales have excellent hearing, which is used to receive communications from other individuals and for echolocation.

Saccus vasculosus

Elasmobranch fishes, ganoids, and teleosts have a highly vascular, thin-walled, ventral evagination of the third ventricle, the saccus vasculosus, suspended from the floor of the diencephalon just behind

Fig. 16-10. Head of an iguanid lizard showing slightly depressed eardrum just behind angle of jaws.

the pituitary gland (Fig. 15-15). It is lined with sensory hair cells and supporting cells. The cilia of the hair cells project into the cerebrospinal fluid; nerve fibers in contact with the hair cells pass to the hypothalamus and other brain centers. The sac evidently monitors the pressure of the cerebrospinal fluid (which varies with the depth of the fish) and the information is apparently used to regulate the volume of gas in the swim bladder, hence the animal's buoyancy, via sympathetic and vagal nerves. The sac is not well developed in shallow freshwater fishes.

Light receptors

Many cold-blooded vertebrates have two sets of photoreceptors, lateral and median eyes. In lateral eyes, reflected light is translated into an image on a photosensitive epithelium and the information is used in maintaining an appropriate orientation of the body in the environment. Median eyes form no image; the light stimulates the neuroendocrine reflex arcs that maintain biological rhythms (Fig. 17-5). Lateral eyes are necessary for moment-to-moment survival of the individual; median eyes are necessary for long-term survival of the species.

LATERAL EYES

The receptor site of the lateral eye is the **retina,** a membrane rich in nervous tissue and synapses at the rear of a fluid-filled vitreous chamber of the eyeball (Fig. 16-11). The retina arises from the em-

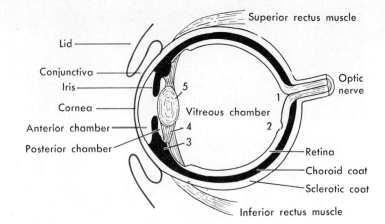

Fig. 16-11. Vertebrate eyeball in sagittal section. **1,** Blind spot; **2,** fovea; **3,** muscular ciliary body; **4,** suspensory ligament; **5,** lens. Red represents the conjunctiva.

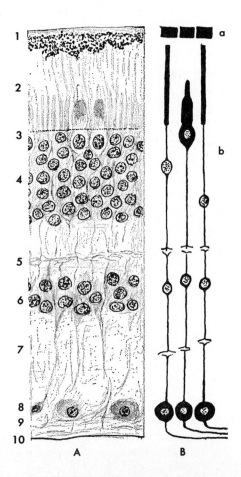

Fig. 16-12. Nervous layer of retina. **A,** Histological appearance. **B,** Areas of synapse, diagramatical. The light enters the retina at layer **10** (base of picture) and passes through the other layers to the rods and cones. **1** and **a,** Pigmented epithelium; **2,** layer of rods and cones; **3,** external limiting membrane; **4,** nuclei of the rods and cones; **5,** outer molecular layer; **6,** layer of bipolar cell bodies; **7,** inner molecular layer; **8,** layer of ganglion cells (cell bodies of optic nerve fibers); **9,** layer of optic nerve fibers; **10,** internal limiting membrane; **b,** rods and cones. (From Bevelander, G., and Ramaley, J.A.: Essentials of histology, ed. 8, St. Louis, 1978, The C.V. Mosby Co.)

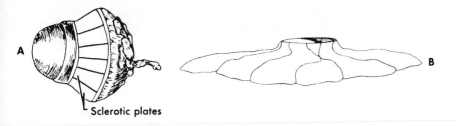

Sclerotic plates

bryonic forebrain as an evagination that soon becomes a double-walled **optic cup** (Fig. 16-4, *B*). The optic cup retains an attachment to the brain via the **optic stalk.** The layer of the optic cup that light first strikes becomes the nervous layer of the retina. Some of the retinal cells become rods and cones, which are the actual photorecep-tors, others become bipolar neurons, and still others become cell bodies of optic nerve fibers (Fig. 16-12). Optic nerve cell bodies (called ganglion cells by the histologist) sprout long processes that grow along the optic stalk and into the brain. These processes consti-tute the optic nerve. From this description it can be seen that the retina arises from the brain and never becomes completely detached from it.

The embryonic mesenchyme surrounding the optic cup forms a pigmented **choroid coat** and a dense **sclerotic coat** (Fig. 16-11). The choroid coat is perforated in front of the lens by the **pupil.** Although usually circular, the pupil is slitlike in snakes and cats and rectangular in many ungulates. The part of the choroid coat surrounding the pupil is the **iris diaphragm.** In tetrapods this diaphragm contains smooth, radially arranged **dilator muscles** and circumferential **constrictor muscles** that change the diameter of the pupil in response to changes in light intensity. (The diameter of the pupil of fishes is usually fixed.) The effect may be demonstrated by shining a flashlight into a dark-adapted eye and watching the pupil constrict. Around the periphery of the iris diaphragm of most vertebrates, encircling the lens, is a fleshy wedge-shaped ring of the choroid coat, the **ciliary body,** from which suspensory ligaments pass to the lens. The ciliary body is mus-cular in tetrapods, and the ciliary muscles control the position and, in amniotes, the curvature of the lens for near and far vision.

The sclerotic coat (sclera) is so named because it is typically scle-rotized (hardened) by cartilage or bone that, in reptiles and birds, takes the form of scleral rings (Fig. 16-13). The sclera is the white of the eye. In front of the iris diaphragm and pupil the sclerotic coat is transparent, this portion being the **cornea.** Through the cornea can be seen the pigmented iris diaphragm surrounding the pupil. The pupil appears black because there is no light emerging from within the eye. Inserting on the outer surface of the sclerotic coat are rectus and oblique muscles that rotate the eyeball within the orbit. These muscles are essentially identical from fish to man except that in birds they are so poorly developed that they are practically useless. As a result, a bird must move its entire head to change the direction of its gaze.

The **lens** arises as a thickened placode of ectoderm that sinks into position in front of the optic cup (Fig. 16-4, *B*). The lens placode is induced to form by organizers (inductor substances) released by the embryonic retina. That the retina serves as the inductor may be demonstrated in an amphibian embryo by exchanging undifferentiated ectoderm from the thigh with that at the site where a lens will form. A lens is induced in the tissue transplanted to the head but not in the potential lens ectoderm that was removed from the influence of the retina. Removal of the optic cup will result in no lens placode.

The chamber behind the lens (**vitreous chamber**) is filled with a jellylike viscous refracting substance, the **vitreous humor.** The small chamber between the lens and iris diaphragm (posterior aqueous chamber) and that between the iris diaphragm and cornea (anterior aqueous chamber) are filled with **aqueous humor.** In teleosts, snakes, lizards, and birds, a pigmented and highly vascular conical or fan-shaped projection of the choroid coat extends into the vitreous chamber nearly to the lens from a position near the entrance of the optic nerve. It is known as the **falciform process** in fishes, **conus papillaris** in reptiles, and **pecten** in birds. It is thought that these may alert the animal to nearby moving objects by casting a shadow on the retina. Their intense vascularity has also led to the hypothesis that they participate in metabolic exchanges between the blood and the interior of the eyeball.

Accommodation of the eye for near or far vision is effected differently in different vertebrates. In lampreys a **cornealis muscle** pulls on the cornea from one side, altering its curvature. In elasmobranchs and most tetrapods the lens of an eye at rest (emmetropic eye) is at a distance from the retina such that distant objects are focused on the retina. In accommodating for near objects the lens is drawn forward by **protractor muscles,** which are the ciliary muscles in tetrapods. The resting eye of teleosts, on the other hand, is focused for near objects, and a **retractor muscle,** the **campanula,** extends from the falciform process (mentioned above) to the lens and pulls the lens backward for distant vision. Snakes accommodate still differently. Increased pressure in the vitreous humor generated by muscles near the iris pushes the lens forward. The lens returns passively to the resting position and shape when the force that displaced it is removed.

Changing the shape of the lens as part of accommodation of the eye is uncommon below amniotes. When the eye is at rest—focused for infinity—the diameter of the ciliary ring is greater than when the eye is focused for near objects. This is because contraction of ciliary muscles for near vision reduces the diameter of the ciliary ring in the manner that a drawstring closes a purse. Since the suspensory ligaments are stretched between ring and lens, reducing the diameter of the ring makes the ligaments less taut; and the lens, being resilient, assumes a more spherical shape. The ciliary muscles are striated in reptiles and birds only; therefore changing focus can be accomplished more quickly in these vertebrates than in mammals.

The surface of the eyeball that you can touch is covered with transparent skin, the **bulbar conjunctiva.** This is continuous with the **palpebral conjunctiva** on the inner surface of the lids (Fig. 16-11). In snakes and many lizards the lids are permanently closed and are transparent, forming a **spectacle.** Each time a snake molts the stratum corneum on the surface of the spectacle is shed, and this carries away any scratches. Epidermal glands in the orbit of terrestrial vertebrates keep the conjunctiva moist and clean. The **lacrimal gland** secretes a watery fluid ("tears"). It is poorly developed in some reptiles and birds, but it is enormous in marine turtles, in which it secretes salt. In many mammals a **harderian gland** secretes a more viscous fluid. It is absent in some mammals, especially those that live permanently in water. Some mammals also have an **infraorbital gland.** The fluids secreted by orbital glands usually drain into a nasolacrimal duct that leads to the nasal cavity or to the vomeronasal organ.

Vertebrates that live in caves or other dark recesses (some fishes, cave salamanders, caecilians, and moles, for example) are frequently blind, or the eyes may even be vestigial. Frequently the lids fail to open. In hagfishes no eyeball whatsoever differentiates.

MEDIAN EYES

Many vertebrates below birds have a functional third eye on the top of the head (Fig. 16-14). Among them are lampreys, ganoid fishes, a few teleosts (especially larvae), anuran larvae, some adult anurans, *Sphenodon,* and some lizards. The median eye is an evagination of the roof of the diencephalon. Primitively, it was one of two evaginations constituting the **epiphyseal complex** (Fig. 16-15). The more anterior evagination becomes a parapineal body, and the posterior one becomes a pineal body. It is usually the parapineal that is photosensitive, but in lampreys both are.

In lampreys the pineal ends as a hollow knob beneath the cornea, an area of skin devoid of pigment between the lateral eyes. The upper wall of the knob consists of several layers of cells that form a lens.

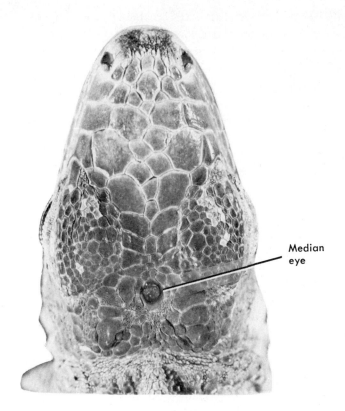

Median
eye

Fig. 16-14. Parapineal eye of an
iguana.

The lower wall contains photosensitive cells and, beneath these, ganglion cells with long processes that pass down the stalk to sensory nuclei in the right side of the diencephalon. The parapineal is similar, but its fibers terminate on the left. The pineal is dominant.

The parapineal of lizards, or **parietal eye,** lies in the parietal foramen immediately under a single, translucent epidermal scale in the midline of the head (Fig. 16-15, *C*). It consists of a cornea, lens, retina with photoreceptive cells resembling those of the vertebrate retina, ganglion cells, and a sensory fiber tract that extends down the epiphyseal stalk and enters the roof of the diencephalon.

In larval frogs the third eye is called the **frontal organ,** or **stirnorgan.** Authorities are uncertain whether this is the pineal or parapineal part of the epiphyseal complex. At metamorphosis the photoreceptive part of this organ regresses, leaving only the glandular component that produced the hormone melatonin in the larva. In at least one tree frog, however, the third eye persists throughout life.

Median eyes, unlike lateral eyes, form no retinal image. Instead, they monitor the duration of photoperiods, and the input affects internal biological rhythms such as daily spontaneous motor activity and

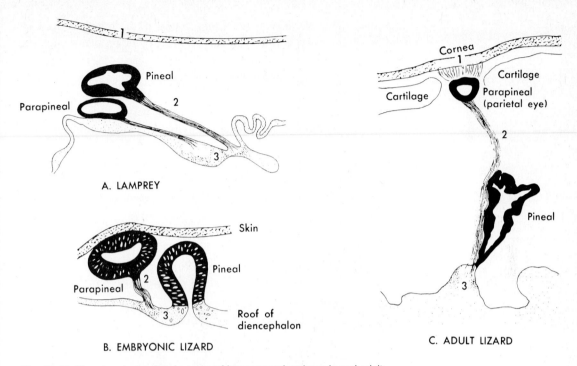

Fig. 16-15. Pineal and parapineal organs of lamprey and embryonic and adult lizard. **1,** Cornea; **2,** fiber tract; **3,** habenular nuclei. The parapineal of the lizard lies within the parietal foramen. (**B** and **C** modified from Nowikoff.[15])

seasonal changes in the gonads. They probably monitor also the intensity of solar radiation. The rates of metabolic processes are correlated with body temperature, which, in turn, depends on how much solar energy is received. Third eyes were present in all major groups of Devonian fishes and in early amphibians and reptiles before being lost in later vertebrates.

Pit receptors of reptiles

Snakes and lizards have pitlike mechanoreceptors and thermoreceptors that open to the surface between epidermal scales. These organs are of several morphological and functional varieties, the most numerous being the **apical pits** of lizards. These tactile receptors are widely distributed over the surface, especially on the trunk, where, as their name indicates, they lie at the posterior free borders, or apices, of scales. Frequently, a filamentous, hairlike bristle projects from the pit. Since typical cutaneous nerve endings lie beneath the scales, apical pits provide more sensitive sites for the input of tactile stimuli. Unlike the receptors discussed next, apical pits are *general* somatic receptors.

A single pair of thermal receptors, **loreal pits,** detect infrared radiation on the head of snakes of the family Crotalidae, which includes North American rattlesnakes, copperheads, and water moccasins. One pit is located at the caudal border of each loreal scale. (The lore of reptiles is the region between the external naris and eye, as shown in Fig. 5-15, *L*.) These pits are readily seen, being directed forward, several millimeters wide, and twice as deep. Because of these pits crotalid snakes are called pit vipers. Physiological and behavioral studies have shown that loreal pits can detect temperature changes of as little as 0.001° C at a distance of several feet. This enables terrestrial species to detect the presence of small warm-blooded prey and strike accurately in the dark.

Pythons and some boas have smaller and less sensitive thermal pits with slitlike openings arranged in a series along the margin of each jaw. Because of their location they are called **labial pits.** Pit receptors on the trunk are innervated by spinal nerves, those on the head by the fifth cranial nerve.

SPECIAL VISCERAL RECEPTORS

There are two varieties of special visceral receptors, **olfactory** (for smell) and **gustatory** (for taste). Both are chemoreceptors that are sensitive to certain amino acids, olfactory receptors being less specific. Differences in sensitivity apparently are related to side chains of the acids. That taste and smell are related phenomena is evident to anyone who has been unable to savor food because of a head cold.

Olfactory organs

The olfactory organs of gnathostomes arise as a pair of ectodermal olfactory placodes that form just cephalad to the stomodeum. The placodes sink into the head to form a pair of nasal pits, the epithelial lining of which differentiates into olfactory, supportive, and mucous cells (Figs. 1-10 and 12-20, *B*). The olfactory cells, which are the receptors, sprout processes that grow toward and penetrate the olfactory bulb of the forebrain (Fig. 16-16).* These processes are the fibers of the olfactory nerve. There are an estimated 50 million olfactory cells in humans. For a substance to act as an odorant, it must have a chemical configuration compatible with that of a binding substance on the olfactory cell membrane, and it must be in solution. Characteristic branched, tubular, mucus-secreting **Bowman's glands** keep the epithelium moist in tetrapods. They are not necessary, and not present, in fishes.

---

*The olfactory cells and rods and cones are neurosensory cells.

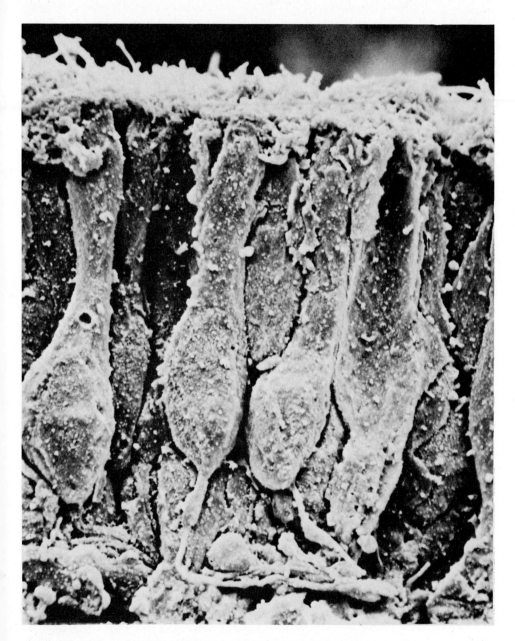

Fig. 16-16. Section of olfactory epithelium from the channel catfish, *Ictalurus punctatus*. Three ciliated olfactory cells and their axons are readily identifiable. Height of the section was approximately 20 microns. (From Caprio, J., and Raderman-Little, R.: Tissue and Cell **10**[1]:1, 1978.)

In fishes other than lobe-fins the differentiating olfactory epithelium becomes surrounded by connective tissue that forms a blind olfactory sac. A current of water into and out of the sac is ensured because each external naris is partitioned into incurrent and excurrent apertures so situated that the forward motion of the fish propels a stream of water into one aperture and out the other. The mucosa containing the olfactory epithelium may exhibit folds that increase the surface area. The olfactory cells monitor the water stream and are stimulated by odorants that may have their source in potential food, mates, or enemies. Probably the most primitive response to olfactory stimuli is reflex contraction of locomotor muscles, which propel the fish closer to, or father from, the source of the odorant.

In lungfishes and tetrapods the olfactory pits push deep into the head to acquire an opening into the oral cavity or pharynx. The openings are internal nares. When this occurs, the olfactory epithelium is confined to a portion of the lining of this newly established nasal canal, so that it is appropriate to distinguish an olfactory epithelium from a respiratory epithelium. The olfactory epithelium contains olfactory cell bodies just as in fishes, but in tetrapods it monitors an airstream instead of a water stream. Odorants in the airstream dissolve on the moist olfactory epithelium and stimulate the olfactory cells.

Olfactory mechanisms are well developed in fishes, least developed in birds, which therefore have a poor sense of smell. In some whales the olfactory nerves disappear during embryonic life. A mammal trying to smell something under water would drown! Loss of the olfactory nerve—a result of mutations—was therefore no disadvantage to the whale.

VOMERONASAL (JACOBSON'S) ORGANS

There has been a tendency among tetrapods, and even among fishes, for a ventral segment of the olfactory epithelium to become more or less isolated from the nasal passageway, to the extent of becoming an accessory olfactory organ in some species. The isolated olfactory area is called a vomeronasal organ because of its frequent location above the vomer bone. It is also known as Jacobson's organ. The epithelium lacks Bowman's glands.

In urodeles the vomeronasal organs are a pair of deep grooves in the ventromedial floor of the nasal canal. In anurans they are blind sacs that open to the canal. In lizards and snakes they lose their connection with the nasal canals and open into the anterior roof of the oral cavity (Fig. 16-17), becoming two moist pockets that receive the tips of the forked tongue each time it darts out of the mouth and back as it monitors chemicals in the environment. Vomeronasal organs ap-

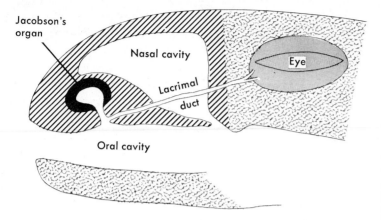

Fig. 16-17. Anatomical relationships of the vomeronasal (Jacobson's) organ in a generalized lizard. Only the left organ is shown. Diagonal lines designate a parasagittal section. The lacrimal duct is also called the nasolacrimal canal.

pear in embryonic crocodilians and birds and then regress—mute testimony to an ancestral function. Their presence in turtles is doubtful.

Most mammals have vomeronasal organs just above the hard palate. They open either in the floor of the nasal canals, as in many rodents, or onto the hard palate via nasopalatine ducts that pass through incisive foramina, as in cats. They are especially well developed in monotremes, marsupials, and generalized insectivores, absent in cetaceans (where they would be as useless as other olfactory epithelia), some bats, and adult higher primates. They and their nerves develop in human embryos, reach maximum size about the fifth month of gestation, and then regress. Those that open into the oral cavity are probably stimulated by food in solution in the cavity. The epithelium of vomeronasal organs is supplied by the vomeronasal nerve, a separate division of the olfactory nerve.

Organs of taste

Taste buds are barrel-shaped clusters of elongated taste cells and supportive cells, the apices of which protrude into a tiny taste pore in a moist epithelium (Fig. 16-18). Taste cells bear microvilli and are transducers of chemical energy. In contact with the base of each taste cell are sensory nerve endings. The functional life of a taste cell is only about 10 days, at which time they die from "wear and tear." They are replaced by the supportive cells, which are reserve taste cells. Supportive cells are constantly replaced by the epithelium.

In fishes, taste buds are widely distributed in the roof, side walls, and floor of the pharynx, where they monitor the stream of water passing to the gills. In bottom feeders or scavengers, such as catfish, carp, and suckers, taste buds are distributed over the surface of the body to the tip of the tail. They are abundant on the "whiskers" of

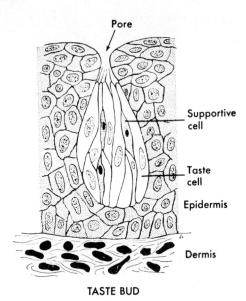

TASTE BUD

Fig. 16-18. Taste bud on the tongue of a monkey. The innervation is not shown.

catfish. The exaggerated size of the sensory nucleus that receives incoming taste fibers in such fishes is illustrated in Fig. 15-13.

In most tetrapods taste buds are restricted to the tongue, posterior palate, and pharynx. There are fewer on the tongue in reptiles and birds than in mammals, and human embryos have more taste buds than children 7 years old as a result of failure to replace some that are lost.

Taste buds from fish to man are supplied by cranial nerves VII, IX, and X *in that sequence* from mouth to the end of the pharynx. Therefore, in man, taste buds on the anterior surface of the tongue are supplied by nerve VII, those on the posterior surface of the tongue by nerve IX, and those in the vicinity of the glottis by nerve X. Nerve VII also supplies all taste buds in the skin of fishes all the way to the tip of the tail.

GENERAL SOMATIC RECEPTORS

There are two categories of general somatic receptors: (1) cutaneous receptors for light touch, pain, temperature, and pressure (touch sufficient to indent the surface) and (2) proprioceptors, found in striated muscles, joints, and tendons.

Cutaneous receptors

The skin of all vertebrates contains free (naked, unencapsulated) endings of sensory neurons that ramify among the epidermal cells everywhere in the skin and are stimulated by contact (Fig. 16-19, na-

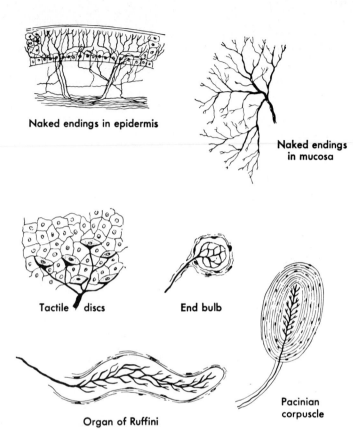

Naked endings in epidermis

Naked endings in mucosa

Tactile discs

End bulb

Organ of Ruffini

Pacinian corpuscle

Fig. 16-19. General somatic and visceral receptors. Encapsulated endings include pacinian corpuscles for touch, end bulbs (of Krause) for cold, and organs of Ruffini for heat.

ked endings in epidermis). These are probably the oldest cutaneous endings in vertebrates, and in cyclostomes they are the only ones. They give rise to what has been called **protopathic sensation.** This is a crude, poorly localized, phylogenetically ancient sensation. It is purely protective. It is not necessary that a fish know the texture of whatever touches it or whether the object is warm or cool. The mere fact of contact indicates possible danger. The impulses ascend to the thalamus, where reflex motor activity is initiated to reorient the animal so that it avoids the stimulus. In mammals these endings give rise to vague, poorly localized, and sometimes unpleasant sensations including pain, as in toothache or when the skin is pricked. Free nerve endings for touch entwine around the base of each hair. Displace a single hair on your arm and note the sensation. Localization of the stimulus is a function of the cerebral cortex.

In addition to free endings ramifying in the epidermis, tetrapods have acquired encapsulated bulblike endings in the dermis (Figs. 5-10 and 16-19). They consist of endings associated with epithelial-like cells surrounded by a thin or thick connective tissue capsule. They may have evolved from free endings by the addition of capsular cells and by withdrawal into the dermal papillae or even deeper. Encapsulated endings seem to have evolved along with the cerebral hemispheres and are employed in **epicritic sensation:** discrimination between small differences in warmth or cold, recognizing texture, or localizing two points that are very close together and being touched simultaneously. Birds and mammals have the largest number and variety of such corpuscles, including some on the beaks of birds, at the end of the snout in mammals that rout in the soil, and on external genitalia and other erogenous areas.

Proprioceptors

Skeletal muscles, tendons, and the bursae of joints are supplied with sensory endings that monitor the extent to which skeletal muscles are contracted at any instant. These proprioceptors are distinguished from exteroceptors, which monitor the external environment, and enteroceptors, which monitor the viscera. Proprioceptors maintain muscle tonus in resting muscles and synergize the activity of functional groups of muscles when muscles are at work.

The sensory endings in most skeletal muscles of higher vertebrates are found in **muscle spindles.** These are tiny fusiform bundles of fewer than a dozen striated muscle fibers that are wrapped together in a connective tissue sheath and located among and parallel to typical striated muscle fibers near the ends of muscles. Each muscle fiber in the spindle (**intrafusal fiber**) is supplied with at least one proprioceptive fiber (Fig. 16-20). Motor neurons supplying intrafusal fibers are

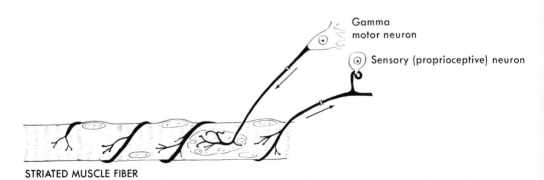

STRIATED MUSCLE FIBER

Fig. 16-20. Innervation of an intrafusal muscle fiber of a muscle spindle. The contraction is monitored by the proprioceptive neuron. The proprioceptive fiber synapses in the central nervous system with motor cell bodies of regular (alpha) motor neurons (not shown) that stimulate extrafusal muscle fibers. The mechanism is essential for muscle tonus and posture.

called **gamma motor neurons** to distinguish them from **alpha motor neurons,** which innervate other muscle fibers.

In maintaining muscle tonus, muscle spindles function as follows. The connective tissue envelope of the spindle is continuous with the connective tissue surrounding extrafusal fibers beyond the spindle, so that any change in the length of a muscle will affect the spindle. When a muscle is relaxed it is elongated, the spindle is slightly stretched, and proprioceptive fibers fire. Since proprioceptive fibers synapse in the central nervous system with alpha neurons, discharge from the spindle triggers contraction of a group of extrafusal fibers, which increases the tonus of the muscle, shortening the muscle slightly. This relieves some of the tension within the spindle, firing of the proprioceptive fibers slows, the muscle tends to elongate once again, and this triggers new discharges from the spindle. Thus feedback from muscle to central nervous system maintains the muscle in a state of dynamic tonicity when the muscle is not working.

The role of spindles when muscles are doing work is more complicated. In maintenance of posture, alpha and gamma motor neurons are being stimulated by motor fibers whose cell bodies are in the brain. Stimulation of gamma motor neurons results in contraction of intrafusal fibers and discharge of proprioceptive impulses at a constant frequency. The resulting steady reflex firing of alpha neurons imposed by the spindle maintains a steady contraction of specific muscle masses, subject to brain controls, whether the vertebrate is locomoting or playing a piano. Other proprioceptive receptors provide input. Pacinian corpuscles are proprioceptors in bursae, and naked endings respond to stretch in tendons. Lower vertebrates have simpler proprioceptive mechanisms than mammals.

Most proprioceptive stimuli do not reach centers of consciousness but are shunted into the cerebellum and elsewhere, where they make reflex connections. To demonstrate conscious proprioception, first close your eyes, then extend your arm or leg. Your awareness of the change in position is an example of conscious proprioception, also called kinesthesia or deep muscle sensibility. That the act was performed smoothly is a result of unconscious reflex responses to volleys of proprioceptive stimuli.

GENERAL VISCERAL RECEPTORS

General visceral receptors are mostly naked endings in the mucosa of the internal tubes and organs of the body, in cardiac muscle, in smooth muscle including that of blood vessels, and in the capsules, mesenteries, and meninges of the viscera (Fig. 16-19). Pacinian corpuscles are also found in mesenteries and some coelomic viscera. General visceral receptors are stimulated mechanically by stretching or chemically by the presence of certain substances, such as acid in the pyloric stomach. They are also stimulated by tactile and thermal stimuli in the pharynx.

Most of the sensory input from general visceral receptors gives rise to no conscious sensation, but to reflex control of smooth muscles and glands. Because the same kind of monitoring of the internal environment must take place in all vertebrates whether in water or on land, general visceral receptors are not subject to so many selective pressures as are somatic receptors. Therefore visceral receptors vary little from fish to man.

Tetrapods have **vascular monitors** associated with the carotid arteries and systemic arch. These chemoreceptors and baroreceptors monitor the oxygen content and pressure of blood coming from the heart. Three such receptors have been described in tetrapods. These are the carotid body, carotid sinus, and aortic body. Similar structures have not been described in fishes.

The **carotid body** lies close to the common carotid or internal carotid artery or embedded in the wall of the vessel from which it receives an arterial supply. It is richly supplied with sensory endings of cranial nerve IX and monitors the oxygen and, perhaps, carbon dioxide in blood passing through the organ. Anoxia evokes a discharge of sensory impulses that reflexly increase the respiratory rate. The **carotid sinus** is a bulbous enlargement on the internal carotid artery at its origin from the common carotid. It is a baroreceptor that monitors arterial blood pressure. Low pressure evokes sensory discharges that provide input to the cardiovascular regulatory center of the medulla. The sinus is supplied by cranial nerve IX and also receives vagal and sympathetic fibers. An **aortic body,** described only in mammals, lies on the arch of the aorta. It is a baroreceptor innervated by sensory fibers in the vagal nerve. Other vascular monitors, including osmoreceptors, are located in the hypothalamus and elsewhere in the brain.

CHAPTER SUMMARY

1. Receptors are transducers of mechanical, electrical, thermal, chemical, or radiant energy.

2. Somatic receptors provide information about the external environment other than taste or smell (exteroception), and about skeletal muscle activity (proprioception).

3. Visceral receptors monitor the internal environment (enteroception) and chemicals in the external environment.

4. Special receptors have a limited distribution in the body. General receptors are widely distributed.

5. Neuromast organs are fluid-filled pits, ampullae, or canals lined with hair cells and supporting cells. They are common in fishes and aquatic amphibians and function in electroreception, mechanoreception, and thermoreception. They are innervated by cranial nerves VII, IX, and X.

6. The membranous labyrinth (inner ear) is a neuromast complex consisting of semicircular ducts, sacculus, utriculus, endolymphatic duct, and lagena or chochlear duct. It is filled with endolymph and surrounded by perilymph.

7. The primitive function of the labyrinth was to monitor the orientation of the body in the environment for reflex maintenance of posture (orientation of head, trunk, tail, appendages). An auditory function performed by neuromasts with a tectorial membrane was a later development culminating in a cochlear duct and organ of Corti.

8. Cristae are receptor sites in the ampullae of the semicircular ducts. Maculae are in the sacculus, utriculus, and lagena. Papillae with tectorial membranes instead of cupulae are in the sacculus close to the lagena of lower tetrapods. Otoliths are associated with maculae and tectorial membranes.

9. In higher tetrapods stimulation of semicircular ducts results in reflex movements of the eyeballs as well as maintenance of equilibrium.

10. Airborne auditory stimuli most commonly reach the labyrinth by a tympanic membrane and ear ossicles. Waterborne stimuli arrive via the swim bladder and weberian ossicles. Stimuli in the substrate arrive via the lower jaw, forelimbs, buccopharyngeal floor, or hyoid, and articulating bones of the skull.

11. Inner ears are found in all vertebrates, middle ears in tetrapods, outer ear canals in amniotes, and pinnas in mammals.

12. The saccus vasculosus of fishes is a midventral evagination of the floor of the third ventricle caudal to the pituitary. The epithelium has hair cells and supporting cells. It may monitor pressure of the cerebrospinal fluid.

13. Vertebrates have paired (lateral) eyes and unpaired (median) eyes. The latter are part of an epiphyseal complex.

14. Lateral eyes arise as paired evaginations of the forebrain. They have a retina, choroid coat, sclerotic coat, and the exposed part of the eyeball is covered by a conjunctiva. Accommodation for near and far vision and for light intensity is chiefly by muscles that insert on the cornea or lens and by dilators and constrictors of the pupil.

15. Median eyes have a cornea, lens, and retina but form no retinal image. They are found in agnathans, some jawed fishes, larval anurans, and some reptiles. The parapineal serves as the photoreceptor more frequently than the pineal.

16. Lizards have apical pits widely scattered on the surface between scales. They are probably mechanoreceptors. Loreal and labial pit organs on the heads of crotalid snakes and boas are thermoreceptors for radiant heat.

17. Olfactory organs, which include vomeronasal organs, are special visceral chemoreceptors that arise from nasal pits. The receptor cells in the epithelia are the cell bodies of sensory neurons (neurosensory cells) whose processes make up the olfactory nerve.

18. Taste buds are special visceral chemoreceptors that are distributed over the surface of the head, trunk, and tail of some fishes, confined to the head in others, and restricted to the oral cavity and pharynx in tetrapods. Specialized epithelial cells (taste cells)

are transducers of chemical energy. They are supplied by cranial nerves VII, IX, and X in all vertebrates.

19. General somatic receptors include cutaneous receptors for touch, temperature, pain, and pressure on the skin, and proprioceptors in striated muscles, bursae, and tendons. Cutaneous receptors are naked endings among epidermal cells and encapsulated endings in the dermis. Proprioceptors are muscle spindles in striated muscles, pacinian corpuscles in bursae, naked endings in tendons.

20. General visceral receptors are mostly naked endings in viscera. They are mostly stretch receptors and chemoreceptors. Carotid bodies, carotid sinuses, and the aortic body are vascular monitors of the neck.

LITERATURE CITED AND SELECTED READINGS

1. Adams, W.E.: The comparative morphology of the carotid body and carotid sinus, Springfield, Ill., 1958, Charles C Thomas, Publisher.
2. Ariëns Kappers, C.U., Huber, G.C., and Crosby, E.C.: The comparative anatomy of the nervous system of vertebrates, including man, New York, 1936, The Macmillan Co. (Republished by Hafner Publishing Co., Inc., 1960.)
3. Botterman, B.R., Binder, M.D., and Stuart, D.G.: Functional anatomy of the association between motor units and muscle receptors, American Zoologist 18(1):135, 1978.
4. Branson, B.A., and Moore, G.A.: The lateralis components of the acoustico-lateralis system in the sunfish family Centrarchidae, Copeia, no. 1, p. 1, 1962.
5. Cahn, P.H., editor: Lateral-line detectors, Bloomington, Ind., 1967, Indiana University Press.
6. Dodt, E.: The parietal eye (pineal and parietal organs) of lower vertebrates. In Jung, R., editor: Handbook of sensory physiology, Part B, vol. 7/3B, West Berlin, 1973, Springer-Verlag.
7. Eakin, R.M.: The third eye, Berkeley, Calif., 1973, University of California Press.
8. Gans, C., Northcutt, R.G., and Ulinski, P., editors: Biology of the reptilia, vol. 9, New York, 1979, Academic Press, Inc.
9. Gans, C., and Parsons, S.T., editors: Biology of the reptilia, vol. 2, New York, 1970, Academic Press, Inc.
10. Hopkins, C.D.: Electric communication in fish, American Scientist 62:426, 1974.
11. Johns, P.R.: Growth of fish retinas, American Zoologist 21(2):447, 1981.
12. Lombard, R.E., and Straughan, I.R.: Functional aspects of anuran middle ear structures, Journal of Experimental Biology 61:71, 1944.
13. Lowenstein, O., Osborne, M.P., and Thornhill, R.A.: The anatomy and ultrastructure of the labyrinth of the lamprey (*Lampetra fluviatilis* L.), Proceedings of the Royal Society, Series B 170:113, 1968.
14. Mates, J.W.B.: Eye movements of African chameleons: spontaneous saccade timing, Science 199:1087, 1978.
15. Nowikoff, M.: Untersuchungen über den Bau, die Entwicklung und die Bedeutung des Parietalauges von aurien, Zeitschrift für wissenschaftliche Zoologie 96:118, 1910.
16. Parker, D.E.: The vestibular apparatus, Scientific American 243(5):98, 1980.

17. Popper, A.N.: Comparative studies of hearing in vertebrates, New York, 1980, Springer-Verlag, Inc.

18. Prince, J.H.: Comparative anatomy of the eye, Springfield, Ill., 1956, Charles C Thomas, Publisher.

19. Quay, W.B.: The parietal eye-pineal complex. In Gans, C., Northcutt, R.G., and Ulinski, P.: Biology of the reptilia, vol. 9, New York, 1979, Academic Press, Inc.

20. Shaw, E.: Schooling fishes, American Scientist 66(2):166, 1978.

21. Sher, A.E.: The embryonic and postnatal development of the inner ear of the mouse, Acta Oto-laryngologica, supplement 285, Uppsala, Sweden, 1971.

22. Wever, E.G.: Reptile ear: its structure and function, Princeton, N.J., 1978, Princeton University Press.

Symposia in American Zoologist

Vertebrate olfaction, 7:385, 1967.

Vertebrate sound production, 13:1137, 1973.

Recent advances in the biology of sharks. Section III. Cranial nerves and sense organs, 17:411, 1977.

CHAPTER 17

Endocrine organs

An endocrine organ is an organ that synthesizes hormones. Hormones are products of specific groups of cells that have a regulatory effect on other cells, often referred to as "target" cells. Target cells may be right next to the cells that regulate them, but more often they are remote and the hormone is transported by the bloodstream.

The term "target cell" might lead to the mistaken notion that a hormone passes only to the "target," as though aimed in that direction. This is not the case. Most hormones are transported in the bloodstream, and the fluid constituents of the stream escape from capillaries everywhere in the body and bathe every living cell. Only those cells having an appropriate molecular "receptor site" on their membranes are able to be affected by the hormone. For example, thyrotropic hormone from the pituitary bathes the cells of the big toe in the same concentration that it bathes the cells of the thyroid gland, which is its target; but only certain cells of the thyroid can be affected. A few hormones appear to have receptor sites on every cell of the organism. These are **general metabolic hormones.**

Some hormones are produced by organs with additional functions. For example, insulin is usually produced by a gland that also produces digestive enzymes. There are endocrine cells in the liver, kidney, epithelium of the digestive tract, and many other locations. In this chapter we will confine the discussion to organs that are solely endocrine, or that produce hormones as one of their major functions. An exception will be the thymus. As a derivative of pharyngeal pouches it is suspected of having an endocrine role, although this role has so far proved elusive.

Most hormones are combinations of amino acids—chiefly polypeptides, proteins, or nucleoproteins—or they are steroids. A few are amines. All these compounds are common products of biochemical synthesis not only among vertebrates but also among invertebrates and plants. They represent chemical taxa that have evolved along with the living organisms that produce them. Steroids, for example,

In this chapter we will study organs whose secretions in most instances adapt vertebrates over a period of time to more or less gradual fluctuations in the internal and external environments. We will learn that the brain is one of these organs, translating cyclical environmental input into hormonal messages. We will find that vertebrates from fish to man have the same array of such organs, that they form from the same embryonic precursors, and that they synthesize the same molecules. We will also note some of the molecular and anatomical mutations that have occurred during phylogeny.

are found in yeast and in many green plants and are universal in the animal kingdom. There is a greater variety of steroids in lower animals than in higher ones.

Endocrine glands as well as their products have evolved. Some of them appear to be phylogenetic descendants of clusters of hormone-secreting cells located in an epithelium in ancestral forms. Thyroid cells are still in the epithelium of the pharyngeal floor of an amphioxus, and in some adult fishes the thyroid retains an open duct to the pharyngeal floor throughout life. The cells that secrete parathyroid hormone are ontogenetic migrants from pharyngeal pouch epithelia. The glandular part of the pituitary evaginates from the roof of the embryonic stomodeum and retains a duct to the oral cavity in some adult fishes. Cells that secrete insulin are still in or near the epithelium of the gut in cyclostomes and dipnoans, and in elasmobranchs they are in the epithelium of small pancreatic ducts; not having escaped from the epithelium during ontogeny as they do in most other vertebrates. Several gastrointestinal hormones that regulate digestive organs are in the epithelium of the digestive tract in all vertebrates. These include gastrin, which causes adjacent cells of the stomach lining to release gastric juice, cholecystokinin, which causes the gallbladder to empty, and pancreozymin, which releases certain enzymes from pancreatic alveoli. Early hormones were probably effective locally by diffusion long before the evolution of vascular circulatory systems. They still function in this manner in coelenterates and in human gonads. The pituitary and adrenal evolved from two entirely separate endocrine tissues that became anatomically associated during phylogeny.

Most importantly, the central nervous system produces hormones. We will begin the chapter with the endocrine roles of the nervous system after which we will discuss other endocrine tissues derived from ectoderm, mesoderm, and endoderm, in that order. Only the more obvious effects of the hormones will be mentioned. Many hormones, especially the smaller polypeptides, have other less noticeable effects.

ENDOCRINE ROLES OF THE NERVOUS SYSTEM

The hormones of the nervous system are **neurosecretions.** They are produced by **neurosecretory neurons.** Neurosecretions should not be confused with neurotransmitters. The latter are amines, the former are small polypeptides.* Neurosecretions are found in the animal kingdom commencing with coelenterates.

---

*Some amines, such as epinephrine and pineal melatonin, serve as hormones in certain localities, and there is evidence that polypeptides may under certain conditions serve as neurotransmitters.

Neurosecretions are synthesized in the cell bodies of neurosecretory neurons located in neurosecretory nuclei (Fig. 17-1). The secretions move along an axon, or neurosecretory fiber, chemically bound to stable proteins (neurophysins) and accumulate in the axon terminals until released into blood sinusoids by reflex nerve impulses. The terminals plus the sinusoids constitute a **neurohemal organ.** The major neurohemal organs of vertebrates are the pars nervosa, or posterior lobe of the pituitary (Fig. 17-2), the median eminence of the diencephalic floor immediately behind the optic chiasma (Figs. 17-2 and 17-3), and the urophysis at the end of the spinal cord of jawed fishes (Fig. 17-4).

Most vertebrate neurosecretions are produced in the hypothalamus. Some of these are released into a hypophyseal portal vein in the median eminence and carried to the adenohypophysis (anterior pituitary), where their target cells are located (Fig. 17-2). Synthesis or release of these hypothalamic neurosecretions is regulated in part by the cyclical external environment and partly by feedback from endocrine glands. The two most obvious environmental influences are the daily cycles of light and darkness, and seasonal changes in temperature, day length, rainfall, salinity, and other variables. These are monitored by sense organs. Of the many effects of this input, one is promotion of gametogenesis and appropriate reproductive behavior

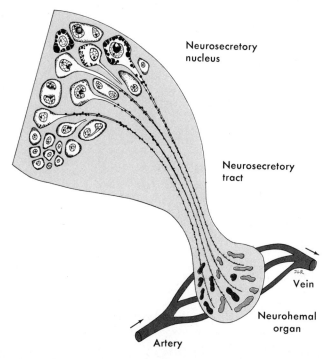

Fig. 17-1. Neurosecretory neurons in a functional neurosecretory unit. The neurohemal organ contains sinusoidal vascular channels. The chief neurohemal organs in vertebrates are urophysis, posterior lobe of the pituitary, and median eminence of the diencephalic floor.

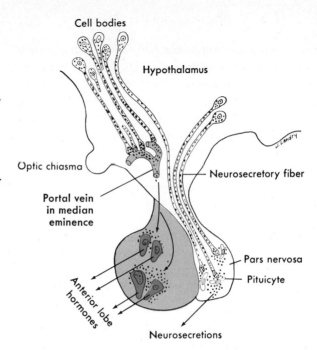

Fig. 17-2. Hypothalamic neurosecretory neurons. Cell bodies in the hypothalamus manufacture neurosecretions (black granules) that flow along the axons (neurosecretory fibers) and are discharged into the hypophyseal portal vein or into vascular channels in the pars nervosa (posterior lobe) of the pituitary. Neurosecretions released into the portal vein help regulate the hormone-producing cells (dark red) of the anterior lobe. Those released in the pars nervosa affect tissue remote from the pituitary.

Cell bodies

Hypothalamus

Optic chiasma

Portal vein in median eminence

Neurosecretory fiber

Pars nervosa

Pituicyte

Anterior lobe hormones

Neurosecretions

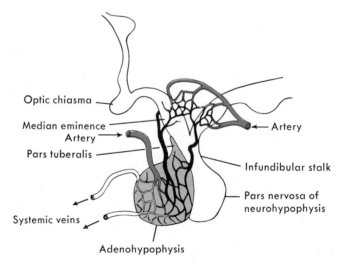

Fig. 17-3. The hypophyseal portal system (black) of mammals, schematic. Arrows indicate direction of blood flow.

Optic chiasma

Median eminence
Artery

Pars tuberalis

Artery

Infundibular stalk

Pars nervosa of neurohypophysis

Systemic veins

Adenohypophysis

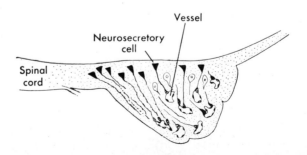

Fig. 17-4. Urophysis (caudal neurosecretory organ) of a carp.

Vessel

Neurosecretory cell

Spinal cord

(migration, territorial defense, mating behavior, nest building, care of eggs and young) at the precise time of year when environmental conditions are most suitable for survival of the offspring at birth (Fig. 17-5). Such adaptive neuroendocrine reflex arcs (receptor–sensory nerve–hypothalamus–neurosecretions–median eminence–hypophyseal portal system–effector) are evidently the result of natural selection. Other hypothalamic neurosecretions are released into the pars nervosa (Fig. 17-2) where they enter the general circulation. Their role is discussed under "Pituitary gland."

Fishes other than cyclostomes have neurosecretory cells in the spinal cord at the base of the tail (Fig. 17-4). Their axons terminate in the **urophysis,** a neurohemal organ that is more or less suspended

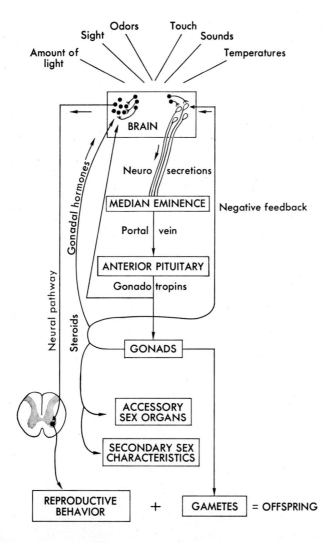

Fig. 17-5. Regulatory effects of the environment on reproduction.

from the cord, depending on the species. The neurosecretions appear to affect a number of functions including thermoregulation and osmoregulation, but their precise role is not yet known.

ENDOCRINE ORGANS DERIVED FROM ECTODERM
Pituitary gland

The pituitary gland, or hypophysis, lies underneath the diencephalon cradled, except in cyclostomes, in a depression in the sphenoid area of the skull. Because of its shape, the depression is called the sella turcica. The gland consists of two major subdivisions with different embryonic origins: a **neurohypophysis** derived from the floor of the diencephalon and an **adenohypophysis** derived from the roof of the stomodeum (Fig. 17-6). Their major subdivisions, with some common synonyms in parentheses, are as follows:

Neurohypophysis (pars neuralis)
    Median eminence
    Infundibular stalk
    Pars nervosa (posterior lobe; neural lobe)
Adenohypophysis (pars buccalis)
    Pars intermedia
    Pars distalis (anterior lobe)
    Pars tuberalis
    Ventral (inferior) lobes of elasmobranchs

NEUROHYPOPHYSIS

The neurohypophysis is the part of the pituitary that forms from the floor of the diencephalon (Fig. 17-6). It contains a recess of the third ventricle that is deepest in mammals, in which the diencephalic floor is drawn out into a long **infundibular stalk** with the **posterior lobe** at its end (Fig. 17-7, cat). Just behind the optic chiasma the neurohypophysis has a swollen area, the **median eminence** (Fig. 17-6, *1*).

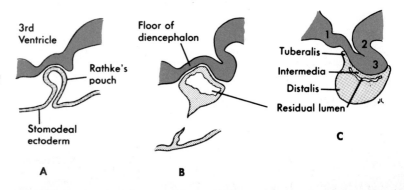

Fig. 17-6. Embryogenesis of amniote pituitary. **A,** Rathke's pouch stage. **B,** Isolation of adenohypophyseal anlage (gray) in contact with the floor of the diencephalon. **C,** Young pituitary consisting of adenohypophysis (gray) and neurohypophysis (blue). **1,** Median eminence; **2,** infundibular stalk; **3,** pars nervosa (posterior lobe). The subdivisions of the adenohypophysis are labeled.

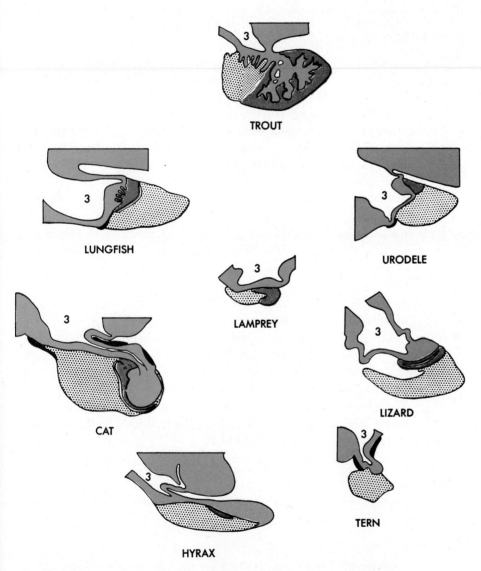

TROUT

LUNGFISH

URODELE

LAMPREY

CAT

LIZARD

TERN

HYRAX

Fig. 17-7. Pituitaries of representative vertebrates, sagittal sections, anterior to the left. Neurohypophysis and adjacent brain, *blue;* pars intermedia, *red;* pars distalis (anterior lobe), *dotted;* pars tuberalis, *black.* The pars distalis of teleosts, as exemplified by the trout, exhibits two cytological regions, a rostral part (large dots) and a proximal part (small dots).

The posterior lobe is a neurohemal organ and produces no known hormones. The hypothalamic neurosecretions released there are carried to the heart for distribution throughout the body. **Arginine vasotocin** is phylogenetically the oldest so-called "posterior lobe hormone." It is the only one in cyclostomes and is found in all higher vertebrate classes, although in mammals it is confined to fetuses. In terrestrial vertebrates it prevents dehydration by causing the kidney tubules to reclaim water from glomerular filtrate and by causing resorption of water stored in the urinary bladder. (The bladder is not an excretory organ in the functional sense. It is a reservoir for water, which, under arid conditions, becomes precious.) Arginine vasotocin also causes absorption of water from soil through the skin of amphibians and lungfishes that burrow during arid conditions. **Arginine vasopressin,** a mutant molecule, regulates water and salt excretion in mammals and is therefore an antidiuretic hormone (ADH) (Fig. 17-8). Another mutant, **oxytocin,** induces uterine contractions during birth of mammals, and causes "letdown" of milk into nipples during nursing. What these and other mutants are able to do for any species depends on whether some of their cells, either contractile or secretory, can respond to (that is, have receptor sites for) the circulating mutant. A mutant molecule will have no effect on a species that has no cells competent to respond.

The median eminence is also a neurohemal organ. Hypothalamic neurosecretions released here enter the hypophyseal portal system and are carried to the adenohypophysis, where they stimulate or, with reference to prolactin, inhibit release of anterior lobe hormones (Fig. 17-2). In teleosts the anatomical relationship between median eminence and adenohypophysis is so intimate that hypophyseal portal systems are rare (Fig. 17-7, trout).

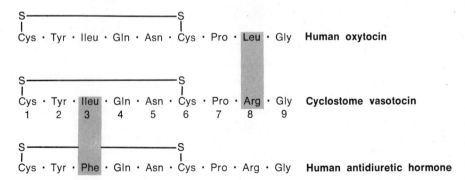

Fig. 17-8. Two evolutionary mutants of arginine vasotocin (cyclostome vasotocin), the oldest known "posterior lobe hormone." Gray bars designate the only differences between cyclostome and human posterior lobe hormones. The human antidiuretic hormone is arginine vasopressin.

ADENOHYPOPHYSIS

The adenohypophysis arises as a bud of ectodermal cells from the roof of the stomodeum. In amniotes and some lower fishes and selachians the bud is hollow and is known as Rathke's pouch (Fig. 17-6, A). In other fishes and in amphibians the bud is solid. When the anlage of the adenohypophysis has made intimate contact over a broad area with the floor of the brain, the connection between the stomodeum and adenohypophysis usually disappears. However, it remains as an open ciliated duct leading to the buccal cavity in *Calamoichthys*, *Polypterus*, and some primitive teleosts. Rathke's pouch may remain in the adult gland as a residual lumen (Fig. 17-6, C).

The origin of the adenohypophysis from the stomodeum suggests that primitively the adenohypophysis may have secreted into the buccal cavity. It was believed at one time that the pituitary (*pitua* means phlegm) was the source of phlegm that falls into the throat. Although they were wrong about the source of phlegm, they may have been naively correct about the primitive site of secretion of the pituitary!

The adenohypophysis typically exhibits three regions—pars intermedia, pars distalis, and pars tuberalis (Figs. 17-6 and 17-7). The pars tuberalis is a paired cephalic extension of the distalis along the floor of the diencephalon or up the infundibular stalk. No pars tuberalis forms in most fishes, snakes, or lizards, but the rostral part of the distalis in teleosts (Fig. 17-7, trout) may be a homologue. In elasmobranchs the adenohypophysis has a fourth subdivision, the inferior lobes (Fig. 15-15).

The pars intermedia lies in intimate contact with the neurohypophysis. However, in some birds and in cetaceans, manatees, and a few other mammals, no recognizable pars intermedia develops. In apes and humans the intermedia grows smaller in size with age, after being relatively large in the embryo. Size differences are probably related to the function of the intermedin (chromatophorotropic hormone and melanophore-stimulating hormone), a product of the intermedia. The hormone causes pigment granules in some chromatophores to disperse, thus darkening the skin. Physiological color changes are characteristic only of cold-blooded animals. Intermedin also initiates melanogenesis in mammalian hair follicles, which results in morphological color changes.

The pars distalis secretes the following hormones:

Somatotropin
Lipotropin
Thyrotropin
Adrenocorticotropin

Gonadotropins
    Follicle-stimulating hormone
    Luteinizing hormone—in males known as
        interstitial cell–stimulating hormone
Prolactin

Somatotropin stimulates synthesis of proteins from amino acids and is therefore a growth hormone. Lipotropin mobilizes fat from storage sites. Thyroid-stimulating hormone stimulates the thyroid gland to accumulate iodine, to synthesize throid hormone, and to release thyroid hormone into the circulatory channels. Adrenocorticotropin affects certain zones of the adrenal cortex that secrete corticoids. Follicle-stimulating hormone acts on ovarian follicles. Luteinizing hormone induces the ovulated ovarian follicle to develop into a new endocrine body, the corpus luteum. In males luteinizing hormone is better known as interstitial cell–stimulating hormone. It induces the interstitial cells of the testes to produce androgens.

Prolactin is a general metabolic hormone with wide-ranging effects. When preceded or accompanied by other hormones, it participates in the osmoregulatory adjustments necessary for migratory (anadromous) saltwater fishes to survive in fresh water, causes red efts to migrate to ponds at the approach of sexual maturity, stimulates production of pigeon milk from the crop sac and mammalian milk from mammary glands, and stimulates secretion of parental skin mucus that nourishes hatchlings of some teleost species. In all vertebrates prolactin has a role in inducing certain parental behavior patterns, such as nest building, protection, turning, and incubation of eggs, and protection of the young. The diverse effects of prolactin may be attributable to a single metabolic effect of the molecule.

Pineal body

The pineal body, an evagination of the roof of the diencephalon, produces the amine **melatonin.** *Mammalian* melatonin causes melanin granules in dermal melanophores of *larval* amphibian skin to aggregate, thereby blanching the skin. The effect is opposite that of intermedin. Experimental evidence indicates that, in some species at least, light impedes the synthesis of melatonin by inhibiting the synthesis of the enzyme hydroxyindole-O-methyl transferase, which synthesizes melatonin from serotonin. The effect of light on the pineal may be direct when the pineal is located under translucent skin. Otherwise, it is mediated via the optic nerves, cranial nuclei, spinal cord, sympathetic trunk, and conarial nerves (nervi conarii) that connect the superior cervical sympathetic ganglion with the pineal body. Darkness facilitates the synthesis of melatonin. Amphibian larvae with intact pineal organs become pale when placed in darkness, and pinealectomy abolishes the response. Melatonin also has an inhibitory effect on the gonads of some mammals, at least, inhibiting sperm formation in seasons when nights are long and melatonin levels are consequently higher. Additional discussions of the pineal will be found in Chapters 15 and 16.

Adrenal medulla and aminogenic tissue

The adrenal in most vertebrates is a gland on the ventral surface of the kidney or near its cephalic pole. In mammals it consists of two components, a peripheral cortex and a central medulla (Fig. 17-9). However, cortex and medulla are two entirely different glands separated from each other in many fishes and more or less interspersed among one another in other vertebrates below mammals (Fig. 17-10). Therefore we must discuss the adrenal as two separate glands, which it really is.

One component of the adrenal complex is ectodermal. This tissue, homologous with the adrenal medulla of mammals, synthesizes cate-

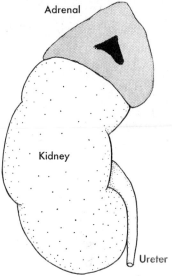

Fig. 17-9. Adrenal of man. The cortex (steroidogenic tissue, gray) surrounds the medulla (aminogenic tissue, black).

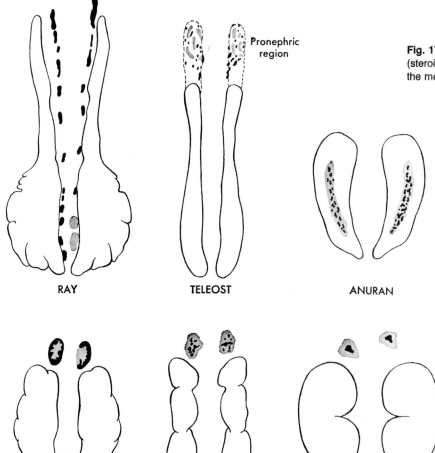

RAY   TELEOST   ANURAN

Pronephric region

LIZARD   BIRD   MAMMAL

Fig. 17-10. Adrenal components in selected vertebrates. Aminogenic tissue (medulla in mammals) is shown in black, steroidogenic tissue (cortex in mammals) in gray. The kidneys are shown in outline.

cholamines, chiefly epinephrine (adrenaline). Because of its staining reaction, this aminogenic component is called chromaffin tissue.*

In lampreys and some teleosts, the aminogenic cells lie in clusters scattered along the postcardinal vein, and in lungfishes they are scattered along the dorsal aorta. In sharks and rays they usually form one or several masses between the caudal ends of the kidneys (Fig. 17-10, ray). In most teleosts they are associated with vestiges of the pronephroi (Fig. 17-10, teleost). In this location they are more or less interspersed among cells of the other adrenal component (steroidogenic tissue).

In most tetrapods the two components are interspersed. However, in some lizards and snakes the aminogenic tissue tends to aggregate, forming an almost complete capsule around the steroidogenic tissue (Fig. 17-10, lizard). This is the reverse of the condition in mammals. But even in mammals there are species in which the steroidogenic

---

*Chromaffin tissue is widely distributed in the trunk. Masses occur in close association with sympathetic ganglia, where they are called paraganglia, and in the gonads, kidneys, heart, and other viscera. However, not all chromaffin tissue is aminogenic.

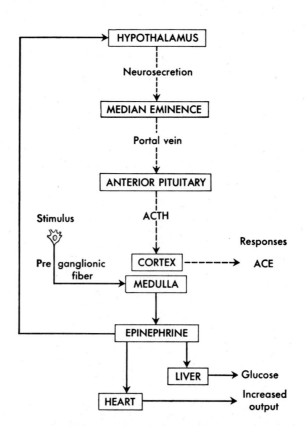

Fig. 17-11. Some regulatory functions of the adrenal medulla. When presented with a suitable neural stimulus (left center), a preganglionic neuron of the sympathetic nervous system stimulates the medulla to release epinephrine. The latter elicits many responses, three of which are indicated at the right. **ACE,** Adrenal corticoids.

tissue does not form a complete cortex. In sea lions, for example, cortical tissue is scattered in the medulla, and medullary tissue is scattered in the cortex.

The adrenal glands of anurans are flattened, elongated masses on the ventral surface of the kidneys (Fig. 14-16). In urodeles they form small bright flecks and nodules along the postcava and are difficult to locate without a lens. In amniotes the adrenals are at or near the cephalic pole of the kidney. For this reason, in erect mammals they are also called **suprarenal** glands.

Epinephrine has a number of endocrine roles (Fig. 17-11). The most prominent are to increase the amount of blood sugar in times of sudden metabolic need (sudden stress) and to stimulate increased production of adrenocortical hormones in times of prolonged stress. Norepinephrine, another amine produced by medullary tissue, is concerned chiefly with maintaining the tonus of the circulatory system through its vasoconstrictor effect.

The aminogenic cells of the adrenal complex and the cell bodies of postganglionic neurons in sympathetic ganglia are the same kind of cells. Both arise from neural crests, both are stimulated by preganglionic neurons, and both produce catecholamines in response to stimulation. The cells of the medulla are postganglionic neurons that failed to sprout processes. They secrete higher ratios of epinephrine than do most postganglionic neurons.

ENDOCRINE ORGANS DERIVED FROM MESODERM
Adrenal cortex and steroidogenic tissue

We have just seen that the adrenal complex of vertebrates is composed of two entirely different components, aminogenic and steroidogenic, which may be intimately associated or spatially separated. The aminogenic component becomes the adrenal medulla in mammals, and the steroidogenic component becomes the cortex.

The steroidogenic component is derived from mesodermal cells that arise from the coelomic mesothelium of the gonadal ridge (Fig. 14-17) and from the underlying nephrogenic mesoderm. Therefore steroidogenic cells are closely associated with kidneys. In elasmobranchs the steroidogenic cells form clusters or elongate masses lying between the kidneys and called, appropriately, **interrenal bodies.** In teleosts the steroidogenic cells most frequently collect in the pronephric region near the aminogenic cells, and in tetrapods they are interspersed among the aminogenic cells to form a more or less discrete adrenal gland on or near the kidney (Fig. 17-10). All such steroidogenic masses are homologous with the adrenal cortex of mammals. Although the term "cortical tissue" is appropriate for these masses in mammals only, it is often used to designate any steroidogenic mass that produces "corticoids" (steroids similar to those of the mammalian adrenal cortex).

Corticoids regulate sodium levels by acting on the gills and kidneys of fishes and on the kidneys of terrestrial vertebrates. The most potent sodium-regulating steroid is **aldosterone.** Other corticoids, such as **cortisone, cortisol,** and **corticosterone,** stimulate the conversion of proteins into sugar (gluconeogenesis).

The origin of steroidogenic tissue from the same mesothelium that gives rise to gonads is interesting because only corticoid tissue and gonads produce steroid hormones in vertebrates. The mammalian adrenal cortex produces some 50 different steroids, including small amounts of male and female sex hormones. The bearded lady is an example of what may happen when the adrenal cortex of a female produces excessive quantities of male hormones.

Corpuscles of Stannius

Embedded in the posterior part of the mesonephric kidneys or attached to the mesonephric ducts of ray-finned fishes are spherical epithelioid bodies, the corpuscles of Stannius. They are easily mistaken for interrenal bodies, but their embryonic origin is different, since they arise as evaginations of the pronephric duct. In most teleosts there are two, but in *Amia* there are 40 to 50. In large salmon the corpuscles may reach 0.5 cm in diameter.

The precise role of the corpuscles remains to be clarified. They are capable of converting one steroid into another in some fishes, but no steroids have been demonstrated in the corpuscles. Ablation of the corpuscles has been followed by changes in calcium and sodium within body fluids. Ablation also causes a fall in arterial blood pressure in freshwater eels, and extracts of the corpuscles raise the blood pressure of rats as well as eels. There seems to be a functional relationship, direct or indirect, between corpuscles and steroidogenic tissue, since ablation of the latter stimulates the corpuscles and vice versa. The secretions of the corpuscles, if any, probably supplement other hormones in the maintenance of electrolyte homeostasis and osmoregulation in fishes.

Gonads as endocrine organs

Gonads arise from the coelomic mesothelium as a pair of gonadal ridges medial to the kidneys (Fig. 14-17). Ovaries and testes of most vertebrates produce three varieties of steroid hormones—**estrogens, androgens,** and **progestogens.** Collectively, these hormones are essential for reproduction.

Estrogens produced by ovarian follicles and androgens produced by interstitial cells of the testes affect other reproductive organs. Differentiation of muellerian ducts to become uteri and oviducts is partly an expression of the effects of estrogens, and failure of muellerian ducts to develop in males may be ascribed, in some lower vertebrates at least, to the dominance of androgens. These steroids are also responsible for secondary sex characteristics, such as mammary glands in female mammals and large muscles and skeleton in males. They also regulate cyclic changes in reproductive organs and behavior.

Progesterone is an intermediate precursor in the synthesis of estrogens and androgens. In female mammals it has achieved an independent role—maintaining the uterus in a progestational state—a state supporting pregnancy. By negative feedback to the hypothalamus it also inhibits the formation of a new wave of ovarian follicles and hence delays the next ovulation in "anticipation" of pregnancy. Much of the progesterone in mammals is a product of the corpus luteum. This is the name given to an ovarian follicle after the cells have undergone luteinization (chemical and morphological change) under the influence of luteinizing hormone from the pituitary.

In addition to steroid hormones, the mammalian ovary produces **relaxin,** a peptide. Relaxin produced during pregnancy softens the ligaments of the pubic symphysis and sacroiliac joints before birth, thus enlarging the birth canal for easier delivery of the fetus.

ENDOCRINE ORGANS DERIVED FROM ENDODERM

The endodermal linings of the embryonic pharyngeal pouches develop thickenings that become parathyroids, thymus, and ultimobranchial bodies, and the pharyngeal floor evaginates to form thyroid tissue. Except in a few lower vertebrates, these organs separate from the pharynx, sink into the surrounding mesenchyme, and migrate some distance from their origin. All have known endocrine functions except the thymus, which is still under study. The endocrine portion of the pancreas is also endodermal and will be discussed first.

Pancreatic islets

In addition to alveoli that secrete digestive enzymes, the pancreas of most vertebrates contains many microscopic islands of endocrine cells (islands of Langerhans) that secrete the hormones insulin and glucagon. However, in most teleosts the endocrine cells are aggregated into a few compact macroscopic masses, often two or three, in the same mesenteries that support the diffuse exocrine pancreatic tissue. In elasmobranchs the endocrine cells are in the epithelium of the pancreatic ductules instead of in islets. In cyclostomes they are in the intestinal wall (lampreys), or they surround the bile duct where it enters the intestine (hagfishes). The seemingly random location of the islands in different vertebrates is understandable when their embryogenesis is known. Potential islet cells at first lie in the lining of the embryonic foregut along with the potential exocrine cells. Later, both types are usually displaced in the growing liver and pancreatic buds (Fig. 11-23). If they are not, the endocrine cells remain in the wall of the gut as in lampreys. If they are displaced along with exocrine cells, they usually bud off from the lining of the pancreatic ductules and become endocrine islands. If they fail to bud off, they remain in the lining of the ducts, as in elasmobranchs.

Insulin seems to regulate utilization of glucose by the tissues. It stimulates conversion of dietary sugar into glycogen (glycogenesis) for temporary storage, and it performs other roles associated with carbohydrate metabolism. The exact metabolic role of insulin remains to be clarified. **Glucagon** stimulates conversion of liver glycogen into glucose (glycogenolysis), thereby maintaining a stable blood sugar level. In times of sudden stress epinephrine from the adrenal medulla produces a more rapid increase in blood sugar.

Thyroid gland

Early in vertebrate evolution some of the cells of the epithelium of the pharyngeal floor had the capacity to accumulate iodine and to bind it to tyrosine, which is what the thyroid does in manufacturing thyroid hormone. Cells of the hypobranchial groove, or endostyle, of the amphioxus perform this synthesis, as does the subpharyngeal gland (endostyle) of larval lampreys (Figs. 2-10, *C*, and 17-12). In both organisms the iodinated protein is secreted into the pharynx and absorbed farther along the digestive tract. When the duct of a lamprey's subpharyngeal gland closes at metamorphosis, the iodinated protein is thereafter secreted into blood vessels from thyroid follicles that have become isolated beneath the pharyngeal floor (Fig. 17-13). A **thyroid follicle** consists of cuboidal epithelium surrounding a colloid-filled cavity that stores, temporarily, the iodinated protein. The follicles in hagfishes are similarly located, but hagfish larvae have no functional subpharyngeal gland.

The thyroid glands of gnathostomes, like endostyles, arise as an unpaired evagination from the pharyngeal floor near the second pharyngeal pouches (Fig. 17-14). After the evagination has reached its adult location, thyroid follicles organize. The embryonic stalk connecting the thyroid to the pharynx usually disappears, leaving a ductless gland. However, a thyroid duct remains in the elasmobranch *Chlamydoselache*. In mammals a small pit on the surface of the tongue near its root marks the site where the thyroid evagination took place; and in human beings short sections of the stalk often persist as

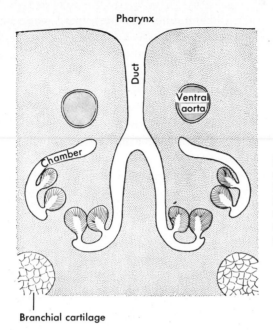

Pharynx

Duct

Ventral aorta

Chamber

Branchial cartilage

Fig. 17-12. Cross section of subpharyngeal gland (endostyle) of a larval lamprey (ammocoete) at site of its duct. All chambers empty into the duct. At metamorphosis the duct closes and some of the isolated glandular cells form thyroid follicles.

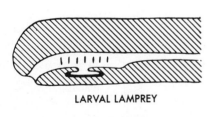

LARVAL LAMPREY

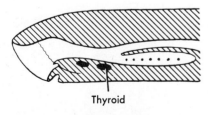

Thyroid

ADULT LAMPREY

Fig. 17-13. Subpharyngeal gland of the larval lamprey (black) and thyroid follicles in the adult.

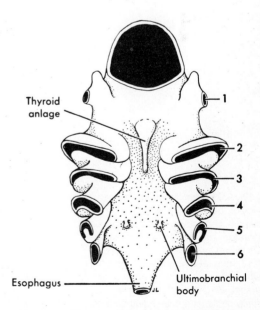

Thyroid anlage

Esophagus

Ultimobranchial body

1

2

3

4

5

6

Fig. 17-14. Pharynx of shark embryo, viewed from below. **1,** Spiracle; **2** to **6,** gill slits. (From Camp.[4])

a cystlike **thyroglossal duct** that occasionally requires surgical removal.

In teleosts, thyroid follicles are usually scattered singly or in small
groups along the ventral aorta under the pharyngeal floor. They may
even accompany some of the afferent branchial arteries into the gill
arches. In a few teleosts they follow the dorsal aorta caudad and even
invade the kidneys. In others they form one or two compact masses
between the bases of the first gill pouches.

Except in cyclostomes and teleosts, the unpaired thyroid evagination develops into either a single gland or a pair. Sharks have a median thyroid just behind the mandibular symphysis near the insertion

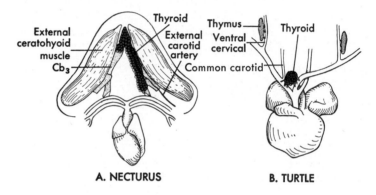

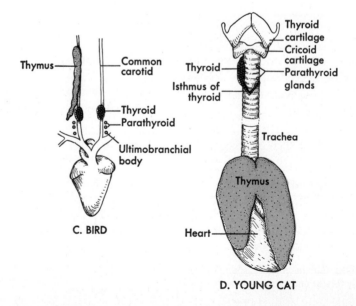

Fig. 17-15. Thymus (light red), thyroid
(dark red), parathyroids, and
ultimobranchial body in selected
vertebrates. The thymus of necturus
lies in the angle between the posterior
ends of the masseter and external
ceratohyoid muscles and is not
illustrated. **Cb₃,** The ceratobranchial
cartilage of the third pharyngeal arch. In
turtles the parathyroids are embedded
in the thymus.

of the coracomandibular muscles. A median thyroid is also characteristic of snakes, turtles, a few lizards, and *Echidna*. Most other adult
vertebrates have paired thyroid glands.

In amphibians the two glands lie in the floor of the pharynx under
cover of the mylohyoid muscle (Fig. 17-15, *A*). In amniotes the
glands migrate caudad for varying distances, taking a position close to
the trachea and common carotid arteries from which they receive a
rich arterial supply (Fig. 17-15, *B* to *D*). The gland was named thyroid because of its location close to the thyroid cartilage in mammals.

The ability to combine iodine into an organic molecule is not restricted to vertebrates or even to animals, but only vertebrate thyroid
cells are known to synthesize the hormones **thyroxine** and **triiodothyronine.** The synthesis is stimulated by thyroid-stimulating hormone
(**TSH**) from the adenohypophysis. The precise role of thyroid hormone is unknown, but an eventual effect is an increase in the rate of
cellular respiration.

The thyroid of mammals produces a third hormone, **calcitonin,**
which, when released, impedes removal of calcium from bone. This
is not the only source of calcitonin. In the thyroid gland it is a product
of parafollicular, or "C," cells that have migrated into the thyroid
from the embryonic ultimobranchial glands.

Parathyroid glands

Parathyroid glands arise as evaginations from pharyngeal pouches
and are so named because they usually lie beside or embedded in the
thyroid gland (Fig. 17-15, *C* and *D*). They have not been identified
in fishes or larval or neotenous amphibians. A few reptiles have three
pairs that arise as endodermal outgrowths from pharyngeal pouches
II, III, and IV, but most tetrapods have two pairs, since the pouch II
anlagen usually fail to mature. When there is only one pair (as in a
few urodeles, crocodilians, chickens, and some mammals), they may
have developed from pouch III or IV, depending on the species, or
the single gland on each side may have contributions from both
pouches.

The parathyroid glands produce **parathyroid hormone** and **calcitonin,** which regulate the levels of calcium and phosphate in the
blood. Abnormally low levels of serum calcium evoke release of parathyroid hormone, which restores serum calcium levels to normal by
releasing calcium from bone and other storage sites. At other times
calcitonin protects these storage sites by impeding release of calcium.

Although fishes have no parathyroids they do not lack a calcium-
regulating factor. Calcitonin is produced in their ultimobranchial
glands.

Ultimobranchial glands

Ultimobranchial glands develop from the epithelium of the last pair of pharyngeal pouches and produce calcitonin (Figs. 17-14, 17-15, *C*, and 17-16). In jawed fishes the glands lie not far from their embryonic origin. In amphibians, reptiles, and birds they are close to the thyroid glands. Adult mammals have none because potential calcitonin-producing cells migrate from the last pouches to the thyroid, where they become parafollicular cells. The precise role of calcitonin in fishes is not yet known.

In birds and mammals that have been studied, potential calcitonin-producing cells arise from neural crests and migrate to the last pouches. If this proves true in lower vertebrates, it would suggest that neural crests may have been the primitive source of calcium-regulating hormones in vertebrates. No ultimobranchial glands have been found in cyclostomes, and no calcitonin has been demonstrated in their serum.

Thymus and bursa of Fabricius

Thymus glands arise as thickenings of the linings of several pharyngeal pouches (Fig. 17-16). The epithelia become invaded by cells that migrate from the hemopoietic regions of the embryonic yolk sac and, later, from the fetal liver. The thymic masses subsequently become separated from the pouches and take a position nearby or remote from their origin.

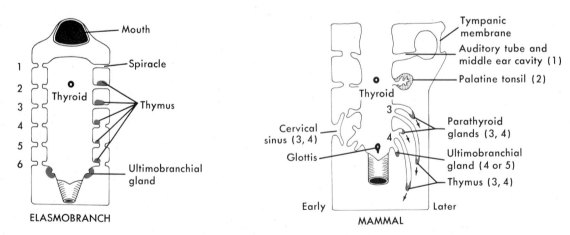

Fig. 17-16. Pharyngeal derivatives of sharks and mammals (diagramatic frontal sections looking down onto pharyngeal floor). Left sides are earlier in ontogeny than the right. Numbers identify ectodermal grooves or pharyngeal pouches. Arrows indicate caudal growth of anlagen. Whether the ultimobranchial gland of mammals is from pouch 4 or from a vestige of pouch 5 is not certain. Endocrine anlagen, except thyroid, are red.

Primitively, thymus probably developed from all pouches. In lampreys it is said to differentiate from all seven. In jawed fishes and tailed amphibians it usually develops from all pouches except the first, and transient thymus tissue has been described from the first. In caecilians the first six pouches participate, and in salamanders, thymus arises from pouches III, IV, and V. Thymus origin is more restricted in some vertebrates. In amniotes pouches III and IV are the sole contributors, and in a few mammals pouch III is the sole source. In frogs pouch II is frequently the sole source.

There is a tendency for successive thymus anlagen to unite during development so there may be fewer adult thymus masses than embryonic anlagen. In fishes, except elasmobranchs, all anlagen more or less fuse to form a single, elongated gland lying above the branchial chambers. In amphibians and reptiles they may fuse or remain separate. The single gland on each side in frogs usually lies just behind the tympanic membrane. In reptiles and birds the thymus may consist of a series of large nodes in the neck extending caudad as far as the thyroid (Fig. 17-15, bird). In young mammals the thymus is a large bilobed mass in the thoracic cavity between the sternum and anterior portion of the pericardium. After puberty it undergoes fatty degeneration. In the larvae of at least one elasmobranch (*Heptanchus cinereus*), ducts lead from the first six lobes of the thymus into the pharynx. These ducts may persist in young adults.

Interest in the thymus as an endocrine organ has alternately waxed and waned over a span of many years as bits of evidence for an endocrine role have been reported in the literature, only to fail the test of reproducibility. Among the facts that had to be taken into account is that the thymus is largest in fetal, neonatal, and young mammals and undergoes fatty infiltration as the animal attains sexual maturity. Recent studies by immunologists have provided one explanation. The thymus is large just before birth and early in life because at that time it is housing and processing stem cells that are released into the general circulation and which, along with their descendants, participate in immune reactions. A hormone, thymosin, has been attributed by some workers to the thymus, but the status of the thymus as an endocrine organ is still debatable.

In young birds the role of the thymus is supplemented by the **bursa of Fabricius,** an organ that arises as an evagination of the cloaca. It resembles the thymus in structure and disappears completely at sexual maturity.

CHAPTER SUMMARY

1. Hormones are products of specific groups of cells that regulate nearby or remote cells of a different nature. They are mostly polypeptides, proteins, nucleoproteins, or steroids. A few are amines.

2. Neurosecretions are small polypeptides produced by neurosecretory neurons and released into circulatory channels of neurohemal organs.

3. Known neurohemal organs of vertebrates are the median eminence, posterior lobe of pituitary, and urophysis.

4. The hypothalamus is the major source of vertebrate neurosecretions. It is regulated partly by the external environment and hormonal feedback. The caudal spinal cord contains neurosecretory neurons in ray-finned fishes.

5. The pituitary consists of a neurohypophysis derived from the floor of the third ventricle and an adenohypophysis derived from the roof of the stomodeum.

6. The neurohypophysis consists of a median eminence, an infundibular stalk (shortest in fishes and amphibians), and a posterior lobe (pars nervosa). It produces no known hormones. Hypothalamic neurosecretions released from the posterior lobe prevent dehydration and stimulate smooth muscles in restricted locations. Those released from the median eminence reach the pituitary via hypophyseal portal vessels.

7. The adenohypophysis usually consists of pars distalis, pars intermedia, pars tuberalis, and, in elasmobranchs, pars inferior. The pars distalis secretes growth-promoting, thyroid-stimulating, adrenal cortical–regulating, gonad-regulating, and fat-mobilizing hormones, and prolactin. The pars intermedia produces intermedin, a melanophore-stimulating hormone that darkens some skin.

8. The role of the caudal neurosecretory neurons is not yet clear. It may be thermoregulatory and osmoregulatory.

9. The pineal produces melatonin, which blanches the skin of larval amphibians and has a gonad-inhibiting influence in some species.

10. Aminogenic tissue, which includes the mammalian adrenal medulla, synthesizes hormones that are amines. In some fishes it is spatially separate from the steroidogenic component of the adrenal complex.

11. Steroidogenic tissue arises from the mesothelial covering of the gonadal ridge and produces adrenal and gonadal steroids.

12. Adrenal steroidogenic tissues include the interrenal bodies of fishes and adrenal cortex of mammals. Corticoids regulate sodium excretion and raise blood sugar by gluconeogenesis.

13. The gonads of both sexes produce steroids that include androgens and estrogens. The ovary also produces progesterone and relaxin, which affect the female reproductive tract.

14. Corpuscles of Stannius are derivatives of the pronephric duct of ray-finned fishes. They affect electrolyte homeostasis, but their status as endocrine organs is not yet clear.

15. The endocrine pancreas produces insulin, which lowers blood sugar by glycogenesis, and glucagon, which elevates blood sugar by glycogenolysis. Its relationship to the exocrine pancreas is less intimate in some fishes than in tetrapods.

16. Thyroid follicles arise from a median evagination of the pharyngeal floor and form discrete median or paired glands except in cyclostomes and teleosts. The hormones thyroxine and triiodothyronine increase metabolic rates. C cells produce calcitonin in mammals.

17. Parathyroid glands are absent in fishes and larval and neotenic amphibians. They are derivatives of pharyngeal pouches II to IV in some reptiles, III and IV in birds and mammals. They produce parathyroid hormone, which elevates serum calcium, and calcitonin, which reduces it.

18. Ultimobranchial glands develop from the last pharyngeal pouches and produce calcitonin. They are absent in adult mammals.

19. The adult thymus is lymphoidal. It is derived from one or more pairs of pharyngeal pouches. Its status as a source of hormones is debatable. The bursa of Fabricius is a similar organ in the cloacal wall of young birds. Thymus and bursa participate in immune reactions.

LITERATURE CITED AND SELECTED READINGS

1. Amoroso, E.C., Heap, R.B., and Renfree, M.B.: Hormones and the evolution of viviparity. In Barrington, E.J.W., editor: Hormones and evolution, vol. 2, New York, 1979, Academic Press, Inc.
2. Barrington, E.J.W.: Hormones and evolution, 2 vols., New York, 1979, Academic Press, Inc.
3. Bentley, P.J.: Comparative vertebrate endocrinology, New York, 1976, Cambridge University Press.
4. Camp, W.E.: The development of the suprapericardial (postbranchial, ultimobranchial) body in *Squalus acanthias*, Journal of Morphology **28:**369, 1917.
5. Glick, B.: The thymus and bursa of Fabricius: endocrine organs? In Epple, A., and Stetson, M.H.: Avian endocrinology, New York, 1980, Academic Press, Inc.
6. Harris, G.W., and Donovan, B.T., editors: The pituitary gland, 3 vols., Berkeley, Calif., 1966, University of California Press.
7. Hoar, W.S., and Randall, D.J., editors: Fish physiology, vol. 2. The endocrine system, New York, 1969, Academic Press, Inc.
8. Holmes, R.L., and Ball, J.N.: The pituitary gland: a comparative account, New York, 1974, Cambridge University Press.
9. Hutchinson, J.B., editor: Biological determinants of sexual behavior, New York, 1978, John Wiley & Sons, Inc.
10. Martin, C.: Textbook of endocrine physiology, New York, 1976, Oxford University Press.
11. Setchell, B.P.: The mammalian testis, Ithaca, N.Y., 1978, Cornell University Press.
12. Turner, C.D., and Bagnara, J.T.: General endocrinology, ed. 6, Philadelphia, 1976, W.B. Saunders Co.

Symposia in American Zoologist

Comparative aspects of parathyroid function, **7:**882, 1967.

Comparative endocrinology of the pineal, **10:**189, 1970.

Comparative aspects of the endocrine pancreas, **13:**565, 1973.

The current status of fish endocrine systems, **13:**710, 1973.

Prolactin in the lower vertebrates, **15:**865, 1975.

Endocrine role of the pineal gland, **16:**1, 1976.

CHAPTER 18

Organic evolution and some other words

THE THEORY OF ORGANIC EVOLUTION: WHAT IT IS AND WHAT IT ISN'T

The theory of organic evolution is a single, simple, easy to understand, unequivocal, yet widely misstated theorem, which is: *The plants and animals on earth have been changing*, and *the ones around us today are descendants of those that were here earlier*.

The conclusion that the animals and plants have been changing is based on geological evidence. It indicates that, if a human being from today could be transported backward in time several hundred million years, the plants and animals he would see would be exotic, alien, and unfamiliar. Five hundred million years ago he would see mostly water, and on the land there would be no land plants. If he happened to bring a fishing pole (!) he would probably catch no fish because the fish would be ostracoderms, and they were filter feeders. Four hundred million years ago fishing would have improved, but there would be no trout, perch, or salmon. The land would be higher and drier, there would be mosses and other simple land plants, and labyrinthodonts would be lumbering in and out of swampy waters, but there would be no frogs or toads. Three hundred million years ago the land would be still higher, and the swamps would be forested with seed ferns and conifers but no flowering plants. Cotylosaurs would be basking in the sun, but there would be no lizards or snakes. One hundred fifty million years ago the birds would have teeth, dinosaurs would be large and specialized, and hairy little animals with pouches to carry their babies in would be scurrying around in the forest, staying out of the way, but there would be no cats, rats, or monkeys. The traveler might be happy to return to the age of the mammals, if only because he is home, and home is familiar. It is in these geological findings that the theory of organic evolution has its roots, but by no means all of them.

The second part of the theorem, that the animals and plants around us today are offspring of the animals of yesterday, is axiomatic. Life comes from preexisting life.

In this chapter we will reduce the theory of organic evolution to its basic premise, look briefly at what Darwin meant by "natural selection," learn how Lamarck explained changes in the structure of successive generations, and be reminded that just because an animal needs a structural change does not mean that this change will come about. We will also examine some words that are used to represent certain evolutionary concepts.

555

This is the theory of organic evolution, stripped of all satellite theories. It doesn't say that multicellular organisms came from protozoa; it doesn't say that man came from a monkey. It doesn't say *where* man came from—that is another theory, or several other theories. Any one of them could be called *the theory of where man came from*, but it is not the theory of organic evolution. Neither does the theory say what caused, or what causes, species to change. That, too, is another theory or several theories. The theory does not state how life began or how the universe began. There are theories about beginnings, but they are not the theory of organic evolution. These satellite or ancillary theories belong to scientific disciplines beyond the intended scope of this book. Finally, it is not a theory about a Supreme Intelligence. Science can neither affirm nor deny the existence of a Supreme Intelligence because it lacks the tools needed to collect the data. And without data science cannot conclude.

The theory of organic evolution might also be called the **theory of the mutability of species.** There is only one alternative, the **theory of the immutability of species.** Proponents of the latter theory must insist that every species on earth today is precisely like it was when it first appeared, and that the first member of the species appeared de novo, coming from no previous living organism. To admit even a single change ("fishes appeared and from these came all kinds of fishes") is to abandon the theory of the immutability of species in favor of organic evolution. If it is accepted that *one* change can occur, it must be accepted that *two* changes can occur. And once this step in logic has been taken, there is no limit to the number of changes that can occur.

NATURAL SELECTION AND THE SYNTHETIC THEORY

The theory of natural selection verbalized by Charles Darwin (1809-1882) is a satellite to the theory of organic evolution. The latter is independent of Darwin's hypothesis—it is neither supported nor negated by it. Natural selection, an example of which is cited on p. 92, was Darwin's attempt to *account for* what he considered the fact of evolution. Variations in organisms, said Darwin, result in varying degrees of success in competition between individuals and with the physical conditions of life. The resulting "preservation of favorable variations [that is, survival of the fittest] and the rejection of injurious variations, I call Natural Selection." Darwin did not know, in 1859, about genetic mutations and recombination of genes whereby hereditary variations arise. A modern biologist might define natural selection as the nonrandom differential reproduction of genotypes as a result of interaction of phenotypes with selective forces in the external environment.

The discussion entitled "The theory of organic evolution: what it is and what it isn't," reduced the theory to a basic premise in order to separate the *premise* from the *mechanics*. The so-called synthetic theory of evolution is a synthesis of the basic premise, current genetic insights (which are subject to change), and the theory of natural selection. Chance mutations and genetic recombination are the presently known sources of hereditary variability, and natural selection seems to dictate evolutionary trends, although it may not be the only directive force. This synthesis combines the basic premise with some of the satellite theories.

THE LAMARCKIAN DOCTRINE

Jean Baptiste de Lamarck (1744-1829) had an explanation for the changes that occur in species. He stated that when a part is employed in successive generations it becomes stronger and better adapted for its role. The animal's use of various structures brings about internal changes that help to perfect these structures. Conversely, when a part is neglected it tends to become vestigial. That is how Lamarck would account for the fact that the olfactory nerves of whales are vestigial. A whale cannot use its sense of smell under water any more than a human being can, because inhaling would lead to drowning! For that reason, according to Lamarck, the whale's olfactory apparatus has become vestigial. The doctrine is not acceptable at present because the current state of our knowledge provides no explanation as to how use or disuse of a part in any individual can be translated into alteration in the hereditary code stored within the sperm and eggs, which are set aside as "germ plasm" early in embryonic life.

NEED AS A BASIS FOR MUTATION

There is no scientific basis for the widespread misconception that, because an animal "needs" a specific structure, the structure will appear as a mutation. Populations that are locked into a changing environment and need some structural or physiological alteration in order to remain successful in that environment and do not acquire it become extinct. Some explanation other than need accounts for adaptive modifications. The best current explanation is to attribute the fulfillment of such needs to chance genetic mutations.

TELEOLOGY

That a population acquires a structure because it needs it is an example of teleological reasoning. Another example is, "Birds have wings *in order that* they may fly." The alternative is, "Birds have wings and therefore they *can* fly." Teleology is the philosophy that natural phenomena take place not by chance but in accordance with a preconceived purpose, intention, or conscious design. It necessitates an intelligence embodied in, or guiding, natural phenomena. Because there are no supporting *scientific data* for this philosophy, science (a body of knowledge and a method based on observable data) cannot adopt it.

ONTOGENY, PHYLOGENY, AND THE BIOGENETIC LAW

All vertebrates exhibit a basic architectural pattern that is dramatically expressed during ontogeny, that is, during development of the individual organism. This concept is incorporated in a generalization formulated in 1828 by the embryologist von Baer that became known as **Baer's law.** It states that *general features* common to all members of a group of animals—in this case, vertebrates—*develop earlier in ontogeny* than do the special features that distinguish the various subdivisions of the group (orders, genera, species). For instance, all vertebrates exhibit very early in ontogeny a notochord, dorsal nervous system, pharyngeal pouches, and aortic arches, and these become modified in the direction of the species as development progresses. These modifications of the basic pattern constitute an important part of the subject matter of this book.

The concept of organic evolution resulted in an addition to Baer's law, namely, that *features that develop earliest are the oldest phylogenetically*, having been inherited from early common ancestors, and that features that develop later in ontogeny are of more recent phylogenetic origin. This is known as the **biogenetic law.** It implies that ontogeny should provide *some indication* of the phylogeny (evolutionary history) of any group.

HOMOLOGY: AN IDEA THAT TRIGGERED A WORD

The idea of homology evolved slowly but persistently in anatomical thought during several centuries before evolutionary theory began to crystallize. As formulated during the seventeenth century, a homologue is "the same organ in different animals under every variety of form and function."[5] Thus the incus in the middle ear of mammals and the quadrate process of the upper jaw cartilage of sharks are homologous structures (homologues). So are the precava of cats and the right common cardinal vein of lower vertebrates. So, too, are the intermaxillary bone of the human embryo (not an independent bone in adults) and the premaxilla of apes.

How can one be sure two organs, or parts, in two different species are the same organs phylogenetically, especially if there has been a change in function? Among vertebrates, at least, evidence with a high probability of validity comes from embryology and, for muscles, from innervation, also. Two parts in two different vertebrates are homologous if they come from the same embryonic precursor. This is equivalent to saying that they are homologous if they have a common ancestry. Some biologists take exception to this definition, justifiably, because it oversimplifies the problem. de Beer presents an easily read analysis of the concept from the viewpoint of an embryologist.[7]

WORDS THAT TRIGGER IDEAS

Words are a necessity for conceptual thought. The more words one can command, the greater the variety of ideas one may entertain. The following words stimulate thinking in relation to evolutionary concepts. You will read them, hear them, and use some of them. There will be differences of opinion with reference to the connotations of most of them. However, if calling attention to these abstract terms stimulates discussion, inclusion of them will have been justified.

Primitive is a relative term. It refers to a beginning or origin. A primitive trait is one that appears in a stem ancestor from which arose an array of subsequent species, some of which may retain the trait. The notochord is primitive, since it occurred in the first chordates. The placoderms were primitive fishes in that they gave rise to an array of later fishes. Ancient insectivorous mammals were primitive *placentals* because they gave rise to an array of later placentals. However, they were not primitive *vertebrates*. Somewhere in phylogeny there was a primitive primate and a primitive species of man. However, one cannot always be certain that a given structure is primitive. For example, the lateral neural cartilages of lampreys are primitive only if they reveal an original condition from which typical vertebrae later evolved.

Generalized refers to structural complexes that, at least in some of the descendants, have undergone subsequent adaptation to a variety of conditions. The hand of an insectivore was, and remains, a generalized mammalian hand. It was competent to evolve into the wing of a bat, the hoof of a horse, the flipper of a seal, and the hand of a primate. A generalized group of animals has demonstrated that it was genetically suitable for divergent evolution, that is, evolution in many directions. Labyrinthodonts were generalized tetrapods. The terms "generalized" and "primitive" come into contrast in that generalized connotes a state of potential adaptability and primitive connotes a state of being ancestral.

A **specialized** condition is one that represents an adaptive modification. Vertebrate wings are specializations of anterior limbs, and beaks are specialized upper and lower jaws. Beaks (Fig. 18-1) may be needlelike for extracting nectar from flowers (hummingbirds), chisel-like for drilling holes (woodpeckers), hooked for piercing and tearing

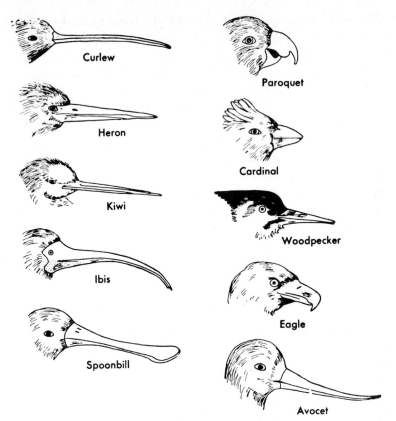

Fig. 18-1. Adaptations of the beak in some birds.

captured prey (raptorial birds, such as hawks and eagles), long and pointed for capturing moving fish, lizards, and other prey (herons), or recurved for extracting grubs from burrows (the female huia of New Zealand). Increased specialization connotes increased adaptation. The greater the specialization, the less may be the potential for further adaptive changes.

Derived, or **modified,** connotes any state of change from a previous condition, a mutated state. If the presence of bone is a primitive trait, wholly cartilaginous skeletons are modifications of the condition. The modification (loss of the potential to form bone) was a specialization if it adaptively modified the animal. Modifications are not necessarily adaptive (students of speciation disagree strongly about this); if they are not, they may portend the demise of the species, since any change is statistically more likely to make the animal less competitive. An exception would be a modification that proved to be preadaptive. (Preadaptations are fortuitous modifications that enable descendants to enter new niches or to cope with conditions not existing at the time of the modification.)

The terms **higher** and **lower** express the relative position of major taxa on a phylogenetic "scale." Birds and mammals evolved from cotylosaurs and hence are said to be higher than cotylosaurs. In this context the words have some meaning. Sometimes the terms are used to express relative mutational distance of a given taxon from a common ancestor when compared with some other taxon—but are mammals to be considered higher than birds? In this context the term may be misleading. The terms may also be meaningless when used to compare a genus within one taxon with a genus within another taxon, as when comparing a modern frog with a perch, or a human being with a hummingbird.

Simple is a relative term connoting a lack of complexity of component parts. A simple state is not necessarily a primitive one. The skull of a human being is simple compared to that of a teleost, but it is not primitive. The primitive may also be far from simple.

The term **advanced** should connote a modification in the direction of further adaptation. Unfortunately the word has overtones connoting progress and hence is subjective and misleading. It is a matter of opinion of one species—man—whether or not a modification in another species represented or represents progress. The phrase "more recent" or "more specialized" may be more informative than the term "advanced."

Degenerate is another value-judgment word. For example, it is sometimes applied to cyclostomes by those who think cyclostomes have lost jaw skeletons, paired appendages, bone in the skin, and other characteristics of typical vertebrates. However, the condition of the cyclostomes represents an adaptation to a semiparasitic state and as such may better be characterized as "specialized." These agnathans may have specialized themselves right into a state of neosimplicity! To call them "degenerate" would seem to discount the value of adaptive modification. Degenerate seems to be a term that should be avoided.

The words **vestigial** and **rudimentary** require explanation. A phylogenetic remnant that was better developed in an ancestor is vestigial. The pelvic girdle of whales is said to be vestigial, since ancestors of whales were tetrapods with functional tetrapod appendages. The yolk sac of the mammalian embryo is vestigial. The term "rudimentary" is used in two different senses, phylogenetic and ontogenetic. In the phylogenetic sense, structures that became more fully exploited in descendants are said to be rudimentary in the phylogenetic precursor. For example, the lagena of the inner ear of fish is sometimes referred to as a rudimentary cochlea, since it evolved into a cochlea in later forms. In the ontogenetic sense, a structure that is undeveloped or not fully developed is said to be rudimentary. The muellerian duct may be considered rudimentary in most male vertebrates. It is not always possible to be certain whether a structure should be called rudimentary or vestigial. The pseudobranch of the shark *Squalus acanthias* is vestigial if it represents a gill that, in ancestral sharks, was a full-fledged functional gill surface. However, if the pseudobranch is a potential future gill surface, then it is rudimentary. The majority opinion is that it is vestigial.

If the foregoing thoughts trigger discussion, no matter how dissonant, the space employed in presenting them will have been well utilized. It must never be forgotten that words are noises made by man to connote a concept. Or, do you wish to object, on a semantical basis, to the word "noise"?

LITERATURE CITED AND SELECTED READINGS

1. Alberch, P., and others: Size and shape in ontogeny and phylogeny, Paleobiology **5**:296, 1979.
2. Ayala, F.J.: Teleological explanations in evolutionary biology, Philosophical Society (London) **37**:1, 1970.
3. Blum, H.F.: Time's arrow and evolution, New York, 1962, Harper & Row, Publishers.
4. Bock, W.J.: The definition and recognition of biological adaptation, American Zoologist **20**:217, 1980.
5. Boyden, A.: Homology and analogy: a century after the definitions of "homologue" and "analogue" of Richard Owen, The Quarterly Review of Biology **18**:228, 1943.
6. Craycraft, J.: The use of functional and adaptive criteria in phylogenetic systematics, American Zoologist **21**:21, 1981.
7. de Beer, G.R.:Homology, an unsolved problem, London, 1971, Oxford University Press.
8. Evolution [a series of articles by Mayr, E., Ayala, F.J., Dickerson, R.E., and others on mechanics, chemical evolution, evolution of earliest cells, evolution of behavior, and other topics], Scientific American **239**(3):46-230, 1978.
9. Gould, S.J.: Ontogeny and phylogeny, Cambridge, Mass., 1977, The Belknap Press of Harvard University.
10. Ho, M.W., and Sanders, P.T.: Beyond neo-Darwinism—an epigenic approach to evolution, Journal of Theoretical Biology **78**:573, 1979.
11. Hull, D.L.: Evolution and circularity in evolutionary taxonomy, Evolution **20**:174, 1976.
12. Lande, R.: Natural selection and random genetic drift in phenotypic evolution, Evolution **30**:314, 1976.
13. Lewontin, R.C.: Adaptation, Scientific American **239**(3):212, 1978.
14. Mayr, E.: Teleological and teleonomic: a new analysis, Boston Studies in the Philosophy of Science **14**:91, 1974.
15. Mayr, E.: Darwin and natural selection, American Scientist **65**(3):321, 1977.
16. Schmidt-Nielsen, K.: Animal physiology: adaptation and environment, ed. 2, London, 1978, Cambridge University Press.
17. Stanley, S.M.: Macroevolution: patterns and processes, San Francisco, 1979, W.H. Freeman and Co., Publishers.
18. Steele, E.J.: Somatic selection and adaptive evolution. On the inheritance of acquired characters, ed. 2, Chicago, 1981, University of Chicago Press.
19. Volpe, E.P.: Understanding evolution, ed. 3, Dubuque, Iowa, 1977, William C. Brown Co., Publishers.

Symposium in American Zoologist

Models and mechanisms of morphological change in evolution, **15**:294, 1975.

APPENDIX I

Abridged classification of the vertebrates

An abridged classification has been provided so that students may readily determine the relationships of animals they meet in the text. If they consult it at once when an unfamilar group of vertebrates is first mentioned, they will find they are gaining a working knowledge of vertebrate relationships without resorting to rote memorization.

Authorities are not in complete accord in matters of classification. This is not unhealthy, since it fosters continual inquiry into the validity of existing schemes. For example, Agnatha are sometimes considered a superclass, or even a subphylum. Since no single classification is universally accepted, the primary consideration in adopting this one was to achieve maximum usefulness.

All classes are included, but subclasses have been omitted if all members are extinct and no representative has been cited. All widely recognized orders containing living members are included except those of Osteichthyes and Aves. Inclusion of the many taxa in those groups would not be in accord with the purpose of the abridgment. Totally extinct groups are indicated by an asterisk.

PHYLUM CHORDATA

Subphylum Urochordata (Tunicata)

Class Ascidiacea
Class Larvacea (Appendicularia)
Class Thaliacea

Subphylum Cephalochordata. *Branchiostoma, Asymmetron,* sole genera

Subphylum Vertebrata (Craniata)

Class Agnatha. Jawless fishes.
    *Order Heterostraci
    *Order Osteostraci
    *Order Anaspida
    *Order Thelodonti (Coelolepida) } Ostracoderms
    Order Petromyzontiformes. Lampreys.
    Order Myxiniformes. Hagfishes. } Cyclostomes
*Class Acanthodii. Armored Paleozoic jawed fishes.
*Class Placodermi. Armored Paleozoic gnathostomous fishes.
    *Order Arthrodira. Arthrodires.
    *Order Antiarchi. Antiarchs.
    Additional extinct orders.
Class Chondrichthyes. Cartilaginous fishes.
    Subclass Elasmobranchii. Naked gill slits.
        *Order Cladoselachii. Primitive Paleozoic sharks.
        *Order Pleuracanthodii. Freshwater Paleozoic sharks with lobed
            fins.
        Order Squaliformes. Sharks.
        Order Rajiformes. Sawfish, skates, rays.
    Subclass Holocephali. Gill slits covered by an operculum.
        Order Chimaeriformes. Chimaeras.
Class Osteichthyes. Higher bony fishes.
    Subclass Sarcopterygii (Choanichthyes). Lobe-finned fishes, many with
      internal nares.
        Order Crossopterygii. Chiefly Paleozoic.
         *Suborder Rhipidistia. Probable ancestors to amphibians.
         Suborder Coelacanthiformes. Specialized crossopterygians,
           internal nares absent; *Latimeria* sole living crossopterygian.
        Order Dipnoi. Lungfishes; *Lepidosiren, Neoceratodus,*
         Protopterus sole living genera.
    Subclass Actinopterygii. Ray-finned fishes.
      Superorder Chondrostei. Chiefly Paleozoic; sturgeons, spoonbills,
        Polypterus, and *Calamoichthys* extant. Ganoids.
      Superorder Holostei. Dominant Mesozoic fishes; *Amia* (bowfin),
        Lepisosteus (gar) sole living genera. Ganoids.
      Superorder Teleostei. Recent bony fishes; 95% of all living fishes.
        Order Clupeiformes. Herringlike fishes.
        Order Cypriniformes. Goldfish, carp, North American catfish,
         buffalo fish; minnows; exhibit weberian apparatus.
        Order Anguilliformes. Eels.
        Order Gadiformes. Codfish, etc.

Order Perciformes. Perchlike fishes; largest order of teleosts.
And up to 35 additional living orders.

Class Amphibia. Highest anamniotes.

 *Subclass Labyrinthodontia. Stem amphibians, precursors of reptiles.

 *Subclass Lepospondyli. Paleozoic; relationships unclear.

 Subclass Lissamphibia. Modern amphibians.

  *Order Proanura. Triassic precursors of Anura.

  Order Anura. Frogs, toads, and tree toads.

  Order Caudata (Urodela). Tailed amphibians.

  Order Apoda (Gymnophiona). Caecilians.

Class Reptilia. Lowest amniotes, mostly extinct.

 Subclass Anapsida

  *Order Cotylosauria. Stem reptiles.

  Order Testudinata (Chelonia). Turtles and tortoises.

 *Subclass Euryapsida (Synaptosauria). Large marine reptiles, including plesiosaurs and ichthyosaurs.

 Subclass Lepidosauria

  Order Rhynchocephalia. *Sphenodon punctatum* sole living species.

  Order Squamata.

   Suborder Lacertilia. Lizards.

   Suborder Amphisbaenia. Amphisbaenians.

   Suborder Serpentes. Snakes.

 Subclass Archosauria. Diapsids; includes bird stock.

  *Order Thecodontia. Stem archosaurs.

  *Order Pterosauria. Flying reptiles (pterodactyls).

  *Order Saurischia. Dinosaurs with reptilelike pelvis.

  *Order Ornithischia. Dinosaurs with birdlike pelvis.

  Order Crocodilia. Crocodiles, alligators, caimans, gavials.

 *Subclass Synapsida. Mammal-like reptiles.

  *Order Pelycosauria. Early synapsids.

  *Order Therapsida. Late synapsids; mammalian precursors.

Class Aves. Feathered vertebrates.

 *Subclass Archaeornithes. Earliest birds, derived from bipedal archosaur; *Archaeopteryx,* sole species.

 Subclass Neornithes. All other extinct and living birds.

  *Superorder Odontognathae. Toothed Cretaceous marine birds; *Hesperornis,* sole species.

  Superorder Neognathae. Ratites and carinates.

   Order Columbiformes. Doves.

   Order Pelecaniformes. Pelicans, cormorants, etc.

   Order Anseriformes. Ducks, geese, other waterfowl.

   Order Falconiformes. Hawks, eagles, vultures.

   Order Galliformes. Chickens, grouse, quail.

   Order Psittaciformes. Parrots, paroquets.

   Order Passeriformes. Perching birds—up to 64 families, including songbirds.

  And about 15 other living orders.

Class Mammalia. Vertebrates with hair.

 Subclass Prototheria. Egg-laying mammals.

  Order Monotremata. Duckbilled platypuses and echidnas.

 Subclass Metatheria. Yolk sac serves as placenta.

  Order Marsupialia. Koala bear, opossum, kangaroo, etc.

Subclass Eutheria. True placental mammals.
  Order Insectivora. Moles, shrews, hedgehogs, flying lemurs, etc.
  Order Chiroptera. Bats.
  Order Primates
    Suborder Lemuroidea. Lemurs, lorises.
    Suborder Tarsioidea Tarsiers.
    Suborder Platyrrhini. South American monkeys and marmosets. Nostrils open to the side.
    Suborder Catarrhini. Anthropoids with nostrils opening downward.
      Superfamily Cercopithecoidea. Old World monkeys.
      Superfamily Hominoidea. Apes and man.
        Family Pongidae. Apes.
        Family Hominidae. Man and extinct prehuman hominids.
          Australopithecus africanus, A. afarensis.
          Homo erectus. Java man.
          Homo neanderthalensis. Sometimes cited as *Homo sapiens neanderthalensis.*
          Homo sapiens. Modern and *Cro-Magnon man.
  Order Carnivora
    Suborder Fissipedia. Land carnivores. Cats, bears, mink, hyenas, etc.
    Suborder Pinnipedia. Marine carnivores. Seals, sea lions, walruses.
  Order Cetacea. Whales, dolphins, porpoises.
  Order Edentata. Sloths, armadillos, South American anteaters.
  Order Tubulidentata. Aardvarks. Insectivorous. One species.
  Order Pholidota. Pangolins. Toothless, insectivorous: *Manis*, sole genus.
  Order Rodentia. Gnawing mammals other than lagomorphs.
  Order Lagomorpha. Rabbits, hares.
  Order Perissodactyla. Ungulates with mesaxonic foot; usually odd-toed. Horses, tapirs, rhinoceros.
  Order Artiodactyla. Ungulates with paraxonic foot; usually even-toed.
    Suborder Suina. Pigs, hippopotami, peccaries—relatively primitive artiodactyls.
    Suborder Ruminantia. Cud chewers with complex stomachs.
      Family Camelidae Camels, llamas.
      Family Cervidae. Deer, caribou (reindeer).
      Family Giraffidae. Giraffes.
      Family Antilocapridae. American pronghorn antelopes sole species.
      Family Bovidae. Cattle, sheep, goats, antelopes (except pronghorns).
      Family Tragulidae. Chevrotains.
  Order Proboscidea. Elephants, *mastodons. Subungulates.
  Order Hyracoidea. Conies. *Hyrax*, sole genus. Subungulate.
  Order Sirenia. Dugongs, manatees; from ungulate stock.
And additional extinct orders.

Anatomical terms*

Following are some of the components of anatomical terms used in the text, with examples. Familiarity with the entries should enable a reader to deduce, within useful limits, the meanings of many additional words, such as hemangioepithelioblastoma, which otherwise may be a meaningless jumble of letters. The list is no substitute for a general unabridged or standard medical dictionary, but it is sufficiently long (nearly 800 entries) and varied to motivate a reader toward habitual use of those standard works should he be so inclined. Such a practice will extend the reader's intellectual horizons far beyond the boundaries of comparative anatomy. Pragmatically, it will result in better recognition and recall and even in more accurate spelling of technical terms.

Meanings are those relevant to the subject matter of the text. Headings that are stems (**acanth-**) are usually the smallest combinations of letters that are common to the derivatives. The symbol > means *hence* and separates a classical from a derived meaning.

a- lacking, without; as in *acelous*, *Agnatha*.

ab- from, away from.

abducens a nerve that abducts (q.v.) the eyeball.

abduct to move a part away from the longitudinal axis, as in raising the arm laterally.

acanth- spine, spiny.

acelous lacking a cavity.

acetabulum a cup for holding vinegar; the socket in the innominate bone.

acr- extremity, highest.

acrodont tooth on the summit of the jaw.

acromion process at proximal extremity of the shoulder (*-omo*).

actin- ray.

Actinopterygii ray-finned fish (see *pter-*).

ad- to, toward, upon.

adduct to draw toward.

adrenal a gland on the kidney.

aden- gland.

adenohypophysis glandular part of the pituitary.

adenoid resembling a gland; a nasal tonsil.

-ae nominative plural ending, as in chordae tendineae (tendinous chords); genitive singular ending as in radix aortae (root of the aorta).

aestivate to spend summer in a state of lowered metabolism.

af- same as *ad-* (to, toward); the *ad-* is changed to *af-* to make the word easier to pronounce.

afferent carrying something to or toward something else (see *-ferent*).

Agnatha *a-* (lacking) + *gnath* (jaws).

ala- wing; see also *ali-*.

alar winglike.

alba white.

alecithal lacking yolk.

---

*Meanings of terms not included here can be located in the text by referring to the index.

ali- wing.

alisphenoid wing of the sphenoid.

alveolus a small chamber or sac.

amel- enamel.

ameloblast a cell that produces enamel.

amphi- both.

amphiarthrosis a joint with severely limited movement.

amphicelous having concavities at both ends.

amphioxus an animal with both ends pointed (*-oxy*).

ampulla a flask > a small dilation.

an- without.

anamniote an animal lacking an amnion.

anapsid lacking an arch.

anura lacking a tail.

ana- up, upward.

anadromous *ana-* + *-dromos* (course) > a migrant from the sea up into freshwater streams.

anastomose to unite end to end.

anatomy *ana-* + *-tome* (q.v.).

anch- gill.

andr- male.

androgen a hormone that induces maleness.

angi- vessel.

ankyl- a growing together of parts.

ankylose to fuse in an immovable articulation.

anlage (pl., **anlagen**) an embryonic rudiment or precursor of a developing structure.

annulus a ring.

annulus tympanicus bony ring to which the eardrum is attached.

ante- before.

antebrachium the forearm; the part before the brachium.

anthrop- refers to human beings.

anti- against, opposite.

antidiuretic inhibiting loss of water (diuresis) via kidneys.

antrum a cavernous space.

Anura *an-* + *uro* (q.v.); tailless amphibians.

apical at the apex.

Apoda *a* + *pod-;* without legs.

aponeurosis *apo-* (away from) +

neuron (a tendon); a broad, flat, tendinous sheet; the meaning of the word cannot be deduced from its parts.

apophysis an outgrowth or process.

apsid refers to an arch.

arch- first, primary, ancient.

archenteron primitive gut.

archetype an early model.

archinephros hypothetical primitive kidney.

archipallium first roof of the telencephalon.

arcuate arched.

arrector pili (pl., **arrectores pilorum**) muscle that erects a hair.

arthro- joint.

arthrodire placoderm with joints, because of dermal plates, in the neck (*-dire*).

artio- an even number.

artiodactyl having an even number of digits.

arytenoid resembling a ladle.

Ascaphus genus of anuran lacking a drum (*scapha*).

ataxia *a-* (lacking) + *taxia* (order); a disorder of the neuromuscular system.

-ate having the property of, as septate: with septa.

atlas the vertebra that supports the head like the mythical Atlas holds up the earth.

atrium the courtyard of a Roman home > a cavity that has entrances and exits.

auricle an ear or earlike flap.

auto- self.

autostyly a condition in which the upper jaw braces (*-styly*) itself against the skull.

autotomy cutting one's self, as when a lizard breaks off the end of its tail.

axial in the longitudinal axis.

azygos *a-* (lacking + *zyg-* (a yoke) > on one side only.

baro- pressure.

baroreceptor a sense organ that monitors pressure.

basi- most ventral; pertaining to a basal location.

basihyal ventral element of hyoid skeleton.

bi- two.

bicornuate having two horns (*cornua*).

bicuspid having two cusps.

bipartite having two parts.

bio- life.

blast- an embryonic precursor; a germ of something.

blastema an embryonic concentration of mesenchyme.

blastocoel cavity of the blastula.

blastocyst the mammalian blastula.

blastula a little (*-ula*) embryo.

brachi- arm.

brachiocephalic associated with the arm and head.

branchi- gill.

branchiomeric referring to parts of the branchial arches.

bucco- cheek.

bulbus bulb.

bulbus arteriosus muscular swelling on ventral aorta.

bulbus cordis term sometimes applied to conus arteriosus in lungfishes, amphibians, and mammalian embryos; part of the heart.

bulla, a bubble > a bubblelike part such as the tympanic bulla.

bursa a sac or pouch.

caecum a blind pouch.

calamus a stem or reed; the stem of a feather.

canaliculus a little canal.

capitulum a little head.

caput head.

cardi- heart.

cardinal of basic importance; chief.

carina a keel.

carn- flesh.

carnivore a flesh-eating animal.

carotid from a word meaning heavy sleep; compression of the carotid artery cuts off blood to the brain.

carpo- wrist.

cat- down.

catarrhine having a nose *(-rhin)* with nares directed downward.

cauda tail.

caudad toward *(-ad)* the tail.

cecum see *caecum*.

cel- see *-coel-*.

ceno- new.

cephal- head.

cerat- horn.

ceratohyal horn of the hyoid.

ceratotrich a horny, hairlike fin support.

-cercal tail.

cerumen wax.

cervical pertaining to the *cervix* (q.v.).

cervix neck.

cheir-, chir- hand.

Chiroptera mammals in which the hand is modified as a wing; bats.

chiasma shaped like the Greek letter chi (X) > a crossing.

choana a funnel-shaped opening.

chole- bile.

chondr- cartilage.

chorion a membrane.

choroid, chorioid resembling a membrane (see *chorion*).

chrom-, chromato- color.

circum around.

clava club.

clavo-, cleido- clavicle.

cleidomastoid a neck muscle attached to clavicle.

cleidoic closed, locked up > a reptilian, bird, or monotreme egg with much yolk and a shell.

cloaca a sewer > common terminus for digestive and urinary tracts.

cochlea a snail with a spiral shell > spiral labyrinth of inner ear.

-coel- hollow, a cavity.

coelom body cavity.

collagen gelatinous, gluelike material.

columella a little *(-ella)* pillar or column.

com-, con-, cor- with, together.

conari of the pineal (q.v.).

conch- shell.

concha the pinna of the ear, shaped like a clamshell.

contra- opposite.

contralateral on the opposite side.

conus a cone.

conus arteriosus chamber of heart after the ventricle.

copr- feces.

coprodeum fecal passage derived from cloaca.

cor- see *com-*.

coracoid shaped like a crow's beak.

corn- horn.

cornified changed to horn by keratinization.

cornu (pl., **cornua**) horn of the hyoid.

corona a wreath or crown.

coronary sinus forms a "wreath" around the heart.

corpus (pl., **corpora**) body.

corpora quadrigemina the two pairs of twins *(-gemini)* of the roof of the mesencephalon of amniotes.

corpus luteum a yellow body of the ovary.

corpus spongiosum spongy body.

costa rib.

costal cartilage a cartilage at the ventral end of a rib.

cotyledonary cup shaped.

coxa hip.

cribriform sievelike.

cricoid resembling a ring.

crista a ridge or crest.

crus leg.

cten- comb.

ctenoid resembling a comb.

cucullaris from a word meaning a hood; the two cucullaris (trapezius) muscles resemble collectively a hood or shawl.

cuneiform wedge shaped.

cusp a peak or point.

cutaneous referring to skin.

cyclo- circular.

cyclostome agnathan with round mouthlike funnel.

cyst fluid-filled sac.

cyt-cell.

dactyl- finger, toe.

decidu- fall off or be shed.

deciduous placenta one in which the uterine wall of the mother is partly shed at parturition.

deltoid resembling the Greek letter delta (Δ).

demi- half.

demibranch gill on one face of a gill arch.

dent- tooth.

dentin bone like that in teeth.

derm- skin.

dermatome layer of a somite giving rise to skin.

Dermoptera mammals in which the skin forms a wing membrane (see *-pter*).

dermato- referring to skin.

dermatocranium skull bones phylogenetically derived from skin.

-deum, -daeum a passageway.

deuter- two.

deuterostome an animal that uses the blastopore as an anus and forms a second mouth.

di- two.

diapophysis one of two lateral processes.

diapsid having two arches.

diarthrosis freely movable joint between two bones or cartilages.

Dipnoi fish with two breathing apertures (external and internal).

dia- through, apart.

diaphragm a separation *(phragma)* between two parts.

-didym- twins > the testes.

digiti- fingers or toes.

digitigrade walking *(-grade)* on the digits.

dino- fearful, terrible.

dinosaur a fear-inspiring reptile.

diphy- double.

diphyodont having two successive sets of teeth.

diplo- double, two.

diplospondyly two vertebrae in each body segment.

dis- separation, taking apart.

dissect to disassemble.

diverticulum an outpocketing

dorsum the back.
  dorsad toward the back.
duodenum 12; the length of the human duodenum is about the breadth of 12 fingers.
dura tough, hard.
dys- bad, faulty, painful.

e- without.
  Edentata an order of mammals lacking teeth.
ect- outer.
  ectopterygoid the outer pterygoid bone.
  ectotherm an animal whose temperature varies with the environment.
-ectomy *ex-* (out of) + *tome* (cut), as in appendectomy.
ectopic *ex-* (out of) + *topo-* (place).
  ectopic pregnancy a pregnancy in which the fetus is implanted elsewhere then in the uterus (in the coelom, for example).
ef- variant of *ex-*.
  efferent that which carries away from; efferent branchial arteries carry blood out of the gills.
elasmo- plate.
  elasmobranch with gills composed of flat plates.
-ella a diminutive, as in columella.
en- in, into.
  encephalon the brain, a structure in the head.
endo- within, inner; see also *ento-*.
  endochondral within cartilage.
  endolymph the lymph within the membranous labyrinth.
  endotherm an animal that maintains a relatively constant body temperature regardless of environmental fluctuations.
enteron the gut.
ento- within, inner; see also *endo-*.
  entoglossal within the tongue.
ep-, epi- upon, above, over.
  epaxial above an axis.
  ependyma an outer garment > the membrane covering the part of the central nervous system exposed to the neurocoel.

epididymis (pl., **epididymides**) a structure lying on the testis *(didym-)*.
epiglottis a skeletal flap over the glottis.
epimere dorsal mesoderm.
epiphysis *epi* + *physis* (q.v.), pineal complex.
epiploic relating to greater omentum.
epithelium a surface layer of cells.
erythro- red.
eso- carrier.
  esophagus carrier of substances that have been eaten *(phag-)*.
estr- female.
ethmoid seivelike.
eu- true.
eury- wide.
  euryhaline able to live in waters with a wide range of salinity *(halo-)*.
ex-, exo- out, out of, away from, outer.
  excurrent pore a pore for the exit of a current of water.
  exoskeleton a skeleton in the skin.
extra- beyond, outside of.
  extraembryonic outside of the embryo.

falciform shaped like a sickle.
fauces throat.
fenestra a window > an aperture.
-ferent, -ferous carrying, as in *afferent* (q.v.).
fil thread.
fimbria fringe.
foramen a small opening, usually transmits something.
  foramen magnum the large foramen in the occipital region.
fore- before, in front.
  forearm the part of the arm before the upper arm.
fossa a pit, cavity, depression, vacuity.
frenulum a little bridle > the membrane that bridles (ties) the tongue to the floor of the oral cavity.
frug- fruit.
  frugivore a fruit eater.

fundus the bottom of a cavity.

gan- bright.
ganglion a swelling > a group of cell bodies outside the central nervous system.
gastr- a belly, a stomach; the digastric muscle has two bellies.
  gastralia ventral abdominal ribs.
  gastrula a little stomach > a stomachlike embryo.
gen- origin.
genio- chin.
genu knee.
geo- earth.
glans acorn > the tip of the penis.
glenoid resembling a socket.
glia glue.
glomerulus a little glomus (ball or skein) > a tiny plexus of blood vessels.
gloss- tongue.
gnath- jaw.
gon- seed > generative, as in glucagon (giving rise to glucose).
  gonad the source of gametes.
gubernaculum a rudder > a governor, as the ligament that (partly) governs the position of the testis.
gula throat.
  gular fold a fold at the throat of some tetrapods.
gustatory related to gustation (taste).
gymn- naked.
gyrus a ridge between gooves.

haem-, hem- blood.
hamate having a hook.
hamulus a little hook.
hemi- half; equal to *demi-*.
hemo see *haem-*.
hepat- liver.
hept- seven.
herbivore an animal that devours grasses (herbs).
hetero- other, different; opposite to *homo-*.
  heterodont having different kinds of teeth.
hex- six.
hilum a notch.
hipp- horse.

hist- tissue.

histogenesis the formation of a tissue.

holo- entire, whole.

holonephros a kidney extending the length of the coelom.

hom-, homeo-, homo-, homoio- like, similar.

homeostasis maintenance of a constant internal environment.

homeotherm an animal that maintains a steady body temperature despite ambient (external) temperature; an endotherm.

homodont teeth all alike.

hyaline clear, glassy.

hyoid shaped like the capital Greek letter upsilon (Y).

hyostyly see *-styly*.

hyp-, hypo-, under, below, less than ordinary.

hypaxial below a given axis.

hypophysis a growth under the brain; the pituitary body.

hyper- above, beyond the ordinary.

ichthy- fish.

-iform having the shape of.

ileo- pertaining to the ileum of the intestine.

ilio- pertaining to the ilium of the pelvis.

impar unpaired.

in- not.

innominate not named.

incus an anvil.

infra- beneath, under.

infundibulum a little funnel.

inguen the groin.

inguinal in the region of the groin.

inter- between.

intercalary plate part of neural arch between neural plates in fishes.

interrenal steroidogenic tissue between the kidneys.

intra- within.

intramembranous within a membrane.

intrasegmental within a segment.

ipsi- the same.

ipsilateral on the same side.

irid- iris of the eye.

iridophore a pigment cell containing refractory bodies that result in iridescence.

ischi- hip, pelvis.

iso- equal, alike.

isolecithal egg an egg having even distribution of yolk.

-issimus a superlative ending; the longissimus dorsi is the longest muscle of the back.

-itis inflammation of.

jejunum empty; part of intestine that is often empty at death.

juga- yoke > something that joins; the jugal bone in mammals is a yoke uniting maxilla and temporal bones.

jugular pertaining to the neck.

juxta- next to, near.

juxtaglomerular near glomeruli.

kat- down; same as *cat-*

keratin from a Greek word meaning horn; a relatively insoluble substance in cornified cells.

kinetic capable of moving.

labium lip.

labyrinth a maze.

labyrinthodont an early tetrapod with greatly folded dentin in the teeth.

lac-, lact- milk.

lacrimal pertaining to tears; from lachryma (a teardrop).

lacuna a lake.

lag- hare.

lagena a flask > flask-shaped part of inner ear.

lambdoidal having the shape of the Greek letter lambda (λ).

lamina a thin sheet, plate, or layer.

laryng- larynx.

latissimus the broadest; see *-issimus*.

lecith- yolk.

lemmo- sheath or envelope.

lemur from a word meaning a nocturnal being or ghost.

lepid-, lepis- scale.

Lepisosteus a ganoid fish with bony scales.

lepto weak, thin, delicate.

leuco-, leuko- white, colorless.

levator that which elevates or raises.

lien- spleen.

lingua the tongue.

lip- fat.

liss- smooth.

longissimus the longest; see *-issimus*.

lumen light > an opening that light can pass through; the cavity in a tube.

lunar, lunate moon shaped.

luteo- yellow.

macula a spot.

magnus, -a, -um large.

malleus a hammer.

mandibula a jaw.

manu- hand.

manubrium a handle.

marsupium a pouch.

mastoid like a breast (*mast-*).

mater mother.

maximus, -a, -um largest.

meatus a canal or passageway.

medulla bone marrow.

medulla spinalis the marrow of the backbone > spinal cord.

meg- great, very large.

melan- dark, black.

melanophore bearing (*-phore*) dark pigment.

meninx (pl., **meninges**) a membrane.

mento- chin.

mental foramen foramen on mandible near chin.

-mer- a segment, a part, one of a series.

mes- middle, midway, intermediate.

mesaxonic foot one in which the weight-bearing axis passes through the middle toe.

mesenchyme a tissue (*enchyme*) that is not yet differentiated.

mesentery associated with the midline of the enteron.

mesonephros an intermediate kidney.

met- after, last in succession.

metacarpal a bone distal to a carpal.

metamorphosis the final change in shape.

metanephros hindmost kidney.

mimetic capable of mimicking; having the characteristics of a mime.

mitral refers to a bishop's miter or headdress; the mitral valve is the bicuspid valve of the mammalian heart.

mono- one.

monotreme a mammal with one caudal opening.

morph- shape, structure, form.

morphogenesis development of form.

morphology study of form; anatomy.

morula a mulberry.

myel- marrow.

myelencephalon the marrow inside the skull > the medulla.

myelin fatty material.

mylo- from a word meaning a millstone.

mylohyoid a muscle attached near the grinding teeth.

myo- muscle.

myocardium muscle of heart.

myomere one of a series of muscle segments.

myotome part of somite giving rise to muscle.

neo- new, recent.

nephr- kidney.

nephrogenic giving rise to kidney.

nephron a functional kidney unit.

nomen- (pl., **nomina**) name.

noto- back.

notochord cordlike skeleton of the back.

nuchal refers to the nape of the neck.

occiput part of the head surrounding the foramen magnum; in mammals, the back of the head.

ocul- eye.

odon-, odont- tooth.

odontognath a bird with teeth on the jaws.

odontoid resembling a tooth.

-oid like, having a resemblance to, as in hominoid (humanlike).

-ole small, as in arteriole.

-oma swelling.

omentum a free fold of peritoneum.

omni- all.

omnivore an animal that eats plants and animals.

omo- shoulder.

ontogenesis *onto* (individual) + *genesis* (origin); the development of an individual.

oö- egg (pronounced oh-oh).

oöcyte egg cell.

oöphoron *oö* + *-phore-* (q.v.); ovary.

operculum a cover or lid.

ophthalm- eye.

opisth- at the rear, at the end.

opisthocelous with a cavity at the end.

opisthonephros hind kidney of anamniotes.

orb- a circle.

orbit cavity for the eyeball.

ornith- bird.

oro- mouth.

-orum of the, as in branchiorum (of the gills).

os bone.

ossicle a small bone.

ossify to become bony.

os mouth.

os uteri entrance to uterus from vagina.

osmoregulation electrolyte homeostasis.

oste- bone.

Osteichthyes bony fish.

osteon unit of bone in concentric layers.

ostium an entranceway > a mouth.

ostraco- shell.

oto- ear.

otic refers to the ear.

otocyst a vesicle that becomes the inner ear.

-ous having the characteristic of.

ovale shaped like a hen's egg; oval.

ovi-, ovo- egg.

oviparous egg laying.

ovipositor a structure for laying eggs.

-oxy- sharp, acute, acid.

pachy- thick.

paed-, ped- child.

paedogenesis reproducing without attaining full maturity.

palae- see *pale-*.

palatine referring to the palate.

pale- old, ancient.

pallium a cloak > a roof.

panniculus a small piece of cloth > a layer of tissue.

papilla a nipple > a nipple-shaped structure.

par-, para- beside, near.

parasphenoid parallel to the sphenoid.

parotid near the ear.

parie- pertaining to the body wall.

-parous bearing, giving birth to.

pars (pl., **partes**) part.

pectoral refers to the chest.

pedicel a slender stalk.

pelvis a basin.

penta- five.

perennibranchiate having permanent gills.

peri- around.

perilymph fluid surrounding membranous labyrinth.

periss- odd.

peritoneum something that stretches over or around > the coelomic lining.

pes (pl., **pedes**) foot.

petro- stone, rock.

petrosal bone the bone surrounding the inner ear, which resembles a steep rugged rock.

phag- eat.

phalanx (pl., **phalanges**) a line of soldiers > a bone of a digit.

pharyng- pharynx.

-phil loving > having an affinity for.

-phore- bearing, one that bears, as in photophore (an organ that emits light).

phrenic refers to diaphragm.

phylo- tribe.

phylogeny evolutionary history of a group.

-physis that which grows.

physo- bellows > lung or air bladder.

physoclistous lacking a duct from air bladder.

physostome a fish that can get air to the swim bladder via the mouth.

pia tender, kind.

pia mater the delicate meninx of the brain.

pilo- hair.

pineal resembling a pine cone.

pisci- fish.

placo- thick, flat, platelike.

placode in embryology, an ectodermal thickening that gives rise to something.

placoderm fish with (bony) plates in the skin.

planta- the sole of the foot.

plantigrade a flat-footed stance.

platy- flat, wide, broad.

pleur- rib, side.

pleural refers to ribs.

pleurapophysis apophysis (process) of vertebral column that is fused with a short rib.

plexus a network.

pneumato- air.

pneumo- lung.

pod- foot.

poikilotherm an ectotherm (q.v.).

poly- many, much.

pons a bridge.

post- after, behind.

posttrematic behind a trema or slit.

pre- before, in front of; see also *pro-*.

pretrematic in front of a trema or slit.

prim- first, earliest.

primate first in rank.

pro- favoring, on behalf of.

prolactin hormone necessary for milk production.

pro- in front of, before, preceding.

procelous with a cavity at the cephalic end.

prostate a gland standing (*stat-*) at the beginning of the urethra.

proboscis a feeding tube > an elephant's trunk.

procto- anus.

proprio- one's own.

proprioception reception of stimuli from muscles, joints, tendons.

pros- toward, near.

prosencephalon the anterior end of the embryonic brain.

proto- early, first.

pseudo- false.

pter-, pteryg- wing, feather.

pterosaur winged reptile.

pterotic wing of the otic complex.

pterygoid resembling a wing.

pulmo- lung.

pyg- rump.

quadrate square.

quint- five.

rachi- vertebral column.

rachis supporting "spine" for feather.

rachitomous vertebra a vertebra consisting of several pieces; see *-tome*.

radix (pl., **radices**) a root.

ramus a branch.

rectus, rectum straight.

rete (pl., **retia**) a network.

rete mirabile a remarkable (*mirabilis*) network of vessels.

reticulum a little network.

retro- behind.

rheo- current, flow.

rhin- nose.

rhinencephalon an olfactory part of the brain.

rhinoceros an animal with a horn (*cerato-*) on the nose.

rhomb- rhomboid.

rhynch- snout.

ruga (pl., **rugae**) a wrinkle.

sacculus a little sac.

sagittal from a word meaning an arrow.

sangui- blood.

sarco- flesh.

Sarcopterygii fish with fleshy lobe at base of fin.

saur- lizard > reptile.

scalene a triangle with sides and angles unequal.

scler- hard, skeletal.

sclerotome part of somite giving rise to skeletal components.

sebum grease, wax.

sebaceous having an oily secretion.

-sect- cut, divide.

sella turcica a seat (*sella*) shaped like a Turkish saddle.

semi- half, partial.

semilunar shaped like a half-moon.

seminal pertaining to seed > to semen.

seminiferous carrying sperm.

serrate notched or toothed along the edge; the serratus muscle is serrate.

sex- six.

sigmoid S-shaped.

sinus a cavity.

sinusoid a thin-walled, sinuslike vascular channel.

soma-, somato- body.

somite a body segment.

sphenoid wedge shaped.

spiracle a breathing hole.

splanchn- viscera.

splen- spleen.

spondyl- vertebra.

squam- scale.

squamous scalelike, flattened; squamate.

stapes a stirrup.

stapedial associated with the stapes.

stato- standing, fixed.

stellate star shaped.

stereo- solid > shape; stereognosis is knowledge (*-gnosis*) of form or weight acquired by feeling or lifting.

stom- mouth.

stratum layer.

strept- twisted, curved.

stria a stripe.

-style pillar > a process such as the urostyle.

styloid having an elongated shape.

-styly braced; in hyostyly the jaws are braced against the hyoid.

sub- under, below, to an inferior degree.

    subclavian under the clavicle.

    subunguis under the nail.

    subungulate not quite an ungulate.

sudor sweat

sulcus a groove.

super-, supra- over, above, in addition.

    suprarenal a gland above the mammalian kidney.

sur- over, above; equivalent to *super-*.

    surangular bone a bone above the angular.

sym-, syn- together.

    symphysis a growing together; see *-physis*.

    synarthrosis an immovable suture-like joint.

    synapse a junction.

    synsacrum sacrum united with other vertebrae.

tarsus ankle; also, a connective tissue plate in the eyelid.

tax- arrangement.

    taxon a taxonomic unit such as a phylum.

    taxonomy the orderly arrangement of taxons; classification.

tectum a roof.

tel-, teleo-, telo- end, complete.

    telencephalon anterior end of the brain.

    teleology the use of design or purpose to explain natural phenomena.

temporal refers to the temple or the side of the skull behind the eye.

teres round.

tetra- four.

theco- a case.

    thecodont having socketed teeth.

therio- an animal with hair, a beast.

thyroid shield shaped.

-tome cut; also, the result of cutting, as a section or thin sheet.

trabecula a little beam > a strand, ridge, rod, or bundle.

trans- across.

    transect to cut across.

trapezoid a four-sided plane with two parallel sides.

    trapezius muscle named for its shape in humans.

-trema a slit.

tri- having three parts.

    trigeminal from word meaning triplets; a nerve with three primary branches.

trochlea a pulley; the trochlear nerve of humans passes through a pulley at its attachment.

troph- nourishment.

truncus trunk.

    truncus arteriosus ventral aorta.

tuber a swelling or knob > a tuberosity, tubercle, or protuberance.

    tuberculum a little tubercle.

tunic a coat or wrap.

tympanum a drum > eardrum.

ulna elbow > the bone at the elbow.

ultimobranchial a gland derived from the last (*ultimo-*) branchial pouch.

-ulus, -ula, -ulum diminutive endings denoting tiny.

uncus a hook.

    uncinate hooked.

unguis nail, claw, hoof.

ungula hoof.

    ungulate hooved.

uro- tail.

    urophysis a growth at the base of the tail.

    uropygium the rumplike tail of a bird.

utricle a little sac or vesicle.

vagina a sheath.

vagus wandering.

vas (pl., **vasa**) vessel.

    vasa vasorum vessels of the blood vessels.

velum a veil > a thin membrane.

venter abdomen; the part opposite the dorsum or back.

ventricle a cavity in an organ.

vesica a bladder or vesicle.

vestibule an antechamber or entrance way.

vitelli- yolk.

vitreous having a glassy appearance.

vivi- alive.

vomer a plowshare; the mammalian vomer bone resembles a plowshare.

-vorous eating, devouring, as in insectivore.

Xanth- yellow.

xiph- sword.

    xiphoid process a swordlike process of the sternum opposite the manubrium or handle.

ypsiloid shaped like the Greek letter upsilon (Y).

zyg- yoke > something that links two things.

    zygapophysis a vertebral process that articulates with a more anterior or posterior one.

    zygomatic arched.

    zygote result of union of gametes.

Comprehensive references

The following are mostly multivolume works relevant to many chapters. Single-volume works of the same nature— a book on the biology of cyclostomes, for example—will be found at the end of Chapter 3. The latter and the present list supplement those at the ends of many chapters. Other entries below have been arbitrarily included.

Alexander, R.M.: The chordates, Cambridge, England, 1975, Cambridge University Press.

Bellairs, A.: The life of reptiles, 2 vols., New York, 1970, Universe Books.

Cole, J.F.: A history of comparative anatomy, London, 1944, The Macmillan Co., Ltd.

Farner, D.S., King, J.R., and Parkes, K.C., editors: Avian biology, 5 vols., New York, 1971-1975, Academic Press, Inc.

Gans, C.: Biomechanics: an approach to vertebrate biology, Philadelphia, 1974, J.B. Lippincott Co.

Gans, C., and others, editors: Biology of the reptilia, 10 vols., New York, 1969-1979, Academic Press, Inc.

Getty, R., editor: Sisson and Grossman's the anatomy of the domestic animals, ed. 5, 2 vols., Philadelphia, 1975, W.B. Saunders Co.

Goodrich, E.S.: Studies on the structure and development of vertebrates, London, 1930, The Macmillan Co., Ltd. (Reprinted by Dover Publications, Inc., New York, 1958.) Some outdated theories but excellent morphology.

Grassé, P.-P., editor: Traité de zoologie, anatomie, systématique, biologie, vols. 11-17, Paris, 1948-1970, Masson et Cie.

Harmer, S.F., and Shipley, A.E., editors: The Cambridge natural history, vols. 7-10, London, 1898-1902, The Macmillan Co., Ltd. (Reprinted by Hafner Press, New York, 1958-1960.)

Hildebrand, M.: Analysis of vertebrate structure, New York, 1974, John Wiley & Sons, Inc.

Hoar, W.S., and Randall, D.J., editors: Fish physiology, 7 vols., New York, 1969-1978, Academic Press, Inc.

Jarvik, E.: Basic structure and evolution of vertebrates, 2 vols., New York, 1980, Academic Press, Inc.

King, A.S., and McLelland, J., editors: Form and function in birds, 2 vols., New York, 1979, 1980, Academic Press, Inc.

Lofts, B., editor: Physiology of the amphibia, 3 vols., New York, 1974-1976, Academic Press, Inc.

Nickel, R., and others: The viscera of the domestic mammals, New York, 1973, Springer-Verlag.

Parker, T.J., and Haswell, W.A.: Textbook of zoology, vol. II (revised by Marshall, A.J.), ed. 7, London, 1962, The Macmillan Co., Ltd.

Prosser, C.L., editor: Comparative animal physiology, ed. 3, vol. 2, Philadelphia, 1973, W.B. Saunders Co.

MEDICAL DICTIONARIES AND ANATOMICAL NAMES

Baumel, J.J., editor: Nomina anatomica avium, an annotated anatomical dictionary of birds, New York, 1979, Academic Press, Inc.

Dorland's illustrated medical dictionary, ed. 25, Philadelphia, 1974, W.B. Saunders Co.

Nomina anatomica, ed. 3, Amsterdam, 1966, Excerpta Medica Foundation.

Nomina anatomica veterinaria, Ithaca, N.Y., 1973, Department of Anatomy, State Veterinary College.

Stedman's medical dictionary, ed. 22, Baltimore, 1972, The Williams & Wilkins Co.

Index

Pages cited in **boldface** contain an illustration only. Other cited pages frequently contain illustrations. Footnotes are designated by "f." Tables are designated by "t."